PRINCIPLES OF

HUMAN GENETICS

A Series of Books in Biology

EDITORS: George W. Beadle

Ralph Emerson

Douglas M. Whitaker

PRINCIPLES OF

HUMAN

GENETICS

Second Edition

by CURT STERN *University of California, Berkeley*

 W. H. FREEMAN AND COMPANY

SAN FRANCISCO AND LONDON

Library of Congress Catalogue Card Number: 60–12098

TO *Evelyn*

AND *Hilde,*
Holly, and
Barbara

PREFACE

Eleven years ago, when the first edition of this book appeared, the principles of human genetics seemed well established. These principles still stand, even though the past decade witnessed breath-taking changes and advances in the field of human genetics. As elementary a fact as the number of man's chromosomes was recognized and, based on this knowledge, human cytogenetics became a fruitful reality. "Classical" pedigrees of special traits were shown to have been unreliable. The sex-determining role of the Y-chromosome was discovered. Much information of value to geneticist, physiologist, and physician came from biochemical research on inborn errors of metabolism and on inborn differences among normal people. With the recognition of the universal existence of polymorphism and with the discovery of relationships between disease and blood group and hemoglobin constitution, the role of genetic selection in human populations acquired new meaning. And of crucial importance to all men living in the Nuclear Age was the demonstration that fewer mutations are produced in immature germ cells by exposure to a dose of radiation over a long period than by exposure to an equal dose over a short period.

Although the book has been extensively rewritten and expanded to take account of recent discoveries, the emphasis remains on principles rather than on detail. This edition, like the first one, is designed to serve many masters: students of genetics concerned primarily with man; students with special medical goals; students for whom the study of human genetics will be one of the foundations for their thinking as educators, psychologists, anthropologists, and social workers. The first ten chapters are intended for all readers; among the later chapters, however, are some that will be of more interest to certain groups of readers than to others. In spite of the wide variety of material covered, the book has a basic unity: the presentation of the principles of human genetics as a means of understanding some of the diversity, as well as the underlying community, of mankind.

This book is based on the work of many persons—some named in the text, but most uncited. Here I can acknowledge only a few who gave specific help. Dr. J. F. Crow commented on the whole manuscript, Dr. Gordon Walls on the sections on color blindness, Dr. J. H. Renwick on linkage, and Dr. W. L. Russell on radiation genetics. Mrs. Eva Sherwood was of constant support in the preparation of the new edition.

Many excellent drawings which Dr. Aloha Hannah-Alava prepared for the first edition have been used again, and many new drawings from the skillful pen of Mrs. Emily Reid have been added. The investigators who generously made new, original photographs available and the publishers and authors who kindly granted permission for the use of copyright material are acknowledged in the figure and table legends. The system of acknowledging borrowed material is explained in the introduction to the references at the end of Chapter 1.

There were more errors in the first edition than I had anticipated. The asked-for corrections came from many sides, and a whole dossier of valuable comments was assembled by Dr. Norman Ford-Walker's keen students at the University of Toronto. Most of the old errors have now been rectified, but how many new ones have slipped in?

In concluding this preface, I take pleasure in referring to the personal relations between Mr. William H. Freeman, his associates, and myself—relations in the distinguished tradition of the publishing craft.

July, 1960   CURT STERN

CONTENTS

ix

CHAPTER 1

INTRODUCTION

The study of human inheritance is concerned with the existence of "inborn" characteristics of human beings: physical and mental, normal and abnormal. In its broadest sense, it deals with those qualities present in all human beings that distinguish them from nonhuman beings, as well as with those qualities which characterize only certain groups of man, certain families, or certain individuals. Thus, it is largely a study of hereditary similarities and differences among human beings. It is concerned with the causes of these similarities and differences and the way in which they are transmitted from generation to generation.

The science of inheritance is called *genetics,* a term derived from the Greek root *gen,* which means to become or to grow into something. It signifies that genetics deals not only with the transmission of hereditary factors but also with the ways in which they express themselves during the development and life of the individual.

The student of human genetics must draw on many sources of information. He obtains his material from studies of families or larger groups—from anthropological, psychological, medical, and sociological investigations. To evaluate the data, he needs the tools of the statistician. Human genetics is based on general principles derived originally from the study of plants and animals —principles which are as valid for man as they are for unicellular and other multicellular organisms. Since these general principles can often be demonstrated more clearly in organisms better adapted to experimental work than man, reference to such studies is often helpful in an analysis of human inheritance.

An understanding of simple inheritance in man was not possible before Mendel's work on peas. Elucidation of the genetics of body size, intelligence scores, and other "quantitative" characters in man was not even begun until Nilsson-Ehle's and East's studies on shades of color in wheat and size of Indian corn paved the way. The peculiar mode of transmission of color blindness in man became clear only after similarly transmitted "sex-linked" traits were found in birds, moths, and flies. The riddle of sex determination was not solved until the cells of grasshoppers and plant bugs had been scrutinized. And no study contributed more toward the clarification of the heredity-environment problem than an investigation of the variability of size in beans. Work on nonhuman organisms will be cited, however, not only for historical reasons, but for the decisive experimental data that illustrate situations in man which are still obscure or that point out possibly significant factors known to play a role in animal or plant genetics but not yet recognized in human genetics.

Man as an Object of Genetic Study.   At first sight, man appears to be an unfavorable object for genetic study. Ideally, the student of genetics works with groups of standardized organisms that are genetically identical or at least approach identity. He tries to breed and raise successive generations under similar environmental conditions. In man, however, the genetic diversity of individuals is great and uncontrolled, and biological and social environments vary greatly. The principal tool of the general geneticist is the experimental crossing of different genetic types. In man, on the other hand, parental unions are entered into with no intent to serve an experimental plan. Studies of inheritance are generally based on knowledge of a series of generations. Consequently, the preferred subjects for genetical study are organisms with rapid succession of parents and offspring. Annual plants and small mammals like mice and rats first served this purpose, with the still shorter-lived fruit flies, molds, and unicellular organisms gaining special favor later. More patience was required for work on fruit or forest trees or on horses and cattle —and relatively less scientific yield was expected. With man, the duration of a generation is alike in the observer and in the object of observation, and personal knowledge of successive generations is therefore restricted. Finally, many factors affecting transmission of hereditary traits obey statistical laws and are best studied when large numbers of offspring are available. In man, these numbers are always small; even large human families fall far short of the size desirable for statistical deductions.

Obstacles to the understanding of nature have always been challenging to the human mind. Even though genetic and environmental diversity in man is largely uncontrollable, the human geneticist can find groups that have similar heredity or similar environments. Even though he cannot arrange for matings in accordance with a research plan, he can collect data from those marriages which happen to fit into his schemes. Even though man's life cycle is longer than that of laboratory organisms, the scientist can devise special methods that enable him to get information from one or two generations, which normally only a longer series would provide. Even though the human family is small, pooling of data from many families may provide enough material for statistical analysis. The human population is large, and its millions of unions give the geneticist an immense amount of material from which to select what he needs.

The Principles of Human Genetics.   This book will present the principles of human genetics, i.e., the general regularities of heredity in man that have been derived from the study of families, pedigrees, and large interrelated groups of individuals called populations. It will describe the various rules of transmission of hereditary traits and some of the methods which enable us to find out what kind of inheritance is involved in specific cases. It will also survey the effects of environment on the action and expression of human genes, the genetic aspects of sex, and the origin of new hereditary traits (mutation). Applications of these principles will be considered under such headings as Genetic Counseling (Chap. 8), Medicolegal Applications (Chap. 12), The Genetic Hazards of Radiation (Chap. 24), Selection in Civilization (Chap. 29), Medical Genetics (Chap. 30), and Genetic Aspects of Race and of Race Mixture (Chaps. 31 and 32).

No attempt will be made to treat systematically the genetics of the seemingly infinite range of normal and abnormal human traits, but many of these will be used as examples to illustrate principles. The reader who wishes to obtain more detailed information on various characters must go to the two-volume work of Gates on human genetics, to the treatise on clinical genetics edited by Sorsby, to von Verschuer's *Genetik des Menschen,* or to other works listed in the bibliography at the end of this chapter. When he consults these books, he will often find fragmentary or apparently conflicting information on the inheritance of specific traits. Only an understanding of the principles of human genetics will make it possible to evaluate such data.

The Scope of Human Genetics.   Human genetics is a young science. When, in the early twentieth century, the modern study of heredity in plants and lower animals resulted in the discovery of the laws of biological inheritance, enthusiastic men drew far-reaching conclusions concerning the hereditary nature of differences among human individuals and of the consequences for mankind of the transmission of these differences to future generations. These conclusions were not just stated as theories, but included plans for "human engineering" involving legal prohibition of reproduction for certain large groups of humans and social incentives that would increase reproduction of other groups. It became evident later that the factual knowledge of man's inheritance was too narrow to justify such actions. The "eugenic movement" became discredited in the eyes of many, and a greater effort was made to accumulate specific information and devise specific methods applicable to human genetics. The work of the past three decades has greatly increased our knowledge, but the preliminary nature of much of it must still be emphasized. This book, accordingly, contains many such phrases as "it is not unlikely" or "it seems highly probable," and even positively worded statements should not be taken as final. Human genetics can claim significant achievements, but, as in any growing science, future discoveries will not only add new facts, but may also invalidate apparently established views.

Knowledge of human genetics does not only satisfy our desire to know about ourselves; it must also form the basis of practical decisions. The physician and public health official need to understand the inheritance of diseases and abnormal characteristics. Every individual should know something about the genetic aspects of selecting a partner for marriage and about the kinds of children he may expect; he should also know that his prospects for physical and mental well-being and for a long or short life are genetically determined. Unavoidably, though often obscurely, social measures affect the type of men and women who will people a country and the earth. In order to gauge such influences, an understanding is needed of the causes of human differences, individual and racial; of the part heredity and environment play in the determination of such differences; and of the role of social organization and education in molding men. If it is proposed to change a population hereditarily, the prospects of successful selection of favored types must first be understood in order to reach rational conclusions; if such a change is feared, the same knowledge is required to evaluate the future.

As will be shown, human genetics has already made important contributions to these practical problems, and there is every reason to believe that its usefulness will increase greatly in years to come.

References

The references listed at the ends of chapters include important sources of the discussion as well as suggestions for further reading. Besides these references, other sources are also cited in the figure legends and table headings. If only the author's name is cited in a figure legend or table heading, the full bibliographical information will be found in the references at the end of the chapter. References in the figure legends or table headings which cite the author's name and, in abbreviated form, the time and place of publication are not given again at the ends of chapters; these are references which should be of further help in tracing the origins and ramifications of the topics treated.

In the figure legends and table headings, an attempt has also been made to indicate whether the illustrative and tabular material borrowed from other authors is unchanged or is in modified form. For both modified and unchanged material, credit is acknowledged in the figure legends and table headings; but for modified material, the author's name is preceded by the word "after."

Some Textbooks on General Genetics

Altenburg, E., 1957. *Genetics*. Rev. ed. 496 pp. Henry Holt, New York.

Colin, E. C., 1956. *Elements of Genetics*. 3rd ed. 498 pp. McGraw-Hill, New York.

Sinnott, E. W., Dunn, L. C., and Dobzhansky, T., 1958. *Principles of Genetics*. 5th ed. 459 pp. McGraw-Hill, New York.

Snyder, L. H., and David, P. R., 1957. *The Principles of Heredity*. 5th ed. 507 pp. D. C. Heath, Boston.

Srb, A. M., and Owen, R. D., 1952. *General Genetics*. 561 pp. W. H. Freeman & Co., San Francisco and London.

Treatises on Human Genetics

The entries marked with an asterisk contain extensive sections devoted to specific organs, organ systems, and disease groups.

*Baur, E., Fischer, E., and Lenz, F., 1931. *Human Heredity*. 734 pp. Macmillan, New York.

*———, 1936. *Menschliche Erblehre und Rassenhygiene*. 4th ed. Vol. I. 601 pp. J. F. Lehmann, Munich.

Boyd, W. C., 1950. *Genetics and the Races of Man*. 453 pp. Little, Brown, Boston.

*Cockayne, E. A., 1933. *Inherited Abnormalities of the Skin and Its Appendages*. 394 pp. Oxford University Press, London.

*Crew, F. A. E., 1947. *Genetics in Relation to Clinical Medicine*. 111 pp. Oliver & Boyd, Edinburgh.

Ford, E. B., 1948. *Genetics for Medical Students*. 3rd ed. 163 pp. Methuen Co., London.

*Francois, J., 1958. *L'Hérédité en Ophthalmologie*. 876 pp. Masson & Co., Paris.

*Gates, R., 1946. *Human Genetics*. 2 vols. 1518 pp. Macmillan, New York.

Giordano, A., 1949. *Avviamento alla Patologia Genetica dell'uomo*. 165 pp. Garzanti, Milan.

Grüneberg, H., 1947. *Animal Genetics and Medicine*. 296 pp. Hoeber, New York and London.

*Gütt, A. (Ed.), 1937–38. *Handbuch der Erbkrankheiten*. 6 vols. Thieme, Leipzig.

Haldane, J. B. S., 1938. *Heredity and Politics*. 202 pp. Norton, New York.

———, 1942. *New Paths in Genetics*. 206 pp. Harper, New York.

———, 1948. The formal genetics of man. Croonian Lecture. *Proc. Royal Society, B.,* **135:** 147–170.

Hogben, L. T., 1931. *Genetic Principles in Medicine and Social Science*. 230 pp. Williams & Norgate, Ltd., London.

———, 1933. *Nature and Nurture*. 143 pp. Norton, New York.

———, 1946. *An Introduction to Mathematical Genetics*. 260 pp. Norton, New York.

Huron, R., and Ruffié, J., 1959. *Les Méthodes en Génétique Générale et en Génétique Humaine*. 556 pp. Masson & Co., Paris.

*Just, G. (Ed.), 1940. *Handbuch der Erbbiologie des Menschen*. 5 vols. in 7. Springer, Berlin.

*Kallmann, F. J., 1953. *Heredity in Health and Mental Disorder*. 315 pp. Norton, New York.

Kemp, T., 1951. *Genetics and Disease*. 330 pp. Oliver & Boyd, Edinburgh.

Komai, T., 1934. *Pedigrees of Hereditary Diseases and Abnormalities Found in the Japanese Race*. 135 pp. Kyoto.

———, 1947. *Pedigrees of Hereditary Diseases and Abnormalities Found in the Japanese Race (1934–1943)*. 225 pp. Hokuryukan.

Lamy, M., 1952. *Précis de Génétique Médicale*. 256 pp. Doin & Co., Paris.

Li, C. C., 1955. *Population Genetics*. 366 pp. University of Chicago Press, Chicago.

*McKusick, V. A., 1960. *Heritable Disorders of Connective Tissue*. 2nd ed. 333 pp. C. V. Mosby, St. Louis.

Mohr, O. L., 1934. *Heredity and Disease*. 253 pp. Norton, New York.

Muller, H. J., Little, C. C., and Snyder, L. H., 1947. *Genetics, Medicine and Man*. 158 pp. Cornell University Press, Ithaca, New York.

Neel, J. V., and Schull, W. J., 1954. *Human Heredity*. 361 pp. University of Chicago Press, Chicago.

*Penrose, L. S., 1954. *The Biology of Mental Defect*. 303 pp. Sidgwick & Jackson, London.

Penrose, L. S., 1959. *Outline of Human Genetics.* 146 pp. Wiley, New York.

Roberts, J. A. Fraser, 1959. *An Introduction to Medical Genetics.* 2nd ed. 263 pp. Oxford University Press, London.

Rostand, J., and Tétry, A., 1955. *Atlas de Génétique Humaine.* 106 pp. Société d'Edition d'enseignement Supérieur, Paris.

Scheinfeld, A., 1950. *The New You and Heredity.* 616 pp. Lippincott, Philadelphia.

————, 1956. *The Human Heredity Handbook.* 276 pp. Lippincott, Philadelphia.

*Siemens, H. W., 1923. *Einführung in die allgemeine und specielle Vererbungspathologie des Menschen.* 2nd ed. 286 pp. Springer, Berlin.

————, 1952. *Grundzüge der Vererbungslehre, Rassenhygiene und Be-völkerungspolitik.* 13th ed. 210 pp. J. F. Lehmann, Munich.

*Sorsby, A., 1951. *Genetics in Ophthalmology.* 251 pp. Butterworth & Co., London.

*———— (Ed.), 1953. *Clinical Genetics.* 580 pp. Butterworth & Co. Ltd., London.

*Touraine, A., 1955. *L'Hérédité en Médecine.* 875 pp. Masson & Co., Paris.

Turpin, R., 1951. *L'Hérédité des Prédispositions Morbides.* 261 pp. Gallimard.

*Verschuer, O. v., 1959. *Genetik des Menschen.* 427 pp. Urban & Schwarzenberg, Muenchen, Berlin.

Vogel, F., 1959. Moderne Probleme der Humangenetik. In: *Ergebnisse der Inneren Medizin und Kinderheilkunde.* **12:** 1–125. Springer, Berlin.

*Weitz, W., 1949. *Die Vererbung innerer Krankheiten.* 2nd ed. 352 pp. Nölke, Hamburg.

Serial Publications Devoted to Human Genetics

The publications marked with an asterisk often consist of separate volumes devoted to specific diseases or disease groups.

Acta Genetica et Statistica Medica (Switzerland).

Acta Geneticae Medicae et Gemellologiae (Italy).

**Acta Psychiatrica et Neurologica Scandinavica.*

American Journal of Human Genetics (United States).

**Analecta Genetica* (Italy).

Annals of Human Genetics (formerly *Annals of Eugenics*) (Great Britain).

Archiv der Julius Claus Stiftung für Vererbungsforschung (Switzerland).

*Copenhagen Universitet: *Opera ex Domo Biologiae Hereditariae Humanae Universitatis Hafniensis* (Denmark).

Eugenics Quarterly (United States).

Eugenics Review (Great Britain).

Human Biology (United States).

Japanese Journal of Human Genetics (Japan).

Journal de Génétique (Switzerland).

Journal of Chronic Diseases: Medical Genetics (a review to be published annually in the United States beginning 1959, by Victor A. McKusick and associates).

Journal of Heredity (United States).

**The Treasury of Human Inheritance* (England).

Zeitschrift für menschliche Vererbungs- und Konstitutionslehre (Germany).

CHAPTER 2

THE BIOLOGICAL BASIS
OF MAN'S INHERITANCE

All the material a human being inherits from his two parents is contained in two cells, the egg and the sperm.

Egg and Sperm

The Human Egg. The human egg (Fig. 1) is a spherical cell about 1/7 of a millimeter, or about 1/175 of an inch, in diameter. Such small measurements are usually given in microns—a micron (μ) being one thousandth of a millimeter; thus the diameter of the human egg is about 130 or 140μ. In spite of its relatively minute size, the egg is one of the largest cells of the human body. Its cellular character is easily recognizable, since it possesses a typical nucleus enclosed in a mass of cytoplasm.

The weight of the human egg has been estimated to be 0.0015 milligram, or approximately one twenty-millionth of an ounce. In this tiny bit of matter is contained the genetic contribution of the mother to her child.

The eggs are produced in two ovaries, organs about the size of walnuts, which are attached to the dorsal wall of the female abdominal cavity. In the ovaries, immature germ cells are found in various stages of growth (Fig. 2). Each egg cell is surrounded by a wall of *follicle cells*. Concurrent with the growth of an egg cell, the follicle cells multiply. Fluid-filled gaps appear between the cells of the follicular wall and, by fusing together, split it into an external and an internal layer. Thus, a mature ovarian follicle originates. It consists of an outer layer of follicle cells, a large, fluid-filled center, and an egg cell located within an inner layer of follicle cells still connected on one side with the outer layer. As growth proceeds, the follicle bulges out on the surface of the ovary. The internal pressure of the follicular fluid stretches the thin sheets of tissue which separate the content of the follicle from the ab-

7

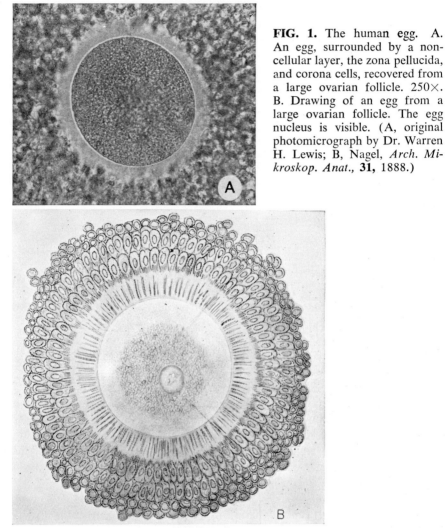

FIG. 1. The human egg. A. An egg, surrounded by a non-cellular layer, the zona pellucida, and corona cells, recovered from a large ovarian follicle. 250×. B. Drawing of an egg from a large ovarian follicle. The egg nucleus is visible. (A, original photomicrograph by Dr. Warren H. Lewis; B, Nagel, *Arch. Mikroskop. Anat.*, **31,** 1888.)

dominal cavity until both the follicle and the wall of the ovary burst. The egg, surrounded by its immediate cover of follicle cells, the *corona,* or *crown,* is released into the abdominal cavity, where it enters the funnel-like opening of the oviduct and starts its journey down the oviduct into the uterus.

If the oviduct is free of sperm, the egg cell disintegrates inside the uterus. If, however, as a result of a recent mating, live sperm are present, the egg may be fertilized in the oviduct and there begin its development. While undergoing the first steps of this process, it will move to the uterus, where it will become embedded in the uterine wall and remain for the nine months of embryonic development.

Normally, only one mature follicle develops during each monthly cycle. It may originate in either the right or left ovary: by and large, each has an

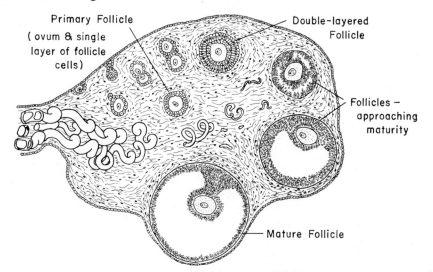

FIG. 2. Diagram of a human ovary with eggs and follicles at various stages of development. (Adapted from Patten, *Embryology of the Pig,* Blakiston, 1931.)

equal share, but one ovary often has several successive ovulations. Occasionally, more than one follicle matures at the same time, either in the same ovary or in both. Consequently, more than one ripe egg may be ready for fertilization at the same time, and a multiple birth may result. Occasionally, too, one follicle may contain more than one egg cell, again setting the stage for a possible multiple birth.

The human egg was discovered in 1827 by Karl Ernst von Bär (1792–1876), the founder of modern embryology. The basic research which led to this discovery was done with dogs. Von Bär obtained a series of female dogs in various stages of pregnancy and succeeded in tracing the embryos back to very small specks of matter—much smaller than the large ovarian follicles which had been thought to be the eggs. Finally, he found that the unbroken follicles contained minute bodies which were identical with the egg and its corona, which at a later stage were present in the oviduct. To confirm that what was true of dogs was also true of man was only a short step.

The Human Sperm.   The father's genetic contribution to a child is contained in the *spermatozoon,* or *sperm* (Fig. 3), which is produced in the testes. Its cellular nature is less obvious than that of the egg. It consists of several parts, called *head, middlepiece,* and *tail.* Their dimensions are:

Head			Middlepiece		Tail	
	Width					
Length	(elliptical face view)	(side view anterior end)	Length	Width	Length	Width
3–5μ	2–3μ	1.8μ	3–6μ	1μ	30–50μ	less than 1μ

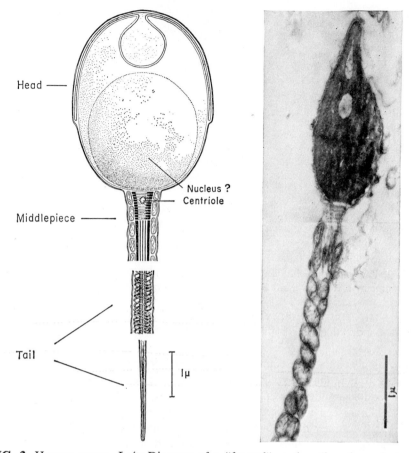

Head

Nucleus ?
Centriole

Middlepiece

Tail

1μ

FIG. 3. Human sperm. *Left:* Diagram of a "frontal" section (based on electron-microscopic studies). *Right:* Electronmicrograph of a somewhat tangential "longi-tudinal" section through head and middlepiece, 19,640×. (Left, Schultz-Larsen; right, Lord Rothschild, *Brit. Med. J., 1,* 1958.)

The different types of immature germ cells, each representing a different stage in the development of mature spermatozoa, are called *spermatogonia, spermatocytes,* and *spermatids.* Each consists of a mass of cytoplasm and a nucleus, and is thus a typical cell. In the course of the transformation of a spermatid into a spermatozoon, striking changes take place (Fig. 4). The nucleus becomes smaller and more compact. It forms a large part of the head of the mature sperm, which is somewhat pear-shaped in side view and oval in face view. A minute body in the cytoplasm, the *centriole,* sends out a bundle of fibers, which, embedded in a thin cylinder of cytoplasm, become the tail. Most of the original cytoplasm of the immature cell is cast off and disintegrates inside the testes: a small part remains in the head, another develops into the conical middlepiece, and a third forms the outer covering of the tail.

Inside the numerous fine tubes (Fig. 5) that constitute the greater part of the testes, many millions of cells are constantly being transformed into mature spermatozoa. They are stored in the ducts that lead from the testes to the outside. A discharge of human semen consists on the average of more than two hundred million spermatozoa suspended in the fluid secretions of glands which form part of the male genital system.

Human spermatozoa were first seen in 1677 by a student named Ham. He reported his observation to the pioneer of microscopy, van Leeuwenhoek (1632–1723), who described the sperm in detail in some of his famous letters to the Royal Society of London. The sperm cells, swimming around in the seminal fluid with their motile tails, appeared not unlike the small animals which Leeuwenhoek had discovered in drops of pond water; he therefore called them spermatozoa, or "seed animals." Although Leeuwenhoek himself believed that the spermatozoa were the essential elements of the male reproductive material, others doubted this and regarded them as independent organisms with no known function. A hundred years later, Spallanzani (1729–1799) tested the two conflicting theories by experiment. He filtered the seminal fluid of dogs and injected either unfiltered semen or a sperm-free filtrate into dogs' vaginas, thus inventing a new method of artificial insemination. (A similar procedure had been practiced much earlier by Arabs in the breeding of horses.) Offspring resulted only from insemination with fluid containing sperm. Spallanzani did not draw the conclusion that the sperm takes part in the development of the egg, but believed that it in some way enabled the seminal fluid to stimulate development. Final proof for the theory that the

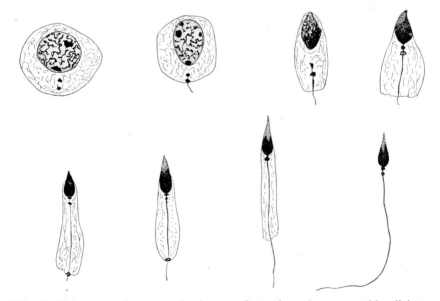

FIG. 4. Eight successive stages in the transformation of a spermatid cell into a mature sperm. (After Stieve, *Hdbch. d. Mikroskop. Anat. d. Menschen,* **7,** 1930.)

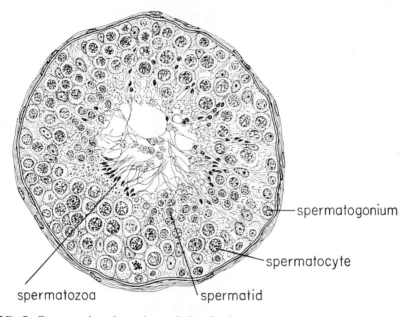

spermatogonium

spermatocyte

spermatozoa

spermatid

FIG. 5. Cross section through a tubule of a human testis. Cells in various stages of spermatogenesis: spermatogonia → spermatocytes → spermatids → spermatozoa. (After Stieve, *Hdbch. d. Mikroskop. Anat. d. Menschen,* **7,** 1930.)

sperm cell is the essential contribution of the male to his offspring was not obtained until 200 years after Ham's and Leeuwenhoek's discovery, when studies on fertilization of sea-urchin eggs showed the fusion of a single egg and a single spermatozoon at the beginning of each new life.

Fertilization. To fertilize an egg, a sperm must penetrate the corona surrounding it. This process is probably facilitated by the action of an enzyme (hyaluronidase) in the seminal fluid that breaks down the substance (hyaluronic acid) which cements the cells of the corona together. As soon as a sperm fuses with an egg, the *zona pellucida,* which surrounds it, undergoes an important change which prevents the entry of other sperm. Conceivably, two or more spermatozoa may make contact with an egg so nearly simultaneously as to accomplish a double or multiple fertilization. There is evidence from other organisms that such fertilizations seldom lead to normal development. If they occur in man, development probably stops at a very early stage, before formation of an embryo.

After the egg and sperm have fused, the head of the sperm cell absorbs fluid from the cytoplasm of the egg, increases in size, and becomes spherical, resuming the appearance of a normal nucleus and resembling the nucleus of the egg, both in volume and morphological detail. The two nuclei approach each other until they are in contact, and finally fuse. This nuclear fusion may be regarded as the ultimate process in fertilization. The fertilized egg cell is called the *zygote*, a term also frequently used to designate the individual who develops from the fertilized egg cell.

The female and male *gametes,* egg and sperm, contain all of the hereditary potentialities of a future child. The small space in which these potentialities lie can perhaps best be comprehended if one considers how large a volume would be required to contain the hereditary potentialities of all men of the next generation. Mankind, at present, comprises somewhat more than 2,500,000,000 individuals, and it is probable that at least 4,000,000,000 persons will be alive when all now living have died. These future 4,000,-000,000 people will originate from 4,000,000,000 egg cells and an equal number of sperm cells. Calculating the volume of a sphere the size of a human egg and multiplying it by 4,000,000,000 yields a total volume of about five quarts: this is the material contribution of all mothers of this generation to all beings of the next. By making a similar calculation for the volume of sperm, it is found that the total hereditary contribution of all fathers of this generation will be contained in a mass smaller than an aspirin tablet!

The Genetic Significance of the Nucleus.   Egg and sperm are greatly unequal in size, but the hereditary influences of the mother and father are about equal. This is not only known from the general observation that children, on the whole, do not resemble the female more than the male parent, but it can be especially well demonstrated by the offspring of interracial crosses. The children from unions of whites and negroes are mulattoes, regardless of whether the mother is negro and the father white or whether they have a white mother and a negro father. If one considers that the sperm consists almost entirely of a nucleus, while the egg is made up both of a nucleus and a considerable amount of cytoplasm, it would perhaps have been expected that the children of negro mothers and white fathers would be darker and, in general, more negro-like than those resulting from "reciprocal matings." The observation that the children are *not* different from each other suggests that the cytoplasm of the egg does not transmit the specific properties which distinguish the two parents, but that the two nuclei, which are strikingly similar, are the material carriers of the hereditary contributions of the parents. It was this reasoning, first suggested by O. Hertwig (1849–1922) in the second half of the nineteenth century, which focused the attention of biologists on the nucleus as the bearer of hereditary qualities.

Chromosomes

Mitosis.   When it was realized that the nuclei were probably the essential agents in the transmission of hereditary differences, it was natural to seek more knowledge about them. It was soon found that such knowledge could be obtained from a study of cell division (Fig. 6).

When a cell divides, it forms two daughter cells, each of which derives its nucleus and cytoplasm from the nucleus and cytoplasm of the mother cell.

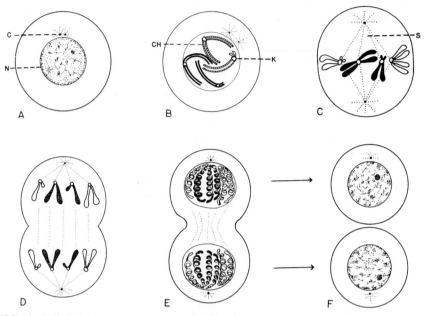

FIG. 6. Cell division and mitosis. C = centriole; N = nucleus; CH = chromosome; K = kinetochore; S = spindle.

Division of the cytoplasm is usually a relatively simple process: a furrow appears on the surface of the cell around its whole circumference and gradually grows deeper and deeper until it separates the cytoplasm into two halves.

While the division of the cytoplasm is under way, the nucleus is also dividing in two—a division that involves a much more elaborate series of events. Inside the nucleus, which in the undivided cell appears as a rather undifferentiated vesicle (Fig. 6, A), well-defined structures become visible (Fig. 6, B–D). They have various shapes: some are short rods and others long rods; some are V-shaped and others J-shaped. Although these bodies can be observed in living cells, they are more frequently studied in cells which have been fixed—that is, killed in such a manner as to cause very little change in their structure—and then treated with special stains. These stains are taken up more intensely by such nuclear structures than by the rest of the cell; some stains are exclusively absorbed by them. They have, therefore, been called *chromosomes* (from the Greek words *chromos* = color, *soma* = body).

At about the time the chromosomes become visible in the dividing cell, the nuclear membrane and the nucleus disappear, and the chromosomes become associated with a new structure, the *spindle,* which now develops inside the cell (Fig. 6, C, D). (It derived its name from the spindle used in weaving, a familiar household object in earlier times.) In most animal cells, including those of man, the spindle is an elongated body that resembles two cones joined at their bases. It is formed as the centriole of the cell is duplicated and the two centrioles move apart (Fig. 6, B): these bodies assume positions on opposite sides of the cell, and the spindle forms between them. The centrioles are thus the poles of the spindle.

By the time the spindle is fully formed, the chromosomes have assembled in its equatorial plane (Fig. 6, C). At this stage, they show clearly the most important feature of nuclear division, which could be seen only indistinctly earlier. Each chromosome appears to be double (Fig. 6, B, C), with two identical strands lying nearly parallel to each other and joined at only one short region: close to the ends of the rod-shaped chromosomes and at the bend of the V- or J-shaped ones. This region has staining properties different from the rest of the chromosomes and is known as the *kinetochore,* or *centromere.* The kinetochores are anchored on the spindle; the rest of the chromosome may extend into the cytoplasm of the cell.

The final separation of the sister strands is initiated by a division of the kinetochores. They divide in such a way that one of the two sister kinetochores becomes connected with one of the sister chromosome strands, and the other kinetochore with the other chromosome strand. The sister kinetochores then move along the spindle to opposite poles, dragging behind them the sister strands. Thus, two groups of chromosomes move along the spindle, one group toward each pole. The two groups are identical in make-up, since each chromosome of one group has a sister chromosome in the other. As they near the poles, the chromosomes become less distinct, a nuclear membrane forms around each group, and, gradually, each daughter nucleus takes on the diffuse appearance which the mother nucleus exhibited before its division (Fig. 6, E, F).

The somewhat thread-like appearance of the chromosomes during the early stages has provided the name *mitosis* (from the Greek *mitos* = thread) for the whole process of nuclear division. Cell division and mitosis are so synchronized that the circular furrow which cleaves the cytoplasm into two halves, and which lies in the same plane as the equator of the spindle, separates the two new cells at the same time that each chromosomal group becomes transformed into a daughter nucleus. The whole process of mitosis and cell division ordinarily takes less than an hour, but wide variations in its duration are found.

Continuity of the Chromosomes.   It is known that the chromosomes never lose their identity in the nucleus. That they are indistinct during the period when the cell is not dividing seems to be due to the fact that they are then long and extended threads which are so thin that they are almost invisible. The relatively thick chromosomes of the mitotic periods are these same long threads concentrated into tightly wound coils.

Chromosome Reproduction.   The continuous existence of the chromosomes in the nuclei accounts for the fact that in general each cell within the same organism has the same number of chromosomes. A man's body is made up of thousands of billions of cells that are all derived, by division, from one fertilized egg. Even in the cells of the adult organism, division and mitosis continue to form new cells in order to replace old or lost ones. Typically, in each dividing nucleus each chromosome duplicates itself, and each daughter nucleus receives one of the duplicates. Thus, mitosis supplies the nuclei of all cells with a complete reproduction of the chromosomes of the fertilized egg.

The chromosomes of the billions of body cells are, however, not simply division products of the original chromosomes of egg and sperm. We must think of the reproduction of chromosomes as a process by which the original chromosome builds a copy of itself out of the materials present in the cell. This process takes place some time before the separation of sister chromosomes. The dual nature of each chromosome can be seen as soon as the chromosomes become visible in mitosis.

The Significance of Mitosis.   As soon as mitosis had been discovered, biologists began to speculate about its meaning. Why should the nuclear material be arranged in thread-like structures, and why should identical sister threads be transmitted to both daughter nuclei? The contrast between the extreme precision of assuring equality of nuclear matter to the daughter nuclei and the less accurate method of dividing the cytoplasm of the original cell between the daughter cells called for an explanation. It was suspected that the nucleus contained many different kinds of essential substances and that, if these substances were present in a haphazard arrangement, simple constriction of the nucleus might not provide each daughter nucleus with part of every one of them. Would not the safest method for a qualitatively equal distribution of the nuclear content during division be the following? Arrange all these different substances in one or several linear structures, let these form identical linear sister structures, and have each double thread send its two representatives into opposite daughter nuclei.

Such reasoning treated cells as if they were constructed in order to achieve a specific purpose—in this case, to insure that every kind of hypothetical self-reproducing nuclear element became equally represented in the daughter cells. To inquire what purpose a biological phenomenon has is not always meaningful, for there are processes and structures that have no significance for the survival of the organisms of which they are a part and may even have slightly harmful effects. In mitosis, however, this inquiry was justified, since it was most unlikely that a process of such universal occurrence could have been retained during the evolution of all species if it were not of great importance to them. The assumption of a linear arrangement of many qualitatively different essential substances was first proposed more than seventy years ago, by Wilhelm Roux (1850–1924). He added the hypothesis that the essential substances were basic units representing hereditary properties. After many years of microscopic studies of chromosomes and after the twentieth-century science of genetics had greatly increased our knowledge,

Roux's ideas were proven to be correct by Thomas Hunt Morgan (1866–1945) and Alfred H. Sturtevant (b. 1891).

The Chromosome Number of Man.   As a rule the nuclei of the mature egg and the sperm each contribute the same number of chromosomes to the zygote. The number characteristic of the gametes of a particular species is called *haploid,* that characteristic of the zygote *diploid* (from the Greek *haploos* = single, *diploos* = double, *-id* from *eidos* = form; i.e., haploid, diploid = single or double number of formative genetic elements). It was easy to establish the haploid and diploid chromosome numbers in many species of animals and plants in which the chromosomes are relatively large and not numerous. In many other species the apparently simple task of counting chromosomes led different investigators to different results. In particular, the chromosomes of mammals proved to be not only rather small and numerous but also difficult to fix. Imperfect penetration of the fixing fluid into the tissues or conditions unfavorable for fixing are common, and this leads to clumping together of chromosomes, thus making it difficult to decide whether an observed "chromosome" is really a single element or a conglomerate of two or even more actually separate chromosomes. These difficulties were at least in part responsible for the many different chromosome numbers in man which were reported by various early observers. Gradually, however, agreement seemed to have been reached. For about thirty years, most students of the subject were satisfied that in man the diploid number was 48 and the haploid number 24.

Unexpectedly, in 1956, the question became open again. Tjio and Levan, in Sweden, had prepared cultures of lung tissue from a number of aborted human embryos. Making use of a special method of handling the cells that leads to contraction of the individual chromosomes but spaces them widely apart, these cytologists obtained unusually clear preparations of fixed cells which, beyond any reasonable doubt, showed 46 chromosomes (Fig. 7, A). Some months later, Ford and Hamerton, in England, produced evidence that the germ cells in the testes of several men likewise possessed 46 chromosomes, present separately in the spermatogonia and as 23 pairs in the first of the two divisions of the spermatocytes (Fig. 7, B; see also Chap. 4). Since these discoveries, many cells from various organs or tissues have been studied. In nearly all, 46 chromosomes have been counted, the few deviations from this number probably being caused by abnormal processes of chromosome distribution which will be described below.

It would then seem that the chromosome number of man is 46, but a reservation has to be added to this statement: Kodani, who studied cells of the testes of Japanese hospital patients, reported that he found different chromosome numbers in different men—46 in most, 48 in some, and 47 in at least one. In cells from the testes of eight American whites, the same investigator counted 46 chromosomes in those from seven, and 48 in those from the other. A comparison of the chromosomes suggested to Kodani that

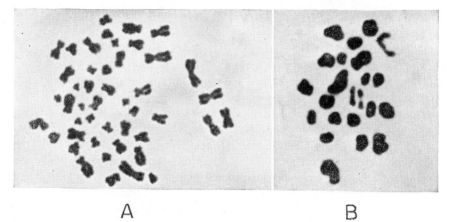

A   B

FIG. 7. The human chromosomes in dividing cells.   A. From a tissue culture of embryonic lung cells. The 46 chromosomes appear as double structures, ready to divide. 1,530×.   B. From a first spermatocyte in a testis. The chromosomes have formed 23 pairs. The elongated pair in the upper-right corner consists of the sex chromosomes; the X-chromosome, which forms approximately the upper four-fifths of the structure; and the Y-chromosome, which forms the lower fifth (see p. 21). 2,610×. (A, Tjio and Levan, *Hereditas,* **42,** 1956; B, Ford and Hamerton, *Nature,* **178,** 1956.)

all men possess 46 normal chromosomes but that some men, in addition, have one or two small "supernumerary" chromosomes. Such supernumerary chromosomes are known to exist in certain plants and some insects, in which they seem to have little importance in the transmission of hereditary properties.

The presence of more than 46 chromosomes in the germ cells of some males is unexpected, since all recent counts, in cells from other tissues from different individuals, including Japanese other than those studied by Kodani, have not revealed the existence of supernumerary chromosomes. In a few animals and plants the chromosome content of cells of somatic and germinal tissues has been found to differ. But before making any analogies, it remains to be seen whether the presence of more than 46 chromosomes in the germ cells of normal humans can be confirmed by other investigators or whether it will be agreed that the normal number is 46. In any case, on the basis of the supposition (here we make an analogy!) that if supernumerary chromosomes occur they are not essential, the fundamental chromosome number of man may be considered to be 46.

The chromosome numbers of other primates have also recently been re-studied. The Rhesus monkey, whose diploid chromosome number had long been given as 48, is now known to possess only 42 chromosomes, but the original finding of 48 chromosomes in the chimpanzee has been confirmed. Other primate species have chromosome numbers as widely different as 34, 42, 44, 54, 60, and 66.

Variations in Chromosome Numbers in the Individual.   Normal mitosis during the development of a human being from the fertilized egg cell is to be expected to produce only cells with the diploid chromosome number characteristic of man, and all cells of his body should contain the same number. Apart from reservations concerning the complete accuracy of the older counts, it can be said that the diploid number of chromosomes has, indeed, been observed in many cells—for instance, in cells of the ovaries, testes, spleen, liver, lungs, and embryonic membranes; in white blood cells, bone-marrow cells, and cells of connective tissues.

There are, however, counts on record which gave considerably lower or higher numbers than the diploid for some cells. Some of these aberrant numbers are clearly the results of faulty technique or misinterpretation. Many, though, are correct: they are a result of the fact that mitosis, in spite of its marvelous accuracy, is a mechanism subject to mishap. It is known that occasionally two sister chromosomes may fail to move to opposite poles ("nondisjunction"; Fig. 8, A). The result is a pair of unlike daughter nuclei, one with one chromosome more than the diploid number, and the other with one

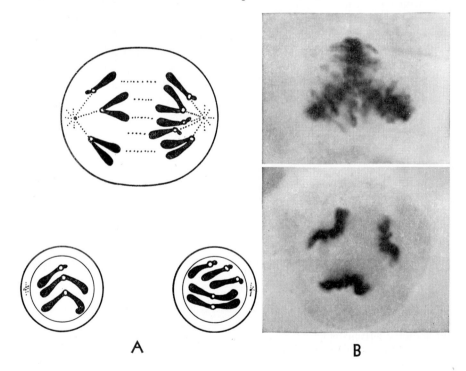

A   B

FIG. 8. Abnormal distribution of chromosomes.   A. "Nondisjunction." *Above:* Two daughter chromosome strands go jointly toward the right spindle pole. *Below:* The resulting two daughter cells, one deficient for a chromosome, the other with an extra chromosome.   B. Two cells with tripolar spindles. The chromosomes divide typically but are distributed irregularly to three instead of two daughter nuclei. (Original photomicrograph from Dr. R. Alava.)

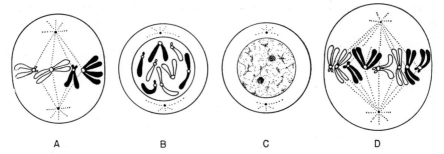

A   B   C   D

FIG. 9. Formation of a cell with doubled chromosome number.   A. 4 chromosomes on spindle.   B. Breakdown of spindle; chromosomes have divided.   C. Formation of resting nucleus.   D. Subsequent mitosis; 8 chromosomes, ready to divide.

chromosome less. In a person who began life with 46 chromosomes, a cell with 47 and another with 45 would thus be formed. Once this has happened, the atypical chromosome numbers will be transmitted to each cell's subsequent generations; later mitosis in the cell with 47 chromosomes will result in two cells with 47 each, and mitosis in the cell with 45 chromosomes will result in two cells with this number. Further mitoses will keep constant the atypical chromosome numbers.

Another type of "accident" results when a nucleus that contains 46 chromosomes goes through mitosis only up to the stage in which the chromosomes and their kinetochores become duplicated (see Fig. 9). Owing to breakdown of the spindle mechanism, separation of sister chromosomes does not take place; and when the new nuclear membrane forms, it encloses the 92 chromosomes. When mitosis occurs again, each of the 92 chromosomes behaves typically and duplicates itself (Fig. 10) so that the two daughter nuclei receive a "tetraploid" number of chromosomes. Still other abnormalities in the distribution of chromosomes have been observed, which account for a wide range of deviations from their typical number (Fig. 8, B).

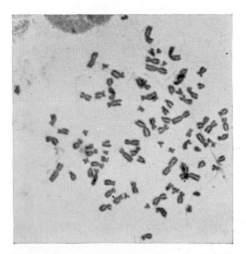

FIG. 10. A tetraploid cell with its 92 chromosomes; from tissue culture. (Original from Dr. S. Makino.)

In many tissues the frequency of cells that do not have the normal diploid number of chromosomes seems to be high. It is very likely, however, that except for tumor cells most cells with aberrant chromosome numbers have low viability—that is, ability to survive—and either disintegrate without further division or, at least, grow and reproduce more slowly than cells with a normal chromosome complement. This view is supported by the results of an experiment in which human cells without nuclei, and hence without chromosomes, were produced in tissue cultures: they retained many normal features of cellular behavior for nearly two days, but then degenerated abruptly. Although this is admittedly an extreme example, the permanence of the body seems to depend on the basic constancy of the diploid chromosome constitution.

The Chromosome Set. A careful study of the diploid chromosomes in man shows (1) that they are of different sizes and shapes (Fig. 11); and (2) that, with one exception, there are two of each type of chromosome in each nucleus. Thus, in the cell whose chromosomes are arranged in pairs in Figure 11, A, each chromosome of the first pair is very large, and the arms of each are almost the same length. The chromosomes of the next pair are about the same length as the first, but with unequal arms; the third are the same shape as the first, but smaller; and so on. About half of all chromosomes in a normal cell can be clearly shown to belong to pairs. Of the remaining chromosomes, all but two can also be arranged in like pairs of "homologous" chromosomes, but a few of them are so similar that a definite assignment of partners is difficult. In other organisms, where differences in size and shape of all chromosomes are more pronounced than in man, it has been proved beyond doubt that there are two of each kind. Purely for convenience in reference, numbers are assigned to the chromosomes, grouping them according to relative length of arms and total size, and, at times, more subtle differences such as the presence or absence of minute terminal structures called _satellites._

A diagram of the chromosomes of the human male, based on average measurements, is shown in Figure 11, B. The different investigators who have supplied the two parts of Figure 11 have come to very similar conclusions about the dimensions and shapes of the chromosomes. (Some discrepancies are apparently due to having given the same chromosome a different number.)

The exception—also encountered in many animals—to the rule that human chromosomes occur in pairs is regularly found in the male. In the cells of females, each chromosome can be matched with another, but in the cells of males, there are two that are unlike any others. The smaller of these, the _Y-chromosome,_ is present exclusively in males. The other, the _X-chromosome,_ occurs as a single chromosome in males, but twice—as a pair—in females. These two types of chromosomes are called _sex chromosomes,_ and their significance will be discussed in the chapters on sex-linkage and sex determination: the "regular" chromosomes are called _autosomes._ In summary, there are basically 22 pairs of autosomes in man, and a twenty-third pair of sex chromosomes, which are alike in the female but unlike in the male.

We have seen that 23 of the 46 chromosomes in the cells of a human body originally come from the egg which formed within the mother, and the other 23 from the sperm produced by the father. It should now be made clear that the 23 chromosomes which an egg or a sperm contains are not an arbitrary collection of 23 chromosomes, but one of each of 23 different kinds. Such an assortment is called a *chromosome set*. Every human being contains within his body (or somatic) cells two sets of 23 different chromosomes—one set derived from his mother, the other from his father.

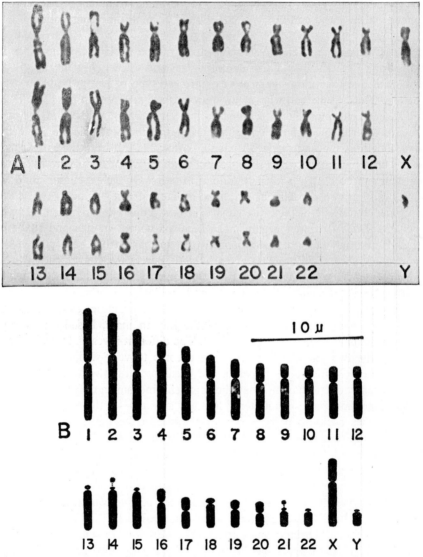

FIG. 11. The human chromosomes (autosomes 1–22, sex chromosomes X and Y). A. From a male cell in culture. The 46 chromosomes are from a photomicrographic print, cut singly, arranged in pairs, and grouped according to sizes and relative lengths of arms. 3,200×. B. Diagram of the 24 different kinds of chromosomes in male cells from cultures, with 46 chromosomes. Chromosomes 14 and 21 each show a satellite. (A, Tjio and Puck, rearranged; B, Chu and Giles.)

Abnormal Chromosome Numbers in Individuals.   The same or similar processes which give rise to variations in chromosome number among somatic cells can also produce gametes with either more or less than 23 chromosomes. Most zygotes with abnormal chromosome numbers are likely to develop abnormally and die at an early stage. Under certain conditions, however, the presence of three like chromosomes instead of a pair is compatible with survival during development and into later life, though the resulting individuals deviate from normal. This is true of Mongolian idiots and some types of individuals with abnormal sexual differentiation, which will be discussed in Chapters 20 and 22.

Even an apparently triploid individual has been discovered. Most of the cells of this severely defective male child have 69 chromosomes (66 autosomes + 2X + Y). Presumably, he came from either a normal haploid egg fertilized by an exceptional diploid sperm, or from an exceptional diploid egg fertilized by a normal haploid sperm, or possibly from fertilization of a haploid egg by two haploid sperm.

Minor Differences in Chromosomal Constitution.   Measurements, made by the same observers, of the length of chromosomes in two Russians and one Japanese were identical for three of the longest chromosomes, but three other long chromosomes were larger in the Japanese than in the Russians. Even within the same individual two homologous chromosomes may differ slightly. (This has been reported for American whites.) Because not only similar differences but others as well have been found in many animals and plants, it may be expected that further differences in man's chromosome structure will be discovered. Some of these may well be characteristic of a single racial group or of several different groups, but others will undoubtedly be found in different individuals in the same group. Chromosomal polymorphism is of no more significance than polymorphism in other traits, such as body size, hair color, or blood group.

The Linear Order of Chromosomal Structures.   A careful study of chromosomes in certain stages of the immature germ cells, in which they are relatively uncoiled long threads, has shown that these threads appear to be covered by a succession of fine beads, the *chromomeres* (Fig. 12). These chromomeres were found to be constant features of each chromosome. They are of different sizes and are arranged differently on each of the 23 pairs of chromosomes. Thus, a chromosome may have a small chromomere at one end, then a series of four slightly larger ones, then two smaller ones, and so on along the length of the chromosome. This is shown in the figure of a specific human chromosome in which it is also seen that the distances between successive chromomeres vary, as do the chromomeres' staining capacities (Fig. 12).

The patterns of chromomeres observed in fixed preparations may not rep-

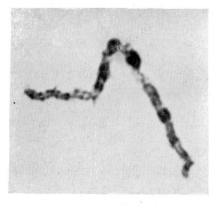

FIG. 12. Human chromomeres. Two closely paired homologous chromosomes of an immature male germ cell. *Above:* Photomicrograph, 2,380×. *Below:* Diagram of the chromomere sequence. (Yerganian, *Am. J. Human Genet.*, **9,** 1957.)

resent well the actual structure of living chromosomes. But their constancy from cell to cell shows at least that constant and linearly arranged structural peculiarities exist in each chromosome and that these determine where, after fixation, a chromomere should appear and what its size and staining properties will be.

Genes

The most detailed insight into the linear arrangement of specific structures along the length of the chromosomes has been gained from study of the so-

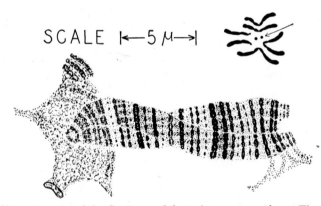

FIG. 13. Chromosomes of the fly *Drosophila melanogaster*. *Above:* The 8 chromosomes of an ovarian cell. *Below:* The two dotlike chromosomes of the ovarian cell as they appear, at the same magnification, in the cell of a larval salivary gland. Note the identical type of cross banding of the two paired chromosomes. (Bridges, *J. Hered.*, **26,** 1935.)

called giant chromosomes of the salivary glands of fly larvae of various species. These chromosomes, instead of resembling threads, look like rather wide cylinders marked by many crossbands or discs (Fig. 13). Just as the size of chromomeres and distances between them vary, so the bands of the salivary gland chromosomes may be thick or thin, close together or far apart; and all this in a manner constant and characteristic of each chromosome of a set, so that it is possible to number every band. Such microscopically visible linear differentiation of the chromosomes is highly suggestive of the linear arrangement of entities representing hereditary properties as postulated by Roux and demonstrated by Morgan. These entities are now called *genes*. It is natural to ask: Are the bands the genes themselves or are they, at least, associated with them? And the answer is: There is much evidence that they are associated; less evidence that they are identical.

The Localization of Genes.   An introduction to human genetics is not the place to give a detailed account of the evidence for the existence of genes and the localization of each gene at a specific point on a specific chromosome. Such a task belongs to a general treatise on genetics. Since, however, the concept of genes underlies all discussions of human genetics, an example of the experimental, factual basis on which the concept is based will be given here. This example is only one of many investigations of plants and animals which, either by similar or by fundamentally different methods, have led to the recognition that the genes are localized in the chromosomes, and in an orderly manner.

Localization by Means of a Deficient Chromosome.   H. J. Muller discovered that X-rays may, besides producing other effects, permanently remove sections of chromosomes. In the fruit fly, *Drosophila melanogaster,* such sections seldom include the ends of a chromosome but are taken out somewhere between them. The remaining end pieces may fuse together at their breakage points, resulting in a chromosome which has a deletion. It is not possible to direct X-rays in such a fashion as to excise any desired section of a chromosome. Rather, the experimenter irradiates the whole fly, after which some of its cells show one or more deletions in different chromosomes or in different regions of the same chromosome. The deletions will be of various lengths, some so short as to be hardly discernible under the strongest microscope and some so large as to leave only the extreme end sections of the original chromosome.

Most offspring of an X-rayed fly are normal, but a few are not: some of the latter have an abnormality called Notch wing. Fruit flies normally have wings whose outline is smooth and continuous (Fig. 14, A); but in Notch flies the wings look as if notches had been cut out of them (Fig. 14, B). This Notch character is transmitted to later generations. Apparently, the irradiation of the parent flies produces a change in some of the gametes which causes loss of ability to produce normal-winged individuals. It is

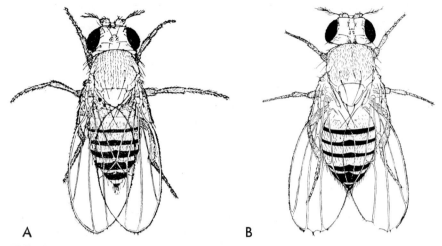

FIG. 14. *Drosophila melanogaster.* A. Normal female. B. Notch female. (A, Morgan, Bridges, and Sturtevant, *Bibliograph. Genet.,* **2**, 1925; B, Mohr, *Zeitschr. Abst. Vererb.,* **32**, 1923.)

possible to study the chromosomes of the Notch-winged flies under the microscope. There is no visible change in the chromosomes of some; the X-rays presumably caused alterations of the hereditary entities in an inter-band region or at a submicroscopic level. In many, however, a specific rod-shaped chromosome shows absence of a specific region (Fig. 15, A). From this, it can be concluded that the ability to cause the development of a normal wing depends on the presence of an entity in the region which is missing from the deficient chromosome. This entity is called a "gene for

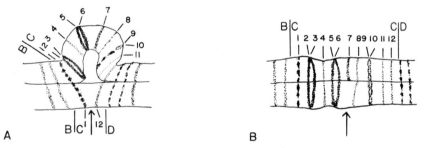

FIG. 15. Notch deficiencies in the chromosomes of two different strains of *Drosophila melanogaster.* A short section of a chromosome pair in a salivary gland nucleus is shown. (The chromosomes of Drosophila have been divided into 102 main sections [1 to 102], each of which is divided into six subsections [A to F]. Within each subsection, a variable number of individual bands are labeled 1, 2, etc. In these figures, subsection C of section 3 is presented ["3C"]). A. The upper chromosome is normal, containing all bands, 3C1 through 3C12. In the lower chromosome the bands in sections 3B and 3D and bands 3C1 and 3C12 are present, so that pairing has taken place. However, bands 3C2 through 3C11 are absent. B. Only band 3C7 is missing from the deficient chromosome.

normal wing outline," or a "gene for not-Notch wings." It may be represented by the symbol N^+ ($+$ = normal).

Genes and Chromosome Bands.   In the giant chromosomes of the salivary gland cell, the location of the gene N^+ may be narrowed down to a very short section. Whenever a visible loss of chromosomal material accompanies the loss of the gene for not-Notch, at least one band in the chromosome, referred to as the 3C7 band, is absent. Some of the deficient chromosomes show loss of this band only (Fig. 15, B), others the loss of a larger number of bands; but all have lost the 3C7 band (Fig. 16). It follows that either

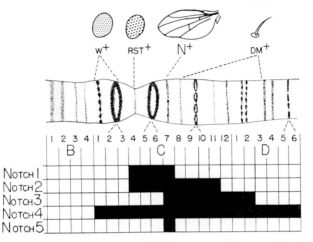

FIG. 16. *Above:* linear arrangement of four genes of Drosophila in relation to bands in chromosome sections 3B–D. *Below:* the extent of five different Notch deficiencies is indicated by the length of the five black bars. The bands located in these sections are absent in the Notch strains; band 3C7 is absent in the chromosomes of all five strains. See text also. (After Slizynska, *Genetics,* **23,** 1938.)

this band or its immediate interband neighborhood is the seat of the gene for not-Notch. In similar ways, other genes have been localized, as indicated in Figure 16. Thus, the gene w^+ ("not-white"), whose loss causes the flies to have white, instead of their normal red, eyes lies to the left of that for not-Notch, within the region indicated by the bands 3C1 to 3C3. Between the genes for red eye and normal wing outline, at the 3C4 band, lies the gene rst^+ ("not-roughest"), whose absence leads to an irregular rough appearance of the eye surface. To the right of N^+ is the gene dm^+ ("not-diminished"), which must be present if bristles are to develop to normal size. Its exact location in the chromosome has not been determined, but it is known to be somewhere between 3C7 and 3D3.

In Drosophila, hereditary differences, such as Notch and normal wing, or rough and smooth eye, can by no means always be traced back to presence or absence of a region or band in a chromosome. Cases of visible loss have been selected for the foregoing analysis, but most inherited abnormalities are found in flies whose chromosomes have all bands present. Furthermore, each different type of abnormality is not distinguished by the presence or absence of some genic content of the chromosomes; rather, all genes are usually present, though in modified form. Notch wings can be caused by the absence of the 3C7 band, but an invisible modification of the gene associated with 3C7 can also cause them. Successful localization of genes has not been restricted to Drosophila and other experimental organisms. In man, too, a beginning has been made in the determination of the linear arrangement and approximate location of genes (see Chap. 15).

We have seen that an individual possesses a pair of each kind of chromosome. Since each chromosome contains a series of *loci* (from the Latin *locus* = place), occupied by different genes, and since the two chromosomes of a pair have the same arrangement of genes, it follows that each individual has two of each kind of gene. Just as each of the 23 kinds of chromosomes has a partner, so has each gene, the two forming a pair of genes occupying homologous loci on a pair of homologous chromosomes. The two partner genes are called *allelomorphs,* or, more commonly, *alleles,* a term which means "the other one." The two alleles of any given gene in an individual may be compared to twins, and the genes making up the hereditary endowment of an individual may be compared to a population in which every individual has a twin.

The Number of Genic Loci in Man

Genes are parts of chromosomes, and it should be possible someday to define them in terms of specific molecular structure. It seems highly probable that genes consist of chemical substances, called deoxyribonucleic acids (DNA), which are typically found only in chromosomes. DNA can be extracted from cells and studied in the test tube. Within the cells each specific DNA compound is able to reproduce, i.e., to make more of itself during growth and chromosomal replication; to undergo occasional changes—*mutations*—and then reproduce itself in the changed form; and to participate in the biochemical reactions which are the basis of the functioning and development of the individual cells and of the whole body. Just as a man is not simply defined by the chemical elements of which his body is composed but rather by their complex organization and dynamic interaction, so the biological term gene refers to the role which the DNA molecules play in the life of an organism.

DNA molecules are long chains of molecular subunits, and it is still not clear whether each gene consists of a specific DNA molecule, separable from all others, or whether two or more genes are part of a single DNA molecule. If we raise the question of the number of genes in an organism, we must specify what we mean by the term gene. Since we cannot study genes in isolation, even if we can study DNA in this way, we must define them by properties recognizable in the living cell or the individual. If we postulate that each gene is directly responsible for a distinct primary property of the cell—for instance, the determination of enzyme specificity—then we might someday estimate the number of genes from the number of discoverable properties of this kind.

Estimates of number of genes in Drosophila have been based on counts of bands in the salivary gland chromosomes and on such indirect approaches as estimating (a) the average frequency of genic changes (mutations) of a single gene, and (b) that of the sum of all genes. The ratio of $b:a$ then gives an estimate of the total number of genes. This leads to estimates of from 5,000 to 15,000 for the haploid set of four chromosomes in Drosophila. Whatever the number, it can be assumed that the number of genes in the chromosome set of man is of the same general order of magnitude. It may be objected that the human body has a higher organization than that of a fly and that man therefore requires a greater number of genes. But it is difficult to rank the complexity of two different organisms and, considering the great similarity in structure and function of cells from the most diverse groups of animals and plants, it may very well be that there are only minor differences between them in numbers and kinds of genes. The striking external differences between diverse species may largely be the developmental outcome of different interactions of similar genic reagents. To use an analogy: the same 26 letters of the alphabet may serve to compose either a nursery rhyme or a philosophical treatise.

Lacking specific information, we may somewhat arbitrarily assume the existence of 10,000 genes in the human chromosome set. It may be surmised, conservatively, that the actual figure deviates by not more than a factor of five from this estimated value. In other words, the true figure is probably not less than 2,000 or more than 50,000. Of course, this is a wide range, but it should be realized that these numbers represent, after all, a *relatively* limited range. Without knowledge of various facts such as those found by Mendel and, later, in combined studies of inheritance and chromosomes, the question regarding a subdivision of the hereditary material might have been answered by as low an estimate as one—that is, no subdivisibility—or as high an estimate as hundreds of millions!

A human individual receives, from his parents, a complete assortment of all genic loci in two sets of chromosomes, those of the egg and the sperm. Thus, the cells of his body harbor two assortments of genes or, assuming the correctness of the foregoing estimate, some 10,000 pairs.

Problems

1. The nucleus of an unfertilized human egg is approximately twenty-five microns in diameter. Calculate the total volume of the nuclei of all eggs from which the present generation of mankind originated.

2. If a newborn baby weighs seven pounds, how many times heavier is the child than the egg from which it originated?

3. Calculate the total volume occupied by the eggs that produced all the children born in a given year in the states of (a) California, (b) New York, (c) Nevada. (Consult U. S. National Office of Vital Statistics, *Vital Statistics of the United States,* for number of births per year.)

4. During an abnormal mitosis of a cell with 46 chromosomes, the daughter chromosomes of one of the long chromosomes are included together in the same daughter nucleus. If nondisjunction also affects one of the short chromosomes, how many chromosomes may there be in the two daughter nuclei?

5. In a cell with 46 chromosomes an abnormal tripolar spindle is formed with three poles: I, II, and III. Eighteen chromosomes send their daughter chromosomes to poles I and II, fifteen to poles I and III, and thirteen to poles II and III. What are the chromosome numbers in the resulting three daughter nuclei?

References

Austin, C. R., and Bishop, M. W. H., 1957. Fertilization in mammals. *Biol. Rev.* **32:** 296–349.

Chu, E. H., and Giles, N. H., 1959. Human chromosome complements in normal somatic cells in culture. *Am. J. Human Genet.,* **11:** 63–79.

Farris, E. J., 1956. *Human Ovulation and Fertility.* 159 pp. Lippincott, Philadelphia.

Fawcett, D. W., 1958. The structure of the mammalian spermatozoon. *Int. Rev. Cyt.,* **7:** 195–234.

Hartman, C. G., Ovulation, fertilization and viability of eggs and spermatozoa. In Allen, E. (Ed.), 1939. *Sex and Internal Secretions.* 2nd ed. pp. 630–719, Williams & Wilkins, Baltimore.

Meyer, A. W., 1939. *The Rise of Embryology.* 367 pp. Stanford University Press and Oxford University Press, Stanford, California, and London.

Muller, H. J., 1947, The gene. Pilgrim Trust Lecture. *Proc. Roy. Soc., B.,* **134:** 1–37.

Schultz-Larsen, J., 1958. *The Morphology of the Human Sperm.* 121 pp. Munksgaard, Copenhagen.

Spuhler, J. N., 1948. On the number of genes in man. *Science,* **108:** 279–280.

Stern, C., 1959. The chromosomes of man. *J. Med. Ed.,* **34:** 301–314 (also *Am. J. Human Genet.,* **11,** 2 Part 2: 301–314).

Swanson, C. P., 1957. *Cytology and Cytogenetics.* 596 pp. Prentice-Hall, Englewood Cliffs.

Tjio, J. H., and Puck, T. T., 1958. The somatic chromosomes of man. *Proc. Nat. Acad. Sci.,* **44:** 1229–1237.

Wilson, E. B., 1925. *The Cell in Development and Heredity.* 1232 pp. Macmillan, New York.

CHAPTER 3

GENIC ACTION

When a human being begins his existence as a fertilized egg, he is completely unlike the organism into which he is to develop. The egg is a cell with a nucleus and cytoplasm, and contains no structures which correspond to the muscles and nerves, the lungs and the brain, the limbs and the eyes, or to any other part of the developed individual. Yet, the nucleus and cytoplasm of the egg constitute a system of wonderfully adjusted parts whose interaction leads, in a few weeks' time, to formation of an embryo with its differentiation of tissues and organs and their arrangement into a harmonious whole.

Genic Action within a Single Cell. Let us consider how the single fertilized egg cell is transformed. We know, from studies of many different organisms, that the genes in the nucleus control the processes of cellular metabolism, the synthesis of proteins and other biochemical compounds; we must, therefore, look at reactions between the genes and the nongenic material of the cell for the basis of the developmental process.

The details of these reactions are little known, but we may obtain some insight into the kinds of processes which take place by pondering over such a scheme as that shown in Figure 17. There we have listed, inside the nucleus of an undivided egg, 6 genes (A, B, C, D, E, and F), whose reactions with substances called *substrates* present in the nucleus (labeled S_1, S_2 . . . S_6) lead to the formation of the products of gene action (P_A, P_B . . . P_F). P may represent either the single product of a reaction between gene and substrate or the sum of the products if more than one kind of material results from the reaction. P_B and P_C, it is assumed, interact within the nucleus to yield a new substance, P_{BC}, which finds its way into the cytoplasm. Similarly, as the diagram suggests, the primary gene products, P_D and P_F, form —inside the nucleus—P_{DF}, which also goes into the cytoplasm. P_A and P_E, on the other hand, leave the nucleus without having undergone changes.

Outside the nucleus, the various products of gene-substrate reaction par-

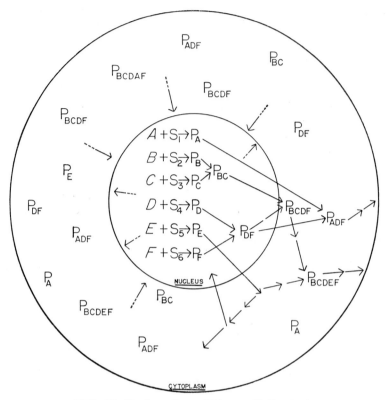

FIG. 17. Genic action within a cell. See text.

ticipate in further reactions with one another or with cytoplasmic components. Two of the reactions are $P_A + P_{DF} = P_{ADF}$ and $P_{BC} + P_{DF} = P_{BCDF}$. A third reaction, P_E + some cytoplasmic material, results in two products: one of these, after a series of intermediary reactions, leads to a compound some of which diffuses back into the nucleus; the other, after intermediary steps, interacts with a derivative of P_{BCDF} to form P_{BCDEF}. While these reactions proceed, many more go on, controlled by other genes, to form an inter-weaving network of sequences which all depend on one another and which, together, make up the life processes of the cell. The specific assumptions which underlie the details of Figure 17 are, of course, arbitrary and, in spite of its apparent complexity, the representation is greatly oversimplified. The assumptions may be replaced by others, but the essential feature should remain, namely, the interdependence of gene-controlled reactions that are presumably biochemical.

Genic Action and Differentiation.   The single egg cell cleaves by repeated divisions into more and more cells. Diagrams of 2-, 4-, and 8-cell stages, as found in the development of many animals, are shown in Figure 18. Externally, the cells of these early embryos are all very similar to one another, but some differentiation is apparent in the 8-cell stage. Here, as a result of slightly unequal divisions, the 4 upper cells are smaller than the 4 lower ones.

There is also an internal difference between the upper and lower cells. The cytoplasm of the original fertilized egg is not identical in all parts of the egg. A stratification can sometimes be observed, with more yolk granules in the lower half than in the upper half, and it has been determined experimentally that other differences in the cytoplasmic composition exist along an axis which extends from the upper to the lower pole of the egg. The cleavage of the egg, which separates its different regions from one another by assigning them to different cells, thus leads to a *differentiation* of the cytoplasmic contents of the cells. Once such a differentiation has begun, it will lead to others. In the 8-cell stage, for instance, the upper group of 4 cells is in contact with the lower group. This contact, however, is restricted to the basal parts of the upper cells, and it seems possible that these basal parts become differentiated by interactions with the underlying cells, as indicated by the stippling in Figure 18, D.

How will the identical genes present in the nucleus of each cell react to

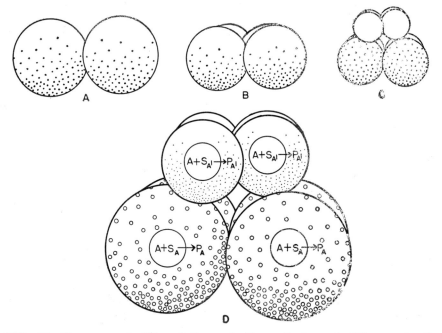

FIG. 18. Cleavage and differentiation.   A. Two-cell stage. A difference in the cytoplasm of the upper and lower halves of the cells is indicated.   B. Four-cell stage.   C. Eight-cell stage. The upper four cells are differentiated from the lower four cells.   D. Eight-cell stage, enlarged. Interaction between the gene A in the nuclei with substrate S_A in the lower cells and substrate S_{A^1} in the upper cells leads to formation of different products P_A and P_{A^1}. Contact between upper and lower cells results in further cytoplasmic differentiation, as indicated by fine stippling in upper cells.

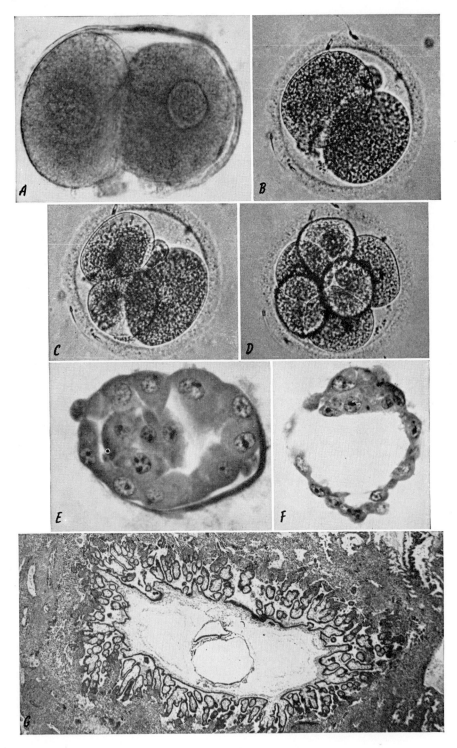

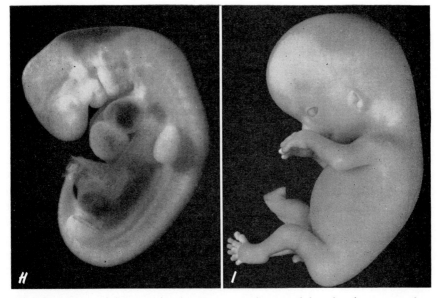

FIG. 19. Stages of human development; supplemented by showing stages from the Rhesus monkey. A. A human egg at the two-cell stage ($\times 512$). This egg, which was recovered from the oviduct of a woman during an operation, shows the earliest known human embryonic stage. Fixed and stained. B–D. Early cleavage in the Rhesus monkey ($\times 288$): Fertilized eggs after or during their first, second, and third divisions. Note some of the spermatozoa outside the developing egg cells. E–F. Blastocyst sections, fixed and stained (E $\times 560$, F $\times 450$). The blastocyst shown in E consisted of 58 cells, that in F of 117 cells. This latter blastocyst was at a stage shortly before implantation in the uterine wall. G. Section through an 18 1/2 day-old embryo implanted in the uterine wall ($\times 22$). Fixed and stained. Compare with Figs. 20 and 21, A. Note the sectioned outgrowths of the chorion; the extraembryonic coelom which corresponds to the large hollow space in the blastocyst shown in F; the cross section of the embryonic shield, above which is the small amniotic cavity and below which is the yolk sac. H. Embryo 28–30 days old, shown without extraembryonic parts ($\times 9$). Note limb buds and tail. I. Embryo ± 47 days old, shown without extraembryonic parts ($\times 2.5$). (A, E, F, Hertig, Rock and Adams; B, C, D, Lewis and Hartman, *Carnegie Inst. Publ.,* **525,** 1941; G, Jones and Brewer, *Carnegie Inst. Contrib. Embryol.,* **29,** 1941; H, I, Carnegie Numbers 8141, 4570.)

these different cytoplasmic "environments" and to the differences in substrates associated with them? If genic action consists of reactions between the genes and other cellular substances, it may well be, for instance, that gene A in an upper cell does not find substrate S_1 as available as it was in the undivided egg, or as it may be in a lower cell. The result (Fig. 18) may be that a different amount of P_A is formed, or that a different substance, S_1', which was present in low concentration in the original egg but is now found concentrated in the upper cell, is transformed into appreciable quantities of a new product, P_A'. It is thought that the sequence that leads to the different fates of these cells as we observe them is:

1. Initial regional differences in the cytoplasm of the egg.
2. Subdivision of the egg into differentiated cells.
3. Production of further differentiation by specific interactions between identical genes and the differentiated cell contents.

The detailed differentiation and organization of the embryo depend on the action of the genes in all cells and interaction among the cells, among whole embryonic regions, and among the parts of the embryo and its surroundings. It may well be that the thousands of genes present in each nucleus are active in every cell, but in qualitatively or quantitatively different fashion. The specific activity may be determined by the different cellular environments in which the genes find themselves, and, by interaction between genes and different substrates, may become enhanced and more manifold. On the other hand, quantitative differences in genic action within different tissues may be so great that some groups of genes are more or less inactive at one stage of differentiation, but are called into action if differentiation has proceeded far enough to provide them with suitable substrates with which to react. The assumption of continuous action of all genes at all times perhaps comes nearer to the truth than does the assumption of restricted activities of fractions of the genic set.

Human Embryology. The development of the fertilized human egg follows in general the same course as that of other mammalian eggs. In particular, the embryology of man is similar to that of other primates, among which that of the Rhesus monkey is best known (see Fig. 19, B–D).

The cleavage of the egg begins while it is still in the oviduct. At first, re-

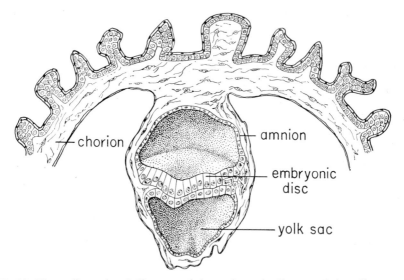

FIG. 20. Three-dimensional diagram of the embryonic disc, amnion, yolk sac, and part of the chorion of an embryo slightly younger than the one in Figure 19, G. (After Arey.)

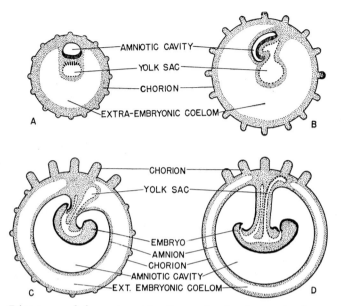

FIG. 21. Diagrams of four stages in the early development of a mammalian embryo. (After Dodds, *The Essentials of Human Embryology,* Wiley, 1946.)

peated divisions of the egg result in the formation of a solid cell ball (Fig. 19, A–E). Within this structure, a space filled with fluid soon develops, so that a stage is reached in which the egg resembles a hollow ball (Fig. 19, F): this is equivalent to the blastula of lower vertebrates and is called the *blastocyst.* Four days after fertilization the blastocyst still consists of less than 100 cells, but it has moved down the oviduct and entered the uterine cavity. At this time an important differentiation becomes visible: the wall of the hollow sphere is of uneven thickness (Fig. 19, F). Most of it consists of a single layer of rather small cells but, at the upper pole, a mass of larger cells has accumulated on the inside. This is the first indication of the very divergent fate of different parts of the blastocyst. Most of its cells do not participate in the formation of the embryo proper, but produce the external embryonic membrane, the *chorion.* The embryo itself develops from the inner cell mass—but again, only from part of it.

During the sixth day the blastocyst attaches itself to the inner surface of the uterus and gradually becomes embedded in its wall. Within its inner cell mass, two new hollow spaces filled with fluid originate: the *amniotic cavity* near the periphery of the embryonic sphere, and the *yolk sac* toward the center (Figs. 19, G; 20; 21, A).

Between the amniotic cavity and the yolk sac, forming the floor for the former and the ceiling of the latter, lies a plate-like layer of tissue, the *embryonic shield* or *disc* (Figs. 19, G; 20). Around the twelfth day, an embryonic streak becomes visible along part of one of its diameters. During the next three weeks the cells of the disc that lie adjacent to the embryonic streak differentiate into the true embryo with skin, brain, neural tube, intestine, heart, body segments, and many other organs and tissues (Fig. 19, H).

Early in this period the amniotic cavity, which is surrounded by a cellular membrane, the *amnion,* enlarges in such a way that all of it but a narrow stalk gradually becomes separated from the external embryonic layer of tissue (Fig. 21, B–D). The amnion, the inner embryonic membrane, thus comes to lie within the chorion.

Still another three weeks are required to transform the embryo, which in many ways resembles not only that of other mammals but also that of lower vertebrates, into a truly human fetus, with a face that foreshadows that of a child, with fingers and toes, and with a progressively smaller tail (Fig. 19, I). Even then, eight weeks after the beginning, the crown-rump length of the fetus is hardly more than 25 mm (one inch), and its weight is less than 2 gm. During the approximately thirty remaining weeks of pregnancy many details of organ formation are elaborated, and general growth increases the length and weight of the fetus to around 340 mm and 3,400 gm.

The first two months, counted from the time of fertilization, represent undoubtedly the most important period in the development of the new human being. As much as later events may still be important in his being born well and progressing after birth, the fundamental organization is laid down very early. Any significant deviation at this stage from the normal course of the differentiation of cells and organs is likely to have far-reaching consequences. Such deviations may be the result of actions of abnormal genes, of abnormal conditions in the surroundings of the embryo, or of combinations of the effects of genes and environment.

Genes and Characters.   The general picture of the role of genes in development which was outlined earlier in this chapter helps us gain an insight into the interrelation between genes and "characters," which is an important aspect of human genetics. A *character,* or *trait,* may be defined as any observable feature of the developing or the fully developed individual: a biochemical property, a cellular form or process, an anatomical structure, an organ function, or a mental characteristic. The genic content of the nuclei of a given individual and his appearance are obviously different things: characters are derived from genic action. They are removed from the genes by at least one and, often, numerous steps. For the genetic constitution, the term genotype has been coined; for the external appearance, the term *phenotype*. The genotype of a given individual is constant, fixed at the time of his origin as a fertilized egg; the phenotype is potentially variable, the result of interaction between the genotype and its nongenetic environment.

The general concepts of genic action lead us to expect (1) that no simple connection will exist between most observable characters of the developed human being and a single gene; and (2) that a single gene, by being part of the network of developmental reactions, will often influence more than a single character. We shall take up these two generalizations separately.

One Character from Many Genes. Most characters are produced by the complex interaction of numerous genes; Figure 17 gives but a glimpse of this interaction. There is no gene "for" eyes, or even for a part of an eye—no "one-to-one" relation between the genic units in the chromosomes and the different tissues and organs of the individual.

The recognition of this situation provides a guide for one's thinking about the effect of external or internal agents on the organs of the developing or fully developed individual and the possible effects of these agents on the genes themselves. If, for instance, exposure to the sun leads to darkening of the skin, should we assume that the many *genes* in the cells of the skin that enter into the interweaving processes of pigment formation have been changed? Or is it not more likely that some of the *reactions* have been altered under the influence of the new environment, "exposure to irradiation"? Or can we reasonably expect that the genes in the cells of the ovaries or testes of a sun-tanned individual were changed when his skin became browned? There are experimental ways of attacking these problems, and we shall return to them later, in Chapter 23, which deals with the causes of genetic changes.

Since most characters depend on many genes, it is obvious that changes in any one of these genes may result in a change in the character. Thus, hereditary blindness is known to be due to any one of very many different genes at different chromosomal loci. Some of these genetically different kinds of blindness are caused by morphologically different effects of different genes, as, for instance, an effect on the retina, on the lens, or on the general growth of the eyeball. Within each kind, it is possible to find effects specific for different types of genes, for example, different processes leading to opacity of the lens (cataract).

Frequently, what appears to be the same abnormality can be shown to be due to different genic loci. Evidence for this is obtainable, for instance, in the disease retinitis pigmentosa, a progressive degeneration of the retina which is accompanied by deposition of pigment. In some pedigrees, the "sex-linked" inheritance (see Chap. 13) of the disease proves that the gene responsible is located in the X-chromosome; in other pedigrees, the type of inheritance assigns the disease to a gene in an autosome. At present, medical examination of individuals with retinitis pigmentosa does not reveal specific differences by means of which the sex-linked and autosomal cases can be separated from each other. New methods of diagnosis, however, may some-day show that the different genes control development of the disease by means of different mechanisms.

This was recently found to be true for the various "bleeder" diseases. Most of them have a property in common: impairment of the formation of fibrin in blood clotting. Fibrin itself is the end product of interactions of a whole series of substances, insufficiency of any one of which will produce a kind of bleeder phenotype. There is evidence of genetic control of at least eight of these substances. Among these the so-called antihemophilic factor is deficient in persons with "classical" sex-linked hemophilia (hemophilia A). Another type of sex-linked hemophilia (hemophilia B) is characterized by a deficiency in the plasma thromboplastin component, also called the "Christmas factor." Three different autosomal bleeder diseases are each characterized by insufficiency of a particular substance: in one, Ac globulin; in another, fibrinogen; in the third, proconvertin. In still another autosomal hemorrhagic condition the blood seems to be normal, and the bleeding may be due to some defect in the capillaries.

It may appear to be a contradiction to speak first of the many genes on which a character depends, and then of "the" gene responsible for it. But this contradiction is only apparent. The starting of an automobile depends on the collaboration of many parts: the battery, the electrical wiring, the pistons, the transmission, and others. The character "not-starting" may be due to a disturbance in any one of the parts which are required for normal function. Therefore, the normal character, "starting," is controlled by many entities; but the difference between starting and non-starting, in any one instance, is usually controlled by a single entity. (Occasionally, inability of a car to start may be due to more than one cause, each of which alone would suffice to cause the effect. Similarly, a person may, in rare cases, be blind for more than one reason—for example, if he happens to possess both the genetic constitution for cataract and for retinitis pigmentosa.)

There are further consequences of the interrelation of gene-initiated reactions. One of these is that individuals carrying identical genic constitutions may look quite different. The reason is that the gene-initiated reactions are subject to environmental influences, as are all other chemical or physical processes. Genes cannot be expected, under all environmental circumstances, to produce the same observable character. Just as a mixture of hydrogen and oxygen in a container will be stable if kept undisturbed but will explode if an electric spark is introduced, or as the speed of many other chemical reactions is low at one temperature and high at another, so a gene-controlled character may appear in one form under some circumstances and in another form under others. The problems of the relationship of heredity and environment in man will form the subject of several chapters in this book (Chaps. 16, 17, and 25–27).

Another consequence of the interrelations of genic action is that the same gene at a given locus may, if other genes at other loci are not alike, lead to different effects in different individuals, even under the same external circumstances. If, for instance, a certain gene controls the presence of an enzyme which enters into some biochemical process, the activity of the enzyme may be influenced by the acidity of the cytoplasm, which may be under the control of another gene. Thus "genetic background" provided by other genes is often important in the study of any one gene. Examples in man will be presented in Chapter 16.

Many Characters from One Gene. We turn now to the second generalization derived from our concept of genic action: a single gene may often influence more than one character.

Such multiple effects of a gene are called *pleiotropic*. Obviously, certain characters may be of such elementary nature that their genic control is immediate or consists of a chain of only a few links. It is possible that some of the inherited antigenic substances—those which characterize man as a species as well as those which distinguish different individuals—are produced by the primary reaction between a particular gene and its substrate. It is also possible that the presence of an enzyme in the blood of most humans, which accelerates the breakdown of a normal product of metabolism, homogentisic acid (also called alkapton), is the direct consequence of the primary action of gene *A*. Likewise, the absence of the enzyme in the exceptional individuals in whom the allele *a* is substituted for *A* is probably a character that is dependent on the immediate activity, or possibly the lack of activity, of *a*. This presumed direct effect of the presence of a specific kind of gene on the pres-

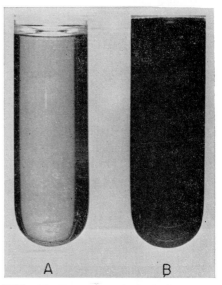

FIG. 22. Two test tubes of urine of a person affected with alkaptonuria. A. Freshly voided, of same appearance as normal urine. B. After prolonged standing, blackened by oxidation. (Original from Dr. R. A. Milch.)

ence or absence of the enzyme has further consequences. The urine of individuals whose blood does not have the enzyme contains the intact alkapton, a substance which darkens if exposed to air (Fig. 22). Individuals with an *A* gene do not excrete alkapton, because the enzyme is present and helps transform it into carbon dioxide and water. There are, then, two characters affected by the allele *a:* absence of an enzyme, and presence of homogentisic acid in the urine. The known interrelation between the two characters accounts readily for the twofold expression of the gene in alkaptonuria.

We know less about the interrelations of the multiple effects of a rare gene, *p,* which controls a related inherited condition, phenylketonuria. Persons affected with this trait—unlike normal persons who possess the allele *P*—excrete in their urine large amounts of phenylpyruvic acid, as readily shown by a deep bluish-green color which develops in the urine after addition of a few drops of a ferric chloride solution. A second trait in phenylketonurics is mental impairment, usually of a severe type, and a third trait a slight pigmentary disturbance resulting in light hair. A fundamental biochemical effect caused by the *p* allele concerns the amino acid phenylalanine. Its abnormal metabolism (see p. 59) is—in a fashion which is only partly understood—the cause of the appearance of the three traits listed.

An instructive example of biochemical pleiotropism has been studied in Drosophila. Presence of a certain gene, called lethal-translucida, results in the accumulation of excessive amounts of blood fluid in the larvae, so that they become bloated and transparent. The chemical composition of the blood fluid differs greatly from that of normal larvae (Fig. 23): the amount of

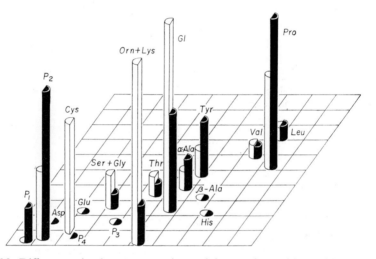

FIG. 23. Differences in the concentrations of free amino acids, amides, and peptides in the blood fluid of normal (light columns) and lethal-translucida (black columns) larvae of *Drosophila melanogaster*. (P1–P4=peptides; Asp=aspartic acid; Cys=cystine; Glu=glutamic acid; Ser + Gly=serine and glycine; Orn + Lys =ornithine and lysine; Thr=threonine; Gl=glutamine; α-Ala=α-alanine; Tyr= tyrosine; β-Ala=β-alanine; His=histidine; Val=valine; Pro=proline; Leu=leucine, isoleucine.) The position of the columns corresponds to the positions of the substances on paper chromatograms (see p. 59). (Hadorn.)

some substances in the abnormal larvae is much greater than in normal ones, and other substances they contain may be absent from normal larvae; still other substances are present in smaller amounts or are lacking completely in abnormal larvae. Undoubtedly, many other biochemical differences will be discovered if tests for further substances in the blood fluid are made, and still more if other parts of the larvae are analyzed.

Inherited Syndromes. If several specific abnormal traits present in the same individual are transmitted to his offspring as a unit, as they often are, it can usually be assumed that they depend jointly on a single gene. In medicine, such a group of characters is called a *syndrome*. A well-known example of a syndrome is Marfan's syndrome, or arachnodactyly (spiderfingeredness), so-called because of the excessive length of the bones of fingers and toes (Fig. 24). This and other skeletal abnormalities are often accompanied by an abnormal position of the eye lens and by heart defects. Another example is the Laurence-Moon-Biedl syndrome, in which mental deficiency, obesity, possession of extra fingers or toes, and subnormal development of the genital organs go together. It is not clear how one gene produces such diverse characters, but it is quite possible that they are all expressions of some single primary genic activity whose consequences are manifold. For example, the different symptoms of Marfan's syndrome, according to McKusick, may all be consequences of a defect in connective tissue. Grüneberg has been able to provide a far-reaching developmental clarification of an inherited syndrome in rats (Figs. 25, 26). In a special genetically atypical strain, individuals are produced who appear normal at birth, but within a few days their growth is retarded, breathing becomes abnormal, and death soon occurs. Anatomical studies show a variety of abnormalities, such as a narrowed windpipe, thickened ribs, bleeding into the lungs, abnormal position of the thoracic viscera, and high hemoglobin content of the blood—all characters that depend in some way on abnormal cartilage formation. Wherever cartilage is formed in the developing animal, it differentiates abnormally and thus leads to various defects, which, in turn, cause further abnormalities in other organs or functions. These abnormalities, singly or jointly, lead to the death of the individual.

This example shows that multiple effects may well be caused by some single primary genic action. It is possible that other syndromes are the result of several independent primary genic actions, but we are touching upon a largely unexplored field here.

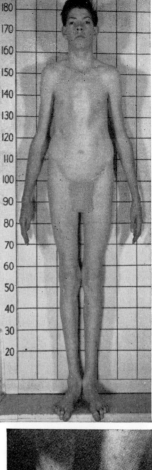

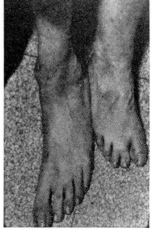

FIG. 24. Arachnodactyly. *Above:* An affected individual; note length of legs and feet, and "pigeon chest." *Below:* Affected and normal foot for comparison. (Above, original from Dr. V. McKusick; below, Rados, *Arch. Ophthalmol.,* **27,** 1942.)

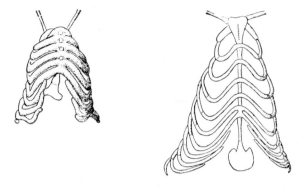

FIG. 25. Thoracic skeletons of two newborn rats: normal (*right*) and a lethal littermate (*left*). Note abnormal sternum and thickened ribs. (Grüneberg, *Proc. Royal Soc., B.,* **125,** 1938.)

Autonomous and Dependent Characters. The existence of syndromes shows that a specific gene may produce effects in different parts of the body. The question arises whether (1) the gene is necessarily present in all tissues or organs which are affected, or whether (2) some basic effect at one stage of development in one particular primary organ may be the decisive factor which controls, secondarily, the production of the specific traits in other parts of the body. If the latter alternative were true, the appearance of the traits would be unrelated to the fact that the organs concerned also happened to contain the gene in their cell nuclei. Answers to this question are provided by work with animals, and two experiments conducted with mice will be described briefly.

In the first of these, color differences of the hair coat were studied. It is known that such differences in color are due to the presence of different kinds of genes. In this case, our question may be formulated in the following terms: Is the fur of a black mouse black because the pigment cells of the animal are genetically black, or because genic action in some other part of the animal sets up a physiological condition which affects the pigment cells and causes them to make the hair black? A decision is made possible by transplanting a piece of skin from a newborn or late embryonic genetically black mouse to a genetically nonblack one. At the time of transplantation, no pigment has been formed. Will the transplant obey its own genic commands or will it respond to the genic influences of the host? The answer is that the transplant forms black pigment, independently of the host, by *autonomous determination* (Fig. 27, A).

It may be wondered whether this autonomy of the transplant is the result of genic action in its own cells, or whether the formation of black pigment is due to some processes which had been initiated in remote parts of the genetically black embryo before transplantation took place. This possibility could be tested by studies in which tissues from very early embryos were transplanted. Such studies have not been done, but essentially similar pro-

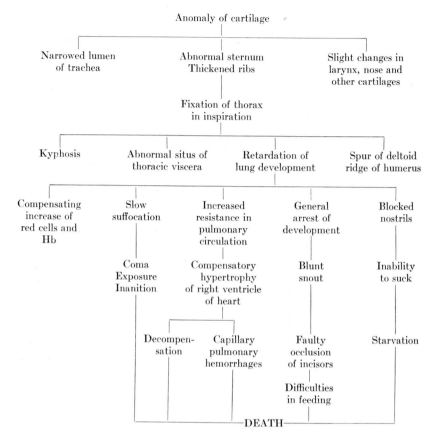

FIG. 26. Interrelation of causes of death in a lethal type of rat. (Grüneberg, *Animal Genetics and Medicine.* Hoeber, New York and London, 1947.)

cedures have confirmed the fact that the genetic control of pigmentation is in the pigment cells themselves.

The second experiment shows that genetic effects are not always brought about by autonomous determination. There is a class of mice in which the normal allele *D* is replaced by *d,* with the result that growth is retarded and the animals remain dwarfs. The pituitary gland of such a dwarf mouse is abnormal. The anterior lobe of this gland normally secretes into the blood stream a hormone which is necessary for normal body growth, but none, or only insignificant amounts, of the growth hormone is produced by the pituitary of the dwarfs. This defect of the gland would be a sufficient explanation for the growth retardation of the animals. The question remains, however, whether the *d* allele, which, in the cells of the pituitary, is responsible for the deficient hormone production, may, in addition, by its presence in the cells of the growing parts themselves, inhibit their growth. A decision is reached by transplanting pituitary glands from normal animals (rats being

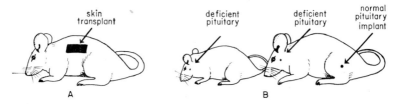

FIG. 27. Autonomous and dependent development. A. Genetically pigmented piece of skin transplanted to an unpigmented host develops its intrinsic coloration. B. *Left:* A genetically dwarf mouse with deficient pituitary. *Right:* Normal growth of a genetically dwarf mouse dependent on implantation of normal pituitary.

the donors) into young dwarf mice, or by injecting the lacking hormone into them. Such experiments result in normal growth of the genetically dwarf mice (Fig. 27, B). Here, then, is an example of *dependent determination*. The dwarf allele causes pituitary deficiency, and the easily observable character, dwarfness, is secondarily dependent on the insufficient production of the hormone.

As in mice, autonomous and dependent determination can be distinguished in inherited human traits, although clear-cut experimental proof is usually not obtainable. It seems likely, however, that autonomous genetic determination in man accounts for hair and eye colors, for the antigens which characterize various blood types, for certain diseases in which specific cells of the nervous system degenerate, for red-green color blindness, and for many other characters. Dependent determination in man probably accounts for the development of certain midgets with adult body proportions who are presumably pituitary-deficient dwarfs; for at least those types of sugar diabetes (diabetes mellitus) in which the abnormal carbohydrate metabolism is a consequence of defective pancreatic glands; and for genetic subnormal functioning of the thyroid in children which may lead to stunted physical and mental development (cretinism). Dependent determination also brings about the development of those traits which are not mediated by hormones but by interrelated physiological processes comparable to some of those active in the development of the lethal syndrome in the rat.

Phenocopies. The skin of many people is heavily pigmented even in those areas which are not exposed to sunlight. This is due to the action of specific alleles. Other people are only lightly pigmented in unexposed regions but become dark when exposed. The latter carry alleles for light skin, but the processes leading typically to limited pigment formation can be reinforced by the external agent "sunlight." Sun-tanned, genetically light individuals thus are copies of genetically dark individuals. The term *phenocopy* has been coined to designate individuals whose phenotype, under the influence of nongenetic agents, has become like the one normally caused by a specific genotype in the absence of the nongenetic agent (Goldschmidt, 1878–1958).

Numerous examples can be cited to show that a given phenotype is either the result of a specific genotype or a phenocopy produced by the interaction of a nongenetic agent with a different genotype. Thus, cretinism can be due to the presence of certain alleles or to the lack of iodine in the diet of a child of any genotype, and cataract can be the result of specific genes or of damage to the lens by ionizing radiation.

The existence of phenocopies is an aspect of genic and gene-dependent action which conforms to expectations based on the general concepts of the relation between gene and character.

Genes and Alleles.   We have seen that every human being receives one allele of each pair of alleles from his father, and the other from his mother. There are perhaps many genes of which only one allelic variety exists, so that certain loci are alike in all humans, carrying identical alleles. Characters common to all men, as contrasted with other animals—characters like the serological properties which differentiate species from one another—may very likely be controlled by genes that have only one allelic form. No specific method for discovering such genes is available, since the discovery of genes normally depends on finding differences among individuals, differences which can then be traced to differences in one or more pairs of loci in the chromosomes. However, many genes are known to have more than one allelic form. For instance, people having a chemical substance in their blood which marks them as belonging to the blood group O have the allele I^O of gene I at a certain locus of their chromosomes, and people belonging to blood group A have a different allele, I^A, at the same locus.

Since we do not know the detailed chemical structure of any gene, we do not know, either, what characterizes different alleles. In general, although alleles may differ, those at the same locus determine the appearance of similar traits—as the alleles I^O and I^A determine properties of the blood antigens. This is otherwise with alleles at different loci. Those at one locus may determine blood properties; those at another, skeletal traits. Differences among alleles seem to be of another order than those among genes. Genes may well be strikingly dissimilar chemical entities, but the alleles of a gene are possibly distinguished from each other only by minor chemical variations, differences in one or a few pairs of bases of the thousands in a DNA molecule. Using a comparison from the field of biological systematics, we may compare the genes at different loci with different species, and the alleles of each locus with different varieties of that species.

The words gene and allele are often used indiscriminately, since an allele is a gene. The term allele is preferred when a specific variety of a gene is meant, or when the existence of different genic varieties is to be emphasized. The term gene is preferred when the emphasis lies on the genic "species" as such, without reference to the gene's one or more varieties.

The number of different known kinds of alleles of a gene, any one of which may be found at a specific locus in a human chromosome, varies from one to many, but no normal individual can carry more than two different kinds, since he possesses only two chromosomes in which the alleles are present.

Homozygotes and Heterozygotes.   If we consider the blood-group gene *I*, we recognize three possibilities in regard to the two alleles, I^O and I^A. An individual may carry the allele I^O in both his chromosomes; he may carry I^O in one and I^A in the other chromosome; or he may carry I^A in both. We speak of the first and third persons, symbolized as $I^O I^O$ and $I^A I^A$, as *homozygotes,* since the two alleles of this locus are alike; of the second, $I^O I^A$, as *heterozygotes,* since the alleles are different. An individual may be homozygous or heterozygous at one or many loci, or he may be homozygous at some and heterozygous at others.

The Phenotypes of Heterozygotes.   We have said that $I^O I^O$ persons belong to blood group O, and $I^A I^A$ persons belong to group A. What is the phenotype of the heterozygous $I^O I^A$ individuals?

In heterozygosity, three main types of phenotypic expression have been encountered:

1. The heterozygote may exhibit only the properties typical of persons with one of the two alleles.
2. The heterozygote may exhibit properties intermediate between those of the two homozygotes.
3. The heterozygote may exhibit the properties of both of the homozygotes.

Dominance and Recessiveness.   The first type is represented by our example of the blood-group alleles I^O and I^A. The heterozygous individuals $I^O I^A$ belong to blood group A, just as the homozygotes $I^A I^A$ do. The allele I^A is said to be *dominant* over the allele I^O, the latter being *recessive* to the former (Table, 1, A).

Dominance and recessiveness are obviously developmental phenomena resulting from genic action, since they refer to the effect of a combination of differing alleles as compared to the effects of a homozygous combination. Dominance of an allele in a heterozygote does not necessarily signify a competitive struggle between the dominant and the recessive allele in which the former is successful. In some instances, there may, indeed, be competition between two different reactions controlled by the two alleles:

$$(1)\ \text{Competition} \quad \begin{array}{c} A \longrightarrow \\ \longleftarrow a \end{array} \Big\} \ \text{effect similar to } AA.$$

But in others it may be true that one allele is inactive while the other is active enough to produce an effect which seems as great as that produced in the homozygote by two alleles:

$$(2)\ \text{Inactivity of one allele} \quad \begin{array}{c} A \longrightarrow \\ a \end{array} \Big\} \ \text{effect similar to } AA.$$

In $I^O I^A$ individuals, this seems to be nearly true, the one I^A allele causing an effect similar to that of two in $I^A I^A$ homozygotes, and the I^O allele seeming to be nearly inactive.

A dominant effect may even result from the joint action of the dominant and recessive allele, since there are known to be recessive alleles whose effect is qualitatively identical or very similar to that of their dominant alleles, although quantitatively weaker than the latter:

(3) Cumulative action of both alleles $\begin{matrix} A \longrightarrow \\ a \rightarrow \end{matrix} \Big\}$ effect similar to AA.

In such cases, the dominant effect of the heterozygote may be the outcome of the addition of a quantitatively strong effect of the dominant allele to the weaker, but similar, effect of the recessive allele.

In human genetics, the term dominance is often used in situations to which it may not fully apply. In order to decide whether two alleles, A^1 and A^2, are related to each other as dominant and recessive or whether they produce an intermediate effect in the heterozygote, it is obviously necessary to compare the effects of all three combinations: $A^1 A^1$, $A^1 A^2$, and $A^2 A^2$. In general,

TABLE 1. *Traits of Homozygous and Heterozygous Individuals.*

Trait	Homozygous for One Allele	Heterozygous	Homozygous for the Other Allele	Allelic Relation
A. Blood groups O, A (dominance involving 2 frequent alleles)	$I^A I^A$ a normal trait	$I^O I^A$ trait as in $I^A I^A$	$I^O I^O$ another normal trait	I^A dominant I^O recessive
B. Polydactyly (dominance of a rare allele)	$A^1 A^1$ normal	$A^1 A^2$ abnormal	$A^2 A^2$ unknown, possibly more abnormal than $A^1 A^2$	A^1 dominant A^2 recessive
C. Albinism (recessivity of a rare allele)	AA normal	Aa normal	aa abnormal	A dominant a recessive
D. Singing voice (intermediateness)	$A^1 A^1$ a normal trait	$A^1 A^2$ intermediate between two homozygotes	$A^2 A^2$ another normal trait	$A^1 \atop A^2 \big\}$ intermediate
E. Blood groups A, B (codominance)	$I^A I^A$ a normal trait	$I^A I^B$ a normal trait showing properties of both homozygotes	$I^B I^B$ another normal trait	$I^A \atop I^B \big\}$ codominant

this comparison is not possible in relatively rare inherited traits. For example, we may take the trait polydactyly, the possession of extra fingers and toes (Table 1, B). Assuming that A^1A^1 is responsible for normal appearance—i.e., five-fingeredness—and A^1A^2 causes the development of extra fingers, it is important to know of what type A^2A^2 individuals are. Such individuals, however, can originate only if they receive the "abnormal" allele A^2 from both parents, and this will usually happen only if two abnormal individuals marry. The union of two individuals with such a rare abnormality as this—and striking abnormalities, by definition, are always rare—is very infrequent. Consequently, in most cases, the abnormal homozygote has not yet been found.

There is reason to believe—by analogy with animals—that the homozygote would often be still more abnormal than the heterozygote, thus making the latter really intermediate. In practice, however, abnormal conditions caused by the presence of a single allele are called dominants even if the homozygous condition for the abnormal gene is unknown, or, if known, is identical with, or more extreme than, the heterozygous condition. We may summarize the usage by the statement that rare alleles are called dominant if they cause an appreciable observable effect in the heterozygote.

Rare recessive alleles do not present a similar problem. Recessive homozygotes must receive an "abnormal" allele from each of their parents, who, as will be shown later, are mostly heterozygotes. Therefore, all three genotypes—homozygotes for the recessive, for the dominant, and heterozygotes—are available for comparison. An example of a relatively rare recessive allele is provided in albinism, which consists of the absence of pigment in skin, hair, and the iris of the eye. Individuals who are aa (homozygous for the allele a) are albinos; homozygotes who are AA, and heterozygotes, who are Aa, are normally pigmented (Table 1, C).

An often quoted example of dominance in two alleles which both act on a normal trait is that of brown and blue eye color. It is usually stated that there is a pair of alleles, B and b, that control eye color, and that BB and Bb produce brown eyes, and bb blue. It is now recognized that this description is only an approximation of the truth. The irises of some blue-eyed persons contain small spots of brown pigment which may not be noticeable without careful inspection. Two such seemingly blue-eyed individuals can have brown-eyed children. The genetics of eye color is complex and not yet fully understood.

Intermediateness. Properties intermediate between those of two homozygotes undoubtedly occur in human heterozygotes as often as they are known to occur in other heterozygous organisms, but there are few well-established examples. This is so in part because, as we have seen, genes that are responsible for abnormal traits in heterozygotes are liable to be classified as dominants, although their heterozygous effects may actually be intermediate between those of the normal and abnormal homozygotes. In part, the difficulty of establishing intermediateness concerns common traits. Such traits often depend on genetic differences at more than one locus—for reasons to be discussed in Chapter 6—so that it is difficult to make clear decisions concerning dominance or intermediateness of alleles at a single locus. Intermediate expression does occur in singing voice: baritones and mezzosopranos are the heterozygotes; tenors and bassos, or altos and sopranos, the homozygotes (Table 1, D; see also p. 318).

It should be pointed out that reference to intermediateness in a heterozygote does not imply that an expressed character lies exactly in the middle between those of the homozygotes. Apart from the fact that no "average" or "mean" can be found between two such qualitatively different conditions as normal-fingeredness and polydactyly, an intermediate character may approach, to varying degrees, that of one of the homozygotes. The limit between intermediateness and dominance or recessiveness is not sharp.

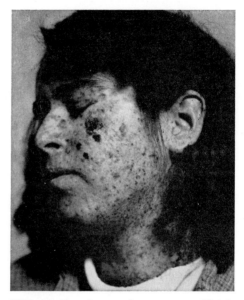

FIG. 28. Xeroderma pigmentosum. (Original from Dr. F. Ronchese.)

Codominance. The blood-group gene I is one for which more than the two different alleles I^A and I^O are known. Another, I^B, dominant over I^O, causes the presence of a B substance in the blood. In dominance over I^O, it resembles the allele I^A. In combination with each other, I^A and I^B present a new relation (Table 1, E). The heterozygote $I^A I^B$ does not show dominance of either allele, nor does it show an intermediate expression. Instead, the substances A and B are found together in the blood of the $I^A I^B$ individuals. Such *codominant effects* in heterozygotes are rare for morphological traits but seem characteristic of the gene-controlled chemical substances to which A and B belong.

We have seen that a gene participates in the developmental network in such a way that it may be involved in the expression of more than one character. Though our procedure of naming a gene for its most conspicuous effect often causes us to forget its varied expressions, most genes seem to have multiple effects. Remembering this, it is not surprising that the same gene may be dominant in regard to one expression and recessive or intermediate in regard to another. For example, the skin disease xeroderma pigmentosum (Fig. 28), characterized by a peculiar type of freckling, degenerating areas, and cancerous growth which invariably leads to premature death, is inherited as a recessive abnormality as far as the serious pathological effects are concerned—i.e., the heterozygotes are normal people—but the freckling shows in many of them, and is thus a dominant expression of the gene.

Gene Symbols.   Repeated use has already been made of gene symbols, and since their use will increase in later chapters, it may be helpful if they are explained here. It is customary to denote the genes of specific loci by one or a few letters of the alphabet printed in italics. Such a designation may be completely arbitrary—as is the use of the letters A, B, M, or X—or the letters chosen may be abbreviations of the names of specific traits or characters: for example, I for blood substances, called isoagglutinogens, or Xe for the locus concerned with xeroderma pigmentosum. Different alleles of a gene are all given the same letter with an additional distinguishing mark: for instance A and A', A^1 and A^2, or I^O and I^A. This makes it easy for the reader to recognize the allelic groupings in a genotype. In the formula $AA'I^OI^A$, it is clear that A and A' are a pair of alleles, and that I^O and I^A are a different pair. When one allele of a pair is recessive to the other, its symbol is not capitalized by many authors. A is used for the dominant and a for the recessive, or D for the dominant and d for the recessive (*not* D versus $r!$).

Sometimes, alleles with particularly similar action are distinguished by such symbols as I^{A_1} and I^{A_2}. Sometimes, also, the same base letters may be used for genes at different loci with distinguishing subscripts: Hb_1 and Hb_2 designate genes at two loci both of which are concerned with hemoglobin properties. Two alleles at the Hb_1 locus, which will be discussed on page 55 and later, are $Hb_1{}^A$ and $Hb_1{}^S$.

Genotype and Phenotype.   The terms genotype and phenotype can be applied either to the totality of the genetic constitution and its expression, or to part of it. They are often used in relation to a single pair of alleles and its expression. Thus, one may refer to the heterozygous genotype Aa and its dominant phenotype.

The simple statement "The phenotype is not always an indication of the genotype" summarizes important discoveries. We have seen that a genotypically dwarf animal can be made phenotypically normal by treatment with growth hormone, and that the phenotype blood group A may be the result of either of the two genotypes I^AI^A and I^AI^O. The two concepts, genotype and phenotype, form a frame of reference in many discussions of human genetics.

Biochemical Genetics

The general picture of genic action which has been developed may now be filled out in more detail. In the final analysis, all genetic differences among human beings must be produced by differences in the physiological processes of their cells. Since it is assumed that genes produce their effects by chemical interaction with other cellular constituents, the study of genic action leads to a study of biochemistry.

Most genetic differences among human beings are naturally described by reference to phenotypic characters that can be distinguished by simple observation: tallness versus shortness, six-fingeredness versus five-fingeredness, straight hair versus curly hair, normal blood clotting versus bleeder's disease, color sensitivity versus color blindness, and idiocy versus normal mentality. Sometimes simple observation constitutes an acknowledgment of obvious chemical differences—for example, pigmented persons versus albinos, the distinction here being the presence or absence of the pigment melanin—but often the chemical basis of phenotypic differences is far removed from the easily observable trait and special studies are required for its determination.

Genetic Control of Properties of Blood.   Blood was the basis of some of the earliest studies of human biochemical genetics. The discovery, in 1901, that men can be divided into different groups according to whether their red blood cells clump or remain separate when their blood is mixed with that of other individuals was the beginning of a long series of studies whose goal, still unattained, is a complete chemical characterization of the substances involved in the reaction. We do know that the *antigens* present in the cells are large molecules composed of sugars and amino acids, the building stones of protein (mucoids, made up of a polysaccharide component associated with an amino-acid complex), and that the *antibodies* in the fluid part of the blood are proteins. However, the differences among the different antigens and among the different antibodies can be only partly defined. One aspect of the control of antibodies by blood-group genes has been uncovered in a study of the molecular weights of antibodies. Homozygous $I^{A_1}I^{A_1}$ individuals (I^{A_1} is one of several I alleles) form large antibody molecules that have an approximate molecular weight of 300,000; and $I^O I^O$ individuals, somewhat smaller molecules with a weight of about 170,000. The $I^{A_1}I^O$ heterozygotes do not have a mixture of the two kinds of molecules but contain a single kind, a very large antibody molecule whose weight is about 500,000.

Among the normal constituents of the blood serum are the α_2-globulins or haptoglobins, proteins which are concerned with the binding of hemoglobin from aged and broken down red blood cells. Two alleles Hp^1 and Hp^2 control the presence of different haptoglobin molecules, which can be distinguished from one another by their different electric charges. This difference causes the haptoglobins to move with different speed when an electric current is applied to a solution containing them (electrophoresis; Fig. 29, A). The biochemical effects of the two Hp alleles are remarkable in that $Hp^1 Hp^1$ homozygotes produce a single type of haptoglobin, Hp 1–1, as judged by the single band of uniformly moving molecules, but $Hp^2 Hp^2$ homozygotes produce a whole series of different haptoglobins, Hp 2–2, as judged by a sequence of bands, all different from Hp 1–1. In $Hp^1 Hp^2$ heterozygotes a whole series of new haptoglobins, Hp 2–1, are formed, all differing from both Hp 1–1 and

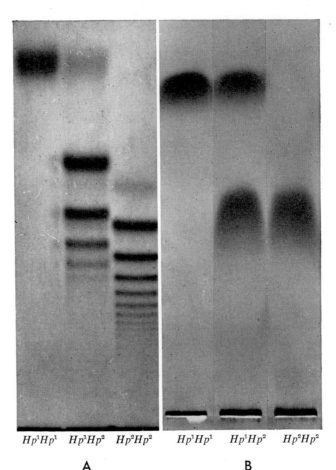

Hp^1Hp^1 Hp^1Hp^2 Hp^2Hp^2 Hp^1Hp^1 Hp^1Hp^2 Hp^2Hp^2

A   B

FIG. 29. The haptoglobins of the three genotypes Hp^1Hp^1, Hp^1Hp^2, and Hp^2Hp^2.
A. Purified haptoglobins.   B. Haptoglobins after chemical treatment. Electrophoresis was carried out in starch gel. (A, Connell and Smithies, *Biochem. J.*, **72**,
1959; B, original from Drs. O. Smithies and G. E. Connell.)

Hp 2–2. These findings show that the substitution of the allele Hp^2 for the
allele Hp^1 is responsible for the appearance of a whole array of new protein
molecules, a biochemical demonstration of the fact that one gene may have
many effects. It seems likely that the haptoglobins are not under the immediate control of the Hp alleles but are produced somewhat farther away
in the chain of reactions along which the Hp alleles exert their effects. This
view is supported by the outcome of experiments in which by chemical treatment a portion of each type of haptoglobin is split off. This portion, too, will
migrate electrophoretically and the results are much simpler than those obtained with untreated haptoglobins (Figure 29, B). Only one haptoglobin
type is found in $Hp^2 Hp^2$, different from the one in $Hp^1 Hp^1$; in the heter-

ozygote the two types are present codominantly and no new "hybrid" types (or types) appear. One may assume that the two simple types of haptoglobin are closer to the primary gene products than the multiple types shown in Figure 29, A.

Other gene-controlled chemical properties of the blood include those of components of the fluid that are concerned with the formation of antibodies in general and with the properties of hemoglobin in the red blood cells. Thus there exists a rare gene which makes its bearers extremely susceptible to bacterial infections by causing the near absence of that blood fraction called gamma globulin, a protein material from which a normal individual forms the antibodies that attack the foreign material produced by bacterial invaders. This hypogammaglobulinemia has been traced back to the near absence of a special type of cells in the lymph nodes, the spleen, and some other organs. These "plasma cells" are apparently essential in the production of antibodies and are thus analogous to the cells of the islets of Langerhans in the pancreas, whose presence is necessary for the production of insulin and whose formation is also under genetic control. Absence of Langerhans cells is a cause of sugar diabetes (diabetes mellitus).

Rapid advances are being made in the study of differences in the chemical nature of *hemoglobin*. This material consists of complex molecules that are composed of the colored, iron-containing heme and a colorless protein, globin. In many populations, particularly those of African stock, there are numerous individuals whose red blood cells take on a sickle-like shape when they are exposed to low oxygen tension outside the body (Fig. 30, a, b). Such persons fall into two classes. The majority are perfectly healthy and inside their bodies less than one per cent of the blood cells are abnormally shaped: they are said to possess the "sickle-cell trait." A small minority, however, has a severe anemia which often becomes fatal before those afflicted reach the age of reproduction, and more than one-third of their blood cells have abnormal shapes: they are called "sickle-cell anemics." The sickle-cell character is controlled by a pair of alleles. Individuals whose cells are not sickle-shaped are homozygous for an allele Hb_1^A ($Hb_1^A Hb_1^A$); possessors of the trait are heterozygous for the allele Hb_1^S ($Hb_1^A Hb_1^S$); and sickle-cell anemics are homozygous $Hb_1^S Hb_1^S$.

The molecular basis of the sickle-cell character began to be understood when it was discovered that a special kind of hemoglobin (S) different from that of normal individuals (A) is present in the blood cells of persons with the sickle-cell trait or the sickle-cell anemia. In solutions, the two kinds of hemoglobin may under certain conditions possess opposite electrical charges, so that if an electric current is passed through a solution in which both types of hemoglobins are present one type moves toward the negative pole and the other toward the positive pole (Fig. 30, c-e). Chemical studies have shown that there is a simple difference between sickle-cell hemoglobin and normal hemoglobin. A hemoglobin molecule consists of two like halves made up of about 4,000 atoms arranged to form about 300 amino acids. A difference in

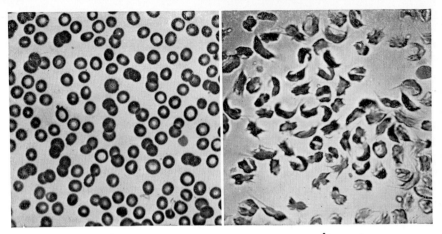

a. b.

c. Normal   d. Sickle-cell anemia   e. Sickle-cell trait

Phenotype	Genotype	Hemoglobin(s)	
Normal	Hb_l^A Hb_l^A	A	
Sickle-Cell Anemia	Hb_l^S Hb_l^S	S	
Hbg. C Disease	Hb_l^C Hb_l^C	C	
Sickle-Cell Trait	Hb_l^S Hb_l^A	S,A	
Hbg. C Trait	Hb_l^C Hb_l^A	C,A	
Sickle-Cell / Hbg. C Dis.	Hb_l^S Hb_l^C	S,C	

f.

FIG. 30. Red blood cells from (a) normal and (b) sickle-cell homozygotes. Movement of hemoglobins in an electric field (c, d, e). The hemoglobins were dissolved and an electric current passed through the fluid. The black areas correspond to the position and amount of hemoglobin after its migration in the electric field. By using the original vertical axes (arrows in figure) as points of reference, it is seen that normal hemoglobin, A, has moved toward the negative pole, sickle-cell hemoglobin, S, toward the positive pole, and that the hemoglobin of the heterozygous individual became separated into two parts: about 60 per cent A and 40 per cent S hemoglobin. Movement (f) of hemoglobins A, S, and C in an electric field on filter paper. The hemoglobins were initially placed on the line at left. Different hemoglobins move with different speed. (a, b, f, originals from Dr. C. L. Conley; c, d, e, after Pauling, Itano, Singer, and Wells, *Science*, **110**, 1949; Conley and Smith, *Trans. Ass. Amer. Phys.*, **57**, 1954.)

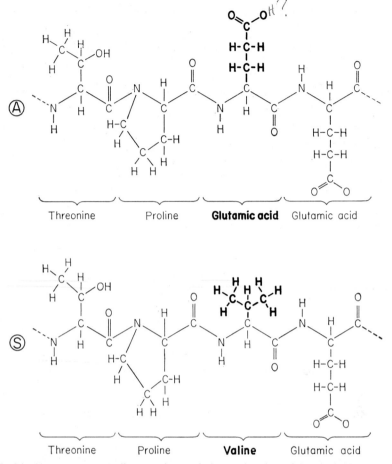

FIG. 31. Short corresponding sections of the molecules of hemoglobin A and S. The amino acid units are the same in both hemoglobins except that glutamic acid in A is replaced by valine in S. (After ingram, *Sc. Am.* **198,** 1958.)

a single one of these amino acids constitutes the difference between sickle-cell and normal hemoglobin: the latter contains glutamic acid; the former, valine (Fig. 31). The presence of a third allele at the Hb_1 locus, Hb_1^C, causes another amino acid, lysine, to replace either glutamic acid or valine in the hemoglobin molecule. Ingram, the discoverer of the molecular difference between hemoglobins A and S, has remarked that "a change of one amino acid in nearly 300 is certainly a very small change indeed and yet this slight alteration can be fatal to the unfortunate possessor of the errant hemoglobin." There are, of course, many compounds synthesized in nature or in laboratories which have ill effects on man, and their chemical structure is often only slightly different from that of harmless or beneficial substances. Hence it is not surprising that the molecular entities called genes are at times responsible

for alterations of molecular cellular material with far-reaching effects in development or functioning.

It is interesting to note that a normal $Hb_1{}^A Hb_1{}^A$ individual forms only normal adult hemoglobin, that an anemic $Hb_1{}^S Hb_1{}^S$ individual has none of it, and
that the heterozygote, $Hb_1{}^A Hb_1{}^S$ with the sickle-cell trait, produces, in codominant manner, both types of hemoglobin, the abnormal one making up
from a quarter to nearly half of the mixture (Fig. 30, e, f). The reader may
want to compare this situation with that described for blood antibodies produced by $I^{A_1}I^{A_1}$, $I^O I^O$, and $I^{A_1} I^O$ individuals.

Besides the S hemoglobin, characteristic of carriers of the gene $Hb_1{}^S$, at
least nine other abnormal hemoglobins have been discovered. They are all
dependent on particular genes, and when occurring in homozygotes are responsible for anemias of varying degrees of severity.

Inborn Errors of Metabolism.   The English physician Garrod (1858–
1936) was the first to analyze in detail the activity of human genes in terms
of biochemistry. His study of alkaptonuria, the abnormal excretion of homogentisic acid in the urine, has been referred to earlier (p. 41). The absence,
in affected individuals, of an enzyme normally involved in the breakdown of
homogentisic acid (Fig. 32) at first causes only the blackening of urine exposed to air; later the development of dark pigmentation of cartilage and
other body parts, externally noticeable in the ears, the sclera of the eyes, and
some other regions; but finally disease of the joints (arthritis), sometimes
incapacitating, is the ultimate consequence of this famous "inborn error of
metabolism" as Garrod called it.

Absence of other enzymes may have still more serious effects. Homogentisic

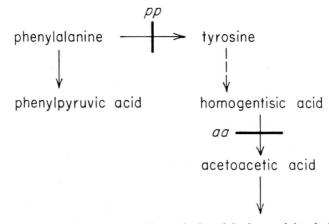

FIG. 32. Some steps in the metabolism of phenylalanine and its derivatives. In
the presence of the gene *P*, phenylalanine is transformed to tyrosine: the genotype
pp blocks this reaction. In the presence of the gene *A*, homogentisic acid is transformed to acetoacetic acid: the genotype *aa* blocks this reaction. (What would
happen in a *pp aa* individual?)

acid is a substance that seems to provide one of the intermediary links in a metabolic chain of reactions which begins with the amino acid tyrosine, which is normally formed in the body from the very similar amino acid phenylalanine (Fig. 32). There are individuals homozygous for the rare recessive gene *p*, who lack the enzyme phenylalanine oxidase necessary for this transformation. Since they cannot convert phenylalanine in the regular way, large concentrations of it are accumulated in the blood, the cerebro-spinal fluid, and the urine. Some phenylalanine is normally converted into phenylpyruvic acid, but in *pp* persons excessive amounts of this substance are produced and excreted in the urine. As stated earlier, the condition is known as phenylketonuria and is usually accompanied by feeble-mindedness. There is reason to believe that the mental deficiency is caused, in some indirect way, by the abnormally high concentrations of phenylalanine or its derivatives.

Absence of an enzyme that acts on milk sugar is responsible for a rare disease of young children, galactosemia, which is transmitted by another recessive gene, *g*. Children who are *gg* lack the enzyme "P Gal transferase," which in *GG* and *Gg* individuals converts compounds of the milk sugar galactose into compounds of the similar sugar glucose. Without this conversion, galactose compounds accumulate in the blood and soon after birth lead to liver damage and mental retardation.

Another genetically controlled biochemical condition is one that affects the utilization of copper in the body. Wilson's disease, characterized by degeneration of certain parts of the nervous system and of the liver, has long been recognized as a peculiar clinical entity, and its dependence on a recessive gene established. Only recently could it be shown that the diverse symptoms of the condition are the results of an inability to synthesize the normal amount of a copper-containing blood protein called ceruloplasmin. As a result of this inability, the copper atoms taken up in food are deposited in the brain, the liver, and other tissues, and there produce their multiple clinical effects.

A modern method of identifying various chemicals, particularly those present only in small amounts, is paper chromatography. In its simplest application a mixture of chemicals is placed on a piece of filter paper near its border and a solvent made to diffuse over the material. The molecular properties of the different chemicals determine the distance the solvent will carry each of them from the place they had first been deposited. In this way they will be separated from one another, and they can then be made visible by reagents. This and similar methods have been applied to urine of different individuals, and a variety of amino acids and other substances present in the urine have been identified. There is evidence of genetic control of the excreted amounts of these metabolic products within groups of normal individuals. In most cases it still remains to be determined where the primary gene effect lies—whether in some general metabolic processes or in the degree to which the kidney controls the excretory processes.

Most normal individuals excrete only six amino acids in easily discernible amounts (Fig. 33, A). Cystinuric persons, characterized by homozygosity

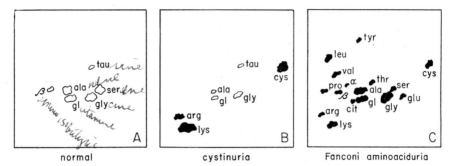

FIG. 33. Paper chromatograms of urine from (A) a normal individual, (B) a cystinuric individual, and (C) an individual with Fanconi syndrome. The square represents the piece of filter paper to whose lower-right corner the urine sample had been applied. Solvents were then run from right to left and from bottom to top, thus separating the various amino acids. (tau=taurine; ser =serine; gly= glycine; ala=alanine; gl=glutamine; $\beta=\beta$-amino-iso-butyric acid; cys=cystine; arg=arginine; lys=lysine; glu=glutamic acid; thr=threonine; leu=leucine, iso-l; val=valine; $\alpha=\alpha$-amino-iso-butyric acid; cit=citrulline; pro=proline.) The normal individual excretes significant though small amounts of only six amino acids. A cystinuric individual is primarily characterized by excessive excretion of cystine, arginine, and lysine. A patient with Fanconi syndrome excretes large quantities of many amino acids. (Dent and Harris, *Ann. Eugen.,* **16,** 1951.)

for a recessive gene, excrete unusually large amounts not only of cystine, as had been known for a long time, but also of arginine and lysine (Fig. 33, B). Some of these individuals do not show any symptoms of disease, but others form a special type of kidney stone composed of cystine and suffer damage to the kidney. An even more generalized "aminoaciduria" occurs in infants with the rare and eventually fatal Fanconi syndrome, which affects bone formation and causes various physiological disturbances; it, too, is caused by a recessive gene. Affected infants excrete large quantities of the majority of amino acids (Fig. 33, C).

Most biochemical analyses of gene effects have been concerned with rare defects. The biochemistry and the genetics of many rather common defects is less well understood, largely because most rare defects are caused by practically complete absence of a normal metabolic process, while the more common defects may be correlated, not with the absence of a biochemical reaction, but only with a quantitative abnormality. Obviously, it is easier to discover which genes result in a reaction's absence than to find which genes lead to less striking quantitative variations in reactions. Yet there is every reason to assume that genes, by regulating biochemical processes, determine not only striking abnormalities but also less striking ones and, above all, much of the variability among normal human beings.

Great advances in biochemical human genetics can be expected within the near future. Recent refinements of the methods of propagating cells of animals and man in culture media—methods similar to those used by microbiologists in dealing with bacteria and molds in glass dishes—have made possible the study of the biochemistry of isolated tissue cultures. The experimental investigation of cell cultures from different tissues of a multitude of genetic types, normal as well as diseased, will undoubtedly result in many new discoveries which will add to the knowledge heretofore obtained by clinical and biochemical studies of whole individuals.

Insight into the biochemistry of genetic variation has already provided tools for overcoming genic deficiencies. Infants with galactosemia can be helped by removing galactose from their diet; a beginning has been made in improving the mental development of phenylketonuric infants by giving them food containing only the minimal necessary amount of phenylalanine; and sugar diabetes, which is often due to a deficiency of the pancreatic enzyme insulin, can be controlled by regular injection of this enzyme. One may even, with Pauling, "foresee the day when many of the diseases that are caused by abnormal enzyme molecules will be treated by the use of artificial enzymes. . . . It may be possible, for example, to synthesize a catalyst for the oxidation of phenylalanine to tyrosine. A small amount of this catalyst could be attached to a framework inside a small open-ended tube, which could be permanently placed within the artery of a new-born child who had been shown by chemical tests to have inherited the mental disease phenylketonuria. Through the action of the artificial enzyme, the child could then develop in a normal way."

In this chapter, we have tried to picture genic action in terms of intracellular reactions and have outlined the role of genic action in the development and the biochemistry of the individual. A few summarized experiments and some deductions from general principles have indicated the relationship between genes and specific traits. Important phenomena and concepts have been discussed and defined: genes and alleles; homozygotes and heterozygotes; dominance, recessiveness, intermediateness, and codominance; genotype and phenotype. The ground has been prepared for a more detailed treatment of many aspects of human genetics.

References

Allison, A. C., 1959. Metabolic polymorphism in mammals and their bearing on problems of biochemical genetics. *Am. Naturalist,* **93:** 5–16.

Arey, L. B., 1954. *Developmental Anatomy.* 6th ed. 680 pp. W. B. Saunders, Philadelphia and London.

Caspari, E., 1952. Pleiotropic gene action. *Evolution,* **6:** 1–18.

Filitti-Wurmser, S., Jacquot-Armand, Y., Aubel-Lesure, G., and Wurmser, R., 1954. Physico-chemical study of human isohaemagglutination. *Ann. Eugen.,* **18:** 183–202.

Garrod, A. E., 1923. *Inborn Errors of Metabolism.* 2nd ed. 216 pp. H. Frowde & Hodder & Stoughton, London.

Gitlin, D., and Janeway, C. A., 1957. Agammaglobulinemia. *Sc. Am.,* **197:** 93–104.

Graham, J. B., 1956. Biochemical genetics of blood coagulation. *Am. J. Human Genet.,* **8:** 63–79.

Grouchy, J. de, 1958. L'Hérédité Moléculaire. Conditions Normales et Pathologiques. *Analecta Genetica.,* **7:** 1–333. Inst. Gregorio Mendel (Ed.), Rome.

Hadorn, E., 1955. *Letalfaktoren.* 338 pp. Georg Thieme Verlag, Stuttgart.

Haldane, J. B. S., 1954. *The Biochemistry of Genetics.* 144 pp. Allen & Unwin, London.

Harris, H., 1959. *Human Biochemical Genetics.* 310 pp. Cambridge University Press, London.

Hertig, A. T., Rock, J., and Adams, E. C., 1956. A description of 34 human ova within the first 17 days of development. *Am. J. Anat.,* **98:** 435–493.

Hsia, D. (Yi-Yung), 1959. *Inborn Errors of Metabolism.* 358 pp. The Year Book Publishers, Inc., Chicago.

Hunt, J. A., and Ingram, V. M., 1958. Allelomorphism and the chemical differences of the human hemoglobins A, S, and C. *Nature,* **181:** 1062–1063.

Jervis, G. A., 1954. Phenylpyruvic oligophrenia (Phenylketonuria). *Res. Publ. Ass. Nerv. Mental Dis.,* **33:** 259–282.

Knox, W. E., 1958. Sir Archibald Garrod's "Inborn errors of metalobism": I. Cystinuria, II. Alkaptonuria, III. Albinism, IV. Pentosuria. *Am. J. Human Genet.* **10:** 3–32, 95–124, 249–267, 385–397.

Lamy, M., Royer, P., and Frézal, J., 1959. *Maladies Héréditaires du Métabolisme chez l'Enfant.* 259 pp Masson & Co., Paris.

Neel, J. V., 1956. The genetics of human hemoglobin differences: problems and perspectives. *Ann. Human Genet.* **21:** 1–30.

Patten, Bradley M., 1953. *Human Embryology.* 2nd ed. 798 pp. Blakiston, New York–Toronto.

Stern, C., 1955. Gene Action. In Willier, B. H., Weiss, P. A., and Hamburger, V. (Eds.). *Analysis of Development.* pp. 151–169. W. B. Saunders, Philadelphia and London.

Wagner, R. P., and Mitchell, H. K., 1955. *Genetics and Metabolism.* 444 pp. Wiley, New York.

Witschi, E., 1956. *Development of Vertebrates.* 588 pp. W. B. Saunders, Philadelphia and London.

CHAPTER 4

MEIOSIS

The cells which make up the body of a man or a woman contain two sets of 23 chromosomes, or 46 chromosomes in all. When, however, a mature egg is formed by a woman, or a mature sperm by a man, each germ cell contains only one set of 23 chromosomes. How is the reduction in number of sets from two to one—in number of chromosomes from 46 to 23—accomplished? This is clearly not just a problem of cellular detail but a question of great significance for human inheritance, since changes in the number of chromosomes involve, by necessity, changes in the number of genes.

It has taken nearly a half-century of the most painstaking study of many animals and plants to determine how chromosome reduction takes place. In the growing ovary or testis of a human, each cell, like the other cells of the individual, contains 46 chromosomes. After many cell divisions, with normal mitotic behavior of the chromosomes, numerous immature germ cells have been produced. These cells—one at a time in the ovary and many at a time in the testis—undergo a unique process called *meiosis,* which results in production of the mature germ cells.

A Preliminary Outline of Meiosis. The essential aspects of meiosis are not difficult to understand, but since several different processes go on simultaneously, it will be helpful to give a simplified description before a more complete account is rendered.

Figure 34, A and B, shows an immature germ cell in which the chromosomes become differentiated in a way characteristic of the early stages of nuclear division. As in the diagram of mitosis (Fig. 6), only two pairs of chromosomes are shown: a pair of long chromosomes with a kinetochore in the middle, and a pair of short chromosomes with a kinetochore near one end.

Figure 34, C, shows the *first* of the unique features of meiosis: homologous chromosomes attract each other and lie side by side. As the diagram indicates, this pairing brings together the homologous chromosomes in such a way that

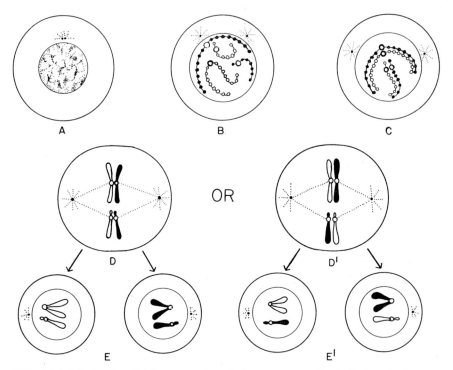

OR

FIG. 34. Meiosis, simplified: two pairs of chromosomes. *Dark:* Paternal chromosomes. *Light:* Maternal chromosomes. A. Nucleus in a premeiotic germ cell. B–C. Pairing of homologous chromosomes. D–D′. The two alternative arrangements of the chromosome pairs on a meiotic spindle. E–E′. The four different types of reduced chromosome constitutions of the gametes.

each chromomere pairs with its homologous chromomere, and kinetochore with kinetochore.

While the relatively uncoiled, paired chromosomes condense into shorter, heavier bodies, a spindle is formed on which they become arranged as in mitosis (Fig. 34, D and D′). At this stage, a *second* important feature of meiosis can be observed. In mitosis, each kinetochore lies apart from its homologue; in meiosis, it lies beside it. In mitosis, the kinetochores divide and lead their associated sister chromosomes to opposite poles. In the meiotic division pictured in Figure 34, D and D′, the paired kinetochores do not divide, but move apart, leading one of each pair of chromosomes to opposite poles. Thus, when cell division takes place, each daughter cell contains only one chromosome of each pair, or, stated differently, only one instead of two sets of chromosomes (Fig. 34, E and E′).

A *third* characteristic of meiosis is shown in the alternative diagrams of Figure 34, D and D′: there is no fixed pattern of arrangement of paternal and maternal chromosomes on the meiotic spindle. On the spindle of Figure 34, D, both maternal chromosomes, the long and the short, lie on one side, and the two paternal ones on the other. On the spindle of Figure 34, D', the two maternal chromosomes lie on opposite sides, as do the paternal ones.

In microscopic preparations of cells, the paternal and maternal partners of a pair of homologous chromosomes are almost always indistinguishable from each other. Occasionally, however, slight permanent differences can be seen, and it has been observed that each pair of homologues acts as if it had been ordered to arrange itself on the spindle without paying attention to any other pair. The result is an independent arrangement of the different chromosome pairs. When division occurs and "reduced" daughter cells with only one set of chromosomes are formed, the meiotic process shown in Figure 34, D, produces one cell containing the long and short maternal chromosomes and another containing the long and short paternal ones (Fig. 34, E). The meiosis in Figure 34, D', leads to one cell with the long paternal and the short maternal chromosomes and another cell with the long maternal and short paternal ones. Since the two arrangments, D and D', are equally common, all four resulting gametes are also equally common. Meiosis thus involves the independent or free assortment of the maternal and paternal chromosomes during the reduction from two to one chromosome set.

The Two Meiotic Divisions.   The preceding simplified description referred to a single division by means of which chromosome reduction is accomplished. In reality, meiosis always includes two successive divisions (Fig. 35). During the *first* meiotic division, the paired homologous chromosomes are present in duplicate, the duplicates being joined by a single kinetochore just as in the early stages of mitosis. Each pair, therefore, consists of four chromosome strands (*chromatids*), two of which are held together by a maternal and two by a paternal kinetochore. When the kinetochores move toward opposite poles, each carries with it two chromosome strands. The two daughter cells which are formed as a result of the first meiotic division immediately divide again. During this *second* meiotic division, the kinetochores with their double strands assemble on the spindles of the daughter cells. As in mitosis, the kinetochores divide, and the daughter kinetochores, each joined to one chromosome strand, move to opposite poles. Thus, a premeiotic germ cell with two sets of chromosomes (Fig. 35, A, A') forms four germ cells, each with a single set of chromosomes (Fig. 35, D, D').

The two meiotic divisions are often called the reduction divisions. The first division reduces to one-half the number of kinetochores in a cell; the second reduces to one-half the number of chromosome strands. An answer to the question of why meiosis takes two instead of only one division will have to await a better knowledge of the forces involved in duplication, pairing, and separation of kinetochores and chromosome strands.

The cells in which meiosis takes place are called *oocytes* in the female, and *spermatocytes* in the male. They originate, by divisions involving ordinary mitosis, from oogonia and spermatogonia. After meiosis has been com-

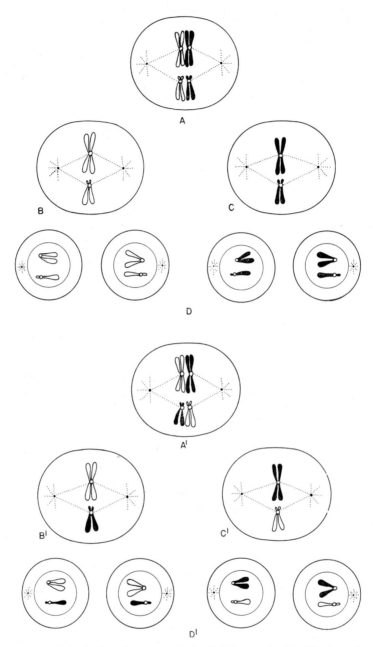

FIG. 35. Meiosis, including the two meiotic divisions.   A–A'. The two alternative arrangements of the chromosome pairs on the first meiotic spindle.   B–D, and B'–D'. The second meiotic divisions and the different types of reduced chromosome constitutions of the gametes.

pleted, the female germ cell is a mature egg, but the male germ cell, the spermatid, has still to transform itself into a mature sperm.

Crossing Over.   Meiosis includes an important additional feature: *crossing
over.* This is a process by which homologous segments of paired maternal
and paternal chromosomes are exchanged. Its effect is that even genes that
are "linked" in a single chromosome do not necessarily remain together from
one generation to another, but are interchanged with their alleles in the homologous partner chromosome. If, for instance, the maternal chromosome
contained, among other genes, the genes *A* and *B*, and the paternal chromosome the alleles *A'* and *B'*, then, after meiosis, some gametes might contain
the original chromosomes with *AB* or *A'B'* (no crossing over) and others
exchange-chromosomes with *AB'* or *A'B*.

Except for their relation to the important study of linkage, the details of
crossing over have little bearing on human genetics. Some readers may therefore prefer to postpone a study of the next three pages until they reach
Chapters 14 and 15, which deal with linkage and crossing over of human
genes.

Examples of crossing over are illustrated in Figure 36. Three pairs of loci
have been indicated in a pair of chromosomes, the maternal alleles by *M*, *N*,
and *O*, and the paternal alleles by *M'*, *N'*, and *O'* (Fig. 36, A). In the

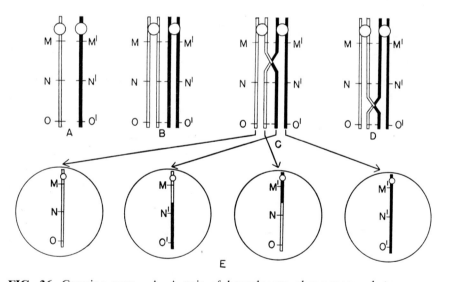

FIG. 36. Crossing over.   A. A pair of homologous chromosomes heterozygous
for three pairs of loci *M*, *M'*; *N*, *N'*; and *O*, *O'*.   B. Four-strand stage.   C.
Crossing over between two of the four strands in the region between *M*, *M'* and
N, *N'*.   D. Same in the region between *N*, *N'* and *O*, *O'*.   E. The four types
of reduced chromosome constitutions of the gametes resulting from the crossing
over shown in C.

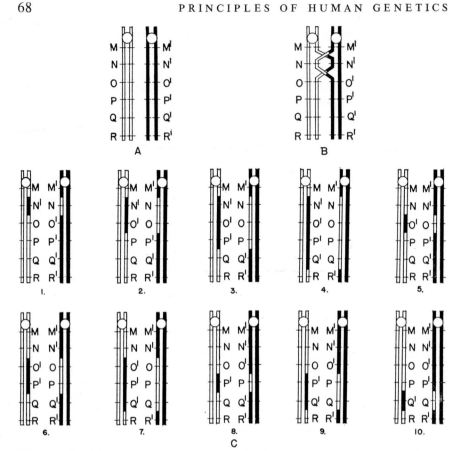

FIG. 37. Double crossing over. A. A pair of homologous chromosomes heterozygous for six pairs of loci. B. A double crossover involving two of the four strands. C, 1. The four chromosome strands resulting from the double crossover shown in B. C, 2–10. Chromosome strands resulting from the other 9 possible types of double crossovers involving two of the four strands in A.

duplicated chromosomes, each locus is present twice: *MMM'M'*, *NNN'N'*, and *OOO'O'* (Fig. 36, B). A crossover between the *M*, *M'* and *N*, *N'* loci is shown in Figure 36, C. Only two of the four chromosome strands are involved in the exchange. Two strands are noncrossovers and have retained the original maternal or paternal sequence of alleles, *MNO* or *M'N'O'*, respectively. The two other strands are crossovers. One of them begins with the maternal allele *M*, but continues with a section containing the paternal alleles *N'* and *O'*. The other begins with the paternal allele *M'*, but continues with a section containing the maternal alleles *N* and *O*. It is as if the crossover strands originated by breakage of two original strands at exactly homologous locations and healed together after they had crossed over, although it is not certain that breakage and fusion are the actual mechanisms involved.

It has been found that the place of a crossover in a given pair of homologous chromosomes varies from cell to cell. Considering only the three pairs of loci—*M*, *M'*; *N*, *N'*; and *O*, *O'*—crossovers can occur between *M*, *M'* and *N*, *N'* in some cells, and between *N*, *N'* and *O*, *O'* in others. These crossovers are seen in Figure 36, C and D. Had more than three pairs of loci been shown in the diagrams, then more than two possible crossover sites could have been indicated. For instance, a pair of chromosomes with six pairs of loci, occupied by the alleles *MNOPQR* in the maternal chromosome and the alleles *M'N'O'P'Q'R'* in the paternal chromosome, could, in different cells, undergo crossing over between any two successive loci, that is, in five different regions.

Any single crossover between two homologous chromosomes affects only two of the four chromosome strands. Since these four strands are distributed into four separate cells by the two meiotic divisions, each of the four cells receives a different type of chromosome. If we follow, as an example, the crossover in Figure 36, C, we see (Fig. 36, E) that one cell receives the maternal noncrossover strand *MNO*, another the crossover strand *MN'O'*, a third the complementary crossover strand *M'NO*, and a fourth the paternal noncrossover strand *M'N'O'*. This may be the reason for the two meiotic divisions: because crossing over takes place at the four-strand stage of paired chromosomes and between two strands only, a single meiotic division would not be able to reduce the number of strands, and many double strands would have homologous sections derived from both parents.

A pair of homologous chromosomes in a given cell may cross over at more than one location. Many double crossovers are found. Such crossovers, if they involve the same two strands, lead to exchanges of middle sections by the strands. This is shown in Figure 37 for two chromosomes on which six pairs of loci are marked. In different immature germ cells of the same individual, middle sections may be exchanged in ten different ways, assuming that only single exchanges take place between successive loci. Triple and even higher-multiple crossovers are also known.

Although only two strands are involved in any individual crossover, three or all four strands may participate in double or multiple crossovers. A "three-strand" and a "four-strand double" are shown in Figure 38.

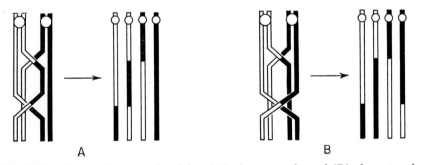

A B

FIG. 38. Double crossing over, involving (A), three strands, and (B), four strands. Note that three-strand double crossing over results in chromosomes that have undergone 1, 2, 1, 0 exchanges, and that four-strand double crossing over results in chromosomes each of which has undergone 1 exchange only.

OOGENESIS   SPERMATOGENESIS

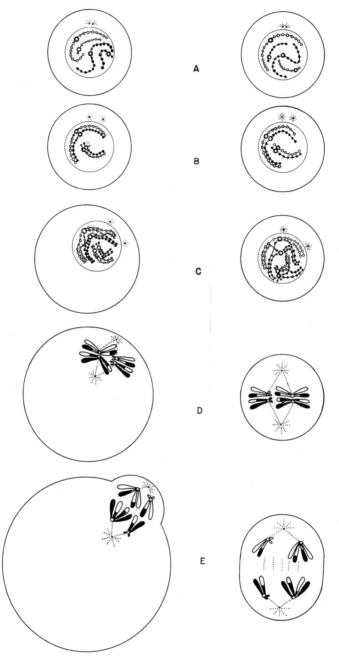

FIG. 39. Meiosis and formation of gametes.   A–C. Chromosome pairing and crossing over.   D–E. First meiotic division.

OOGENESIS   SPERMATOGENESIS

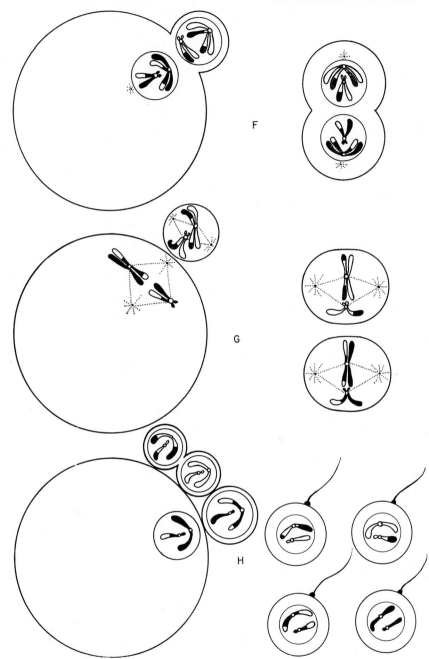

FIG. 39. (*continued*). F. Products of first division. G. Second meiotic division. H. Egg with polar bodies (left), sperm cells (right).

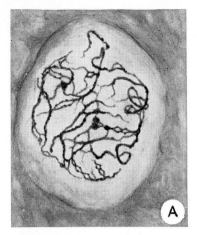
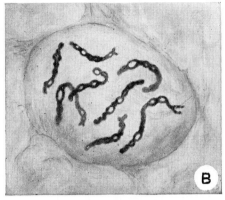

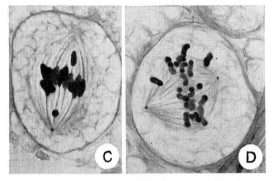

FIG. 40. Meiosis in human spermatogenesis. A–B. Pairing of homologous chromosomes (only 8 pairs shown). The four-strand nature of the chromosome pairs is not visible. C. First meiotic division (note the X- and Y-chromosomes which have separated ahead of the autosomes). D. Second meiotic division. (Severinghaus, *Am. J. Anat.,* **70,** 1942.)

Meiosis and the Formation of Egg and Sperm.   Many of the important phenomena of meiosis are summarized in Figure 39, and a careful study of the figure is advisable. The formation of both mature eggs and sperm is illustrated. Essentially, meiosis is alike in both, but one difference is significant. In the male, the first meiotic division results in two cells of equal size; the second meiotic division, which occurs simultaneously in these two cells, leads to the formation of four equal-sized cells, each of which becomes a mature, functional sperm (Fig. 39, D-H, right). In the female, the two divisions do not yield four cells of equal size. The cytoplasm of an immature egg cell has been organized in a special way in preparation for development and has been loaded with reserve food material, so that its growth has made it one of the largest cells in the human body. The meiotic divisions occur in such a fashion that the structure and size of one of the four cells which are being formed are almost the same as the original cell. This is accomplished by the first meiotic spindle being near the periphery of the cell, with the spindle's long axis lying along a radius of the egg. Only a small bud of cytoplasm, including the peripheral daughter nucleus, is pinched off the main body of the cell. The second meiotic division occurs simultaneously in the large cell and in the pinched-off cell, which is called the first polar body. In the latter, the second division results in two equal-sized polar bodies, provided the division is completed, which is not always the case. In the large cell, the second meiotic spindle occupies the same asymmetrical position as the first meiotic spindle and, again, this results in an unequal cell division: a second polar body is separated from the now-mature egg, which has maintained a volume almost equal to that of the original egg cell. Four viable sperm cells but only one viable egg cell and three degenerating polar bodies are thus formed by meiosis of a single cell.

Cells of a human testis in various stages of meiosis are shown in Figure 40. The paired and condensed chromosomes at the time of the first meiotic divisions in human testes have already been shown in Figure 7, B.

Genetic Consequences of Meiosis

The cellular details of meiosis will now be translated into the language of genetics. We shall first follow the fate of a single pair of alleles, then that of two or more pairs located in different pairs of homologous chromosomes, and, last, that of pairs of loci which are linked by being carried in the same pair of chromosomes.

Segregation of a Single Pair of Alleles. In the early stages of meiosis, every pair of alleles—A and A', for example—that is present in a pair of homologous chromosomes of the immature germ cells is duplicated when the chromosomes double. Therefore, the genotype is temporarily $AAA'A'$ (Fig. 41). The separation, during the two meiotic divisions of the four strands and

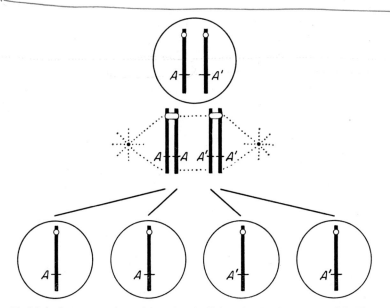

FIG. 41. Meiotic segregation of a pair of alleles A, A'. Compare with Figure 35.

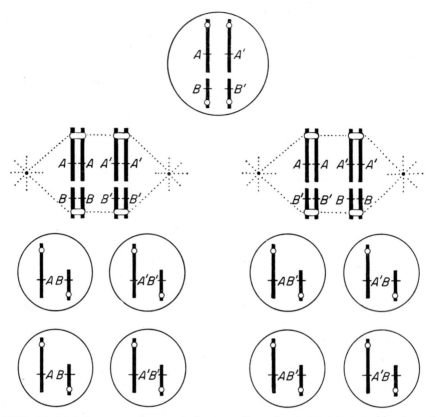

FIG. 42. Meiotic segregation, and the two alternative types of recombination of two pairs of alleles *A*, *A'* and *B*, *B'*. Compare with Figure 35.

their final enclosure within four cells, assigns one, and only one, of these alleles to each cell. This process, called *segregation,* results in mature germ cells that are *pure* for either the maternal or the paternal allele; or, as we might say, the alleles segregate themselves from each other, uninfluenced by the fact that they have resided together in the same nuclei since the individual began his existence as a fertilized egg.

Segregation of Two Pairs of Alleles. In order to understand the distribution of two pairs of alleles located in two pairs of chromosomes, it will be best to assume at first that no crossing over takes place. We have seen (Fig. 35) that the pairs of homologous chromosomes take their positions on the spindle independently of each other, so that different, but equally frequent, arrangements of maternal and paternal partner chromosomes are found in different meiotic cells. In Figure 42, these arrangements are recognizable by the position of the alleles. *A* and *B* represent the maternal alleles in the two nonhomologous chromosomes, and *A'* and *B'* the paternal ones. The division at the left segregates the two original parental combinations, *AB* and *A'B'*, from each other; and the division at the right, the two new combinations, AB' and $A'B$.

Four types of gametes are thus formed, as is illustrated by the following example. Assume that an individual received from his mother the allele A^2 for polydactlyly in one chromosome and the allele I^A for blood-group property A in another, and that the father had contributed the allele A^1 for five-fingeredness and the allele I^O for blood-group property O. At maturity, the individual will form gametes with one, and only one, of either A^2 or A^1 in equal proportion, and in addition, with one, and only one, of either I^A or I^O in equal proportion. Therefore, one-quarter of the gametes will be like that of the mother, carrying both A^2 and I^A; one-quarter, like that of the father, with both A^1 and I^O; one-quarter will contain the mother's A^2 and the father's I^O; one-quarter, the father's A^1 and the mother's I^A.

Segregation of Many Pairs of Alleles.   Independent assortment of maternal and paternal alleles belonging to genes located in different chromosome pairs occurs not only for two pairs of alleles but for as many pairs of alleles as there are pairs of chromosomes. It is easy to calculate how many different kinds of gametes may be formed by an individual whose 23 chromosome pairs are all marked by a pair of alleles. If only one pair, A and A', is considered, two kinds of gametes can be produced, A and A'. If two pairs of loci, A, A' and B, B', are assumed to exist, a gamete with A may have either B or B', a gamete with A' may have either B or B', and four kinds of gametes, AB, AB', $A'B$, and $A'B'$, would thus be formed. When a third pair of loci, C, C', is taken into account, each of the four kinds of gametes just mentioned may contain either the maternal (C) or the paternal (C') allele of the third pair of loci, and this leads to eight kinds of gametes. ABC, ABC', $AB'C$, $A'BC$, $AB'C'$, $A'BC'$, $A'B'C$, and $A'B'C'$. With each further pair of loci added, the number of possible kinds of gametes is doubled. This is shown graphically in Figure 43. The regularity can also be expressed in numerical form, as in Table 2, where it is seen that the number of kinds of gametes

TABLE 2.   *Number of Potentially Different Gametes in Relation to Number of Pairs of Alleles.*

No. of Heterozygous Pairs of Alleles	No. of Kinds of Gametes
1	$2 = 2^1$
2	$4 = 2^2$
3	$8 = 2^3$
4	$16 = 2^4$
.	.
23	$8{,}388{,}608 = 2^{23}$
.	.
n	$= 2^n$

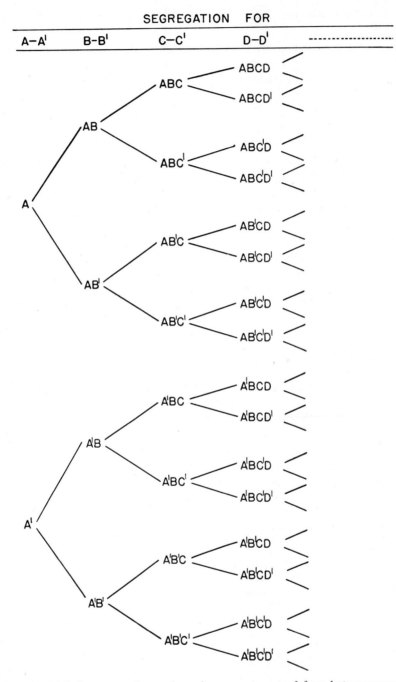

FIG. 43. Meiotic segregation and random assortment of four heterozygous pairs of alleles, and the resulting different kinds of gametic constitutions.

(which is equal to the number of combinations of maternal and paternal alleles) is 2^n, where n signifies the number of allelic pairs.

When 23 allelic pairs, on the 23 pairs of chromosomes, are involved, 2^{23} or 8,388,608 kinds of gametes could be produced. This number may seem astoundingly large, particularly when we remember that it represents the combinations of only 23 elements, each of which occurs in only two forms.

In order to help the reader realize the significance of 8,388,608 possible combinations, we may cite a few of the individual combinations which are included in the total. First, there are two combinations with either all 23 maternal or all 23 paternal alleles. Second, there are combinations of 22 maternal and 1 paternal and of 22 paternal and 1 maternal alleles, each of which occurs in 23 different ways, since the 1 paternal or the 1 maternal allele of these combinations may be either the allele in the first pair of chromosomes, or that in the second pair, and so on, up to the twenty-third pair. Third, there are no less than 253 different ways in which 2 maternal and 21 paternal alleles, and 253 different ways in which 2 paternal and 21 maternal alleles, may be segregated and assorted as a result of meiosis. The two maternal alleles may belong to pairs 1 and 2, 1 and 3, 1 and 4, and so on to 1 and 23, adding up to 22 combinations. Or they may belong to pairs 2 and 3, 2 and 4, and so on to 2 and 23, adding up to 21 combinations. Similarly they may belong to pairs 3 and 4, etc., to 3 and 23, adding up to 20 combinations. The sum of all these combinations of 2 maternal and 21 paternal chromosomes cited up to this point is $22 + 21 + 20$.

Many more combinations are furnished by the maternal alleles of pair 4 with the maternal alleles of pairs 5, 6, ... 23; of the maternal allele of pair 5 with the maternal alleles of pairs 6, 7, ..., 23; and so on until, finally, the combination of the 2 maternal alleles of pairs 22 and 23 is reached. It should be apparent, then, that the sum total of all combinations that contain 2 maternal alleles (plus, necessarily, 21 paternal alleles) is $22 + 21 + 20 + 19 + 18 ... + 1$, which is 253. As the number of maternal alleles approaches that of paternal alleles, the number of combinations increases, until there are no less than 1,352,078 ways in which 12 maternal alleles of different loci may be combined with 11 paternal alleles of other loci, or 11 maternal with 12 paternal ones. (This large number is obtained from the expression $23!/(12! \; 11!)$, which is explained on page 131.)

The Number of Combinations. As large as the figure 8,388,608 may seem, it is by no means large enough to give a true description of the number of possible combinations of maternal and paternal genetic elements in the gametes of a single individual. A chromosome pair contains not only one pair of loci, but a great many. If crossing over did not occur, then the existence of many pairs of loci in a pair of homologous chromosomes would not add to the number of allelic combinations in the gametes, since the alleles in a maternal chromosome would always segregate as a unit from the paternal alleles. But crossing over, as we have seen, breaks up the original combina-

[handwritten annotation at top: 20^{23} possible allelic combinations]

tions and recombines maternal and paternal alleles in new chromosome strands. It thus increases greatly the number of hereditarily different kinds of gametes that one individual is potentially able to form.

This number depends, of course, on the degree of heterozygosity of the individual. All the gametes of a completely homozygous person are alike genetically, and only a heterozygote will produce different kinds of gametes. It is impossible to estimate the total number of heterozygous genes in an individual. Surely, this number will vary from one person to another, but it seems conservative to assume arbitrarily that 2 per cent of all genes are heterozygous. Making use of the earlier assumption of a total of 10,000 loci in a chromosome set, the present assumption would mean that 9,800 of the genes supplied by the mother are exactly the same as those supplied by the father, but that the two parents contributed different alleles at 200 loci. On the average, each of the 23 chromosome pairs would be heterozygous for nearly 10 different loci.

In different cells of the same individual, crossing over could occur in any one of the 9 consecutive regions delimited in each chromosome by 10 heterozygous loci. If only single crossovers occurred in each chromosome pair, the gametes could contain 20 different combinations of maternally and paternally derived alleles in one pair of chromosomes: namely, 2 noncrossover combinations and 18 different crossover combinations.

Since crossing over in one pair of chromosomes takes place largely irrespective of its occurrence in other chromosome pairs, and since segregation of the four strands of each original pair of chromosomes is independent of segregation in other pairs, the total number of possible combinations is the product of the combinations in each of the 23 pairs. This product, under the assumptions made—which do not include double or multiple crossovers—is $20 \cdot 20 \cdot 20 \ldots = 20^{23}$. The magnitude of this figure is beyond comprehension. It is, of course, equivalent to $2^{23} \times 10^{23}$, or our former figure of 8,388,608 followed by 23 zeros. A woman, during her reproductive years, produces only about 400 mature egg cells. Clearly, these 400 eggs are an infinitesimally small sample of the overwhelming variety of germ cells which she has the potentiality of forming. A man's total production of germ cells is much larger than that of a woman: it has been estimated to be in the neighborhood of 1,000,000,000,000 (1,000 billion). Even this immense number is negligible if compared to 20^{23}, the total number of possible combinations of maternal and paternal alleles in his sperm; it is only about one billion-billionth of 20^{23}!

The Shuffling of Genes. Because meiosis assorts and recombines the genetic contributions of an individual's parents, it has been compared to the shuffling of a deck of cards. The recombining of genes in meiosis explains why each child of a couple, excepting identical twins, has many genetic characters that the other brothers and sisters do not have. Even if individuals lived for geologic periods and had a litter of children each year, the chance of forming two identical gametes would be so small as to make it practically certain that no two children would have the same genotype.

We are prone to emphasize those genes which a child inherits from his parents. It is important not to forget the genes which he does *not* inherit. Of every pair of alleles a parent possesses, a child gets only one. As far as that child is concerned, the other allele is lost to the future, since segregation in meiosis excluded it from the germ cells which led to the child's being. Segregation explains some of his similarities to his parents, those due to his having half of the genes of each; and it also explains some of his dissimilarities, those due to his not having obtained the other half of their genes. Pride of ancestry is, at best, a questionable attitude, since an individual's value depends on himself rather than on properties of others. If the pride is based on the assumption that one has the same genes as a distinguished ancestor, it is well to remember that half of a person's genes are not transmitted to his child, and that this process of halving takes place in each generation.

The argument may also be used in a different situation. Undesirable traits among ancestors are not uncommon, even though family tradition may seldom preserve their memory. Should these traits be based on a specific genotype, there may be consolation in the knowledge that only half of any ancestor's genetic material reaches the next generation.

Problems

6. A woman received from her father the five genes *ABCDE* and from her mother the alleles *A'B'C'D'E'*. Which of the following combinations of alleles may be present in the eggs from which her children originate: *ABCDE, A'B'C'D'E', ABCC'DE', A'BCDD', ABCD'E, AB'DE?*

7. A man is heterozygous for ten pairs of genes, each pair in different chromosomes. (a) How many different types of gametes may be formed by him? (b) Had the ten pairs of genes been located in five pairs of chromosomes, each chromosome pair with two pairs of genes, how would you have answered Part a?

8. What kind of crossover (single, double, two-strand, etc.) has occurred in the rod-shaped chromosome pair drawn in Figure 39? In the V-shaped chromosome pair?

9. (a) Redraw figures 39, D (left and right) with a different arrangement of the chromosome pairs. How many different arrangements are possible in each case? (b) On the basis of your redrawn stages D, make corresponding drawings of stages E–H. (Note that additional alternative arrangements are possible at the second meiotic division, giving a total of 16 possible kinds of gametes.)

10. Redraw Figure 39, C, assuming a three-strand double crossover in the V-shaped chromosome pair. Redraw D–H on the basis of your new Figure 39, C.

11. Assume that a man is heterozygous for five pairs of loci arranged in the order *ABCDE* on one chromosome and *A'B'C'D'E'* on the other. (a) What

are all possible genotypes of the spermatozoa? (b) State for each genotype whether it was derived from a noncrossover or a crossover, and, if the latter, from what kind?

References

Sharp, L. W., 1934. *Introduction to Cytology*. Chapter 16, pp. 250–283. McGraw-Hill, New York.

Sturtevant, A. H., and Beadle, G. W., 1939. *An Introduction to Genetics*. Chapters 5 to 7, pp. 63–126. W. B. Saunders, Philadelphia and London.

Swanson, C. P., 1957. *Cytology and Cytogenetics*. Chapters 3 and 8, 62– 81, 235–290. Prentice-Hall, Englewood Cliffs.

White, M. J. D., 1954. *Animal Cytology and Evolution*. 2nd. ed. Chapter 5, pp. 77–108. Cambridge University Press, London.

Wilson, E. B., 1925. *The Cell in Development and Heredity*. 1232 pp. Macmillan, New York.

PROBABILITY

We have seen that each of an individual's genes comprises a pair of alleles and that one allele of each pair is obtained from the mother and the other from the father. When the individual produces eggs or sperm, only one allele of each pair is transmitted to a gamete—one-half of the gametes receive the maternal allele, and the other half the paternal.

A child, therefore, receives only one allele from each of his mother's pairs of alleles and only one from each of his father's pairs. Whether any specific allele is the one which the parent received from the child's grandmother or from its grandfather is a question which cannot be answered with certainty. It is a matter of chance, depending on whether the fertilizing gametes happened to contain the maternal or paternal allele. Chance is not a vague concept but can be expressed quantitatively. Its evaluation in terms of probability plays a major role in all human activities. The probability that a healthy person will still be alive the next day determines much of his behavior. It also determines the behavior of all other persons with whom he has contact —although everyone is aware of the possibility of death. The probability that the sales volume of a store will not vary greatly for corresponding periods is the basis of ordering new merchandise. The probability that an automobile accident will occur is decisive in determining the rates of accident insurance. Most human actions are based on the probability that a certain event will or will not occur.

Probability Expressed as a Fraction. In tossing a coin, there is an even chance that heads or tails will turn up. The probability of throwing heads is therefore 1 out of 2, or 1/2. In throwing a die, the probability of obtaining a specific number—for example, three—is 1 out of 6, or 1/6. In general, *probability* is defined quantitatively as *the fraction obtained when the favorable event is divided by all possible events*—"favorable" denoting the event whose probability is under discussion. For the coin, the probability of turning up a

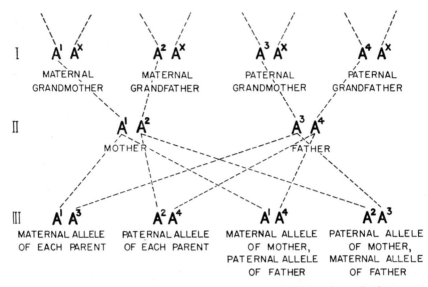

FIG. 44. The distribution of maternal and paternal alleles through three generations. I. Generation of grandparents. II. Generation of parents. III. Present generation. A^X = alleles which were not transmitted to the parents in generation II.

head is the fraction formed by dividing this one favorable event by the sum of the possible events, head or tail, which is two. If the problem should be the probability of picking, blindfolded, a red marble out of a container in which 30 red, 50 white, and 20 black marbles are mixed, this probability is 30 out of 100, or 3/10.

Applying the above to human genetics, we may ask: What is the probability that a child will inherit from its father the allele which the father received from his father? In other words: What is the probability that a child will inherit a certain allele from its paternal grandfather rather than from its paternal grandmother? The answer is 1/2, since the child could receive from its father either the "favorable" paternal allele or the "unfavorable" maternal allele.

The Probability of Independent Events Coinciding. A common problem is that of determining the probability that two independent events will both occur. What, for example, is the probability that a child will obtain from his mother the grandmother's allele (i.e., the mother's maternal allele) and from his father the grandfather's allele (i.e., the father's paternal allele)? Let us enumerate all possible cases and then obtain a fraction by dividing the favorable one by the total number of possible cases (Fig. 44):

    1. A child may receive the maternal allele of each parent.
    2. A child may receive the paternal allele of each parent.
    3. A child may receive the maternal allele of the mother and the paternal allele of the father.

4. A child may receive the paternal allele of the mother and the maternal allele of the father.

Obviously, the four combinations are equally probable. The third is the favorable combination, whose probability we wish to determine. This combination takes place in 1 out of 4 cases, and the probability is thus 1/4.

We can derive this result in a different way. Since the probability of obtaining the paternal grandfather's allele is 1/2 and that of obtaining the maternal grandmother's allele is also 1/2, the first event is realized in only 1/2 of the cases in which the second occurs. This means that the chance of both events happening together is 1/2 of 1/2, or 1/4.

If, in a given population, half of all individuals are men and 1/10 of them belong to blood group B, then the probability of choosing at random an individual who is both a man and belongs to blood group B is 1/10 of 1/2, or 1/20. Generalizing, we obtain the theorem: *The probability of two independent events occurring together is the product of the two separate probabilities.* This theorem can be extended to any number of independent events; the probability that they will occur together is the product of the separate probabilities of each of the events.

The Probability of One or Another Event Occurring.   What is the probability that *either* one *or* another of two mutually exclusive events will occur? (It is implied here that either alternative is "favorable.") For example, what is the probability that a child will inherit his two alleles either from the two grandfathers or from the two grandmothers, and not one allele from a grandfather and the other from a grandmother? Inheritance of the alleles from the two grandfathers has a probability of 1/4, and the probability of inheriting them from the two grandmothers is also 1/4. The over-all probability that a favorable event will occur is thus 1/4 *plus* 1/4, or 1/2. Generalized: *The probability that one or the other of any number of mutually exclusive events will occur is the sum of the separate probabilities.*

The limits of probability are 0 and 1. A probability of 0 signifies impossibility; that is, absence of a favorable possibility. For example, the chance that a child will inherit both alleles of a pair from its father and none from its mother is 0, since no such alternative is listed among the four possible cases on page 82. A probability of 1 means certainty; that is, *all* possible events are favorable. For example, the chance that a child will inherit either its father's paternal or maternal allele is 1, since these two alternatives are the only ones that exist.

Aspects of Probability in Human Genetics.   It can be predicted with certainty that a child will receive from each parent one of the two alleles of all genic pairs, but it cannot be predicted which specific combination of either parent's maternal and paternal alleles will be received. In the gametes of an individual who is heterozygous for one pair of loci in each of the 23 chromosomes, 8,388,608 different combinations of alleles are possible, and equally probable. Therefore, the probability that a child will inherit any one specified combination is 1/8,388,608: there are 8,388,607 other combinations, any one of which the child is as likely to receive as the one specified. Thus, the chance of his receiving the specific combination is close to the lower limit of probability—zero.

Every person is a "half-breed" in the sense that he has inherited half of each pair of genes from one parent and the other half from the other parent. No one should be called "half-blood," since blood is no more transmitted directly than are limbs or eyes or gastric juices. The expression "quarter-blood," or any other designation which attempts to express the fraction of a genotype which a person owes to an ancestor more remote than his parents, is even more misleading. The genotype of each individual may well be considered to consist of two halves, namely, two complete single sets of genes; but neither of these single sets is composed of two equal parts, each contributed by one of the grandparents. The set of genes that the individual has received from his father may consist solely of the grandfather's alleles or solely of the grandmother's alleles, or any one of the numerous combinations of alleles of both grandparents. It is true that among the many combinations there are some in which one-half consist of alleles from the grandfather and the other half of alleles from the grandmother. In this sense, one could defend a statement like the following: It can happen that one-quarter of the genes of an individual may be derived from his father's father, one-quarter from his father's mother, and one-half from his mother—this latter half consisting of any one of the numerous combinations of the alleles of his mother's parents.

This would be a biologically meaningless formulation. Each locus is a unique entity among a set of loci. To speak of one-quarter of all alleles of a set would be equivalent to enumerating all the different parts of a complex machine and then designating any randomly chosen quarter of these parts as "one-quarter of the machine."

Many times in this book, questions on human genetics and their answers will be expressed in terms of probability. One of the important things that can be learned from the study of human genetics is that many of the problems of inheritance are statistical ones.

Correlation.   The height of individuals varies and so does the color of their hair. Should we seek to determine whether the color of hair is related to stature or whether these two variables are independent, one of at least three possibilities might be found to be true: (1) the taller the person, the darker the hair; (2) the taller the person, the lighter the hair; and (3) a short person is as likely to have light—or dark—hair as a tall one. If the last were true, we would say that there is no correlation between the two traits; if the first were true they would be "positively correlated"; if the second, "negatively correlated."

These terms are also applicable when a single trait is considered in different

TABLE 3.   *Relation between Height of Parents and Their Adult Children.*
(After data of Galton's from Johannsen, *Erblichkeitslehre*, Jena, 1909.)

Mean Height of Parents (in inches)	Height of Children (in Inches)							
	60.7	62.7	64.7	66.7	68.7	70.7	72.7	74.7
64	2	7	10	14	4	—	—	—
66	1	15	19	56	41	11	1	—
68	1	15	56	130	148	69	11	—
70	1	2	21	48	83	66	22	8
72	—	—	1	7	11	17	20	6
74	—	—	—	—	—	—	4	—

individuals. Thus, if we ask whether height is correlated in parents and off-spring, we might expect to find that (1) the taller the parents, the taller the child; (2) the taller the parents, the smaller the child; or (3) the height of a child is unrelated to that of its parents.

The actual finding here is that there is a positive correlation between the heights of parents and offspring (Table 3). Such a correlation does not by itself indicate anything about its cause or causes. It could, for instance, signify that most tall parents grow up in homes in which nutrition and other environmental factors are favorable to the attainment of tallness and that they, in turn, provide the same favorable circumstances for their children. Or it could mean that tall parents come from a part of the country where conditions are favorable for growth and that their children share this geographic background. Or it could mean that tall parents have genes for tallness and that their children share some of these genes. A decision among these hypotheses would have to depend on independent evidence.

It is usually desirable to be able to express the strength of a given correlation. When, for example, an increase in the measurement of a given trait is accompanied by a proportional increase in the measurement of another, there is complete positive correlation. When an increase in the first is usually, but not always, accompanied by an increase in the second, or if the increase in the second is not always strictly proportional to the increase in the first, the correlation is positive, but incomplete (Table 3). When there is a tendency for the second to decrease when the first increases, the correlation is negative; it, too, may be complete or incomplete. The *correlation coefficient, r,* is a measure of the strength of correlation. No formula for r will be given here, but it should be noted that it is so defined that for complete positive correlation $r = +1$, and for complete negative correlation $r = -1$. In the absence of any correlation, $r = 0$, and the various degrees of incomplete positive and negative correlation are expressed by coefficients which lie between $+1$ and -1.

Data for the calculation of correlation coefficients are often presented in the form of "scatter diagrams." Two such diagrams based on measurements

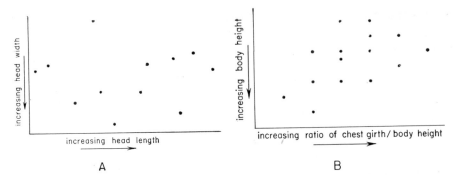

FIG. 45. Scatter diagrams of the relation of two variable measures in groups of individuals. A. Absence of correlation between head length and head width. B. Incomplete negative correlation between chest girth/body height and body height. (After Weber, *Variations–und Erblichkeits–Statistik,* J. F. Lehmann, Munich, 1935.)

of only a few individuals are shown in Figure 45. In part A, the absence of any trend indicates lack of correlation between length and width of the head in a sample of 12 adult males; in B, the increasing ratio of chest girth to height with decreasing height is evidence for incomplete negative correlation between chest girth:height and height. A tabular presentation of incomplete positive correlation—between height of parents and offspring—has been given in Table 3. Numerical values of some correlation coefficients follow. In one study the correlation coefficient for the relation between the length of the first joint of the forefinger on the right hand and the length of that on the left hand of the same individuals was found to be $+0.92$; in other studies, that between stature of husband and wife, $+0.28$; between stature of fathers and sons, $+0.51$; between height and body temperature, 0.00; and between adult age and body temperature, -0.15. In later chapters various coefficients of correlation will be given and their genetic significance discussed.

Problems

12. Assume the probabilities for a birth to occur are alike for all days of a year: (a) What is the probability of a girl having her birthday on Christmas? (b) A man was born on May 1. What is the probability of his marrying a woman born the same date? On June 1? On October 12? (c) In a random sampling what is the probability of finding a husband and wife who have their birthdays on May 1?

13. What is the probability that a child will inherit either the allele I^O or the allele I^A from his $I^O I^A$ mother?

14. What is the probability of a person inheriting one of the alleles of a given pair of his genes from his paternal grandmother and the other allele from his maternal grandmother?

15. A man's maternal grandfather belongs to blood group AB, but all other grandparents are O. What is the chance of the man being: (i) A? (ii) B? (iii) AB? (iv) O?

16. A man received the following genes, all located in different chromosomes: from his father *ABCDE* and from his mother *A'B'C'D'E'*. What is the probability of his giving to his child the combination (i) *AB'C'D'E?* (ii) Either *ABCDE* or *A'B'C'D'E?*

17. If the genotypes of the parents are $I^A I^O$ and $I^A I^A$, what is the chance of their two children both being (i) $I^A I^O$? (ii) $I^A I^A$? (iii) $I^O I^O$?

18. (a) What fraction of his genes does a parent have in common with any one of his children? (b) What fraction have two sibs in common?

19. Assume that the probabilities of the birth of a boy or a girl are 1/2. What are the probabilities of the following sequences of births in a hospital: (a) A succession of 30 boys? (b) 15 of each sex born alternately?

20. If no crossing over occurs, what is the probability that a woman will inherit: (a) None of her 22 maternal autosomes from her grandmother? (b) All of her 22 maternal and all of her 22 paternal autosomes from her two grandfathers?

21. What is the probability that a man will transmit a specific allele to his great-granddaughter?

22. Assume that a certain desirable trait of an individual depends on the presence of the following rare alleles: *A'B'C'D'E'* in heterozygous combination with their alleles *ABCDE*. What is the probability that a grandchild of this individual will receive the alleles *A'B'C'D'E'* from this grandparent?

23. Would you expect positive, negative, or no correlation between the following variables: (a) Degree of schooling and longevity, (b) Degree of schooling and income, (c) Length and importance of a research report, (d) Age of adult and number of healthy teeth?

References

See the books on statistics cited in references to Chapter 9.

CHAPTER 6

SIMPLE SINGLE FACTOR INHERITANCE

Genetic differences between two individuals may consist of differences between the alleles at a single pair of loci or between those at more than one pair of loci. In general, different individuals have different alleles at *many* pairs of loci. Mendel taught us not to attempt the study of the inheritance of all genetic differences at once, but to follow separately the inheritance of differences dependent upon single pairs of loci. This we shall do in the present chapter, as indicated by the words "single factor inheritance" in the title. The title includes another word—"simple"—and this implies that the discussion will be restricted to cases in which a given genotype is always expressed in the same manner in the phenotype. Later, we shall discuss inherited conditions for which this is not true.

Normal and Abnormal Traits. Phenotypic differences between two individuals may be such that one can be regarded as normal and the other abnormal, or both may be variants of either normal or abnormal traits. The study of all kinds of differences is important. The difference between normal and abnormal is particularly significant to medical men and to psychologists who are interested in the inheritance of mental defects; the difference between normal variants is of interest to anthropologists and psychologists who investigate the normal variability of mankind. Studies have shown that many persons afflicted with striking abnormalities are genetically distinguished from normal persons by a difference at no more than a single pair of loci, while the genetic differences between persons who have differing normal variants of a trait are often polygenic—that is, differences at many pairs of loci. That this is so is not surprising when we remember the concepts of genic action developed in Chapter 3. A trait depends on numerous genic loci, and differences between the alleles at any one of these loci may cause variations in the phenotype.

The slight differences between normal individuals are, therefore, likely to be due to the sum of minor differences in the action of several pairs of loci. A rare, striking difference between a normal and an abnormal person, on the other hand, could conceivably be also due to a combination of minor genic differences; but it is more likely to be brought about by the failure of a single pair of loci to control a reaction necessary for normality. An analogy with an automobile might again be made. The "normal" variation between two different models often consists of a large number of minor differences in many parts; but the difference between a "normal" automobile, which starts, and an "abnormal" one, which doesn't, is likely to be traceable to a single cause.

These developmental relations make the genetic study of abnormal traits easier than the study of normal ones, and consequently we know more about the inheritance of defects than of normal variants. The examples used in this book cannot help reflecting this.

Pedigrees.   Data of human genetics are frequently presented in the form of diagrammatic pedigrees (Fig. 46). In some countries, including the United States, females in these pedigrees are symbolized by circles and males by squares; in some countries, females by the sign ♀ and males by ♂. Symbols of parents are joined by a horizontal *marriage line,* and their offspring's symbols are placed in a horizontal row below a line to which they are connected by verticals. The horizontal line above the symbols for the children is itself connected to the parents' marriage line by a vertical line. The symbol for a single child is directly attached to this vertical line. The children of a parental pair form a *sibship,* and the individual children, regardless of sex, are called *sibs,* or *siblings.* Thus, sibs can be brothers, sisters, or brothers and sisters. In a pedigree the sibs are listed from left to right in order of birth. The term *family* is usually applied to a pair of parents and

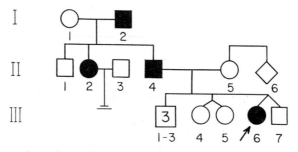

FIG. 46. A sample pedigree. For explanation, see text. The marriage of II-2 and II-3 was childless. The twins, III-4 and III-5, are identical, as indicated by the short vertical line descending from the sibship line. The twins III-6 and III-7 are nonidentical, as indicated by their separate connection with the sibship line. II-5 and II-6 are sibs whose parents are not included in the pedigree.

their children but may also refer to a larger circle of relatives, although this larger circle of persons who are interconnected by descent and marriage is generally called a *kindred.*

Often, each individual in a pedigree is designated by a number in order to facilitate reference to him. The numbering system may be consecutive from the earliest generation to the most recent, or each generation may be denoted by a Roman numeral and the individuals within a generation by Arabic numerals. Thus, II-4 identifies the fourth individual listed in the second generation of a pedigree.

Many additional symbols are used for special purposes. They are usually explained in the legend of the pedigree in which they occur. Some of these are used in Figure 46: a diamond denotes that the sex of the person was unknown to the recorder of the pedigree; a number enclosed in a large symbol indicates the number of sibs who are not listed separately; twins are represented by two symbols connected by lines to the same point on the sibship line. If an individual possesses the trait whose inheritance forms the subject of the pedigree, he is said to be "affected" and is designated by a black symbol. A hollow circle or square signifies absence of the trait ("not-affected").

Sometimes, to save space in extensive pedigrees, different generations are listed in consecutive concentric curves (Fig. 73, p. 122) rather than in horizontal rows.

Dominant Inheritance

We shall begin our discussion of transmission of hereditary traits by considering a dominant allele, *D,* whose presence or absence is made immediately apparent by the presence or absence of the corresponding phenotype. If the dominant allele is rare, then most individuals carrying it will have it singly—that is, heterozygously with the recessive allele *d.* Homozygosity for *D* could only result from its presence in both parents—and this combination would be so much rarer than the postulated rarity of the gene that almost no doubt would exist that a person with the dominant phenotype was heterozygous. If, however, the dominant gene is a common one, then both homozygous (*DD*) and heterozygous (*Dd*) individuals should be common, and the *D* phenotype could no longer serve as a complete indication of the genotype.

An individual heterozygous for a dominant gene (*Dd*) will produce equal numbers of gametes with the alleles *D* and *d.* Marriages between such a person and another without the dominant gene—that is, *dd*—would result in children any one of whom would have an equal chance of receiving either *D* or *d* from the *Dd* parent, and all of whom would receive *d* from the other parent (Fig. 47). Consequently, half of the children of such marriages will carry the trait dependent on *D* (i.e., will be affected), and the other half will lack it. Furthermore, it is obvious that only affected parents can have af-

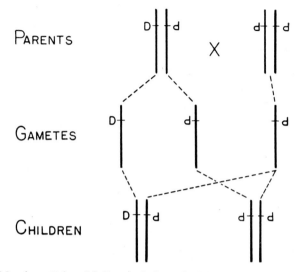

FIG. 47. Marriage *Dd* × *dd*. Transmission of alleles from parents to children.

fected children—that all affected children have at least one affected parent. In simple dominant inheritance, a trait never skips a generation.

It should be emphasized that the statement that half of the children with *Dd* and *dd* parents will carry the trait dependent on *D* does not mean that in any one family one-half of the sibs will have it and the other half will not. The distribution of the trait is governed by the laws of probability (see Chap. 5), and any generalization concerning it is valid only for a large population. All the children of one pair of *Dd* and *dd* parents may have the trait; none of the children of another pair may have it. More will be said about this in Chapter 9, Genetic Ratios.

Woolly Hair.   An example of simple dominant inheritance is found in Figure 48. This extensive pedigree shows the inheritance of a rare type of unusually woolly hair (Fig. 49) in a Norwegian kindred. The curled or fuzzy texture of this woolly hair is similar to, but not identical with, that of negroes' hair. Though of good growth, it breaks off at the tip and never gets very long. It has been propagated for at least five generations. Nothing is known about the first appearance of the trait, but it seems certain that it is not due to admixture of negro alleles, since the possibility of early inter-marriage of Norwegians and negroes is very remote. What appears to be the same condition has also been observed in Holland, in "Old American" stock, and elsewhere.

The pedigree demonstrates the principle of direct transmission from af-fected parent to half of the children. Summing all affected and nonaffected children from all 20 marriages in which one parent was affected, we find 38 individuals with woolly hair and 43 without it (omitting 3 persons, long

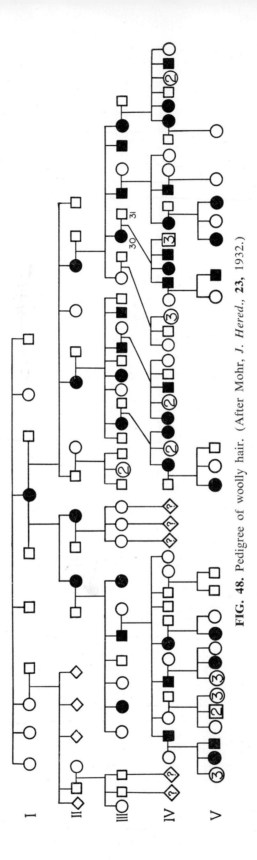

FIG. 48. Pedigree of woolly hair. (After Mohr, *J. Hered.*, **23**, 1932.)

FIG. 49. Segregation for woolly hair. Parents III-30 and III-31 (Fig. 48) and their children. (Mohr, *J. Hered.*, **23,** 1932.)

deceased, for whom the hair type could not be ascertained). Studies from various countries of all similar pedigrees recorded up to 1936, show 145 children with woolly hair and 130 with normal hair in sibships from marriages of one affected and one nonaffected parent. These numbers deviate from the ideal 1:1 ratio (137.5:137.5), but as no one expects, for example, when throwing a coin 276 times, to obtain exactly 138 heads and 138 tails, so the ratio of Dd to dd children cannot be expected to be exactly 1:1, since it is a matter of chance whether a gamete with D or one with d fertilizes a d gamete of the opposite sex when a child is conceived. We shall later discuss methods of judging whether the deviation between an observed and expected ratio may be considered as simply due to chance or whether it is so large as to be statistically significant.

More Rules of Dominant Inheritance. Other facts about the appearance of simple dominant traits may be learned from the study of pedigrees of inheritance of woolly hair:

1. There were 64 men and 66 women among the affected persons whose sex was given in the pedigrees. Thus, the trait does not appear more frequently in one sex than the other.

2. Altogether, woolly-haired fathers had 24 woolly-haired and 36 nonwoolly-haired children, and woolly-haired mothers had 34 woolly-haired and 26 nonwoolly-haired children. Thus, both affected men and women

transmitted the characteristic hair type to their children. Furthermore, regardless of whether the father or the mother was affected, the proportion
of woolly to nonwoolly-haired children deviated from the 1:1 ratio by no
more than would be expected as a result of chance.

The facts derived from the genealogical charts are in agreement with expectations derived from the theoretical principles of transmission of a dominant gene in a chromosome and the chance fusion of sperm and egg carrying
different alleles at a pair of loci. Whenever such facts are found in studying
the inheritance of a rare trait, we may conclude that it is transmitted as a
simple dominant. This conclusion is subject, however, to the provisions
(1) that the pedigree is representative of the facts and is not a biased
selection, and (2) that large enough numbers of individuals are covered
to make the data truly representative.

It may be asked: What would result from the marriage of two individuals
who both possessed woolly hair or some other simple dominant trait? Since
each of the parents would normally possess one allele for woolly and one for
nonwoolly hair, and since each of them would form the two kinds of germ
cells, D and d, with equal frequency, chance fusion of egg and sperm would
lead to the genotypes DD, Dd, and dd in the proportions 1:2:1.

Egg		Sperm		Child
D	$+$	D	$=$	DD
D	$+$	d	$=$	Dd
d	$+$	D	$=$	Dd
d	$+$	d	$=$	dd

If the dominance of D is complete, DD and Dd individuals would be indistinguishable and we would expect 3 woolly-haired children to 1 nonwoolly-
haired child. Should DD produce a phenotype different from that produced by
Dd, three types of offspring would result: the new DD type, woolly (Dd),
and nonwoolly (dd)—in the Mendelian ratio 1:2:1. Since no marriages of
two woolly-haired individuals have been recorded, the phenotype of a DD
person is unknown.

Homozygotes for Dominant Alleles.   Although the likelihood is great
that any woolly-haired person is the offspring of one woolly-haired and one
nonaffected parent, it is still possible that he might be the DD offspring of
two affected parents. He would then endow all his germ cells with the D
gene, so that if he married a nonaffected person, all his children would be
Dd and, thus, woolly-haired. It would, however, be very difficult to establish
his homozygosity for D unless he had an unusually large number of children.
If only woolly-haired children are produced by one affected and one nonaffected parent, it may either be due to the DD homozygosity of one parent
or be nothing but a chance deviation from the theoretical 1:1 ratio expected
from a Dd parent.

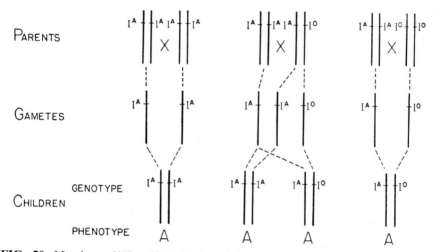

FIG. 50. Marriages $I^A I^A \times I^A I^A$, $I^A I^A \times I^A I^O$, and $I^A I^A \times I^O I^O$ and the resulting offspring.

Pedigrees of unions of homozygous dominant individuals with (1) other homozygous dominants, (2) heterozygotes, and (3) homozygous recessives are known for traits other than woolly hair. If a dominant allele is common enough in the population to permit numerous marriages between heterozygotes, homozygous dominant offspring will be encountered. Marriages of blood group A persons homozygous for $I^A I^A$ to individuals who are either $I^A I^A$, $I^A I^O$, or $I^O I^O$ all lead to group A children only (Fig. 50). Observational proof of this is not so simple as in the case of woolly hair, where the existence of a phenotype is practically an assurance of a heterozygous genotype. The phenotype of a person in the A blood group does not tell us whether he is heterozygous $I^A I^O$ or homozygous $I^A I^A$. Even his offspring may not give us the answer. Although the diagnosis of heterozygosity can be made whenever both parents belong to group A and have an O group child, no certain diagnosis is possible when only A group children result. An O group child is genetically $I^O I^O$, which signifies that he received an I^O allele from each parent and reveals the parents' heterozygosity, $I^A I^O$. The absence of $I^O I^O$ children, however, does not prove that either parent is homozygous $I^A I^A$, since even if the parents were both $I^A I^O$, they might have no $I^O I^O$ children; for, when the number of offspring is small, it is possible that only fertilizations involving I^A may occur.

To be certain that an A group phenotype is based on $I^A I^A$ homozygosity, special pedigrees have to be selected. The best are those in which both parents are in the AB group, because of the codominant action of their genotype $I^A I^B$. Since such parents can produce only gametes with either I^A or I^B, and since presence of the I^B allele in the offspring would be phenotypically apparent, group A offspring from such a marriage can only be $I^A I^A$.

The discussion of the dominant inheritance of the blood-group property

A shows the difficulties encountered in pedigree studies of a common trait. We shall see later that these difficulties can be overcome by applying statistical methods to pooled data from large samples of a population.

Further Examples of Dominant Inheritance. The examples of simple single dominant factor inheritance of relatively rare traits that follow will not teach any new principles, but they will serve to indicate the wide range of traits so transmitted.

Figure 51 is a pedigree of a family in which a white forelock (Fig. 52) has been observed for five consecutive generations. It fulfills all requirements necessary to show dominant transmission of the trait. (This pedigree omits symbols for the spouses of affected parents, as is frequently done when a trait is rare and it can be taken for granted that the spouses are not affected unless there is specific evidence that they are.)

The trait, white forelock, is akin to the piebaldness which is so common in the color patterns of animals (e.g., Holstein cattle, black and tan dogs). The reproduction of an old engraving in Figure 53 correctly suggests the analogy between human and animal spotting.

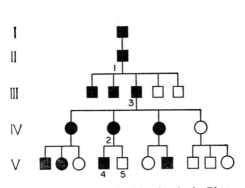

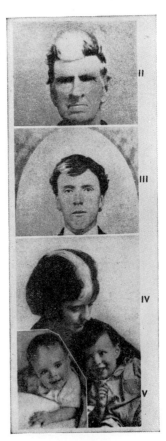

FIG. 51. Pedigree of white forelock. Photographs of the individuals II-1, III-3, IV-2, V-4, and V-5 are shown in Figure 52. Note the uninterrupted line of transmission of the trait, its occurrence in both men and women, and its presence in both sexes of the offspring of an affected parent. (After Fitch, *J. Hered.*, **28,** 1937.)

FIG. 52. White forelock in four generations. The individuals shown are marked by numbers in the pedigree Figure 51. (Fitch, *J. Hered.*, **28,** 1937.)

FIG. 53. White spotting. Old engraving with inscription: "The spotted negro boy. George Alexander Opattan, the spotted boy died on the 3. Febr. 1813 aged 6 years, was buried at Great Marlow in Buckingham. . . . Painted from life by Dan. Orme and engraved under his Direction by his late pupil P. R. Cooper." (Goldschmidt, *Einführung in die Vererbungslehre,* 2nd ed., Engelmann, Leipzig, 1913.)

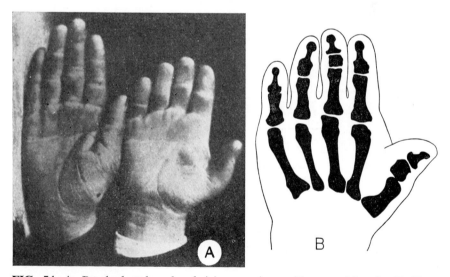

FIG. 54. A. Brachydactylous hand, in comparison with normal hand.   B. Note the abnormally short two distal phalangeal bones in the middle finger and the fusion of these bones into a single element in the second, fourth, and fifth finger. (A. Drinkwater, *Proc. Roy. Soc. Med.,* **10,** Sect. Path., 1917.   B. After Drinkwater, in Lewis, *Treas. Hum. Inher.,* **1,** IVa, 1912.

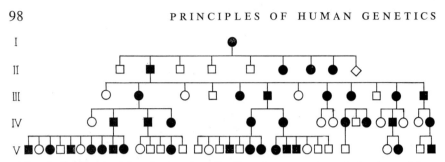

FIG. 55. Pedigree of brachydactyly. The first demonstration of dominant Mendelian inheritance in man. (After Farabee, *Papers Peabody Mus.*, Harvard Univ., **3,** 1905.)

Simple dominant inheritance can also be illustrated by various types of brachydactyly, or short-fingeredness (Fig. 54). One pedigree of this skeletal abnormality, from an American kindred, provided the first demonstration of dominant Mendelian inheritance in man (Fig. 55). In England, a similar trait has been traced back at least fourteen generations. A man living late in the nineteenth century showed fusions of the first and second phalangeal

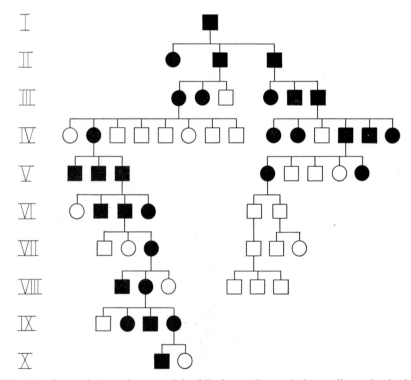

FIG. 56. Congenital stationary night blindness. Part of the pedigree beginning with Jean Nougaret, born about 1637. (After Nettleship, *Ophthal. Reviews,* **26,** 1907; Dejean and Gasseng, *Bull. Soc. Opth. France,* **1,** 1949; and François, Verriest, De Rouck, and Dejean, *Ophthalmologica,* **132,** 1956. The pedigree sections in the last two publications do not fully agree with each other.)

bones. He was a lineal descendant of the first Earl of Shrewsbury (b. 1390), whose skeleton became available for study during repair of his burial place. The same types of fusions were said to have been present in the remote ancestor as in the descendant.

Another abnormality inherited as a dominant is congenital stationary night blindness, a type of defective twilight vision. One pedigree, famous for its extension over many generations, comes from France. Jean Nougaret, who was born about 1637, had, in the course of ten generations, 139 or more affected individuals among his descendants (Fig. 56).

A very thoroughly explored American pedigree of dominant dwarfism is reproduced in Figure 186 (p. 448). These dwarfs belong to the chondrodystrophic type, in which the size of the trunk and head is similar to that of unaffected people but in which the limbs are very short (Fig. 57).

Our final example of a dominant phenotype is a trait found in various families, but particularly well documented from the Hapsburg dynasty. Many members of this house had a narrow, undershot lower jaw and protruding underlip, which resulted in a half-open mouth (Fig. 58). Thanks to the existence of portraits, the trait can be traced back to the fourteenth century. It was present in, among others, Emperor Charles V (1500–1558), Maria Theresa of Austria (1717–1780), and Alfonso XII of Spain (1886–1941).

FIG. 57. Chondrodystrophic dwarfism. Painting by Jens Juel: The Roman dwarf, Francesco Ravai, called Bajozzo (1773). (After Krabbe, *Bibliot. f. Laeger,* **122,** 1930.)

It appears likely that many of the traits which characterize specific families are controlled by single dominant alleles. Family resemblances are often due to the recurrence of rather specific features—form of nose or mouth, position of eyes, shape of eyebrows, and so on. If such traits reappear in successive generations and are transmitted by affected parents only, a dominant allele may be the cause of such family-specific, relatively rare variants within the normal range of phenotypes.

Recessive Inheritance

A single recessive allele will not affect the phenotype of a person; only when both of a pair are present is there any effect. Therefore, both parents

FIG. 58. The Hapsburg lip through the centuries. A. Emperor Maximilian I (1459–1519).   B. Emperor Charles V, grandson of A (1500–1558).   C. Archduke Charles of Teschen (1771–1847).   D. Archduke Albrecht, son of C (1817–1895). (Strohmayer, *Nova Acta Leopoldina,* **5,** 1937.)

of children with a recessive trait must carry at least one of the specific recessive allele. Three different types of marriages fulfill this condition (Table 4, where *d* denotes, as before, the recessive allele and *D* the dominant). The offspring can be expected to be exclusively *dd* in the first type of marriage, 50 per cent *dd* in the second, and 25 per cent *dd* in the third. Clearly, simple recessive inheritance is identical with simple dominant inheritance, but here the observer's emphasis is shifted from the dominant to the recessive allele.

All three types of marriages can be found when both the dominant and the recessive alleles, *D* and *d*, are common in an intermarrying population. This is true for the blood-group types A and O which depend on the dominant allele I^A and the recessive I^O. The three types of marriages involving these two alleles from which homozygous $I^O I^O$ children can arise are $I^O I^O \times I^O I^O$, $I^O I^O \times I^A I^O$, and $I^A I^O \times I^A I^O$. They yield the different kinds of children in the relative proportions postulated by the theory, provided sufficient data are accumulated and analyzed.

Another recessive allele frequently found in man is one that transmits the inability to taste the substance phenylthiocarbamide (PTC) or related compounds. The majority of people are "tasters," a large minority "nontasters." Marriages of nontasters to nontasters yield, with few exceptions, nontaster children only. Marriages of tasters to tasters, or of tasters to nontasters, may bring forth children of either type. This suggests that nontasters are homozygous recessives, *tt*, and tasters homozygous or heterozygous dominants, *TT* or *Tt*. Support for this hypothesis cannot easily be supplied by a study of pedigrees alone but has been provided by the interesting method of allele frequency analysis, which is described and illustrated by the taster example in Chapter 10.

Two other common traits that seem to be inherited on the basis of single gene loci concern the excretion in the urine of some special chemicals contained in food. After eating asparagus, 46 out of 161 Englishmen excreted the strongly odorous substance methanethiol; after eating red beets, only 10 out of 104 excreted the red pigment betamin or a brown product of it. Family data suggest that excretion of methanethiol is recessive to nonexcretion, and that nonexcretion of betamin is recessive to its excretion. Each of the excretory properties seems to depend on a separate pair of alleles.

If the gene *d* that is responsible for a recessive condition is a rare one, *dd* persons will be very rare and even *Dd* persons uncommon. Only once in a great while will two affected people marry. Marriages between homozygous *dd* persons and normal-appearing but heterozygous *Dd* persons will also be rare. Most likely, *dd* individuals will marry *DD* persons, and children from such marriages will all be *Dd*. When they, in turn, marry normals of the genotype *DD*, half of their children will be *DD* and half *Dd*, all of normal phenotype. The heterozygotes will probably marry normal homozygotes, and the same will be the rule for later generations. Thus, the allele *d* may be

TABLE 4. *Marriages Which Yield Homozygous Recessive Offspring (dd).*

Parents	Eggs	Sperm	Offspring
$dd \times dd$	all d	all d	dd
$dd \times Dd$	all d	$\frac{1}{2}D, \frac{1}{2}d$	$\frac{1}{2}Dd, \frac{1}{2}dd$
$Dd \times Dd$	$\frac{1}{2}D, \frac{1}{2}d$	$\frac{1}{2}D, \frac{1}{2}d$	$\frac{1}{4}DD, \frac{1}{2}Dd, \frac{1}{4}dd$

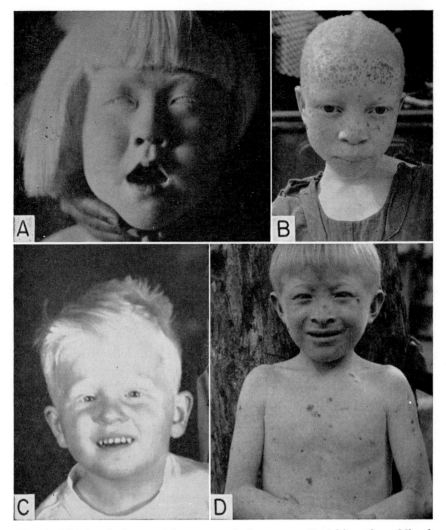

FIG. 59. Albinism in four racial groups.   A. Japanese,   B. African from Nigeria, C. Caucasian,   D. American Indian from San Blas, Panama. (A, original from Dr. M. Ito; B, Barnicot, *Ann. Eugen.,* **17,** 1952; C, original from Dr. J. V. Neel; D; original from Dr. C. E. Keeler.)

carried "unseen" and unknown for centuries, even though the trait it produces in homozygotes is a striking one.

We shall see later that a *d* allele occasionally originates by the permanent transformation (mutation) of a *D* allele to *d* in one chromosome of a human cell. In a hypothetical population in which only the dominant *D* allele was originally present, a *d*-containing germ cell, newly created by the mutation of *D* to *d,* can meet only a *D* germ cell from the opposite sex in fertilization. The child originating from this fertilized egg will be *Dd;* consequently, the *d* allele will be segregated to half of his germ cells, and thus potentially transmittable to his children. In the course of many generations, various *Dd* individuals, all going back in their pedigree to the first *d* germ cell, will be present in the population. A marriage of two such *Dd* persons may then, for the first time in the history of that population, produce a homozygous *dd* child. There may be only one such child—a "sporadic" case—or there may be more than one, since two of the parents' *d* germ cells will theoretically meet in one-fourth of all fertilizations, and may conceivably meet in every one. The appearance of several affected individuals in a sibship or in a larger family group has been called "familial" incidence of an abnormal trait.

All these facts are consonant with the general concepts of inheritance of alleles. They stress the point that inheritance is based on transmission of genes and not of traits. A trait may appear sporadically or familially; it may show up in consecutive generations or it may skip one or many. But the allele responsible will have been transmitted in an uninterrupted line to its carrier from a parent, a grandparent, and so on back to the earliest ancestor in whom the allele originated.

Recessive Albinism. Albinism is a good example of inheritance of a trait dependent on a rare recessive gene. It forms the topic of a monumental collection of pedigrees and data from all over the globe compiled by Pearson (1857–1936) and his collaborators. In individuals who are not albinos, microscopically small but numerous granules containing melanin pigment are deposited in the skin, hair, and iris, giving these parts pigmentation. Albinos are unable to transform the substances from which melanin is formed into the pigment. They are, consequently, light-skinned (this is particularly striking in individuals belonging to "colored" races), have white or light hair, and their eyes are red, because reflected light passes through the red blood vessels in the eyes. Eye abnormalities of different kinds, as well as the peculiar texture of the hair, pictured in Figure 59, are usually part of the multiple expression of the albino gene.

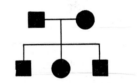

FIG. 60. Pedigree of recessive albinism. Marriage of two affected individuals. (Snyder, *Principles of Genetics,* D. C. Heath, 1947.)

Homozygous recessive albinos are rare. It has been estimated that in various European countries about 1 in 20,000 individuals is an albino. If this low figure should also apply in the United States, there would still be nearly 9,000 albinotic individuals in this country. In certain other populations albinos are relatively more common. Thus, 5 albinos were found among 14,292 negro children in Nigeria, giving a ratio of about 1 in 3,000; and among 20,000 San Blas Indians in Panama the ratio was 1 in 132.

The pedigrees (Figs. 60–63) demonstrate the validity of the conclusions about the transmission of recessive traits which we have derived theoretically.

1. Marriages of albino with albino give albino children only (Fig. 60).

2. Marriages between an albino and a nonalbino either give no albino children (Fig. 61, II, IV), in which cases the normal mates were probably homozygous, or give both types of children (Fig. 62), obviously because of heterozygosity of the normal spouse.

3. Marriages between nonalbinos that result in albino offspring also yield normals (Fig. 63).

That both sexes must be equally involved in the transmission of the albino gene is obvious from its recessive nature, and that either sex may express the trait is seen from the pedigrees.

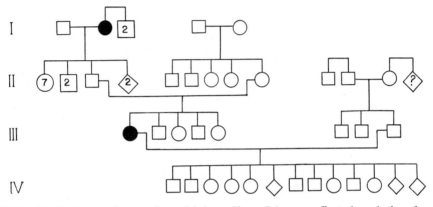

FIG. 61. Pedigree of recessive albinism. Since I-2 was affected and therefore homozygous, all her children must be heterozygous. As shown by the affected state (homozygosity) of III-3, the youngest daughter of the second sibship was also heterozygous. (After Pearson, Nettleship, and Usher. Pedigree 98.)

Phenylketonuria. An example of familial occurrence of a rare recessive trait, phenylketonuria, is given by the pedigree reproduced in Figure 64. This condition consists of a metabolic abnormality which results in mental deficiency, as mentioned earlier. Affected individuals reproduce very rarely, so that nearly all marriages from which the abnormality arises are between two normal-appearing persons who are both heterozygous for the recessive allele, usually without knowing it. Proof of simple single factor inheritance

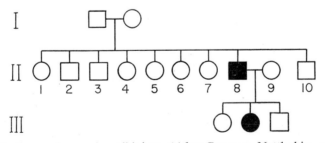

FIG. 62. Pedigree of recessive albinism. (After Pearson, Nettleship, and Usher. Pedigree 54.)

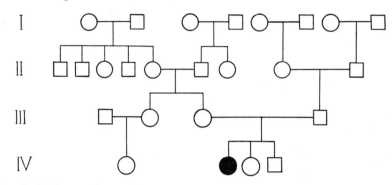

FIG. 63. Pedigree of recessive albinism. (After Pearson, Nettleship, and Usher. Pedigree 113.)

in cases like these involves special statistical techniques that make it possible to determine whether the theoretical expectation for recessive offspring from heterozygous parents is quantitatively fulfilled in that the homozygous affected children represent one-quarter of all sibs. The data on phenylketonuria agree with this theoretical expectation.

Further Criteria for Recessive Inheritance.   Even when homozygous recessives usually produce offspring—as do nontasters and albinos, in contrast to phenylketonurics—evidence for single factor inheritance can often be obtained only by special analyses of ratios of affected to nonaffected sibs (see Chap. 9) and by a special criterion, an increased frequency of cousin marriages among the unions that produce affected children. Such marriages are likely to bring together in the offspring two recessive alleles carried by one of the common grandparents of the parents (see Chap. 18). A cousin marriage, with its offspring, is recorded in the center of Figure 64.

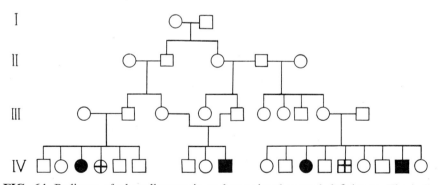

FIG. 64. Pedigree of phenylketonuria and associated mental deficiency. The individuals marked with a cross were probably affected. They died young. These families lived in an isolated group of small islands in Norway. It may well be that certain apparently unrelated normal persons have some early ancestor in common from whom they inherited the recessive allele which made them heterozygous carriers. (After Følling, Mohr, and Ruud.)

The reader will readily understand that the appearance of affected off-spring from normal parents who, themselves, have only normal ancestry may not always be due to a recessive allele, but, for example, to special combinations of alleles at two or more genic loci, to a new dominant mutation, or even to externally caused developmental irregularities.

Different Genotypes for Albinism. It has been pointed out earlier that one and the same inherited phenotype, appearing in different pedigrees, may be the result of different genetic constitutions, all of which may bring about the same effect in development. Certain unusual pedigrees of albinism have been thought to be examples of this. One of these is that of two English albino parents whose three children were all nonalbinos. If the family history is correct, it would suggest that the two parents were albinotic for different genetic reasons, one containing the usual albino genotype aa and the other a genotype bb at a different locus. In this case the genotypes of the parents must be expressed in terms of a more elaborate genetic formulation, in which the first parent would be $aaBB,$ and the second $AAbb$. This would imply that most normal persons are $AABB$ and that replacement of either AA by aa or BB by bb blocks the formation of melanin. The children from marriages of $aaBB$ to $AAbb$ individuals would be $AaBb$ and, because of the dominance of A over a and B over $b,$ be fully pigmented. Whether this genetic scheme, for which other arguments can be adduced (see p. 386), actually fits the English family is not known, particularly since no tests have been made which would exclude illegitimate paternity of the children. The few other known marriages between two albinos have produced albino offspring only—including that of an albino white and an albino negro, who had an albino mulatto child.

Other unusual pedigrees of albinism have suggested dominant inheritance of the trait. Such type of inheritance might be suspected in the pedigree shown in Figure 62, where the albino male of the second generation (II-8) married a nonalbino and had one albino and two nonalbino children. Although this fits the pattern of dominant inheritance, it fits that of recessive inheritance equally well, provided II-8 was homozygous aa and married a heterozygote Aa. The parents of II-8 were nonalbinos, but they may well have each carried one a allele. The hypothesis of a dominant gene for albinism would here require additional assumptions—for example, that II-8 had obtained a newly mutated dominant gene, or that a dominant gene was present in one of his parents but failed to produce its effect.

The hypothesis of a dominant gene for albinism is somewhat more reasonable when the trait appears not only in two but in three successive generations, as in the pedigree of an American Negro kindred shown in Figure 65. Here the father of the three albinos in generation II is unknown, but the albino II-3 had an albino daughter by a normally pigmented wife, and this daughter married a nonalbino man and had albinos among her children. Once more, however, the assumption of a dominant albino gene can be countered by

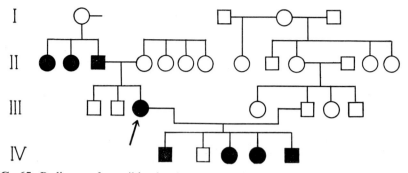

FIG. 65. Pedigree of possibly dominant albinism in negroes, The proposita, i.e., the woman through whom the pedigree became known, is marked by an arrow. (A. C. and S. B. Pipkin, *J. Hered.,* **33,** 1942.)

assuming that the albinos were typical recessive *aa*'s and that the normal mates of the albinos in both generations II and III were *Aa*. Since *Aa* individuals are not too uncommon, it is reasonable to expect that, occasionally, successive generations of parents will include such heterozygotes. Moreover, in the pedigree under discussion, it is possible that the apparently unrelated males in the different generations actually shared a common ancestor in an earlier, unrecorded generation from whom the *a* allele was transmitted to all of them.

A similar situation is known for alkaptonuria. Most pedigrees fit recessive inheritance, but at least one, in which affected individuals descended from affected parents for three generations, has been frequently claimed to be evidence for dominant inheritance. However, recent genealogical studies show connections between members of this kindred with others in which the trait is undoubtedly recessive. This suggests that the same recessive allele is responsible for alkaptonuria in all these kindreds.

Hereditary Deaf-mutism. Deafness that is present at birth and is later followed by muteness unless special training is provided can be caused either by external agents, such as infection of the fetus by the rubella virus in mothers who have an attack of German measles, or by genetic factors. Many genetic types of deafness seem to be caused by homozygosity for a pair of recessive alleles, since hearing parents who are both heterozygous carriers of such a gene usually have both hearing and deaf children in a ratio of 3 to 1; a heterozygous hearing person and a deaf-mute usually have equal numbers of both types of children; and two deaf-mutes usually have only deaf-mute children. Two of these relations are shown in generations I-III of Figure 66: the deviations from the theoretical ratios are explainable as chance phenomena.

The last generation (IV) consists of individuals who are not what we would expect them to be. Although both parents are deaf-mutes, presumably by heredity, their six children all hear normally. This suggests that III-7 and

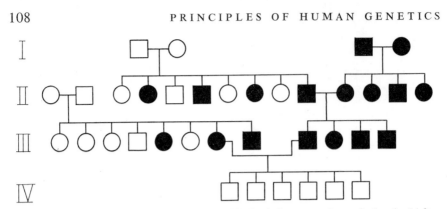

FIG. 66. Pedigree of deaf-mutism in a kindred from northern Ireland. (After Stevenson and Cheeseman.)

III-9 are deaf-mute for different reasons: III-7 may be considered to be affected because she is homozygous for a genotype *dd;* and III-9 to be homozygous for a genotype *ee,* which also causes the defect. Using the genetic scheme mentioned on page 106, III-7 would be *ddEE;* III-9, *DDee;* and their children, *DdEe.* This general genetic interpretation is supported by a detailed analysis of several hundred kindreds of hereditary deaf-mutism in Northern Ireland, made by Stevenson and Cheeseman. Moreover, it appears that there are considerably more than two recessive types of hereditary deafness: *ddEEFF, DDeeFF, DDEEff,* etc. In addition, many of the pedigrees of deaf-mutism from Northern Ireland can be accounted for only by assuming either dominant genes or interaction of genes at more than one locus (see p. 364).

Trait and Type of Inheritance

The example of deaf-mutism contains an important lesson: It is not possible to state without reservation that "deaf-mutism is a simple recessive." It is true that the majority of deaf-mutes owe their phenotype to a homozygous recessive genotype but, in any individual case, only a compilation of a pedigree and its study can result in a reasonably accurate statement about the type of inheritance involved. Even if all known pedigrees indicate clearly only one common type of inheritance for a trait, it cannot be assumed a priori that new cases may not belong to another class—to a different kind of recessive or dominant genotype.

Abnormalities which are based on dominant alleles in some pedigrees, and on recessive alleles in others, often differ from each other in their severity. This is not surprising, since different genes or different alleles may be expected to produce variations in effect. It is, however, remarkable that recessive genes usually cause greater deviations from normality than dominant genes which affect the same trait. It has been suggested that this phenomenon may be the result of natural selection. If alleles causing a severe abnormality arise in a population, and if some are dominant and others recessive, then, it is argued, the dominant alleles will be weeded out by selection but the recessive alleles will not. The dominant alleles will cause such serious defects that their carriers will probably die before having reproduced or even before having been born; therefore, the dominant alleles will not be retained. The recessive alleles, however, will be carried invisibly by heterozygotes and thus remain in the population. Genes causing slight abnormalities will be retained, whether they are dominant or recessive.

Although this selectionist explanation of the greater severity in effect of recessive genes may have some validity, a biochemical interpretation is probably of more general application. When normal genes control the production of specific enzymes, their abnormal alleles often fail to do so. Homozygotes for such abnormal alleles will lack the enzyme completely. This will be so in affected individuals who are recessive homozygotes. In heterozygosity, which is the common genotype for dominantly affected individuals, the one normal allele may well produce some of the enzyme. Obviously, absence of an enzyme would have a greater effect than its presence in a reduced amount. And though we have only limited evidence, it is likely that when homozygous dominants occur, they are as severely affected as homozygous recessives.

Before we conclude the main section of this chapter, it should be pointed out that the genes we have been considering are all located in one or another of the 22 autosomes of man, not in the pair of sex chromosomes. The genes in this pair follow the rules of the sex-linked types of inheritance and will be dealt with in Chapter 13. Among them is at least one more gene for deaf-mutism.

Extranuclear Inheritance in Man?

Most inherited properties of organisms have been traced back to chromosomal genes. Nevertheless, it is known that some specific phenotypes of various plants and animals depend on the transmission of replicating units that are located outside the nucleus, i.e., in the cytoplasm of the cell. These include certain chlorophyll abnormalities in plants, which are determined by the properties of the chloroplasts independently of nuclear genes, and the killer-nonkiller alternative in *Paramecia,* in which the trait is determined by the presence or absence of visible "self-reproducing" bodies in the cytoplasm. Sometimes it is difficult to decide whether such extranuclear inheritance is a result of genetic variations in normal constituents of cells or whether it is really an infection in which the infectious agent is regularly transmitted in the cytoplasm (or perhaps even in the nucleus, but not as part of the chromosomes).

In man, there is no clear example of transmission of a trait that requires the assumption of extranuclear inheritance. The best indication of such a type of inheritance would be the absence of segregation, or at least the

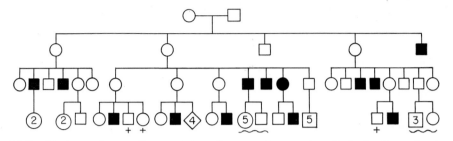

FIG. 67. Part of a pedigree of hereditary optic atrophy (Leber's disease). A plus sign means died young. The wavy lines under two sibships indicate that the birth order was unknown to the recorder of the pedigree. (After Waardenburg from Julia Bell, *Treas. Hum. Inher.*, **2,** 1931. Pedigree 708.)

absence of the regular kind of segregation that is based on the behavior of chromosomes in meiosis. In the simplest case—one encountered in other organisms—the extranuclear "plasmagene" might be transmitted by an affected mother through the cytoplasm of the egg to all her children, while an affected father would be unable to transmit his plasmagenes through the minute amount of cytoplasm in his sperm to any of his offspring. Possibly this interpretation can be applied to a very unusual case of a kindred in which 72 daughters and no sons were born (see p. 440).

The transmission of a type of degeneration of human optic nerves known as Leber's disease is not understood on simple assumptions of either nuclear or extranuclear inheritance. Among the pedigrees of this affliction, which may represent a number of different genetic types, there are many which show the following unusual features: much higher frequency of affected men than woman, a tendency for most men of a sibship to be affected and most women to be carriers, and, particularly remarkable, almost no transmission of the disease to any of the descendants of an affected man. Some of these features are shown in the pedigree in Figure 67. Various authors have attempted to explain this peculiar type of inheritance, but none with full success.

Exceptions in Simple Single Factor Inheritance

Simple single factor inheritance supplies the clearest insight into the working of two of the basic processes of human heredity: segregation, and chance combination of gametes. Nevertheless, occasional deviations from the simple expectations for single factor inheritance should not cause consternation. No single gene pair that is involved in making a person affected or nonaffected works by itself. It takes part in an interaction among many or all genes of the genotype—an interaction whose course is in many ways determined by the environment. An unusual genotype at some locus other than that of the pair of alleles in question, or an unusual factor in the environment, may, for instance, result in the occasional production by *Aa* of the phenotype characteristic for the recessive *aa* or even of the phenotype charac-teristic for one of the two homozygotes, *AA* or *aa,* by the other homozygote.

Furthermore, as indicated in Chapter 2, occasional mishaps in the distribu-tion of chromosomes—such as nondisjunction—are known to take place in meiosis. Such deviations from regular distribution of chromosomes should result in deviations from regular transmission of their associated genes. If during meiosis, for instance, the two chromosomes which carry the alleles *A* and *a,* respectively, should move together to the same pole instead of going to opposite poles, a gamete would be formed which contains both *A* and *a,* and another which contains neither of them. Evidence of such unusual situations will be presented later.

Problems

In Problems 24–29 assume that a person affected with a rare dominant trait is heterozygous.

24. Construct a representative pedigree (i.e., one showing *all* essential features of dominant inheritance) of the three generations of a hypothetical family in which woolly hair occurs. Do not include more than a total of 15 persons. List the geno-types of all individuals.

25. A woman is woolly haired. What is the chance of woolly hair in: (a) Her first child? (b) Her first and second child? (c) All her six children? (d) In any one of her great-grandchildren?

26. A man of blood group O marries a woman of blood group A. The wife's father is of blood group O. What is the probability that their children will belong to blood group O?

27. A brachydactylous man marries a woolly-haired woman. (a) What are their genotypes? (b) Give all the possible genotypes and phenotypes of their prospective children. (c) What are the expected proportions of genotypes?

28. If two chondrodystrophic dwarfs marry, what genotypes, and in what pro-portions, would be theoretically expected among their children?

29. What type of inheritance is involved in the pedigree in Figure 73? (a) De-termine the proportion of affected to nonaffected among the offspring of all relevant marriages. (b) What is the proportion of males to females among the affected? (c) What is the proportion of males to females among the nonaffected in sibships from an affected parent? (d) What is the proportion of males to females among the offspring of nonaffected parents?

In Problems 30–33 on recessive inheritance, assume that individuals unrelated to an affected person are homozygous dominant **unless evidence to the contrary is available.**

30. Construct a representative pedigree of three generations in which albinism is sporadic in the second generation. Let the first generation consist of two pairs of parents, the next of two sibships of three children each, and the last of a single sibship of six. Give the most likely genotype or, if more than one genotype is likely, give all alternatives, of all individuals.

31. Two normal parents have an albino son and a normal daughter. The normal daughter marries a man from a family with all normal members. The third offspring (a daughter) of this marriage is an albino. What is the probability of an albino among many offspring if the albino son mentioned above marries: (a) Someone normal in the general population? (b) A sister of his brother-in-law?

32. A man with normal pigmentation and woolly hair marries a woman with normal pigmentation and normal hair. Their first child is an albino with normal hair. (a) What other phenotypes may they expect in their children? (b) What will be the theoretical expectation of the proportions of all phenotypes?

33. In the pedigree in Figure 64, what are the genotypes of the following individuals: III–1, III–2, IV–3, IV–5, II–1, I–2? If more than one genotype is possible, give the alternatives.

34. (a) If a man and his wife both are excretors of betamin (from red beets) and nonexcretors of methanethiol (from asparagus), what types of children can they expect? (b) A sibship contains excretors and nonexcretors of betamin and methanethiol, what are the possible genotypes and phenotypes of the parents?

35. From marriages of two hereditary deaf mutes, the children are sometimes of two types, normal and deaf, in equal frequencies. How can this be explained?

36. A deaf mute of the genotype $ddEE$ is married to a person with normal hearing of the genotype $DdEd$. What are the possible genotypes and phenotypes of their children? What are their expected proportions?

References

Blakeslee, A. F., and Fox, A. L., 1932. Our different taste worlds. *J. Hered.*, **23:** 96–110.

Chung, C. S., Robinson, O. W., and Morton, N. E., 1959. A note on deaf mutism. *Ann. Human Genet.*, **23:** 357–366.

Følling, A., Mohr, O. L., and Ruud, L., 1945. *Oligophrenia Phenylpyrouvica*, a recessive syndrome in man. *Norske Videnskaps-Akademi Oslo I. Mat.-Naturv. Klasse*, **13:** 1–44.

Hogben, L., Worrall, R. L., and Zieve, I., 1932. The genetic basis of alkaptonuria. *Proc. Roy. Soc., Edinb.*, **52:** 264–295.

Imai, Y., and Moriwaki, D., 1936. A probable case of cytoplasmic inheritance in man: a critique of Leber's disease. *J. Genet.*, **33:** 163–167.

Mendel, Gregor, 1866. Versuche über Pflanzen-Hybriden. *Verhdlg. Naturf. Verein Brünn*, **4**, 3–47. (Facsimile reproduction of the original manuscript in Gedda, L. (Ed.), 1956. *Novant'-Anni delle Leggi Mendeliane*. Instituto "Gregorio Mendel," Rome. Facsimile reproduction of the original printed paper in *J. Hered.*, **42:** 1–47, 1951. Translation: Experiments on plant hybridization. 41 pp. Harvard University Press, Cambridge.)

Pearson, K., Nettleship, E., and Usher, C. H., 1911–1913. A monograph on albinism in man. *Draper's Company Research Memoirs. Biometr. ser.* **6, 8, 9.** Dulau & Co., London.

Stevenson, A. C., and Cheeseman, E. A., 1956. Heredity of deaf mutism with particular reference to Northern Ireland. *Ann. Human Genet.*, **20:** 177–231.

CHAPTER 7

LETHAL AND SUBLETHAL GENES

Different genes influence the ability of an organism to survive in varying degrees. The measurement of *viability,* as this ability is called, depends on the criteria used to define it. Some genotypes, for example, have greater ability to survive under adverse conditions than others, and viability of a given genotype may thus be defined in terms of frequency of survival relative to some standard genotype. A slightly different definition of viability may use for its criterion the average life span attained under normal conditions by individuals of a given genotype: this definition of viability will be used in the present chapter. From studies of other organisms, we know that different genes cover a whole spectrum of degrees of viability—from better than normal, through normal, to subnormal.

Average, Favorable, and Unfavorable Alleles. The normal variability of many human traits is due to the presence of somewhat different alleles in different individuals. The viability of these different, although normal, individuals is not affected strikingly by the slight differences in their alleles.

The discovery of unusually favorable alleles or genic combinations is made difficult because, in general, definitions of normality are not sharp, and all those phenotypes which are not clearly inferior are called normal. Consequently, superior traits are classified together with average traits instead of being classed separately, and the distinction is lost. It seems to be true that there are alleles that endow their bearers with unusually favorable characters, such as immunity to tuberculosis or other infectious diseases, or a lower than average tendency to the development of cancer. Similarly, the existence of special genotypes for longevity is probable, although it is not known whether they provide a person with a generally higher over-all vitality of tissues and

113

organs, or whether they act primarily by way of single organs, such as the heart or some hormone-producing gland.

The discovery of *unfavorable* alleles is easier. Although there must be numerous genotypes which lower viability so slightly that an exact analysis in man is impossible, there are others which cause such decided physiological or morphological defects that their inheritance can be clearly traced.

Lethals and Sublethals.   The lethals and sublethals constitute a special class of alleles. *Lethal* alleles are defined as those which do not permit survival of the embryo or infant. *Sublethals* (also called *semilethals*) lead to death during childhood or, at the latest, before the reproductive age has been reached. The time of death may, however, vary considerably from one affected individual to another: a lethal phenotype may survive for several years, and a sublethal phenotype may die shortly after birth or may, on the contrary, even occasionally survive into the reproductive period.

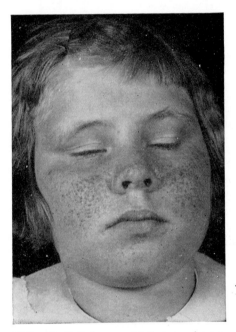

FIG. 68. Epiloia, a sublethal syndrome. Note the "butterfly rash" which is part of the syndrome (adenoma sebaceum). (Original from Dr. V. McKusick.)

Dominant Lethals and Sublethals. Both lethal and sublethal alleles may be dominant or recessive. A child who carries a dominant lethal allele cannot be the offspring of an affected parent, since, by definition, the bearer of this kind of dominant allele does not reproduce. Occasionally, however, a person with a dominant sublethal allele may become adult and reproduce, and afflicted children among his offspring demonstrate the dominant nature of the allele. For example, most persons with the inherited condition known as epiloia (Fig. 68), in which abnormal growth of the skin occurs, accompanied by severe mental deficiency and epilepsy, as well as tumors in the heart, kidneys, and other parts, die young; a few, however, who are mildly affected, may reproduce (Fig. 69).

If one assumes that typical lethal or sublethal phenotypes, which *never* reproduce, are caused by dominant alleles, it must further be assumed that the appearance of such phenotypes is the consequence of a new mutation. One of the normal parents must have formed a gamete in which a dominant lethal replaced a normal allele, and thus an abnormal child was formed.

There is no intrinsic flaw in such a hypothesis, but it cannot be proved directly. Its support lies, rather, in the exclusion of alternative explanations, one of which might be that the lethal or sublethal phenotype had been caused by a homozygous recessive geno-type; another, that during embryonic life an unusual accident, purely environmental, had produced the abnormality of the fetus or child. The first alternative, recessiveness, can often be excluded by showing that in pedigrees in which a specific, suspectedly dominant phenotype is found only a single individual is usually affected. If a recessive gene were involved, more than one affected child would be expected in many sibships. The second alterna-

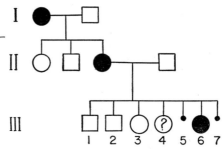

FIG. 69. A pedigree of epiloia. Individuals III-5 and III-7 were miscarriages or stillbirths (After Gunther and Penrose, *J. Genet.*, **31**, 1935.)

tive, the occurrence of a prenatal environmental accident, is more difficult to test, and there seems to be no example in which this alternative to the assumption of a dominant lethal or sublethal allele can be excluded with certainty.

Recessive Lethals and Sublethals.   Recessive lethal or sublethal alleles are responsible for a considerable number of defects of the embryo or infant. Examples are abnormal leathery skin with deep, bleeding fissures (ichthyosis congenita, Fig. 70); a congenital paralysis called Werding-Hoffmann's disease;

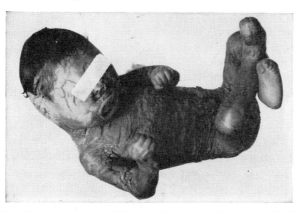

FIG. 70. Ichthyosis congenita, a sublethal. (Courtesy of the Atomic Bomb Casualty Commission, National Academy of Sciences–National Research Council. This child, born in 1948, was the fifth in its sibship. The first child, born in 1938, also had had ichthyosis; the other three children were normal. The parents were first cousins. The mother was in Hiroshima in 1945, about two miles from the center of the atomic explosion.)

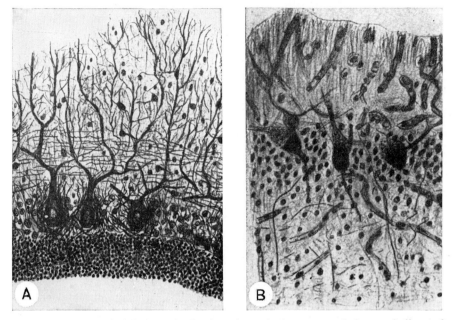

FIG. 71. Amaurotic idiocy.   A. Section through the cortex of the cerebellum of a normal individual.   B. Same in an affected individual. Compare with A, and note the absence of the granular layer and of the centripetal fibers. The large Purkinje cells are naked. (Bielschowsky, *J. f. Psychol. u. Neurol.,* **26,** 1920.)

and the infantile form of amaurotic idiocy (Tay-Sachs disease) in which abnormal fatty substances accumulate in the central nervous system, leading to complete mental degeneration, blindness, and wasting-away of the infant (Fig. 71). The heterozygous parents of such homozygous affected children are fully normal.

A relatively common cause of early death either by abortion or stillbirth is anencephaly, absence of a brain. This defect, present in approximately 1 out of 500 births is probably initiated as early as during the third week of embryonic life, the time when the sides of the broad anterior part of the medullary plate normally become elevated and, forming a vault, grow together to become the roof of the brain. In anencephalic embryos this process either takes place only incompletely or not at all. A homozygous recessive genotype seems to be responsible for many instances of this lethal malformation; but there is some variability in expression of the genes, which complicates the genetic analysis. Thus, a similar malformation, spina bifida, nonclosure of a posterior part of the neural plate resulting in incomplete formation of the neural tube, is lethal only when extensive. Anencephaly and spina bifida often occur together in the same individual, and both may be found in different members of a sibship or kindred. It is suspected either that these two inborn errors of development are variable expressions of the same homozygous, often lethal genotype or that spina bifida results from occasional expression of the heterozygous genotype carrying the lethal allele. The latter interpretation is, in part, based on X-rays of the seemingly unaffected parents of defective children, many of which show that one parent had defects of the spine. Like other abnormalities of development, anencephaly and spina bifida can probably be produced by more than one genotype, and also by external agents.

It is probable that many very early abortions are the result of embryonic malformations caused by lethal genotypes. This can be easily demonstrated in experimental animals such as mice: if parents are raised which are known to be heterozygous for recessive lethals, about a quarter of the embryos will die in the oviduct or uterus. An interesting phenomenon has been observed, particularly in Drosophila but likely also occurring in man. A gene will exert its lethal effect at a specific developmental stage; but, as usual, there will be some variability in the genic action, so that a few individuals will pass successfully through the critical period and, once having passed it, will develop normally. Such homozygous lethal survivors have been called "escapees from death" (Hadorn).

Some types of lethality are related to sex. Among aborted fetuses with certain kinds of severe malformations, males are more common than females; among those with other kinds, females are more common. A rare condition called incontinentia pigmenti may possibly belong in this group. This syndrome is found almost exclusively in females, although its symptoms, which include abnormal pigmentation areas of skin, have no obvious relation to any sex difference. Because affected mothers have approximately twice as many daughters as sons—half of the daughters being affected—W. Lenz has suggested that the gene responsible for incontinentia pigmenti is a dominant nonlethal in females but, usually, is an embryonic lethal in males.

Dominant Alleles with Recessive Lethal or Sublethal Effects. Some recessive lethals or sublethals produce harmless phenotypic effects when present heterozygously. Homozygosity for a specific recessive allele is responsible for xeroderma pigmentosum, a sublethal condition in which skin abnormalities and, finally, multiple cancerous growths occur in those parts of the body that are exposed to light. Many carriers, although of normal health, are heavily freckled, obviously on account of the presence of the allele in heterozygous state (Fig. 28, p. 51).

Another example is that of a shortened or crooked forefinger and second toe in a Norwegian family studied by Mohr and Wriedt—a slight abnormality that does not interfere in the least with normal viability. In the pedigree (Fig. 133, p. 311), a marriage of two affected people is recorded (I-1 × I-2). Of the two children born to them, one had the typical short forefinger, but the other was a cripple—without fingers and toes and with severe disorders of the whole skeletal system. It is probable that this infant, who died at the age of one year, was homozygous for the allele responsible for short-forefingeredness. This allele, then, may be defined as dominant in regard to short-forefingeredness and as a recessive in its sublethal action. Another way of describing the genic action would be to say that heterozygotes with the allele have a skeletal system that is intermediate between those of normal and abnormal homozygotes.

Multiple telangiectasia is a third example of an allele which produces a minor defect in the heterozygote, but is lethal when present homozygously. In the heterozygous phenotype some of the finer blood vessels of the nose, tongue, lips, face, or fingers are enlarged. This trait is usually inherited as a typical, rare dominant which is transmitted from one of the two parents to about half of the children. The pedigree (Fig. 72) shows the marriage of two affected individuals. Their newborn child possessed many abnormally dilated blood vessels; within a few weeks, other severe symptoms of multiple telangiectasia appeared; and after less than three months, breaking of numerous blood vessels resulted in death. The probability that this child was homozygous for the so-called dominant gene is high.

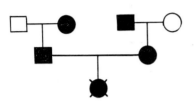

FIG. 72. Pedigree of multiple telangiectasia. The offspring of the affected parents is a sublethal child, probably because of homozygosity for the dominant gene for multiple telangiectasia. (Snyder and Doan, *J. Labor Clinic. Med.,* **29,** 1944.)

Hypercholesteremia, the presence of excessive quantities of cholesterol in the blood, is an inherited trait which frequently leads to disease of the coronary arteries in later life. A dominant gene often seems to be responsible for it. In a kindred with such dominant inheritance, two nonrelated, typically affected individuals had a severely affected sublethal child, probably a homozygote.

Still another sublethal condition is the hemoglobin disease thalassemia (Cooley's anemia). Homozygotes for the allele c die at an early age, but the health of Cc heterozygotes is very nearly as good as that of the normal CC individuals.

Lethal genes usually cause death of a child before birth. Some may exert their fatal effect either prenatally or in early infancy. Others will invariably terminate life at some early embryonic stage. In man, such cases are not well known, since causes of early abortions have rarely been studied from the genetic point of view. We are, however, familiar with genetic conditions in many animals that lead to termination of development in the earliest stages of cleavage, or at various later steps in embryogeny. An example is provided by the yellow mouse, whose yellow fur is caused by a dominant allele for which it is heterozygous. Cleavage of a homozygous egg and formation of the hollow, ball-shaped blastocyst proceed normally, but disintegration occurs before the embryo has become embedded in the uterine wall. Thus, the allele for yellow fur acts as a recessive lethal. In man, such early failure of development would probably remain unnoticed, since the small embryo would be resorbed by the maternal tissue.

Other lethals in mice are known to end life at a later stage by causing incomplete development of the notochord, correlated with nonformation of the nervous system, of the tail, or even of legs. Still other homozygous lethal embryos never develop kidneys, form no (or inconspicuous) external genitalia, and have abnormalities of the anal region. Aborted human embryos exhibiting defects like those in mice are familiar to physicians, and many of the defects probably have similar genetic causes.

Sterility. It is often asked whether sterility in humans may be due to the production of lethal genotypes. It may be, but very rarely. More common causes are absence of normal eggs or sperm, or circumstances which prevent fertilization even though normal gametes are present. Fertilization may be prevented by abnormal form or function of the internal or external genital organs. In other types of sterility, fertilization takes place but normal development of the embryo does not. Any of these phenomena may, of course, be caused by some abnormal nongenetic factor, either physiological or developmental. Thus, in rats, deficiency of vitamin E in the diet causes sterility.

Although sterility is rarely caused by the production of lethal genotypes, its occurrence frequently has a genetic basis. From studies of domesticated animals, mice, and Drosophila, we know that specific alleles at various genic loci are responsible for nonformation or abnormal formation of eggs or sperm, for the development of abnormal genitalia, or for physiological conditions in the female which prevent the development of viable offspring. In man, genes causing abnormalities in gametes have not as yet been recognized, but their existence would not be unexpected. Other genes that produce striking abnormalities in the genital organs are well known.

A special type of genetically controlled interference with fertility results from an antagonism between the blood of the mother and that of the embryo. Most frequently, alleles of the Rh factor are involved. We shall defer a description of this type of partial sterility to Chapter 17, Prenatal Interactions.

None of the alleles which cause sterility fall strictly under the definitions of lethals. If both parents are heterozygous for a truly lethal allele, then embryos homozygous for this allele may die early. However, only one-quarter of the pregnancies will involve homozygous zygotes, which means that three-quarters of the zygotes can develop normally.

At one time, it would have been a contradiction in terms to speak of the inheritance of lethality or of sterility. Modern knowledge of the transmission of genes, as opposed to traits, has removed the apparent contradiction.

Problems

37. List the genotypes of all individuals recorded in the pedigree in Figure 72. If additional children were present in the last generation, what phenotypes and genotypes, and in what proportions, would be expected?

38. A man is heterozygous for the recessive sublethal gene for ichthyosis. His wife is not a carrier for the ichthyosis gene, but is heterozygous for amaurotic idiocy. What are the prospects of their future children being affected?

39. A man is known to have been heterozygous for a very rare recessive gene that, in the homozygous state, causes death during infancy. He married his half-sister (the daughter of his father and another mother) and had two children, one affected and one normal. (a) Draw a pedigree of the case and give the genotypes of all individuals. (b) With the genotypes of the parents as outlined above, what were the chances of both children being normal?

References

Bedichek, S., and Haldane, J. B. S., 1938. A search for autosomal lethals in man. *Ann. Eugen.,* **8:** 245–254.

Böök, J. A., and Kostmann, R., 1956. Prospects of biochemical genetics in man. *Ann. Human Genet.,* **20:** 251–252.

Böök, J. A., and Rayner, S., 1950. A clinical and genetical study of an-encephaly. *Am. J. Human Genet.,* **2:** 61–84.

Dunn, L. C., 1940. Heredity and development of early abnormalities in vertebrates. The Harvey Lectures, **35:** 135–165.

Eaton, O. N., 1937. A summary of lethal characters in animals and man. *J. Hered.,* **28:** 320–326.

Grebe, H., 1953–54. Familienbefunde bei letalen Anomalien der Körperform. *Acta Genet. Med. et Gemel.,* **2:** 447–470; **3:** 93–111.

Gregory, P. W., Regan, W. M., and Mead, S. W., 1945. Evidence of genes for female sterility in dairy cows. *Genetics,* **30:** 506–517.

Hadorn, E., 1955. *Letalfaktoren.* 338 pp. Georg Thieme Verlag, Stuttgart.

Mohr, O. L., 1926. Über Letalfaktoren, mit Berücksichtigung ihres Verhaltens bei Haustieren und beim Menschen. *Zeitschr. Abstgs.- und Vererbungsl.,* **41:** 59–109.

Robertson, G. G., 1942. An analysis of the development of homozygous yellow mouse embryos. *J. Exp. Zool.,* **89:** 197–227.

CHAPTER 8

GENETIC COUNSELING

The recognition of simple dominant or recessive inheritance of a given trait permits statements of practical value about the genotypes of individuals. Persons affected with unfavorable traits, and their close relatives, rightly wish to know whether their future children are likely to have the same traits.

Genetic counseling makes use of a wide range of information on human inheritance. In the present chapter, counseling problems connected with simple single factor inheritance will be stressed, because only this type of inheritance has been covered in the preceding parts of this book. It may appear premature to discuss problems of genetic advisers before more facts have been presented; yet even at this stage of the discussion, it seems worthwhile to show how knowledge of human genetics can be applied to problems of individuals and of society. In later chapters—for instance, those on multiple alleles, sex-linkage, and medical genetics—further material will be presented which may provide a basis for genetic counseling.

Dominant Traits. The answer to questions about the prospects of persons in families with affected individuals having affected children is simple when the trait is dominant. Even the closest relatives of affected individuals, as long as they are normal themselves, will not transmit the trait, either to their immediate offspring or to later generations. Affected persons will transmit the dominant allele to one-half of their children, although there is always a possibility that none or all will receive it.

There are numerous more or less serious defects that are transmitted in simple dominant form. For example, a pedigree of cataract is shown in Figure 73. The condition, opacity of the lens of the eye, is present in many members of this family group from childhood on. Blindness can be avoided by an operation; but even after the operation and after providing the affected individuals with special glasses, they are greatly handicapped. The trait is clearly dominant. Before having been advised by a medical geneticist, the members of this

121

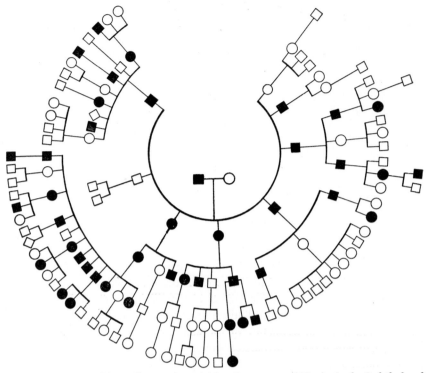

FIG. 73. Pedigree of juvenile cataract. (After Lutman and Neel, *Arch. Ophthalmol.,* **33,** 1945.)

kindred were aware that the affliction was hereditary, but they did not know the rules of its transmission. They knew only that it was uncommon for all children of an affected parent to develop cataracts and that all children of such a parent might be normal.

The apparent irregularity of appearance had kept the members of the family group from realizing that cataracts never appeared among the offspring of parents who were both normal. The physician who drew up the pedigree on the basis of information willingly supplied by the family was able to explain to them why cataract appeared in only some children of a sibship and why, in some small sibships, all the children were defective or all normal. Having supplied this enlightenment, he could further assure normal sibs of affected persons that they did not need to worry about transmitting cataract to their children. This example shows that much harm may be avoided and much worrying relieved if consultants in human genetics become widely available to the public.

Recessive Traits. Although the genotypes of individuals can be given with certainty if simple dominant inheritance of a rare condition is involved, some genotypes of rare recessive conditions are less easy to define. An affected person, of course, is *dd*, but nonaffected relatives are either *DD* or *Dd*. If they are phenotypically normal sibs of a *dd* individual, and if their parents were normal, their genotypes could be either *DD* or *Dd*, since both parents must have been heterozygous. The two genotypes, *DD* and *Dd*, occur in a ratio of 1:2, which makes the probability that a normal sib does not have the recessive allele 1/3, and that he is a carrier 2/3.

These two probability fractions may seem to contradict the expectation that *Dd* × *Dd* marriages will yield 1/4 *DD* and 1/2 *Dd* children; but they do not. The probabilities 1/4 and 1/2 express the frequency with which any child from two heterozygous parents may be expected to be *DD* or *Dd*, considering also that he may be *dd*. The fractions 1/3 and 2/3, on the other hand, are derived from the number of individuals who are phenotypically normal, that is, those who are certainly not *dd*. This may be illustrated by an example: If two normal parents who have an affected child want to know the probability that their unborn second child will be homozygous normal, the answer would be 1/4, since he could be *dd*, *Dd*, or *DD*. If, however, the second child is normal, the answer to the same question would have to be 1/3, because his phenotype shows with certainty that he is not *dd*.

Determination of the probability that an affected individual or phenotypically normal relatives of such an individual will have affected homozygous recessive offspring has to take into account the various types of marriages possible, and also the frequency of the condition in the population at large. Marriages in which both partners are affected will, of course, result in affected children only. If one prospective parent is affected and the other normal and drawn from the general population, it is necessary to estimate the probability that a normal person chosen at random is heterozygous, i.e., a carrier.

A formula which permits such an estimate will be derived in Chapter 10, The Hardy-Weinberg Law. Here, it may be stressed that even very rare conditions that are due to a homozygous recessive constitution are quite often carried by heterozygotes.

Probability of Affected Offspring If One Parent Is Affected.   Knowledge of the frequency with which carriers occur enables a genetic consultant to predict the chance of affected offspring occurring in a marriage (Table 5). For example, it has been estimated that about 1 in 70 persons is a carrier of recessive albinism. Consequently, the probability that an albino will marry a normally pigmented unrelated person who is heterozygous for the albino allele is 1/70. If enough children come from such a marriage to make it reasonably certain that both genotypes, *Dd* and *dd*, will actually occur, the probability that an albino with a normally pigmented spouse will have some affected offspring is 1/70. Expressed in a different way: if prospective parents, one of whom is an albino, ask, "If our family is large, what chance is there of having albino children?" the answer is 1/70. Should, however, the couple ask, "What chance is there that our first child, or any specific child, will be an albino?" then the answer is 1/2 × 1/70 = 1/140, since the probability of *dd* offspring from *dd* × *Dd* parents is 1/2.

TABLE 5. *Some Probabilities of Affected Offspring for Recessive Genotypes.*
(The probability that an individual in the general population is a carrier is h.
For albinism h is about $1/70$, and for other rare recessives it usually lies some-
where between $1/40$ and $1/200$.)

		Second Child If First Is:	
Parents	First Child	Nonaffected*	Affected
Both nonaffected; no affected relative	$\frac{1}{4}h^2$	$\frac{1}{4}h^2$	$\frac{1}{4}$
One affected	$\frac{1}{2}h$	$\frac{1}{2}h$	$\frac{1}{2}$
Both nonaffected; one has affected sib	$\frac{2}{3}\cdot\frac{1}{4}\cdot h$	$\frac{2}{3}\cdot\frac{1}{4}\cdot h$	$\frac{1}{4}$
Both affected	1	—	1

* Approximation; if the first child is nonaffected, then the probability that both parents carry
the recessive allele is slightly decreased.

**Probability of Affected Offspring If One Parent Is the Normal Sib of an
Affected Person.**   In marriages between normal sibs of affected persons and
normal individuals who are not related to them, the probability that any specific child will be affected is determined by multiplying the probability that
the sib is a carrier (which is $2/3$) by the probability that the spouse is a
carrier (which is $1/70$ in albinism) and by the probability that the child will
obtain d from each heterozygous parent (which is $1/4$). Thus, $2/3\cdot1/70\cdot1/4
= 1/420$. This is a rather small chance; yet it is much higher than that in a
marriage of two normal individuals who have no reason to suspect the presence of the d gene in their genotypes. In the latter marriage, the chance that
any specific child will be an albino is $1/70\cdot1/70\cdot1/4 = 1/19,600$: the probability if one parent is a sib of an albino is almost fifty times as great.

Any statement about the probability that an affected child will be born to
normal persons is subject to change when new information gives more specific knowledge of the genotypes involved. If a normal sib of albinos and his
normal fiancée should ask how probable it is that any of their future children
will be albinos, the best estimate possible is 1 in 420. Should the same couple
ask for the same information after an albino child had already been born to
them, the answer would be 1 in 4, since it would now be certain that both
parents are heterozygotes.

Further Probabilities of Being a Carrier.   It is possible not only to determine the probability that individuals who are sibs of an affected person are
heterozygotes, but also to calculate the probability of heterozygosity among
individuals who are related to affected persons in other ways. These probabilities are consequences of the mechanism of genetic transmission, and many

can be found by applying the theorem that the probability of two or more events occurring together is the product of the separate probabilities. Let us give a few examples: (1) The probability that the normal child of an affected parent is heterozygous is 1, or certainty. (2) The probability that a normal parent of an affected person is a carrier is 1, while that for the affected's uncles or aunts is usually 1/2. This follows from the fact that a heterozygous parent himself almost always comes from a marriage of a normal homozygote and a heterozygote and the chance that any offspring from such a marriage will be *Dd* is 1 out of 2. (3) The probability that the children of these aunts and uncles will be carriers is 1/2 that of their parents, or 1/2 of 1/2, i.e., 1/4. This last calculation does not take into consideration the rather rare chance that the spouse of the uncle or aunt may also be a carrier. All these probabilities are greatly increased when individuals from families with affected members marry close relatives (see Chap. 19).

The Independence of Probabilities from Preceding Events. It is important to stress that, if the genotypes of the parents are known, the probability prediction for any one child is not influenced by the type of offspring already born.

"Chance has no memory!" The truth of Le Châtelier's remark is obvious to the geneticist, who knows that the formation of any one combination of genes at the conception of a child depends solely on the union of gametes present at that time and not on any preceding, independent union of gametes. Thus, two parents heterozygous for a recessive allele that causes an abnormality have one chance in four that their first child will be affected. If the first child is affected, then the chance that the second child will also be affected is likewise one in four. However, the chance that two children will be affected is the product of the independent chances, or one in sixteen.

In a relevant case reported by Mohr, a couple had a child who developed a paralysis causing death before it was a year old. Since it was known that the condition is due to a rare recessive gene, the parents were marked as heterozygotes. They were informed that the risk was one in four that any other child would also be doomed. The couple greatly desired a healthy child and were willing to take the risk of another tragedy. They had a second child, and it too developed the deadly paralysis. When a third child was conceived, the dice of destiny determined finally that it was normal.

There are many traits for which a definite genetic interpretation is not available, and, for these, counseling cannot be based on theoretical ratios. However, the data that have been collected on a number of such traits show how often children or other relatives of affected individuals are similarly affected. Such *empiric risk figures* can be used in order to predict the probability of recurrence of the trait. Examples of risk figures are given in Tables 87 and 92 (pp. 565 and 581).

Human genetics counseling involves more than the statement of probabilities. Prospective parents may have to decide whether it is genetically desirable for them to have children and what the consequences will be, both for their personal lives and for society at large. These and other general problems will be discussed in Chapter 30, Medical Genetics.

Problems

40. In Figure 56: (a) What is the probability that the first child born to individual IX–2 is affected with night blindness? (b) What is the probability for the first child of her brother IX–1?

41. A normal woman has three sibs affected with juvenile cataract. Her father and paternal grandmother were also affected. What are the prospects of her future children being affected?

42. A couple, of normal ancestry, have two normal children and an amaurotic idiot. The sister of the husband wishes to marry the brother of the wife. Assume that they may have many children. What is the chance of their having affected offspring?

In Problems 43–48, assume that all individuals are homozygous normal **unless there is evidence to the contrary.**

43. In Figure 63, what is the probability that IV–3 is a carrier for albinism?

44. In Figure 63, what is the probability that IV–1 is a carrier for albinism?

45. List the genotypes of all individuals given in Figure 63. If more than one genotype is likely, list the alternatives and their probabilities.

46. If a man and his unrelated wife each have an albino sib, what is the probability: (a) That their first born will be an albino? (b) That albinism will occur if they have many children? (c) That if they will have three children, all will be albinos? (d) That if their first child is an albino, the next two will also be albinos?

47. (a) If the normal sister of an amaurotic idiot wants to know if her expected child will be affected, what would be your prognosis? (b) If it turned out that her husband had an amaurotic cousin, what would your prognosis be then?

48. In Figure 64, individuals III–1 and III–10 were carriers for phenylketonuria. In addition, carriers must have been present among the individuals of generation II. Could the appearance of the affected individuals in generation IV be explained if the following individuals in generation II had been heterozygous: II–1 and II–2; or II–1 and II–4; or II–2 and II–3; or II–2 and II–4; or II–1 and II–5?

References

See also paragraph two of remarks under references to Chapter 30 and the books by Hammons, Reed, and Scheinfeld listed there.

Lutman, F., and Neel, J. V., 1945. Inherited cataract in the B. genealogy. *Arch. Ophthalmol.*, **33:** 341–357.

Oliver, C. P., 1945. A report on the organization and aims of the Dight Institute. *Bull. Dight Inst. Univ. Minnesota*, **1:** 1–7.

———, 1945. The collection of records in the study of human heredity. *Bull. Dight Inst. Univ. Minnesota*, **2:** 1–34.

Roberts, J. A. Fraser, 1959. *An Introduction to Medical Genetics*. Chapter 11, pp. 228–251. Oxford University Press, London.

CHAPTER 9

GENETIC RATIOS

We have already seen that certain ratios of affected to nonaffected children are to be expected in various types of marriages. The two most important are the 1:1 ratio (in heterozygous *Dd* × homozygous *dd* marriages) and the 3:1 ratio (in *Dd* × *Dd* marriages). These ratios do not represent certainties in the sense that they can be predicted with accuracy for any one family, but are the result of chance occurrences that lead to predictable probabilities.

Chance Phenomena

It may be well to recount these chance occurrences. We know that in a *Dd* man (♂) spermatogenesis leads to the formation of equal numbers of *D* and *d* sperm and that in a *dd* woman (♀) oogenesis leads to *d* eggs exclusively. The role of chance in the production of *Dd* and *dd* children if such persons marry rests on at least three circumstances:

1. Some sperm cells, because of accidents in development, do not become mature sperm. Since there is no reason to believe that either the *D* or the *d* sperm is more subject to such accidents than the other, the cells will degenerate at random. Therefore, it is unlikely that exactly the same number of *D* and *d* cells will be eliminated, and slight inequalities in the two kinds of mature sperm will thus result from chance elimination.

2. Even if absolutely equal numbers of both kinds of sperm should be present in the female ducts, the endowment of the new child would depend on the fusion of either a *D* or a *d* sperm with the *d* egg. Again, there is no reason to believe that either kind of sperm is more likely to fertilize a *d* egg—at least, such "selective fertilization" has not been demonstrated. Thus, it seems a matter of chance whether a *D* or a *d* sperm fertilizes the egg. If the first pregnancy happens to be the result of fertilization by a *D* sperm, a later fertilization will not be influenced by this; the chance that the later fertilization will result in a *Dd* embryo is just as great as it was

127

the first time, and equal to the chance that fertilization by a *d* sperm will occur and result in a *dd* embryo.

3. Even assuming absolute equality in the number of *Dd* and *dd* embryos in early pregnancy, birth of equal numbers of the two kinds of children will depend on normal completion of development. Since an appreciable number of pregnancies are not successfully brought to term, and since it may be assumed here that *Dd* and *dd* fetuses are equally viable, there would, once more, be an equal chance that a *Dd* or a *dd* child would not survive.

In the reciprocal marriage, *Dd* ♀ × *dd* ♂ , we have only one kind of sperm, *d*, to consider. Two main chance processes determine the genotype of a child of this marriage. The first concerns the fate of the *Dd*-containing chromosome pair on the meiotic spindles of the egg cell. Two of the four chromosome strands of the pair possess a *D* allele and the other two a *d* allele, but only one of the four strands is included in the egg nucleus. Whether this strand contains a *D* or a *d* allele depends on the arrangement of the strands on the meiotic spindles—a matter of chance. Thus, there is equal probability that a *Dd* or a *dd* embryo will result from fertilization by the one kind of sperm produced by the *dd* man. The second chance process in the marriage *Dd* ♀ × *dd* ♂ , is identical with the third in the marriage *dd* ♀ × *Dd* ♂ . It is the equal probability that either a *Dd* or a *dd* embryo will die before birth.

In a *Dd* × *Dd* marriage, the various chance processes involved in the development of sperm cells into mature sperm, in the production of *D* or *d* eggs, in the fusion of *D* or *d* sperm with *D* or *d* eggs, and in the survival of *DD*, *Dd*, and *dd* embryos will all play a role.

Ratios in Small Families

Ideal Ratio 1:1. It is possible to express numerically the expected chance deviations from an ideal ratio. If, for instance, a *Dd* × *dd* marriage results in 2 children, the probability that either child will be *Dd* or *dd* is 1/2 each. Consequently, the probability that both the first and second child will be *Dd* is the product of the separate probabilities: $1/2 \cdot 1/2 = 1/4$. The probability of the first being *Dd* and the second *dd* is also 1/4; that of the first being *dd* and the second *Dd,* again 1/4; and that of the first and second being *dd*, once more 1/4. This means that among *Dd* × *dd* marriages with 2 children, chance will cause one-quarter of the families to have only *Dd* children, another quarter to have only *dd* children, and half to have one of each kind.

Similarly, we may calculate the chance deviations from the "ideal" expectations for any given number of children in a sibship. Before giving the general procedure, let us consider sibships with 3 children. The expected probability of either type of child remains, of course, 1/2. All 3 children will be *Dd* in $1/2 \cdot 1/2 \cdot 1/2$, or 1/8, of all sibships. Another 1/8 of all sibships will have 3 *dd* children. Two *Dd* children and 1 *dd* child are possible in three sequences: *Dd–Dd–dd, Dd–dd–Dd,* and *dd–Dd–Dd,* each sequence having the probability of $1/2 \cdot 1/2 \cdot 1/2 = 1/8$. Thus, the probability of 2 *Dd* children and 1 *dd* child is 3/8. Likewise, 3 out of 8 sibships will consist of 1 *Dd* child and 2 *dd* children.

It is evident that the procedure employed is the determination of all possible combinations of two events, the birth of a *Dd* or a *dd* child, in sets of three. A mathematical "recipe" for obtaining the results consists in expanding the binomial $(a + b)^n$. Applied to our example, a equals the probability of the occurrence of the genotype *Dd*, which is 1/2; b, the probability of the genotype *dd*, which is likewise 1/2; and n, the number of children in the sibship.

For sibships of 2, the binomial is $(1/2\ Dd + 1/2\ dd)^2$, which, expanded, becomes

$$\tfrac{1}{4}(Dd)^2 + \tfrac{2}{4}(Dd)\cdot(dd) + \tfrac{1}{4}(dd)^2.$$

The exponents assigned to the genotypes indicate how often they occur in any given sibship of 2 children: $(Dd)^2$ signifies 2 *Dd* children; $(Dd)\cdot(dd)$ signifies 1 *Dd* and 1 *dd* child; and $(dd)^2$ signifies 2 *dd* children. The fractions 1/4, 2/4, and 1/4 designate the probabilities of occurrence of the particular combinations of 2 children in a sibship.

For sibships of 3, the binomial is $(1/2\ Dd + 1/2\ dd)^3$, which, expanded, becomes

$$\tfrac{1}{8}(Dd)^3 + \tfrac{3}{8}(Dd)^2\cdot dd + \tfrac{3}{8}Dd\cdot(dd)^2 + \tfrac{1}{8}(dd)^3.$$

The four terms of this series give the probabilities of the four kinds of sibships possible with 3 children: 1/8 that all 3 children will be *Dd*; 3/8 that there will be 2 *Dd* children and 1 *dd* child; and so on.

In the general case, where n indicates the number of children in a sibship, the expansion of the binomial $(1/2\ Dd + 1/2\ dd)^n$ yields the following series:

$$(\tfrac{1}{2}Dd)^n + n\cdot(\tfrac{1}{2}Dd)^{n-1}\cdot(\tfrac{1}{2}dd) + \frac{n(n-1)}{1\cdot2}\cdot(\tfrac{1}{2}Dd)^{n-2}\cdot(\tfrac{1}{2}dd)^2 +$$
$$\cdots n\cdot(\tfrac{1}{2}Dd)\cdot(\tfrac{1}{2}dd)^{n-1} + (\tfrac{1}{2}dd)^n.$$

This may be written in the form

$$\tfrac{1}{2^n}\cdot(Dd)^n + n\cdot\tfrac{1}{2^n}\cdot[(Dd)^{n-1}\cdot dd] + \frac{n(n-1)}{1\cdot2}\cdot\tfrac{1}{2^n}\cdot[(Dd)^{n-2}\cdot(dd)^2] +$$
$$\cdots n\cdot\tfrac{1}{2^n}\cdot[(Dd)\cdot(dd)^{n-1}] + \tfrac{1}{2^n}\cdot(dd)^n.$$

Expressed in genetic terms, the series states, that $1/2^n$ of all sibships can be expected to have only *Dd* children, that $n\cdot 1/2^n$ of all sibships have $(n-1)$ *Dd* children and 1 *dd* child, that

$$\frac{n(n-1)}{1\cdot2}\cdot\tfrac{1}{2^n}$$

of all sibships have $(n-2)$ *Dd* and 2 *dd* children, and so on. If we take as an example sibships with 8 children, then $1/2^8$ or 1/256 of all sibships have only *Dd* children, 8/256 have 7 *Dd* and 1 *dd*, 28/256 have 6 *Dd* and 2 *dd*, and so on.

TABLE 6. *Probabilities of All Possible Combinations of Dd and dd Children in Sibships of from 1 to 8 Children of Dd × dd Marriages.*

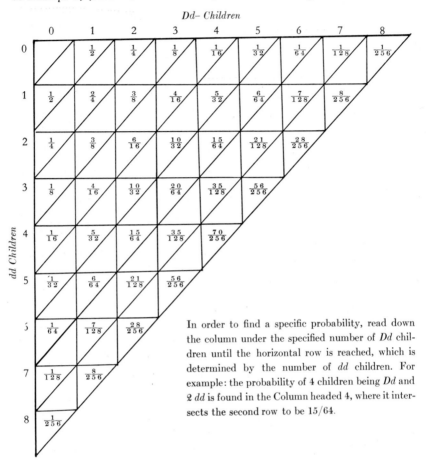

In order to find a specific probability, read down the column under the specified number of Dd children until the horizontal row is reached, which is determined by the number of dd children. For example: the probability of 4 children being Dd and 2 dd is found in the Column headed 4, where it intersects the second row to be 15/64.

In order to determine the probability that a sibship of 8 will consist of 5 Dd and 3 dd children, it is necessary to find the probability corresponding to $(Dd)^5 \cdot (dd)^3$. This may be done by introducing one more general algebraic expression. If n is the total number of children per family, and x the number of Dd children, then $(n - x)$ is the number of dd children. The general binomial term that signifies the probability of a sibship with x Dd and $(n - x)$ dd children is

$$\frac{n!}{x!(n-x)!} \cdot (\tfrac{1}{2}Dd)^x \cdot (\tfrac{1}{2}dd)^{n-x},$$

or

$$\frac{n!}{x!(n-x)!} \cdot \tfrac{1}{2^n} [(Dd)^x \cdot (dd)^{n-x}].$$

An exclamation point following a letter or a combination of letters in parentheses, indicates that they are "factorials," that is, the product of all integers
from 1 to the number signified; for example, if n = 5, then "n factorial" = n!
= $1 \cdot 2 \cdot 3 \cdot 4 \cdot 5$. Applying the binomial to the family of 8 children (n = 8),
the probability that it consists of 5 *Dd* (x = 5) and 3 *dd* (n − x = 3) children is

$$\frac{8!}{5!\,3!} \cdot \frac{1}{2^8} = \frac{1 \cdot 2 \cdot 3 \cdot 4 \cdot 5 \cdot 6 \cdot 7 \cdot 8}{1 \cdot 2 \cdot 3 \cdot 4 \cdot 5 \cdot 1 \cdot 2 \cdot 3} \cdot \frac{1}{256} = \frac{56}{256} = \frac{14}{64}.$$

[handwritten margin note: Why this instead of 129 ? Why is the same]

This calculation, then, shows that, in 14 out of 64 sibships of 8 children
with *Dd* × *dd* parents, it is expected that 5 of the children will be *Dd* and
that 3 will be *dd*.

Table 6 gives the probabilities of the occurrence of all possible combinations
of heterozygous dominant (*Dd*) and homozygous recessive (*dd*) children in
sibships of from 1 to 8 children with *Dd* × *dd* parents. This table reveals
many interesting facts. It shows, for example, that the ideal 1:1 ratio in sibships of 4 is found in only 6 out of 16 families, i.e., 37.5 per cent, and that
in sibships of 8, the 1:1 ratio is even less common, being found in 70 out
of 256 families, or approximately 27 per cent. On the other hand, the larger
the sibship, the more likely it is to be close to the 1:1 ratio. Thus, in sibships
of 4, 10 out of 16, or 63.5 per cent, have ratios of 3:1, 1:3, or "worse";
while in sibships of 8, only 70 out of 256, or 27.3 per cent, show equally
great deviations. Furthermore, in families with 4 children, a ratio of 3 *Dd*:
1 *dd* will be found in 4 out of 16, or 25 per cent, and a ratio of 1 *Dd*:3 *dd*
in another 25 per cent, although the ideal expectation is 1:1. Among sibships
of all sizes, there are some in which only one genotype, *Dd* or *dd*, occurs.

Ideal Ratio 3:1. When both parents are heterozygous for a specific recessive allele, the ideal ratio is 3 dominant to 1 recessive offspring. Again, it is
obvious that chance processes will not only permit, but necessarily cause,
deviations from the ideal ratio.

Let us consider, in detail, families with 4 children.

Five different types of 4-child sibships with *Dd* × *Dd* parents are possible:
4, 3, 2, 1, or 0 *dd* children, or, stated differently, 0, 1, 2, 3, or 4 *D−* children
(*D−* signifies either *DD* or *Dd*). In the second column of Table 7, all 16
possible combinations of *D−* and *dd* children in a set of 4 are enumerated.
In the third column, the probabilities of the combinations are listed. These
probabilities follow from the fact that (1) the occurrence of a *D−* child has
a probability of 3/4; (2) the occurrence of a *dd* child has a probability of
1/4; and (3) the probability of any specific combination of 4 children is the
product of the four separate probabilities. The fourth column gives the total
number of *D−* and *dd* children, calculated on the assumption that 256 families are being studied. As shown in the third column, 81 families out of 256
would have *D−* children only, yielding a total of $4 \cdot 81 = 324$ *D−* and no *dd*

TABLE 7. *Types and Probabilities of Sibships of 4 from Dd × Dd Marriages.*

Type of Sibship	Sequence of Children				Probability of Sibships	No. of D– and dd in 256 Families	
	First	Second	Third	Fourth		D–	dd
4D–:0dd	D–	D–	D–	D–	$\frac{3}{4}\cdot\frac{3}{4}\cdot\frac{3}{4}\cdot\frac{3}{4}=\frac{81}{256}$	324	0
3D–:1dd	D– D– D– dd	D– D– dd D–	D– dd D– D–	dd D– D– D–	$4\cdot\frac{3}{4}\cdot\frac{3}{4}\cdot\frac{3}{4}\cdot\frac{1}{4}=\frac{108}{256}$	324	108
2D–:2dd	D– D– dd D– dd dd	D– dd dd dd D– D–	dd dd D– D– dd dd	dd D– D– dd D– dd	$6\cdot\frac{3}{4}\cdot\frac{3}{4}\cdot\frac{1}{4}\cdot\frac{1}{4}=\frac{54}{256}$	108	108
1D–:3dd	D– dd dd dd	dd D– dd dd	dd dd D– dd	dd dd dd D–	$4\cdot\frac{3}{4}\cdot\frac{1}{4}\cdot\frac{1}{4}\cdot\frac{1}{4}=\frac{12}{256}$	12	36
0D–:4dd	dd	dd	dd	dd	$\frac{1}{4}\cdot\frac{1}{4}\cdot\frac{1}{4}\cdot\frac{1}{4}=\frac{1}{256}$	0	4
Grand total						768	256
Total, omitting the 4D–:0dd sibships						444	256

children. Similarly, 108 families have 3 *D–* and 1 *dd*, giving a total of $3\cdot108$ = 324 *D–* and 108 *dd*, and so on.

The ideal ratio of 3 *D–*:1 *dd* is realized in only 108 out of 256 sibships; that is, in less than 42 per cent of all sibships of 4 can the "expected" ratio (3:1) actually be expected. Instead, 54 sibships will have a 1:1 ratio; 12 sibships, a 1:3 ratio; 81 sibships, a 4:0 ratio; and 1 sibship, a 0:4 ratio!

Rather than laboriously enumerating all combinations, we may again use the binomial theorem to calculate the probabilities. In *Dd* × *Dd* marriages, the binomial takes the general form

$$(\tfrac{3}{4}D- + \tfrac{1}{4}dd)^n,$$

with any member of the series of terms equal to

$$\frac{n!}{x!(n-x)!}\cdot(\tfrac{3}{4}D-)^x\cdot(\tfrac{1}{4}dd)^{n-x} = \frac{n!}{x!(n-x)!}\cdot(\tfrac{3}{4})^x\cdot(\tfrac{1}{4})^{n-x}\,[D-^x\cdot dd^{n-x}].$$

An example may demonstrate the usefulness of this formula: The probability that a sibship of 8 children with two *Dd* parents, will consist of 7 *D–* children and 1 *dd* child is

$$\frac{8!}{7!} \cdot \left(\frac{3}{4}\right)^7 \cdot \frac{1}{4} = 8 \cdot \frac{2,187}{65,536} = \frac{2,187}{8,192},$$

or approximately 1/4; the remaining 3/4 of such sibships will be made up of all other combinations of $D-$ and dd children.

It would be instructive to work out a table similar to Table 6 that would list the probabilities of all combinations of $D-$ and dd children from $Dd \times Dd$ marriages in sibships of from 1 to 8.

Ratios in Pooled Data

Dominant Traits. It should now be clear that there are great deviations from expected "ideal" ratios in single families. An obvious way to correct the incomplete picture that study of single families conveys would seem to be to pool many sibships with identical parental genotypes and study them as a single unit. The chance deviations which make certain ratios too large in some, it might be reasoned, would be compensated for by the chance deviations which make the same ratios too small in others. This is fully true for a *dominant* trait, if we pool the offspring of all marriages in which one of the parents has the dominant phenotype. Here, sibships in which the ratio of affected to nonaffected children is greater than 1:1 will be compensated for by sibships in which it is small. Similarly, in extreme cases, sibships consisting only of affected children and those of nonaffected children only will counteract each other.

Even in dominant inheritance, systematic deviations from expected ratios will be encountered if the genotypes of the parents are unknown and the persons studied come from sibships that are detected only because they contain affected individuals. This may be shown by an example dealing with the sex ratio. If we count all the boys and all the girls in a community, the number of each will be nearly the same. If, however, we restrict the inquiry to those families which contain at least 1 girl—by asking, for example, all girls in the community to state the sex ratios in their sibships—a ratio other than 1 ♂ :1 ♀ will be found. Among 2-child families, for example, the ratio of sibships with 2 girls (♀ ♀) to sibships with 1 girl and 1 boy (either ♀ ♂ or ♂ ♀) is 1:2. Consequently, the ratio obtained if these sibships are pooled is 4 girls to 2 boys, or 2:1. A still different ratio is obtained if we begin our inquiry by selecting at random girls of a given age and determine the sex ratio in the sibships of those from 2-child families. Here the chance that a 2-girl sibship will come to notice is twice as great as that a 2-child sibship with 1 girl only will be discovered. Therefore, there will be 2 ♀ ♀ sibships for each ♀ ♂ and ♂ ♀ sibship, and the resulting ratio will be 6 girls to 2 boys, or 3:1.

Ascertainment. This example, in which three different sex ratios were obtained, shows how important the *method of ascertainment*—that is, the method used in gathering data—is in human genetics. The 1:1 ratio of girls to boys was obtained when ascertainment was "complete," that is, based on all available data; the 2:1 ratio, when ascertainment was by "truncate selection," a method that excluded an entire group (here, all families with no girls); and the 3:1 ratio, when ascertainment was by "single selection" of individual girls. Unless the specific method of ascertainment is known and understood, it is difficult or impossible to draw valid conclusions.

Many pedigrees become known when a specific affected individual comes to the attention of a physician or some other investigator. The ascertainment of the family or kindred depends, therefore, on the discovery of the affected individual. He or she is called the *propositus* or *proposita* (or *proband* or *index case*) and is often marked in pedigrees by an arrow or a pointer. Many kindreds are ascertained more than once by independent discoveries of different propositi.

Recessive Traits.   If two parents are heterozygous for a recessive gene, a 3:1 ratio of normal to affected children is to be expected among their offspring. Any individual sibship from such parents may show deviations from the expected ratio—from all normal to all affected—but a pooling of many sibships will have the 3:1 ratio.

Usually, in recessive inheritance of uncommon traits, ascertainment of sibships is not through the parents, who are normal, but through the fact that one or more sibs are affected. Under these circumstances a certain compensatory effect of pooling data still holds, but this compensation is not complete: a systematic error remains. It is due to the sibships from $Dd \times Dd$ parents, in which no affected (dd) children occur in spite of the "ideal" expectation that they will. Sibships from two heterozygous parents, in which all children appear normal ($D-$), make up $(3/4)^n$ of all sibships, where n is the number of sibs. When n = 4, these all-normal sibships constitute 81/256 or nearly 1/3 of all sibships of 4 children (Table 5), and the proportions of all-normal sibships are still higher when there are fewer children.

Ascertainment of sibships through affected sibs misses the all-normal sibships from $Dd \times Dd$ parents (truncate selection). Thus, there is no compensation, when data are pooled, for those sibships which happen to contain too many dd children. Consequently, the ratio of dominants to recessives in pooled data of sibships from heterozygous parents is shifted from the expected 3 $D-$:1 dd value toward a higher value for the dd group. This is shown for 4-child sibships in Table 7. As seen earlier, none of the sibships of 4 $D-$ children—81 out of 256—will be recognized. The 108 sibships with 3 $D-$ and 1 dd children yield 324 and 108; the 54 sibships with 2 $D-$ and 2 dd contribute 108 of each; the 12 sibships with 1 $D-$ and 3 dd add 12 and 36; and the 1 sibship with 4 dd adds 4. This makes a total of 444 $D-$ and 256 dd, or a ratio of 1.734:1, instead of 3:1 (or, stated differently, the fraction of dd individuals is $1/2.734 = 0.366$ instead of $1/4 = 0.25$).

The size of the deviation from the 3:1 ratio in pooled data decreases as the number of children per sibship increases, since the proportion of "lost," all-

TABLE 8. *Observed and Expected Proportions from Heterozygous Parents of Normal (D–) to Affected (dd) Children in Sibships with at Least One Affected.* (Data on albinism from Roberts, 1940; on phenylketonuria from Munro.)

Trait	Sibs per Sibship	D–	dd	Proportion D–:dd Observed	Proportion D–:dd Expected
Albinism	1–4	—	—	0.9:1	—
	5–7	—	—	1.6:1	—
	8 or more	—	—	2.3:1	—
Phenylketonuria	1	—	6	0:1	0:1
	2	6	8	0.75:1	0.75:1
	3	8	10	0.80:1	1.31:1
	4	12	8	1.50:1	1.74:1
	5	22	13	1.69:1	2.05:1
	6	18	12	1.50:1	2.29:1
	7	10	4	2.50:1	2.46:1
	8	16	8	2.00:1	2.60:1
	9	7	2	3.50:1	2.70:1
	10	15	5	3.00:1	2.77:1
	11	9	2	4.50:1	2.83:1
	12	9	3	3.00:1	2.87:1
	13	9	4	2.25:1	2.90:1

normal sibships decreases. Three-fourths of all children from 1-child sibships are normal, and in 9/16 of 2-child sibships both children are normal; but in 8-child sibships only $(3/4)^8$ or 6,561/65,536, approximately 1/10, consist of all normal children, and in 12-child sibships only $(3/4)^{12}$, or about 1 in 32 sibships.

In Table 8, the expectation for pooled data from sibships of varying sizes is compared with data concerning two recessive traits, albinism and phenylketonuria. Normal and albino children were pooled from three groups of sibships, arranged according to size. In the group of smallest sibships (from 1 to 4 sibs) there are more albinos than normals, but with the increasing number of children the proportions approach more and more closely the 3 D–:1 dd ratio. For phenylketonuria, Table 8 shows even more strikingly the rise in the proportion of normals with increasing size of sibship. The occasional rather large differences between observed and expected ratios are probably due to chance.

Methods for Correcting Ratios from Pooled Data. Since, theoretically, a 3:1 ratio is one of the fundamental attributes of simple single factor recessive inheritance, the deviation due to truncate selection stands in the way of recognition of this important type of heredity. However, there are methods to correct for the systematic bias that results from the failure to detect many sibships from heterozygous parents, so that the corrected data may be compared with ideal expectations.

The Simple Sib Method.   One such correction is based on the "simple sib method" proposed by the physician Weinberg (1862–1937), who was one of the first to recognize clearly the peculiar statistical problems of human genetics. The simple sib method corrects for the fact that not enough normal ($D-$) sibs are recorded or, stated in a different way, that relatively too many affected (dd) sibs are recorded. The record, one may say, is biased, because only families with affected children are selected. Often, in surveys of specific populations, all or most affected children are propositi, since they can be ascertained independently of one another, but their normal sibs become known only because they have affected sibs. In order to eliminate the bias due to the "complete truncate selection" of dd individuals, the ratio $D-$:dd should be determined among the sibs of each propositus. Pooled, these data would give the true ratio.

How this method works may be demonstrated by applying it to the example of 4-child sibships (Table 7) in which, without correction, the total observed ratio of $D-$:dd types is 444:256. The sibship correction will be applied to the four different types of sibships:

1. The 108 (out of 256) sibships with 3 $D-$ children and 1 dd child yield $3 \cdot 108 = 324$ $D-$ sibs of affected propositi and no dd sibs of these children.

2. In the 54 sibships with 2 $D-$ and 2 dd children, each of the 2 affected propositi has 2 nonaffected sibs, or $2 \cdot 2 \cdot 54 = 216$ $D-$ sibs, and 1 affected sib, or $2 \cdot 54 = 108$ dd sibs.

3. In the 12 sibships with 1 $D-$ and 3 dd children, each affected propositus has 1 nonaffected sib, or $3 \cdot 1 \cdot 12 = 36$ $D-$ sibs, and 2 affected sibs, or $3 \cdot 2 \cdot 12 = 72$ dd sibs.

4. Finally, in the one sibship with 4 affected propositi, each child has 3 affected sibs, or $4 \cdot 3 = 12$ dd sibs. Adding the four numbers for $D-$ and dd sibs, the values 576 $D-$ and 192 dd are found, or a ratio of 3:1.

The simple sib method may also be applied to our earlier example of the sex ratio as ascertained from 2-child sibships which contain at least 1 girl. Weinberg's method restores the true 1:1 ratio from the "raw" 2:1 ratio in the following way: Instead of being asked the sex ratio in her family, each girl of a 2-child family would be asked the sex of her sib. The result would be that *each* of the 2 girls of the ♀ ♀ families would state that she has 1 sister, and the girl of every ♀ ♂ or ♂ ♀ family would state that she has 1 brother. The total of the recorded sibs would thus show equality of sexes.

The simple sib method has been described not because it is necessarily the most suitable means for the recognition of true ratios—and thus a tool for testing for simple single factor inheritance—but as an illustration of the procedure necessary in any such corrective method. (It should be mentioned that there is confusion in the literature about the naming of the various methods for correcting ratios. Bailey has pointed out that the "sib method" of English authors is not the same as Weinberg's "simple sib method" and that the term "proband method," applied sometimes to the direct method [see following], is used in a different sense from Weinberg's "general proband method.")

The application of the simple sib method presupposes completely unselected sibship material and complete information on each sibship, and these premises are often not fulfilled. One source of bias is that families with many affected children have a higher chance of being recorded than families with only one or few such children. Another results from pooling data from sibships recorded by various authors. Many such pedigrees owe their publication to peculiarities in the number of affected individuals or to other unusual characteristics—they represent a conscious "selection for oddity-interest"—and since, for a general analysis of inheritance, ordinary cases are as valuable as "interesting" ones, their omission tends to give a false picture of a hereditary problem.

A Direct Method Based on an A Priori Expectation.   While the simple sib method attempts to derive a true ratio without any preconceived theory regarding the nature of this ratio, other methods presuppose a specific ratio, e.g., 3:1, and endeavor to determine whether the observed ratio agrees with the a priori expectation; if it does, it is assumed that the observed ratio is of the kind being tested for. Such methods have been devised by Bernstein, Hogben, Haldane, Fisher, Macklin, and others. The procedure is to work out the ratio that should be expected in the observed selected sibship material on the assumption that unbiased data will give the a priori ratio. An application of this method will now be shown for the same type of sibships as before, namely, for sibships from $Dd \times Dd$ marriages which were recognized because they had at least 1 affected dd child.

The a priori expectation for $D-$ children is $p = 3/4$, and that for dd children, $q = 1/4$. We wish to find the fraction of dd children (q') to be expected in the sibships which supply our data.

The sum of (A) the fraction of all sibships in which no affected child appears, and (B) the fraction in which at least 1 appears, is 1. It was shown (p. 134) that fraction A is p^n, where p is the probability of $D-$ children (i.e., $3/4$) and n the number of sibs per family. It follows that fraction B is $(1 - p^n)$.

Affected children make up the proportion q (i.e., $1/4$) of the children from all sibships, detectable and undetectable. Since these affected children are concentrated in the detectable sibships, the proportion q' in these sibships is larger than q; namely,

$$q = q'(1 - p^n).$$

Solving for the desired q', we have

$$q' = \frac{q}{1 - p^n}.$$

p^n = those $\bar{c}$ 0 dd

$1 - p^n$ = those $\bar{c}$ dd

We may apply this formula to 4-child sibships (n = 4). The expected, observable fraction of dd children is

$$q' = \frac{\frac{1}{4}}{1 - (\frac{3}{4})^4} = 0.366.$$

This value agrees with the value which was derived from our enumeration of all types of 4-child sibships (p. 134).

It is often useful to determine the expected average *number* of affected children per sibship instead of the expected observable *fraction*, q'. This number of affected children is obtained by multiplying q' by n, the total number of children in the sibship. It is listed, for families with from 2 to 10 children, in Table 9. A comparison of the actual expectation with the "naïve," uncorrected expectation based on direct use of the probability q = 1/4 shows how great the difference between the two expectations is in the small sibships, and how it decreases with increasing number of children per sibship.

TABLE 9. *Average Number,* q'·n, *of Affected Children in Sibships with at Least One Affected Sib from Dd ×Dd Marriages.* (Total number of children in sibship, n, from 2 to 10. A priori probability q of $dd = 1/4$.) (Bernstein.)

Children in Sibship	n								
	2	3	4	5	6	7	8	9	10
Expectation q'·n	1.143	1.297	1.463	1.640	1.825	2.020	2.222	2.433	2.649
Uncorrected expectation q·n(q = ¼)	0.500	0.750	1.000	1.250	1.500	1.750	2.000	2.250	2.500

We shall, finally, demonstrate the use of the a priori method on data collected from Swedish families in which one or more children from normal parents were afflicted with a special type of progressive epilepsy (myoclonic epilepsy). The genetic hypothesis is that the diseased children are the dd offspring of Dd parents. Affected children were found in 9 sibships, ranging in size from 1 to 9 children. They are listed in the first two columns of Table 10. The third column gives the average number of affected children per sibship expected according to the a priori ratio. The fourth column gives the number obtained when the number of affected children is multiplied by the number of sibships, and it should be compared with the observed number listed in the final column. When we consider the small amount of data involved, observation and expectation diverge little: in fact, the total numbers of expected and observed affected children, 16.666 and 17, agree remarkably well. It may be concluded that myoclonic epilepsy fulfills the condition imposed by the hypothesis that it is based on a simple single recessive gene.

In the preceding paragraphs, we have seen that a 3:1 ratio is *not* to be expected in recessive inheritance if the pooled sibships have been ascertained

TABLE 10.   *Application of the A Priori Method for Determining the Presence of Recessive Inheritance to Myoclonic Epilepsy.* (Data from Bernstein after Lundborg, simplified.)

Size of Sibship (n)	No. of Sibships (x)	q'·n (from Table 9)	Total Affected Expected q'·n·x	Total Affected Observed
1	1	1	1	1
4	1	1.463	1.463	2
5	1	1.640	1.640	2
6	3	1.825	5.475	7
8	1	2.222	2.222	1
9	2	2.433	4.866	4
Total: 54	9		16.666	17

because they include affected children. Before this was recognized, it was mistakenly believed that simple recessive inheritance was proved when pooled sibships gave a 3:1 ratio! Conversely, when the proportion of affected children was found to be higher than 1 in 4, it was—equally mistakenly—thought that simple recessive inheritance was excluded, although an excess of affected sibs was just what would have been expected.

Goodness of Fit of Ratios

We have investigated the varieties of individual sibships expected as a result of chance. The frequencies of sibships with ratios different from any of the ones expected follow binomial distributions. We have seen how pooling sibships and making necessary corrections can result in a ratio equivalent to the expected. It is, however, clear that an expected ratio is a probability fraction and not an absolute value. Even in pooled and corrected data, we do not expect *exact* agreement with, for example, a 1:1 or a 3:1 ratio. Deviations from the expected ratio can be predicted, and their degree estimated quantitatively.

The Probability That a Specific Deviation from Expectation Is Due to Chance.   When an observed ratio deviates from expectation, the question arises whether the deviation should be considered to be due to chance or whether one should assume that some specific cause is responsible for it. In order to decide this question, we calculate the probability that a deviation of the given magnitude may occur purely as a result of chance. If that probability is high, then the observed ratio may be considered compatible with the expected one. If it is low, then the observed ratio is not considered compatible.

Two different questions may be raised regarding an observed ratio which

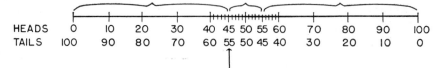

| HEADS | 0 | 10 | 20 | 30 | 40 45 50 55 60 | 70 | 80 | 90 | 100 |
| TAILS | 100 | 90 | 80 | 70 | 60 55 50 45 40 | 30 | 20 | 10 | 0 |

FIG. 74. The range of possible results of flipping a coin one hundred times. The bracket in the center includes those ratios that deviate from 50:50 less than 45:55, or 55:45. The two other brackets include all ratios that deviate from 50:50 as much as, or more than, 45:55 or 55:45.

differs from that expected: First, we may want to know the probability that the observed ratio will occur. Thus, particularly in small samples, one may be interested in determining the probability of finding a *specific* ratio. This kind of question has been dealt with earlier in this chapter, in examples such as that concerning the probability of finding a sibship of 2 affected and 6 nonaffected when the expectation is 1:1. Second, we may want to know the probability of finding a ratio that differs as much from expectation as the observed ratio does. This second way of looking at the deviation divides, so to speak, the whole range of possible deviations into two sections: one includes all possible ratios that are closer to the expected ratio than the observed ratio; the other includes the observed ratio and all possible ratios that are further from expectation than it.

It is the second question which is of interest if we wish to judge whether an observed ratio should be considered a chance deviation from the expected one. This will be apparent if we consider an example: Assume that a coin is tossed 100 times and that 45 heads and 55 tails are counted (Fig. 74). The probability of obtaining exactly this ratio is

$$\frac{100!}{45!55!} \cdot \frac{1}{2^{100}},$$

or about 1 in 20. This is a low probability. Should we, then, conclude that the observed deviation from 50:50 is not due to chance but that some specific cause is responsible for it—for example, an inherently biased coin? This seems to be unreasonable, since the probability of observing any specific ratio in a set of 100 tosses is small, even that of the ideal ratio 50:50 being only about 1 in 13. If one calculates (in a way to be shown), as an alternative, the probability of obtaining a sample which deviates as much from 50:50 as 45:55, or even more, it is found that such deviations occur about once in three series of 100 tosses. This high probability of a deviation as great as, or even greater than, 45:55 appears quite compatible with the hypothesis that the coin was not biased and that the observed ratio deviated from the expected as a result of chance.

How was the last probability calculated? One method would be to add up the probability of occurrence of the observed ratio 45:55 and of all probabilities of occurrence of larger deviations, namely, 44:56, 43:57, 42:58 . . . 0:100. This sum of all probabilities would still have to be multiplied by 2, since the question "What is the probability of obtaining a deviation from 50:50 as great as, or greater than, the observed ratio 45:55?" refers equally to the ratios 45 heads:55 tails and 55 heads:45 tails; 44 heads:56 tails and 56 heads:44 tails; and so on. This elaborate method of calculation is not used in practice. A much simpler procedure, the "chi-square test," will be presented in the following pages.

The Significance of Various Probabilities. What meaning shall we attribute to various probabilities of deviations? It can be calculated that, in a group of sibships totaling 30 individuals, a deviation from a 1:1 ratio as great as, or greater than, 12:18 will be found in about 1 out of 4 cases. Obviously, such a deviation will not be regarded as unusual; therefore, the 12:18 ratio may be considered a chance deviation from the expected 1:1.

Had a ratio of 8:22 been found, calculation would show that a deviation as great as, or greater than, this would occur in only 1 out of about 100 cases. It would be a mistake to conclude from this that the 8:22 ratio *cannot* be a deviation from a 1:1 ratio. The possibility that even the greatest possible deviation is a result of chance, although small, is not excluded, but it must be regarded as improbable. A more probable explanation of the 8:22 ratio would be to assume that it represents a less extreme and, therefore, more probable deviation from some other theoretical ratio, e.g., 1:3. An investigator confronted with the 8:22 ratio would, therefore, retrace the hereditary analysis of his material in order to find out whether the facts in the pedigrees are compatible with some other type of interpretation leading to a theoretical ratio other than 1:1 and closer to that actually observed.

Had a ratio of 10:20 been found, calculation would show that this or a greater deviation from 1:1 would have a probability of about 1 in 15. Obviously, no definite statement about its compatibility with the 1:1 expectation can be made. However, by common agreement, a probability higher than 1/20 that an observed ratio is a chance deviation from an expected one is regarded as signifying that chance is a reasonable cause for the deviation, and a probability lower than 1/20 is interpreted as signifying that the deviation is not the obvious result of chance.

Specifically, observations are said to deviate from expectation "nonsignificantly," in a statistical sense, if the probability that any deviation as great or greater will occur is higher than 1/20 (0.05). If a probability lies between 0.05 and 0.01 (1/100), we speak of statistically "doubtful significance"; and if the probability is lower than 0.01, of statistical "significance." Alternatively, one refers to a result as "significant at the 5 per cent (or 1 per cent) level." The term "significance" denotes that some specific reason or reasons, and not chance, probably underlies such a deviation.

The Chi-square Test of Goodness of Fit. Various tests of significance by means of which the "goodness of fit" of observed ratios can be measured have been devised. Only one of them, the χ^2 test (read: chi-square, Greek letter χ) of Pearson, will be described briefly. It consists of (1) <u>calculating</u> <u>the absolute difference between observed and expected numbers in each</u> <u>class of a given sample</u>; (2) <u>squaring each difference and dividing the square</u> <u>by the number of expected</u>; and <u>(3) adding the figures obtained in (2)</u>. This final sum is called χ^2. It is 0 if there are no differences between observed and expected numbers, and increases with increasing size of the differences. The probability, P, that any deviation of observed from expected ratios is due to chance has been calculated for many values of χ^2 and can be read directly from tables.

The Chi-Square Test Applied to a Sample Consisting of Two Classes. The procedure will be illustrated for the frequency of woolly and nonwoolly hair in sibships in which one of the parents was woolly-haired (p. 93).

	Class 1 (affected)	Class 2 (nonaffected)	Total
Observed	145	130	275
Expected (1:1)	137.5	137.5	275
Absolute difference (observed − expected)	7.5	7.5	

$$\chi^2 = \frac{(\text{obs.}-\text{exp.})^2}{\text{exp.}} + \frac{(\text{obs.}-\text{exp.})^2}{\text{exp.}} = \frac{(7.5)^2}{137.5} + \frac{(7.5)^2}{137.5} = 0.818$$

This value, 0.818, of χ^2 corresponds to a specific probability of obtaining by chance a set of observed results as far from the expected as 145 woolly and 130 nonwoolly, or further. This probability can be obtained by consulting Table 11. The first column of this table is headed "Degrees of Freedom." This expression refers to the fact that if we know only that a given number of observations, say, 275, fall into two or more classes, the number in each class is still undecided ("free"). When, however, the number in Class 1 of a group with only two classes has been determined—in our example, 145—

TABLE 11. *Table of Chi-square.** (Depending on the row in which it is entered, a listed χ^2 value corresponds to the probability given at the top of obtaining, by chance, results deviating from the expectation by as much as, or more than, the observed results.)

Degrees of Freedom	Probability, P				
	.70	.50	.30	.05	.01
1	.15	.45	1.07	3.84	6.63
2	.71	1.39	2.41	5.99	9.21
3	1.42	2.37	3.66	7.81	11.34
4	2.19	3.36	4.88	9.49	13.28
5	3.00	4.35	6.06	11.07	15.09
6	3.83	5.35	7.23	12.59	16.82

* Table 11 is abridged from Table III of Fisher, *Statistical Methods for Research Workers*, Edinburgh: Oliver and Boyd Ltd., by permission of the author and publishers.

the number in Class 2 is fixed, not "free," since it is the difference between the total (275) and the number in Class 1 (145), that is, 130. The number of degrees of freedom in any group consisting of two classes is therefore 1, because only one number is "free," and the degrees of freedom in a group of more than two classes is usually 1 less than the number of classes. In the woolly-nonwoolly study there was only one degree of freedom; so the probability corresponding to the calculated χ^2, 0.818, is to be found in the top row in Table 11. It lies between two values, 0.45 and 1.07. The heading of the table shows that these χ^2 values correspond to the probabilities 0.50 and 0.30, respectively. Thus, the probability of obtaining a χ^2 value of 0.818 or larger lies between these two probabilities. The deviation of observation from expectation is, therefore, statistically nonsignificant, since in from 30 to 50 per cent of all samples of 275 individuals it would be pure chance that the observed ratio would deviate from the expected 1:1 ratio as much as 145:130, or even more. Accordingly, the statistical analysis shows agreement with the hypothesis of dominant inheritance, which is the basis of the 1:1 expectation.

For the sake of accuracy the chi-square test applied to two classes needs a correction when an expected class is smaller than 50, but the correction is usually unimportant unless *the expected class is 5 or smaller*. The correction consists in subtracting 0.5 from each of the two absolute differences between the observed and expected values.

The Chi-Square Test Applied to Samples of More than Two Classes. Genetic data are sometimes subdivided into three or more classes. For example, progeny from marriages between two parents of the genotype $I^A I^B$ belong to three blood groups: A, AB, and B. They are expected in the proportion 1:2:1, and we may want to compare a specific observation with this expectation. The procedure, using the chi-square test, is practically identical with that applied to data which fall into two classes. The only difference is that the calculated value signifies a different probability if it is derived from three instead of two classes.

Three classes permit 2 degrees of freedom for any given number of observations: any of a variety of numbers of these observations may be expected in the first of the classes, and hence it is "free"; even after the number in the first class has been determined, the second class is also "free," since any one of many different numbers of remaining observations may be found in it;

TABLE 12. *Computation of χ^2 for Frequencies of the Three Blood Groups A, AB, and B among 151 Children from AB $\times$ AB Marriages.*

Frequencies	A	AB	B	Total
Observed	39	70	42	151
Expected (1:2:1)	37.75	75.5	37.75	151

$$\chi^2 = \frac{(1.25)^2}{37.75} + \frac{(5.5)^2}{75.5} + \frac{(4.25)^2}{37.75} = 0.920$$

but after the numbers in two classes have been determined, the number in the third class is fixed, because it must be the difference between the total and the sum of the other two classes. An example of the chi-square method applied to three classes is presented in Table 12, where $\chi^2 = 0.920$. This value must be related to the probabilities listed in Table 11 under 2 degrees of freedom. It lies between two values listed there, 0.71 and 1.39, which correspond to probabilities of 0.70 and 0.50. There is, therefore, a probability greater than 0.5, but smaller than 0.7, that deviations as large as those observed, or larger, would occur by chance, and the deviations are statistically nonsignificant.

When more than three classes are studied, the calculated χ^2 value must be related to the values listed in the row of Table 11 that is 1 less than the number of classes.

Comparison between Two Sets of Observations. We have earlier noted (p. 93) that offspring of (A) woolly-haired fathers consisted of 24 woolly and 36 nonwoolly children, and of (B) woolly-haired mothers consisted of 34 woolly and 26 nonwoolly children. Do the two ratios, 24:36 and 34:26, deviate from each other by chance only? In order to answer this question, both observations A and B must be compared with a theoretical expectation. This expectation is not based on any a priori genetic ratio; the problem is, rather, whether the observed ratios deviate significantly from those that would be expected if both sets of observations were samples of the same general population of children with one parent with woolly hair, or, expressed in another way, whether the two observations do not differ from one another significantly ("null hypothesis"). The expected numbers are given in Table 13 and were calculated as follows: There was a total of 58 woolly-haired (Class 1) individuals. If both sets of observations, each of 60 individuals, came from the same general population, the 58 woolly-haired individuals

TABLE 13. *Computation of χ^2 for a Comparison of Two Sets of Observations on Offspring of Parents. One of Whom Is Woolly-haired.*

| | Parents | | Children | | |
	Woolly	Non-woolly	Class 1 Woolly	Class 2 Nonwoolly	Total
Observation A.	Father	Mother	24	36	60
Observation B.	Mother	Father	34	26	60
Total			58	62	120
Expectation A.	Father	Mother	29	31	60
Expectation B.	Mother	Father	29	31	60
Total			58	62	120

$$\chi^2 = \frac{(24-29)^2}{29} + \frac{(34-29)^2}{29} + \frac{(36-31)^2}{31} + \frac{(26-31)^2}{31} = 3.34$$

should ideally have been divided into an equal number from both types of parents, namely, 29. Similarly, the expected division of the 62 nonwoolly-haired (Class 2) individuals from both types of parents would have been 31 and 31.

It is now possible to apply the chi-square test in the same manner as in former examples by calculating the squares of the differences between the four observed and the four expected numbers, dividing each square by the expected number and adding the quotients. The value of χ^2 is 3.34. This comparison has only 1 degree of freedom, since determination of the number in one group fixes the numbers in the three other groups. The 29 individuals of Class 1 expected in set A require that there be 29 from Class 1 in set B because 58 individuals of Class 1 have been observed, and the same 29 individuals of Class 1 in set A require that there be 31 individuals of Class 2 in set A, since that set contains 60 individuals. Finally, that there must be 31 individuals of Class 2 in set B follows rigidly from the observed totals and the single "free" expectation.

The probability for 1 degree of freedom which corresponds to $\chi^2 = 3.34$ lies between 0.30 and 0.05 (Table 11), rather close to the latter. The deviation in proportions of woolly to nonwoolly offspring from the two sets of parents could, therefore, be attributed to chance only.

The two sets of observations on the offspring of woolly-haired parents consisted of equal numbers of individuals. More often than not, we must compare two sets in which the number of observations is different. Many such comparisons will be made in later chapters of this book, and here one of these is chosen for illustration. It is a comparison of frequencies of feeble-mindedness in one or both (A) identical twins and (B) nonidentical twins. As shown in Table 14, there were 219 pairs of twins, 126 identical and 93 nonidentical. In order to test whether the difference between the two sets of data is statistically significant, the expected numbers are calculated by divid-

TABLE 14. *Computation of χ^2 for a Comparison of Two Sets of Observations on Feeble-mindedness in Twins.* (Data from Table 98.)

Twins	Class 1 (both affected)	Class 2 (one affected)	Total
Observation A. Identical	115	11	126
Observation B. Nonidentical	42	51	93
Total	157	62	219
Expectation A. Identical	90	36	126
Expectation B. Nonidentical	67	26	93
Total	157	62	219

$$\chi^2 = \frac{(115-90)^2}{90} + \frac{(42-67)^2}{67} + \frac{(11-36)^2}{36} + \frac{(51-26)^2}{26} = 57.67$$

ing the number of doubly affected pairs, 157, into two numbers that have the same proportion as the two whole samples A and B, namely, 126:93. This yields expectations of 90 and 67 for Class 1 in A and B, respectively, and by simple subtraction, 36 and 26 for Class 2. The calculated χ^2 value is very large, corresponding to an extremely low probability that observations would be so different from expectations if the two kinds of twins were basically alike in regard to feeble-mindedness. The two sets of observations are thus said to differ at a highly significant probability level.

Comparison between any number of sets of observations each of which may contain any number of classes can also be made. The procedure follows from the foregoing discussion. The degrees of freedom to which the obtained value of χ^2 must be related in Table 11 may usually be found by multiplying (number of sets of observations minus one) $\times$ (number of classes minus one): e.g., number of sets of observations is 3, number of classes is 4; therefore, number of degrees of freedom $= (3 - 1) \cdot (4 - 1) = 6$.

This chapter has dealt with some intricate considerations of ratios in small families, ratios in pooled data, and statistical tests of the variability inherent in many phenomena which are influenced by chance. For a more thorough treatment of these topics, one must study books especially devoted to them, such as those by Fisher, Snedecor, Neyman, and other statisticians.

As we look back over these discussions, we may well be impressed by the ingenuity of the human mind, which has been able to overcome some of the difficulties in understanding caused by the smallness of human families and the working of chance.

Problems

49. A man is brachydactylous, his wife normal. If they have ten children, what is the probability of their having: (a) The first, third, fifth, seventh and ninth child brachydactylous, the others normal? (b) Only the first five brachydactylous? (c) Five brachydactylous? (d) All brachydactylous?

50. Two taster parents have a nontaster child. (a) What is the probability of the second child being a nontaster? (b) What is the probability of a sibship of four children in which the first born is a nontaster, the second born a taster, the third born a nontaster, and the fourth born a taster? (c) What proportion of families with four children from heterozygous taster parents will have two tasters and two nontasters?

51. Owing to a recessive lethal condition, a couple's first child is stillborn. After this stillbirth, what is the probability of the couple having: (a) Five conceptions, all resulting in homozygous normal genotypes? (b) Five conceptions, all resulting in viable children? (c) Five conceptions, two of which result in homozygous normal and three in heterozygous children?

52. A man is brachydactylous, his wife is normal. Both are tasters, but both of their mothers were nontasters. (a) Give the genotypes of the couple. If they have 8 children, what is the probability: (b) Of no brachydactylous child among them? (c) Of all being brachydactylous? (d) Of all being nontasters? (e) Of all

being tasters? (f) Of four being brachydactylous? (g) Of four being tasters? (h) Of the first, third, fifth, seventh being brachydactylous and nontasters, and the others having normal fingers and being tasters?

53. Assume that the probability of the birth of a boy or a girl is $1/2$. What are the probabilities of the following proportions of births in a hospital: (a) A total of 10 boys to 10 girls? (b) A total of 15 of one sex to 5 of the other sex? (c) At least 2 girls in a total of 30?

In Problems 54–56, assume that no crossing over occurs.

54. What is the probability of a child inheriting only one chromosome from his paternal grandmother?

55. What is the probability of a man inheriting 2 of his paternal and all of his maternal autosomes from his grandmothers?

56. What is the probability of a child inheriting 11 of his 22 paternal autosomes from his grandmother?

57. Assume that uncorrected, pooled data of sibships with at least one albino child from normal parents gave a ratio of normal to albino of 1.8:1 in the preceding century, but of only 0.8:1 in the present one. Assume that the data are reliable and that the difference between the two ratios is statistically significant. What cause can be suggested for the occurrence of these ratios and their difference?

58. What proportion of sibships with two children will have no boys?

59. What proportion of boys from two-children sibships will have a brother? A sister?

60. What sex ratio do you expect from a random sample of 27 two-children sibships each of which contains at least one boy?

61. In a certain population, it is found that from normal parents there are 50 sibships containing at least one albino. Of these sibships, 6 consist of one child only, 7 of two children, and 37 of three children. (a) How many of each type of sibship would be expected to have one, two, or three albinos? (b) What ratio of normal to affected would be expected from pooling all data?

62. Pooling of sibships from several marriages of woolly-haired × normal parents yields 37 woolly-haired and 53 normal children. Calculate χ^2 and P. Do you regard these data as conforming to expectation?

63. In a group of children, there are 15 girls and 25 boys. (a) Is this a significant deviation from an expected 1:1 ratio? (b) Had there been ten times as many children in the same proportions, what would your answer have been?

64. If you expect a 3:1 ratio in the offspring of parents both known to be heterozygous, but observe 14:1 in a sibship, would you regard this deviation as significant?

65. The frequency of tasters in a general population is 70 per cent. In a specific group of 150 people, 135 were tasters. Is the deviation significant?

66. Of the 15 grandchildren of a certain individual, 4 are college graduates. In the general population the proportion of college graduates in the social class of this family is only 10 per cent. Does the family under discussion represent a significant deviation from general expectation?

67. The frequency of illegitimate children in the white population of Mississippi in 1957 was 12.8 per cent. If, in a certain town, 25 per cent of 20 children born were illegitimate, would you regard this as a significant increase?

68. Among 240 families with 3 children each, the children in 50 of them were either all girls or all boys. Compare this observation with the expectation, based on a sex ratio of 1:1, and judge the significance of the deviation.

69. In two samples each of 1,000 African Pygmies, two investigators found that 270 in one sample and 300 in the other belonged to the blood group O. Are these results consistent with each other?

70. Among 100 Chinese from Canton, 6 were AB; among 100 Chinese from Szechwan, only 3 were AB. Do these data indicate a significant difference?

71. In classes at the University of California in Berkeley, there were 178 whites who could taste PTC and 68 who could not. There were also 36 oriental tasters and 4 nontasters. What is the statistical significance of the difference in taster frequency between the two groups?

References

Bailey, N. T. J., 1951. A classification of methods of ascertainment and analysis in estimating the frequencies of recessives in man. *Ann. Eugen.*, **16:** 223–225.

Bernstein, F., 1929. *Variations- und Erblichkeitsstatistik.* Hdbch. Vererbgswiss. 1C. 96 pp. Gebrüder Bornträger, Berlin.

Fisher, R. A., 1934. The effect of methods of ascertainment upon the estimation of frequencies. *Ann Eugen.*, **6:** 13–25.

———,1954. *Statistical Methods for Research Workers.* 12th ed. 361 pp. Harper, New York.

Haldane, J. B. S., 1932. A method for investigating recessive characters in man. *J. Genet.*, **25:** 251–255.

Hogben, L., 1931. The genetic analysis of familial traits. I. Single gene substitutions. *J. Genet.* **25:** 97–112.

Kempthorne, O., 1954. *Statistics and Mathematics in Biology.* 632 pp. Iowa State College Press, Ames.

Mather, K., 1947. *Statistical Analysis in Biology.* 2nd ed. 267 pp. Interscience, New York.

Morton, N. E., 1958. Segregation analysis in human genetics. *Science,* **127:** 79–80.

Munro, T. A., 1947. Phenylketonuria: data on forty-seven British families. *Ann. Eugen.,* **14:** 60–88.

Neyman, J., 1950. *First Course in Probability and Statistics.* 350 pp. Henry Holt, New York.

Snedecor, G. W., 1946. *Statistical Methods.* 485 pp. Iowa State College Press, Ames.

Steinberg, A. G., 1959. Methodology in human genetics. *J. Med. Ed.,* **34:** 315–334 (also *Am. J. Human Genet.,* **11,** 2 Part 2: 315–334), see pp. 315–323.

Weinberg, W., 1912. Weitere Beiträge zur Theorie der Vererbung. 4. Über Methode und Fehlerquellen der Untersuchung auf Mendelsche Zahlen beim Menschen. *Arch. Rass. u. Ges. Biol.,* **9:** 165–174.

———, 1927. Mathematische Grundlagen der Probandenmethode. *Zeitschr. Abstgs. u. Vererbgsl.,* **48:** 179–228.

CHAPTER 10

THE HARDY-WEINBERG
LAW

It is obvious that individuals owe their genotypes to their parents. It is somewhat less obvious, but equally true, that the kinds of genotypes and their frequencies in any one generation of a particular group of persons— we call such a group a *population*—depends on the kinds of genotypes and their frequencies that are found in all parents in the preceding generation of the population. If, among these parents, the three genotypes AA, AA', and $A'A'$ occur, the proportion with any one genotype will depend on the frequency of the two alleles. Thus, for instance, if most of the alleles are A, and only a few A', we would expect more persons to be AA than AA' or $A'A'$. In the present chapter, we shall consider such questions as these: What are the proportions of different genotypes in a population? How will the proportions existing in one generation be related to those in the next generation?

Selective Forces. The answers to these questions will depend on a number of variables. Among these, selective agents may play a role. If a certain allele should lead to a serious defect in persons endowed with it, such persons may be more likely to die before they become parents than persons without it; or their chances of marrying may be decreased; or, if they marry, the number of children they produce may be below the average. As a result, there will be fewer persons in the next generation who have the allele with the unfavorable effect than there would have been had it not had the adverse effect.

An allele with a low survival property does not necessarily produce a phenotype which is defective. A genetic endowment that enables a man or woman to achieve unusual intellectual or artistic distinction often seems to be accompanied by a reduced rate of reproduction.

Mutation. Mutations also may affect the composition of the population. If inheritable changes from *A* to *A'* occur in the germ cells of the parent generation, then the frequency of specific genotypes in the next generation will depend not only on their frequency in the preceding one but also on the mutation rate *A* → *A'*. If mutations should occur not only in one direction but also in reverse (*A* ← *A'*), both rates would have to be taken into account in predicting the genotypes and their proportions in the next generation.

Systems of Mating. Still another factor, sometimes referred to as the system of mating, is significant. Given individuals of three genotypes and assuming that all three types of persons are equally likely to marry and have offspring, those of any one genotype may select their spouses without showing preference for any one of the three genotypes, or they may prefer spouses of a particular genotype. The former type of mating is called _random mating_, or _panmixis;_ the latter *nonrandom,* or *assortative, mating.*

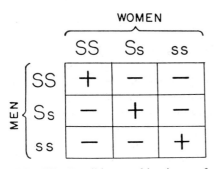

FIG. 75. Possible combinations of short, medium-sized, and tall spouses. Plus sign indicates marriages between identical genotypes, minus sign between nonidentical.

Assortative mating is not uncommon. One of the best-known examples involves body size: tall people prefer to marry tall ones; short people, short ones. Since body size is dependent on specific genetic constitutions, like genotypes occur more often among couples than would be expected by chance (Fig. 75). If we assume that assortative mating by body size is absolute, so that all marriages are between genotypically identical spouses, and if (in deliberate oversimplification) we write the genotypes of short, medium, and tall people as *SS, Ss,* and *ss,* it is obvious that the marriages *SS × SS* and *ss × ss* will give rise to *SS* and *ss* homozygotes only, while *Ss × Ss* will lead to *SS, Ss,* and *ss* children in the ratio 1/4:2/4:1/4. The total number of heterozygotes (*Ss*) in the children's generation will then be equal to one-half of the children issuing from marriages between heterozygotes, and, if the sizes of the parental and filial generations are the same, there will be only one-half as many heterozygous children as parents in the population. Any system of mating other than this absolute assortative mating will lead to a higher proportion of heterozygotes, since, in addition to the *Ss × Ss* marriages, marriages between unlike spouses will also produce heterozygotes. The matings *SS × ss* will produce heterozygotes only, and in the mating *SS × Ss* and *ss × Ss* half of the offspring will be heterozygous. Thus, a union between an *Ss* and either of the two other genotypes will produce the same number of heterozygotes as a union between two *Ss,* and unions between *SS* and *ss* will lead to still more heterozygotes.

Assortative mating, on the contrary, leads to fewer heterozygotes in each successive generation, since only one-half of the children from $Ss \times Ss$ unions are Ss, like their parents.

Assortative mating has been demonstrated for traits within the range of normality, such as body size and intelligence (as measured by test performance; see p. 585), as well as for such abnormal traits as deaf-mutism, and, though not conclusively, a mental disease (schizophrenia). The assortative mating demonstrated is never absolute and consists of a limited preference for similar partners. Of course, even in random mating, marriages of persons with the same specific traits are bound to occur, but the frequency of such marriages is no higher than expected by chance.

Besides preference for similar marriage partners (positive assortative mating, or *homogamy*), there seems also to be preference for opposite types (negative assortative mating) among persons with certain traits, or even an aversion to persons with the same trait. Possibly this is true of red-headed persons, since marriages between two of them seem to be rarer than would be expected from random mating—but no careful studies have been conducted to verify this supposition.

In spite of the fact that individuals are, in general, highly aware of the factor of conscious choice in the selection of their marriage partners, such choice does not extend to numerous hereditary conditions. This is true when the differences between the phenotypic expression of the different genotypes either remain unknown or are of no importance to the people concerned. Examples of such differences are the blood groups, or the common situations in which one genotype, $A'A'$, is extremely rare, and the other two, AA and AA', because of dominance, are indistinguishable, so that preferential mating in the AA-AA' population is not even possible.

Random mating is, therefore, of very wide occurrence. In the present chapter its consequences for the composition of populations will be discussed, using for our example the simplest situation, namely, one in which selection for survival or reproductive ability plays no role, and in which mutations are absent.

The Results of Random Mating

Mixture of Equal Numbers of AA and A'A'.   Let us assume that a certain population consists of AA individuals only, and that another population is made up exclusively of $A'A'$ persons. Let these two populations be of equal size, and let them mix and form a new population in which random mating occurs. What will be the genotypes and their proportions among the children of this panmictic group?

The children will come from four different types of marriages:

$AA \, ♀ \times AA \, ♂$ $A'A' \, ♀ \times AA \, ♂$

$AA \, ♀ \times A'A' \, ♂$ $A'A' \, ♀ \times A'A' \, ♂$

Since the two genotypes are assumed to be equally common, it follows that, with random mating, the four kinds of marriages are also equally common.

It does not make any difference in final results whether, in marriages of unlike genotypes, the female or the male has one or the other genetic constitution. We may, therefore, simplify our enumeration, letting a fraction indicate the proportion of all marriages which each specific type represents:

$$
\left\{
\begin{array}{l}
\frac{1}{4}AA \times AA \\
\frac{1}{2}AA \times A'A' \\
\frac{1}{4}A'A' \times A'A'
\end{array}
\right.
$$

It is important to understand why marriages of unlike types are twice as common as marriages of either one of the two like types. One way of making this clear is provided by our enumeration of all four types of marriages, which shows two between unlike types and only one between each kind of like types. Another approach is: For each genotype, there is only one way in which both spouses are alike, but there are two ways in which they are unlike—the first spouse may be of type 1 and the second of type 2, or the first of type 2 and the second of type 1. Still another method of showing the relationship makes use of the checkerboard scheme as given in Table 15.

TABLE 15. *Types and Frequencies of Marriages in a Random-mating Population Consisting of Equal Numbers of Two Homozygous Allelic Genotypes.*

		Women	
		$\frac{1}{2}AA$	$\frac{1}{2}A'A'$
Men $\left\{\begin{array}{l} \frac{1}{2}AA \\ \frac{1}{2}A'A' \end{array}\right.$	$\frac{1}{2}AA$	$\frac{1}{4}AA \times AA$	$\frac{1}{4}A'A' \times AA$
	$\frac{1}{2}A'A'$	$\frac{1}{4}AA \times A'A'$	$\frac{1}{4}A'A' \times A'A'$

Having established the types of marriages and their relative frequencies, we can now find the genotypes of children and their proportions in the population. We assume, of course, that the average number of children from each marriage type is the same. Marriages $AA \times AA$, one-quarter of all marriages, yield AA children only; consequently, one-quarter of all children are of this type. Similarly, $A'A' \times A'A'$ marriages yield another quarter, all $A'A'$ children. The $AA \times A'A'$ marriages produce AA' offspring, and since these marriages constitute one-half of all marriages, one-half of all children are theirs. Adding all progeny, we obtain:

Marriages		Offspring		
Type	Frequency			
$AA \times AA$	$\frac{1}{2} \cdot \frac{1}{2}$	$\frac{1}{4}AA$		
$AA \times A'A'$	$2 \cdot \frac{1}{2} \cdot \frac{1}{2}$		$\frac{1}{2}AA'$	
$A'A' \times A'A'$	$\frac{1}{2} \cdot \frac{1}{2}$			$\frac{1}{4}A'A'$
Sum of all marriages	1	$\frac{1}{4}AA + \frac{1}{2}AA' + \frac{1}{4}A'A'$		

Our conclusion is that random mating leads to all three possible genotypes in the proportion 1:2:1.

What proportion of these genotypes will be found in the next generation, after further random mating? We may investigate this problem by enumerating again all types of marriages, their relative frequencies, and their offspring:

Marriages		Offspring
Type	Frequency	
$AA \times AA$	$\frac{1}{4} \cdot \frac{1}{4}$	$\frac{1}{16}AA$
$AA \times AA'$	$2 \cdot \frac{1}{4} \cdot \frac{1}{2}$	$\frac{1}{8}AA + \frac{1}{8}AA'$
$AA \times A'A'$	$2 \cdot \frac{1}{4} \cdot \frac{1}{4}$	$\frac{1}{8}AA'$
$AA' \times AA'$	$\frac{1}{2} \cdot \frac{1}{2}$	$\frac{1}{16}AA + \frac{1}{8}AA' + \frac{1}{16}A'A'$
$AA' \times A'A'$	$2 \cdot \frac{1}{2} \cdot \frac{1}{4}$	$\frac{1}{8}AA' + \frac{1}{8}A'A'$
$A'A' \times A'A'$	$\frac{1}{4} \cdot \frac{1}{4}$	$\frac{1}{16}A'A'$
Sum of all marriages:	1	$\frac{1}{4}AA + \frac{1}{2}AA' + \frac{1}{4}A'A'$

The types and proportions of children in the second generation of random mating have remained unchanged! Consequently, these proportions of genotypes will remain the same in all successive generations, provided that no changes in the system of mating occur. (Here, of course, we disregard the fact that the frequency of each type of marriage may vary slightly from the expected figure and that the average number of children from each may not be exactly the same.)

Mixture of AA and $A'A'$ in Ratio 9:1.   We have followed a population consisting originally of equal numbers of AA and $A'A'$ individuals. It may be thought that the final result, the consistent proportions of the three genotypes, AA, AA', and $A'A'$, is due to the special "Mendelian" setup of the original matings, $AA \times A'A'$. This, however, is not true. Although the actual proportions of the three genotypes will depend on the proportions of types present at the beginning, the constancy in the composition of later generations is determined by a law that has general validity. Before deriving this general law, we shall consider one more special case. Let us assume that the original mixed population consists of 90 per cent (9/10) AA and 10 per cent (1/10) $A'A'$ persons. Under these circumstances the frequency of each type of marriage and the resulting children will be:

Marriages		Offspring
Type	Frequency	
$AA \times AA$	$\frac{9}{10} \cdot \frac{9}{10}$	$\frac{81}{100}AA$
$AA \times A'A'$	$2 \cdot \frac{9}{10} \cdot \frac{1}{10}$	$\frac{18}{100}AA'$
$A'A' \times A'A'$	$\frac{1}{10} \cdot \frac{1}{10}$	$\frac{1}{100}A'A'$
Sum of all marriages:	1	$\frac{81}{100}AA + \frac{18}{100}AA' + \frac{1}{100}A'A'$

All three genotypes occur among the children, but not, this time, in any well-known proportions.

In the next generation, the following results are to be expected:

Marriages		Offspring
Type	Frequency	
$AA \times AA$	$\frac{81}{100} \cdot \frac{81}{100}$	$\frac{6561}{10000}AA$
$AA \times AA'$	$2 \cdot \frac{81}{100} \cdot \frac{18}{100}$	$\frac{1458}{10000}AA + \frac{1458}{10000}AA'$
$AA \times A'A'$	$2 \cdot \frac{81}{100} \cdot \frac{1}{100}$	$\frac{162}{10000}AA'$
$AA' \times AA'$	$\frac{18}{100} \cdot \frac{18}{100}$	$\frac{81}{10000}AA + \frac{162}{10000}AA' + \frac{81}{10000}A'A'$
$AA' \times A'A'$	$2 \cdot \frac{18}{100} \cdot \frac{1}{100}$	$\frac{18}{10000}AA' + \frac{18}{10000}A'A'$
$A'A' \times A'A'$	$\frac{1}{100} \cdot \frac{1}{100}$	$\frac{1}{10000}A'A'$
Sum of all marriages:	1	$\frac{8100}{10000}AA + \frac{1800}{10000}AA' + \frac{100}{10000}A'A'$

We see that the proportions of the three genotypes have remained unchanged from one generation to the next. They are still 81 AA:18 AA':1 $A'A'$.

Mixture of AA and $A'A'$ in Ratio p:q. To establish the general law, we designate the proportion of AA individuals in the original population by p, and the proportion of $A'A'$ individuals by q. It is obvious that $p + q = 1$, since the two kinds of people together make up the whole group. We then obtain:

Marriages		Offspring
Type	Frequency	
$AA \times AA$	p^2	p^2AA
$AA \times A'A'$	$2pq$	$2pqAA'$
$A'A' \times A'A'$	q^2	$q^2A'A'$
Sum of all marriages:		Sum of all offspring:
$p^2 + 2pq + q^2 = (p + q)^2 = 1^2 = 1$		$p^2AA + 2pqAA' + q^2A'A'$

Thus, the first generation produced by random marriage of the two original populations contains the three genotypes AA, AA', and $A'A'$ in the proportion p^2:$2pq$:q^2.

Random mating among the individuals of the offspring generation leads to the following marriages and their offspring:

Marriages		Offspring
Type	Frequency	
$AA \times AA$	$p^2 \cdot p^2$	p^4AA
$AA \times AA'$	$2 \cdot p^2 \cdot 2pq$	$2p^3qAA + 2p^3qAA'$
$AA \times A'A'$	$2 \cdot p^2 \cdot q^2$	$2p^2q^2AA'$
$AA' \times AA'$	$2pq \cdot 2pq$	$p^2q^2AA + 2p^2q^2AA' + p^2q^2A'A'$
$AA' \times A'A'$	$2 \cdot 2pq \cdot q^2$	$2pq^3AA' + 2pq^3A'A'$
$A'A' \times A'A'$	$q^2 \cdot q^2$	$q^4A'A'$

By addition, the proportion of all AA offspring is found to be $p^4 + 2p^3q + p^2q^2$, which is equal to $p^2(p^2 + 2pq + q^2) = p^2(p + q)^2$. Since $p + q = 1$, this term reduces to p^2. Similarly, the proportion of AA' offspring is $2p^3q + 4p^2q^2 + 2pq^3 = 2pq(p^2 + 2pq + q^2) = 2pq$, and the proportion of $A'A'$ offspring is $p^2q^2 + 2pq^3 + q^4 = q^2(p^2 + 2pq + q^2) = q^2$. Thus, the proportions of the three genotypes have remained the same as in the preceding generation, i.e., $p^2:2pq:q^2$.

Allele Frequencies and the Hardy-Weinberg Law. Having arrived at this conclusion by a consideration of the kinds and proportions of various marriages, we shall now investigate the same problem—that of the constitution of a random-mating population—by a less familiar but really much simpler method. The essential biological entities in the origin of a generation are not the individual parental pairs, but the gametes supplied by them—the eggs and sperm. Random mating primarily signifies random union of different types of germ cells in the process of fertilization. We can, therefore, determine the composition of a population simply by enumerating the kinds and relative frequencies of the gametes produced by the preceding generation and by finding out how frequently the different combinations of genotypes are formed in fertilization. In a population made up of individuals with A and A' in any possible combination, A and A' gametes will be produced. The relative frequencies of these gametes will be the same as the relative frequencies of the alleles A and A'. The allele frequencies in a population may lie anywhere between two extremes: in the first, $A = 1$ and $A' = 0$ (i.e., all individuals are AA); in the other, $A = 0$ and $A' = 1$ (i.e., all individuals are $A'A'$). In the three examples of mixed populations which have been considered in the preceding pages, the frequencies were:

1. Equal numbers of AA and $A'A'$ individuals, representing equal frequencies of A and A' alleles in the original population. Expressed in decimal fractions, the frequency of A is 0.5 (1/2), and A' likewise 0.5.
2. Ninety per cent AA and 10 per cent $A'A'$ individuals in the original population. Thus, the proportion of A and A' alleles is 9:1: i.e., the frequency of A is 0.9; of A', 0.1.
3. Frequency of original AA individuals p; of $A'A'$ individuals, q. Therefore, frequencies of A and A' alleles are p and q, respectively.

We see that p and q signify a character of a population much more fundamental than the original proportions of homozygotes in a mixture of two groups homozygous for different alleles (Fig. 76). Rather, they represent the relative frequencies of the two alleles present in the mixed population, regardless of how these alleles are distributed among the individuals in the population. The allele frequency of A or A' is 0.5, not only in a population in which half of all people are AA and the other half $A'A'$, but also in one in which, for example, three-sevenths are AA, one-seventh AA', and three-sevenths $A'A'$; in one in which one-eighth is AA, six-eighths AA', and

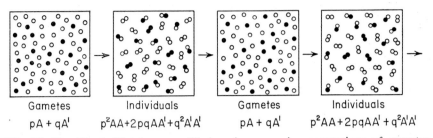

Gametes	Individuals	Gametes	Individuals
$pA + qA'$	$p^2AA + 2pqAA' + q^2A'A'$	$pA + qA'$	$p^2AA + 2pqAA' + q^2A'A'$

FIG. 76. The Hardy-Weinberg equilibrium in successive generations of gametes and individuals of a population with allele frequencies p for A, and q for A'.

one-eighth $A'A';$ or in one in which every individual is AA' (Fig. 77, generation 0). Each of these different populations, after one generation of random mating, will have the *same* composition: AA individuals will originate by fertilization of A eggs by A sperm in the frequency $1/2 \cdot 1/2 = 1/4$; AA' individuals, by fertilization of A eggs by A' sperm and of A' eggs by A sperm in the frequency $2 \cdot 1/2 \cdot 1/2 = 1/2$; and $A'A'$ individuals, by fertilization of A' eggs by A' sperm in the frequency $1/2 \cdot 1/2 = 1/4$ (Fig. 77, generation 1). Even an infinite number of populations containing various proportions of the three genotypes will fit the general allele frequencies, p and q. Again, each of these different populations, after one generation of random mating, will have the same composition: AA individuals in the frequency p^2, AA' individuals in the frequency $2pq$, and $A'A'$ individuals in the frequency q^2.

It is now obvious, without further deductions, that the next and all future generations will repeat the $p^2 + 2pq + q^2$ composition of the first randomly produced generation. Since both preferential survival of one or the other allele and mutation were excluded in this discussion of random mating, the relative frequencies of the alleles will remain the same, namely, p and q. In any generation, therefore, pA and qA' eggs would be met by pA

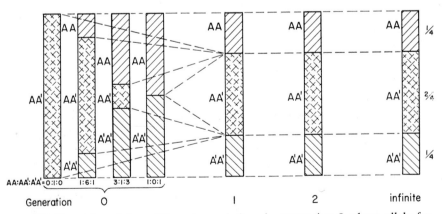

FIG. 77. Examples of four different populations in generation 0 whose allele frequencies p_A and $q_{A'}$ are 1/2 each. Attainment of the Hardy-Weinberg proportions in one generation of panmixis.

and qA' sperm, $(pA + qA') \cdot (pA + qA') = (pA + qA')^2$, and the composition of the resulting population would be $p^2AA + 2pqAA' + q^2A'A'$. The constancy, for later generations, of the specific proportion $1/4:2/4:1/4$ ($1:2:1$) is shown on the right side of Figure 77.

As long as the allele frequencies p and q remain unchanged, a random-mating population in which the three genotypes occur in the proportions $p^2:2pq:q^2$ is said to be *in equilibrium,* since even if a temporary intervention of assortative mating or some other disturbance causes a different proportion of the three genotypes, AA, AA', and $A'A'$, to be produced, future generations will return to this proportion. These facts were independently discovered in 1908 by the mathematician Hardy and the physician Weinberg. The formula $p^2AA + 2pqAA' + q^2A'A'$ and its implications are known as the Hardy-Weinberg Law, which states that a population in which the two alleles A and A' occur in the frequencies p and q will consist, after one generation of random mating, of the three genotypes AA, AA', and $A'A'$ in the equilibrium proportion $p^2:2pq:q^2$.

Human Populations and the Hardy-Weinberg Law

The MN Blood Groups. The red blood cells of an individual carry on their surfaces a variety of chemical substances called *antigens*. Different individuals may possess either the same or different antigens. The next chapter will give a more detailed description of the different antigens and of the methods of recognizing them. Here, for an application of the Hardy-Weinberg Law to human populations, we shall select two specific antigens, M and N, and simply state that there are three kinds of persons: those who have M, others who have N, and still others who have both M and N.

Genetics of MN Blood Groups. Family data show that these blood groups are determined genetically. Inheritance is by the transmission of a single pair of alleles which will be labeled L^M and L^N, though it has been customary to use the letters M and N not only for the antigens of the blood cells, but also for the alleles responsible for the antigens. Table 16 shows the results

TABLE 16. *Heredity of MN Blood Groups in 286 Families.* (After Wiener.)

Parents		No. of	Offspring*		
Phenotypes	Genotypes	Families	M	MN	N
M × M	$L^M L^M \times L^M L^M$	24	98	—	—
N × N	$L^N L^N \times L^N L^N$	6	—	—	27
M × N	$L^M L^M \times L^N L^N$	30	—	43	—
M × MN	$L^M L^M \times L^M L^N$	86	183	196	—
N × MN	$L^N L^N \times L^M L^N$	71	—	156	167
MN × MN	$L^M L^N \times L^M L^N$	69	71	141	63

* Two exceptions, probably caused by illegitimacy, have been omitted.

TABLE 17. *Frequencies of MN Blood Groups in Different Populations.* (Wiener.)

No. of Individuals	Population		Percentages of Blood Groups			Allele Frequencies	
			M	MN	N	L^M(p)	L^N(q)
6,129	Whites	obs.	29.16	49.58	21.26	0.540	0.460
	(U. S.)	exp.	29.16	49.68	21.16	—	—
278	Negroes	obs.	28.42	49.64	21.94	0.532	0.468
	(U. S.)	exp.	28.35	49.89	21.86	—	—
205	Indians	obs.	60.00	35.12	4.88	0.776	0.224
	(U. S.)	exp.	60.15	34.81	5.04	—	—
569	Eskimos (E.	obs.	83.48	15.64	0.88	0.913	0.087
	Greenland)	exp.	83.35	15.89	0.76	—	—
504	Ainus	obs.	17.86	50.20	31.94	0.430	0.570
		exp.	18.45	49.01	32.34	—	—
730	Australian	obs.	3.00	29.6	67.4	0.178	0.882
	aborigines	exp.	3.17	29.26	67.57	—	—

of the six possible kinds of marriages. If both parents are type M, all children are M, and type N parents have N children only. Marriages of M and N individuals lead to MN children exclusively. M and MN spouses have one-half M and one-half MN children; marriages of N and MN lead to one-half N and one-half MN offspring; and, finally, MN and MN parents have children of all blood types in the proportion 1/4M:1/2MN:1/4N. Clearly, the phenotypes M and N are homozygotes $L^M L^M$ and $L^N L^N$, respectively, and the heterozygote $L^M L^N$ has the codominant phenotype MN.

Proportions of MN Blood Groups. If the principle of random mating, as expressed in the Hardy-Weinberg Law, is valid for M and N blood groups, the proportions of M, MN, and N individuals in a population should conform to the formula $p^2:2pq:q^2$. This expectation may be tested by comparison with the proportions of the three blood groups actually observed. These proportions in six different populations are listed in Table 17. It is seen that the frequencies vary from one population to another, and hence each population provides independent material with which to test whether expectation and observation agree with each other.

The Frequencies of the Alleles L^M and L^N. In order to test this, it is necessary to find the frequencies of the alleles L^M (p) and L^N (q). They are easily derived from the frequencies of M, MN, and N individuals. Each

M individual represents two L^M alleles; each N individual, two L^N alleles; and each MN individual, one L^M and one L^N allele. The total number of L^M alleles is, therefore, twice the number of M individuals plus the number of MN individuals. Correspondingly, the number of L^N alleles is twice the number of N individuals plus the number of MN's.

The total number of alleles in a population is twice the number of individuals. It then follows that the frequency p of the allele L^M, expressed as a fraction of all alleles, is

$$p = \frac{2\overline{M} + \overline{MN}}{2(\overline{M} + \overline{MN} + \overline{N})},$$

where $\overline{M}$, $\overline{MN}$, and $\overline{N}$ signify the relative frequencies of the three blood groups observed in the population. Expressed in percentages, as in Table 17,

$$\overline{M} + \overline{MN} + \overline{N} = 100,$$

so that

$$p = \frac{\overline{M} + \frac{1}{2}\overline{MN}}{100}. \tag{1}$$

Similarly, the frequency of allele L^N is

$$q = \frac{\overline{N} + \frac{1}{2}\overline{MN}}{100}. \tag{2}$$

This frequency can also be derived from the formula $p + q = 1$, which yields $q = 1 - p$ (i.e., substracting the frequency of L^M from 1).

The allele frequencies p and q may also be obtained in a different way. Since, according to the Hardy-Weinberg Law, the frequency of $L^M L^M$ homozygotes (M) is p^2,

$$p = \sqrt{\overline{M}}, \tag{3}$$

and correspondingly

$$q = \sqrt{\overline{N}}. \tag{4}$$

Using equations (3) and (4) is, however, less efficient than using (1) and (2), since (3) and (4) do not take into account the information obtainable from the MN heterozygotes.

By applying formulas (1) and (2), the allele frequencies p and q have been found for each of the six populations listed in Table 17. Among the whites, for example, the frequency p of allele L^M is

$$\frac{29.16 + (\frac{1}{2} \times 49.58)}{100} = 0.54,$$

and the frequency q of allele L^N is $(1 - p) = 0.46$. These allele frequencies are given in the final column of the table.

The MN Blood Groups and the Hardy-Weinberg Law.   The frequencies of the three blood groups M, MN, and N that are expected according to

TABLE 18. *"Observed" and Expected Frequencies of the MN Blood Groups in an "Artificial" Population.*

No. of Individuals		Percentages of Blood Groups			Allele Frequencies	
		M	MN	N	L^M(p)	L^N(q)
1,000	obs.	56	33	11	0.725	0.275
	exp.	52.6	39.8	7.6	—	—

the Hardy-Weinberg Law are calculated from the values found for p and q. Thus, among the whites, $p^2 = (0.54)^2 = 0.2916$, $2pq = 2 \cdot 0.54 \cdot 0.46 = 0.4968$, and $q^2 = (0.46)^2 = 0.2116$. This expected distribution of the three blood groups agrees well with that observed, and similarly close agreement is shown for the other populations (Table 17). Though the gene frequencies p and q vary in different populations, the ratio $q^2:2pq:p^2$ is closely approximated within each population. This indicates that the MN groups in the populations are derived from random mating in preceding generations.

The significance of this finding will be appreciated more clearly if we consider an artificially constructed population. Let us assume that an investigator has found a population of 1,000 individuals that consists of about 56 per cent M, 33 per cent MN, and 11 per cent N persons. In this population, the frequency of the allele L^M (p), is $0.56 + (1/2 \cdot 33) = 0.725$, and that of L^N (q) is 0.275. Under random mating, the allele frequencies should be reflected in the proportions of phenotypes of M (p^2), which is 52.3 per cent; of MN ($2pq$), which is 39.9 per cent; and of N (q^2), which is 7.6 per cent. In this population, the expectations do not conform closely to the observed frequencies (Table 18), and a chi-square test would indicate an extremely small probability that the deviation is due to chance. It may therefore be considered that the allele frequency test has established that the population did not arise from random mating in the preceding generation. Indeed, the artificial population was obtained by combining data from equal numbers of American whites and Eskimos from East Greenland. Within each of these groups, the Hardy-Weinberg Law holds true, as shown in Table 17, but the artificial mixture is not a result of random mating and does not obey theory. It can be predicted, however, that after a single generation of random mating the offspring of such a mixture would have approximately the expected proportions listed in Table 18. This example shows the importance of the Hardy-Weinberg formula in finding out whether a population is interbreeding panmictically or whether it consists of subgroups that are more or less separated reproductively. Such subgroups are known as *isolates*.

The Proportions of Genotypes in Recessiveness

The MN blood groups supply a complete test of the Hardy-Weinberg formula, since all three genotypes are distinguishable by their phenotypes.

Whenever the heterozygote of two alleles resembles one of the homozygotes, such direct comparison between expectation and observation is not possible. In these cases, the formula may be used to find the proportions of homozygotes and heterozygotes. Such procedure, of course, presupposes the existence of random mating in regard to the pair of alleles under discussion.

Recessive Albinism.   Recessive albinism may be used as an illustration. Since approximately 1 out of 20,000 individuals is an albino and therefore genotypically *dd,* some of the remaining 19,999 will be *DD* and some *Dd.* It is the proportion of the latter, the carriers of the undesirable allele *d,* which is significant for both the population and the individual. The frequency (q) of the recessive albino allele can be calculated from the known frequency of homozygotes (q²). Since q² = 1/20,000, q = 1/141 and p (the frequency of the normal nonalbino allele) =140/141. Therefore, the frequency of persons who are *Dd* is

$$2pq = 2 \times \tfrac{1}{141} \times \tfrac{140}{141} = \text{(about) } \tfrac{1}{70}.$$

(Because the estimate of the frequency of albinos is only approximate, it is sufficiently accurate to consider the fraction 140/141 as equivalent to 1.)

The result of this calculation comes as a surprise to most persons, who are inclined to reason that the great rarity of albinism must signify a comparable rarity of carriers. The quantitative estimate, however, shows that nearly 1.5 per cent (1/70 = 1.4 per cent) of all normally pigmented persons are heterozygous for the albino allele: there are 280 times as many carriers as affected individuals.

A number of different frequencies for homozygous recessive traits are listed in Table 19, together with the corresponding frequencies of heterozygotes and the ratio of these to affected persons. It is seen that the frequency of carriers decreases with decreasing frequency of homozygotes. Since carrier frequency decreases more slowly, the ratio between the two increases. Thus, an extremely rare recessive condition like alkaptonuria (p. 41), which has been estimated to occur in approximately 1 out of 1,000,000 persons, is carried heterozygously by 1 out of 500 persons; i.e., it is carried

TABLE 19.   *Frequencies of Affected and Carrier Individuals under Random Mating in Various Cases of Simple Single Factor Recessive Inheritance.*

Frequency of Affected (q²)	Frequency of Carriers (2pq)	Ratio of Carriers to Affected (2pq/q² = 2p/q)
1 in 10	1 in 2.3	4.3:1
1 in 100	1 in 5.6	18:1
1 in 1,000	1 in 16	61:1
1 in 10,000	1 in 51	198:1
1 in 100,000	1 in 159	630:1
1 in 1,000,000	1 in 501	1,998:1

by 2,000 times as many people as show the character. It should be clearly apparent that these facts are significant if one wishes to propose public measures intended to eliminate, or at least reduce, the incidence of undesirable genetic traits in a population. An explicit discussion of the problem will be found in Chapter 29, Selection in Civilization.

The Frequencies of Different Types of Marriages. The principle of random mating provides a means for determining the relative frequencies of all different kinds of marriages between individuals of the three genotypes *DD, Dd,* and *dd.* Listing only those marriages which may produce affected (*dd*) offspring and designating by q the frequency of the recessive allele *d,* we obtain

Marriages		*dd Offspring*
Type	Frequency	
$Dd \times Dd$	$4p^2q^2$	p^2q^2
$Dd \times dd$	$4pq^3$	$2pq^3$
$dd \times dd$	q^4	q^4

In a rare recessive condition, where q is small, most affected children will come from marriages of two carriers. In albinism, when $q = 1/141$, the term $q^4 = 1/400,000,000$ signifies that, in a population of 400,000,000, only one albino with two albino parents would be expected. Only two out of more than 2,750,000 would be albinos who had one albino parent. All other albinos would come from normally pigmented heterozygous parents. In other words, more than 99 per cent of all albinos should be the offspring of parents who look normal.

Limitations of Random Mating. Although an analysis such as the one just given leads to considerable insight into the genetics of a human population, it must be realized that the underlying assumption of random mating is at best only an approximation. Slight deviations from random mating are common. Marriages of close relatives are more frequent than would be expected by chance, and, since such relatives have a greater probability of sharing the same genes than two unrelated persons, such marriages represent a certain degree of assortative mating of like genotypes. However, the effect of marriages of close relatives on the genetic composition of a population is not very great (see Chap. 19).

It may also be true that marriages of two homozygous albinos are more common than expected by chance. Several marriages in which both spouses were albinos who were traveling in a circus troupe have been recorded. Considering the rarity of homozygous albinos, such preferential mating, if it really occurs, will have no appreciable effect on the composition of the population.

A more important exception to random mating, namely, significant negative assortative mating, has been reported from the San Blas tribe of Central American Indians. It has been known for nearly three centuries that this tribe contains an appreciable number of albinos. In a recent survey of 20,000 San Blas Indians, 152 albinos were found. It is reported that the group prohibits marriages between albinos; consequently, in contrast to a population mating at random, there would be no albinos who are the offspring of albino × albino marriages. This slight deficit would, of course, be partly counteracted by the greater number of marriages of albinos to heterozygous or homozygous normals, which would increase the number of albinos and heterozygotes. Clearly, under this system of mating, the composition of a population would not agree with the distribution expected from the Hardy-Weinberg Law. It may be added that the San Blas Indians also take selective measures against albinism: not only are albino women prohibited from marrying albino men, but many of them do not marry at all. In the course of generations this introduces further deviations from the structure of the population to be expected from random mating.

In determining the relative frequency of individuals homozygous for a given recessive gene, the larger the sample, the more reliable the estimate. In countries with compulsory military training, for instance, this sample may comprise the total number of young men. Or, where persons with certain afflictions must be hospitalized or registered, data from the whole population may be available for use in determining the frequency of a trait. It is, however, generally known that even the most thorough census is likely to underestimate the number of affected individuals because of the tendency of such persons or their relatives to suppress unfavorable information.

Isolates. Even if the determined frequency is close to the actual one, there are difficulties in equating it with q^2 in applying the Hardy-Weinberg formula. Most populations are composed of subgroups which were originally relatively separate and have not yet intermingled enough to permit random mating in the strictest sense of the term: the existence of isolates within populations is the rule, not the exception. Such isolates may be, for example, whole villages or small towns, to which there has been little immigration for several generations, or various socioeconomic or racial strata in larger cities or in whole countries. Whenever a group of individuals that is part of a larger population has had a tendency to intermarry for several generations and thus limit the exchange of alleles with the rest of the population, the distribution of alleles within the whole population will be uneven. Isolates, whether large or small, are actually relatively inbred associations, and many rare genes present in one such group may be absent in another. Consequently, the proportions of homozygous dominant, heterozygous dominant, and homozygous recessive affected persons may be quite different in the two isolates, and also different in the population that is the sum of these isolates.

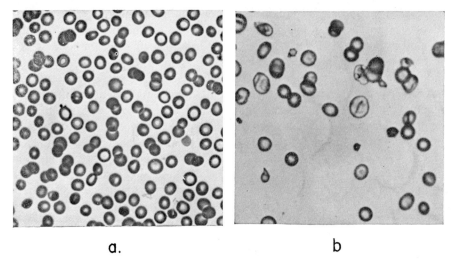

a.   b

FIG. 78. Blood picture in thalassemia.   a. Normal blood.   b. Anemic blood. The red blood cells contain little hemoglobin and the shape of many cells is irregular. (Original from Dr. C. L. Conley.)

Cooley's Anemia, or Thalassemia.   As an example approximating the situation just outlined, we will discuss Cooley's anemia (Fig. 78). This blood disease, which is fatal within the first years of life, is caused by homozygosity for the recessive allele Th^T. The trait is known in various parts of the world, and its frequency has been studied in a medium-sized American city. Hospital records showed that 11 individuals with the disease were born between 1928 and 1942. Since the total number of births during this fifteen-year span was approximately 100,000, it would seem that the frequency of carriers, 2pq, could be derived from the frequency of those affected, $q^2 = 11/100,000$. The calculation indicates that about 1 in 50 persons in the city was a carrier of this rare disease.

Cooley's anemia is known not only by the name of the physician who first gave a clear description of it but also as Mediterranean anemia or thalassemia (from the Greek *thalassa* = sea; meaning anemia occurring near the sea), because it is largely confined to people living on or near the shores of the Mediterranean—Greeks, Italians, Syrians, Armenians—or to their descendants. It happens that the American city studied contains a rather large isolate of persons of Italian descent: all 11 cases of the disease on record came from within this group. The total number of births in the Italian isolate from 1928 to 1942 was estimated to have been about 26,000. Thus the frequency of thalassemia was 11 in 26,000, or slightly less than 1 in 2,400 in the Italian isolate. Since random mating is probably reasonably approximated in this group, an application of the Hardy-Weinberg formula, when $q^2 = 1/2,400$, gives the frequency of carriers (2pq) as about 1 in 25.

The over-all frequency of carriers in the city may be obtained if one assumes that the groups of non-Italian descent do not contain carriers.

Since the total population consists of 25 per cent who are of Italian descent and 75 per cent who are not, the over-all frequency of carriers is (1 in 25) + (0 in 75), or 1 in 100 persons.

It is seen that the original estimate, based on failure to associate thalassemia with ancestral background, gave a figure between the zero frequency figure for the non-Italian group and the high value of 1 in 25 for the Italian group. As the Italian isolate is broken down by intermarriage with the population at large, shifts in the relative frequencies of the genotypes will occur.

The Breakdown of Isolates. Let us assume that a population is composed of two isolates, I and II, each consisting of 100 individuals, and that a deleterious recessive allele a has a frequency $q_I = 0.2$ in I, but is absent in

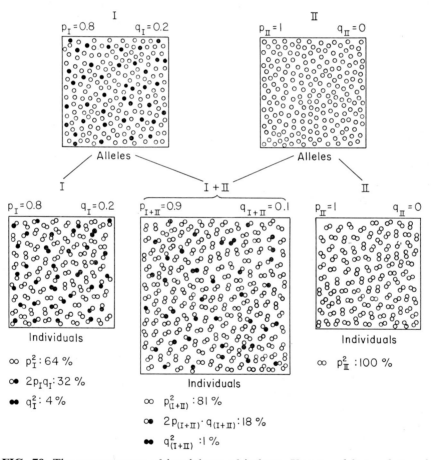

FIG. 79. The consequences of breakdown of isolates. *Upper and lower, left and right:* Two isolates I and II with different allele frequencies, $q_I = 0.2$ and $q_{II} = 0$, produce two groups of individuals with 4 and 0 per cent homozygous recessive individuals, respectively. *Lower middle:* A panmictic population derived from I and II produces 1 per cent homozygous recessives.

II ($p_{II} = 1$, $q_{II} = 0$). Then the frequency of affected individuals (*aa*) in I is $q_I^2 = 0.04$, or 4 in the group. There are no affected persons in II. If we take a census of *aa* persons in the *total* population, which is the sum of I and II, we obtain a frequency of 4 in 200, or 2 per cent. What will happen if the two isolates merge and give rise to a panmictic population?

The answer is provided by the Hardy-Weinberg Law (Fig. 79). Since the frequency of *a* alleles in isolate I is $q_I = 0.2$ and that in isolate II is $q_{II} = 0$, the mean frequency in the joint population is $q_{I+II} = 0.1$. Therefore, after random mating, the frequency of affected individuals (*aa*) is $(q_{I+II})^2 = 0.01$, or 1 per cent: the frequency of affected individuals has decreased from 2 per cent to 1 per cent.

This result is of general significance and highly important, since it typifies the fate of all recessive alleles, which are present in frequencies that differ from one isolate to another, in isolates that merge with each other or with the general population. Breakdown of isolation followed by panmixis must result in a lowering of the incidence of affected individuals. The mean allele frequencies are, of course, not changed by panmixis, but any reduction of high allele frequencies in some isolates by "dilution" with the lower frequencies in others results in a proportionally greater reduction in the number of affected persons: it is greater because the frequency with which two recessive alleles form a homozygote is proportional to the square of the frequency of a single allele. This may be illustrated by one more example. If isolate I has an allele frequency $q_I = 0.01$ and in isolate II, the frequency $q_{II} = 0$, and if isolate I constitutes only one-tenth of the joint population of I and II, then the frequency of affected individuals in the whole population before panmixis is $1/10 \cdot (0.01)^2$, or 10 in 100,000; but after panmixis it is $(1/10 \cdot 0.01)^2$, or 1 in 1,000,000. The number of affected persons is thus reduced from 10 to 1.

The Use of the Hardy-Weinberg Law When Different Genes Cause Similar Phenotypes. We have seen in our discussion of genic action that phenotypic similarities may be due to agents other than identical genotypes. Different genes may produce similar, or identical, end effects and thus cause similar-appearing traits. Unrecognized cases of this type are another obstacle to the uncritical application of the Hardy-Weinberg formula. Although there is, at present, no proof that recessive albinism may be caused by genes at different loci, the assumption is by no means unlikely. Even if it is assumed that the frequency of albinism, 1 in 20,000, is truly characteristic of large random-mating populations, we may not be justified in giving q^2 this value. Should, for instance, two different recessive alleles, *a* and *b*, of different loci, each cause albinism homozygously, then the number of observed albinos would be made up of the sum of the frequencies of *aa* (q_a^2) and of *bb* (q_b^2)—neglecting the very small number of individuals who are simultaneously homozygous for both *aa* and *bb*. If q_a and q_b were equal, q_a^2 and q_b^2 would each be 1 in 40,000, so that q_a and q_b would each be $1/200$.

Therefore, the number of carriers for each albino allele would approximate 1 in 100—a considerably lower estimate than 1 in 70, which was derived earlier from the assumption that a single locus was responsible for the condition.

Since, if two different loci are involved with equal frequency, 1 out of 100 persons is a carrier of the allele a and 1 out of 100 of b, it may be thought that the frequency of carriers should be given as the sum of the two kinds of carriers, or 1 in 50. Genetically, however, each kind of carrier must be considered by itself, since only marriages between individuals who both transmit the same recessive allele can give rise to affected offspring. Therefore, a statement of frequency of carriers is more meaningful if made separately for each locus.

Allele Frequency Tests of Genetic Hypotheses

When a character is present in two alternative forms in a population and the indications are that it is genetically determined, a first working hypothesis is that it is due to a specific pair of alleles: one dominant and the other recessive. If both phenotypes are relatively frequent and no good reasons exist for doubting the existence of random mating, the allele frequency analysis can be used for a test of the working hypothesis.

"Taste-blindness."   This will be shown for the so-called taste-blindness for the organic compound phenylthiocarbamide (PTC). It has been found that in an American white population, about 70 per cent experience a striking, bitter taste if this substance is applied to the tongue, and about 30 per cent find the substance tasteless. (The few individuals who have different taste experiences will be disregarded.) The reaction of any one individual is more or less constant, and pedigree data show inheritance of the trait. By adding the offspring of numerous marriages of the three possible phenotypes, namely, taster to taster, taster to nontaster, and nontaster to nontaster, Snyder obtained the data given in Table 20.

If the ability or inability to taste phenylthiocarbamide is due to the pair of alleles T and t, persons with one of the two phenotypes must be homozygous recessive, and those with the other can be either heterozygous or

TABLE 20.   *Data on the Inheritance of Ability to Taste Phenylthiocarbamide.* (After Snyder.)

Parents	No. of Families	Offspring		Fraction of Nontasters among Offspring
		Tasters	Nontasters	
Taster × Taster	425	929	130	0.123
Taster × Nontaster	289	483	278	0.366
Nontaster × Nontaster	86	5	218	0.978

homozygous dominant. The table shows that the tasters belong to the group which includes the heterozygotes, since parents who are both tasters have both types of children in appreciable numbers. Consequently, the nontasters are the homozygous recessives, and nontaster couples should be expected to have nontaster offspring exclusively. This expectation is closely approached but not completely fulfilled, since 5 tasters were found among 223 children. Such discrepancies do not need to be taken too seriously in genetic interpretation. In a large collection of human data, errors of misclassification are difficult to exclude, and there is always a possibility that some children in any group are illegitimate. Moreover, it is now known that variations in the expression of the taster genotypes are not uncommon. Different individuals have different degrees of taste sensitivity: some can taste PTC in very low concentration; others only in higher concentrations.

If the taster parents actually consist of both TT and Tt genotypes, the allele frequency relations, assuming random mating, give the proportion of these types as p^2 and $2pq$, and that of the nontasters (tt) as q^2. By the use of these frequencies, it is possible to predict the proportions of taster and nontaster children resulting from *groups* of marriages of two tasters, even though it is unknown whether an *individual* taster parent is homozygous or heterozygous.

Phenotypically, there are two kinds of relevant marriage: (A) that in which one spouse is a taster and the other a nontaster; and (B) that in which both are tasters.

A. Marriages between a taster and a nontaster are of two types. These two types, their frequencies, and their offspring are as follows:

Marriages		Offspring	
Type	Frequency	Tasters	Nontasters
$TT \times tt$	$2p^2q^2$	$2p^2q^2$	—
$Tt \times tt$	$4pq^3$	$2pq^3$	$2pq^3$

Adding all offspring, we find the total to be $2p^2q^2 + 4pq^3$. Among these there are $2pq^3$ nontasters; hence, the expected *fraction of nontasters* among all offspring of these marriages is

$$\frac{2pq^3}{2p^2q^2 + 4pq^3} = \frac{q}{p + 2q} = \frac{q}{1 - q + 2q} = \frac{q}{1 + q}. \tag{5}$$

B. Similarly, we can calculate the fraction of nontaster offspring from marriages of tasters to tasters. There are three types of such marriages.

Marriages		Offspring	
Type	Frequency	Tasters	Nontasters
$TT \times TT$	p^4	p^4	—
$TT \times Tt$	$4p^3q$	$4p^3q$	—
$Tt \times Tt$	$4p^2q^2$	$3p^1q^2$	p^2q^2

Here, the fraction of nontasters among all offspring is

$$\frac{p^2q^2}{p^4 + 4p^3q + 4p^2q^2} = \frac{q^2}{p^2 + 4pq + 4q^2} = \left(\frac{q}{p + 2q}\right)^2 = \left(\frac{q}{1 + q}\right)^2. \quad (6)$$

Formulas (5) and (6) enable us to test the hypothesis of single factor inheritance of taster ability, provided the frequency, q, of the t allele is known. It may be derived from the combined data on the population sample listed in Table 20. Of the 3,643 persons tested, 70.2 per cent were tasters and 29.8 per cent nontasters. Therefore, $q^2 = 0.298$, and $q = 0.545$. Given this value for q, the expected fraction of nontaster children from marriages of tasters to nontasters,

$$\frac{q}{1 + q},$$

is 0.354; and

$$\left(\frac{q}{1 + q}\right)^2,$$

the fraction of nontaster children from marriages of tasters to tasters, is 0.124. The observations listed in Table 20 yielded 0.366 and 0.123, respectively, in close agreement with expectation. From this, it may be concluded that the assumption that a single pair of alleles T and t and random mating are responsible for the inheritance of taste reactions to phenylthiocarbamide fits the facts.

The Hardy-Weinberg Relations for Two Pairs of Genes

The Hardy-Weinberg Law states that, for a single pair of alleles, a panmictic population reaches equilibrium in a single generation. Such immediate attainment of equilibrium after panmixis is not characteristic for the combinations of alleles at more than one locus. Let us consider a population with the two alleles A and A', at an A locus, and the two alleles B and B', at a B locus; and let p_A and $q_{A'}$ each equal $1/2$, and p_B and $q_{B'}$ each equal $1/2$. At equilibrium, this population will contain nine different genotypes, namely, $AABB$, $AABB'$, and $AAB'B'$; $AA'BB$, $AA'BB'$, and $AA'B'B'$; and $A'A'BB$, $A'A'BB'$, and $A'A'B'B'$. Each one will have a frequency that is the product of the two independent genotype frequencies at the two loci. Thus, $AABB = 1/4 \cdot 1/4 = 1/16$; $AABB' = 1/4 \cdot 2/4 = 2/16$; and so on. Generalizing for any values of the allele frequencies, the genotypic frequencies for $AABB$ will be $p_A^2 \cdot q_B^2$; for $AABB'$, $p_A^2 \cdot 2p_Bq_{B'}$; and so on.

Now let us consider a population which initially consisted exclusively of $AA'BB'$ heterozygotes. The gametes produced will be of four kinds (AB, AB', $A'B$, and $A'B'$) and will occur in equal frequencies ($1/4:1/4:1/4:1/4$). Although these can combine in 16 different ways, they can produce only nine different genotypes, as indicated in the upper half of Figure 80, where the frequencies are also noted. This first generation population, so different from

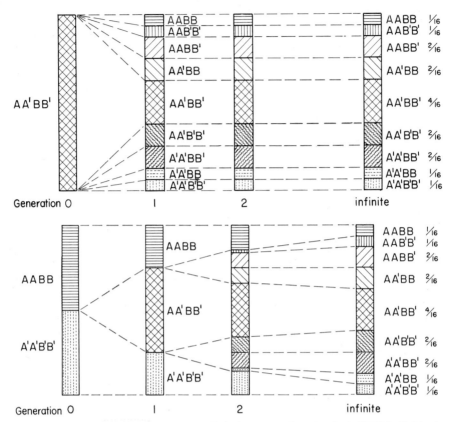

FIG. 80. *Above:* A population consisting, in generation 0, of *AA'BB'* individuals only. Attainment of equilibrium in one generation. *Below:* A population consisting, in generation 0, of equal numbers of *AABB* and *A'A'B'B'* individuals. Stepwise attainment of equilibrium in successive generations.

the original one, is thus in equilibrium, just like the first generation in a population with only one pair of allelic differences.

   Ordinarily, however, equilibrium for two allele pairs is not attained in a single generation. Indeed, only if the initial population consists solely of *AA'BB'* heterozygotes is the equilibrium attained so speedily. Let us consider another initial population: one that consists of equal numbers of *AABB* and *A'A'B'B'* homozygotes and undergoes panmixis (Fig. 80, lower half). Since only two types of gametes segregate in the population, namely, *AB* and *A'B'*, only three genotypes, *AABB*, *AA'BB'*, and *A'A'B'B'*, will be present in the next generation in the ratio 1/4:2/4:1/4. All four possible kinds of gametes, *AB*, *AB'*, *A'B*, and *A'B'*, will be produced by this first panmictic generation. The double heterozygote *AA'BB'* will contribute equal numbers of these, but the *AABB* and *A'A'B'B'* homozygotes will supply only *AB* and *A'B'*. The result will be a second generation in which all nine possible genotypes occur but not at random frequencies. There will be too many *AABB*, *AA'BB'*, and

$A'A'B'B'$ genotypes and too few of the other six genotypes, particularly $AAB'B'$ and $A'A'BB$. With later generations the excesses and deficiencies will disappear until equilibrium is reached.

The gradual approach to equilibrium is characteristic for populations which segregate for more than one pair of alleles, no matter whether the frequencies of all alleles are equal or whether the values of p_A, $q_{A'}$, p_B, $q_{B'}$, and so on, vary greatly. In his first paper on population genetics, Weinberg recognized the essential difference between the attainment of equilibrium for a single locus and its attainment for multiple loci.

The approach to equilibrium in populations which segregate for two alleles at each of two loci is comparatively rapid, provided that the two loci recombine freely. If they are linked, the stronger the linkage, the slower the approach to equilibrium. However, given enough generations, equilibrium is reached even with close linkage. This important fact will be discussed in more detail in Chapter 14.

The Recognition of Recent Intermixture in Populations.   If two populations containing different alleles at any given locus intermarry panmictically, equilibrium for the two alleles of any one locus will be reached in one generation.

Let us assume that two populations differ in two traits that depend on two separate pairs of genes. To be specific, let us assume that one pair of alleles governs the color of eyes and the other the color of hair, and that the heterozygotes are intermediate in both (in reality, differences in these traits are seldom controlled by single pairs of genes). Population I is to consist entirely of individuals who have light eyes and light hair; population II, of persons who have dark eyes and dark hair. Given panmixis between the two populations, the proportion of dark-eyed to light-eyed persons after a single generation, and forever after, will follow the Hardy-Weinberg Law, and so will the proportion of dark-haired to light-haired. Studying the proportions of either trait alone will not reveal whether the presence of dark and light individuals is the result of recent or long-past intermixture, or whether it arose independently by mutation.

But if both traits are studied together, the proportions of persons having the various possible combinations will change with each successive generation. After a single generation of panmixis, only three types of persons will exist: those who, like population I, are dark-eyed and dark-haired; those who are light-eyed and light-haired, like population II; and those who are first-generation hybrids for both traits. There will be no light-eyed and dark-haired, or dark-eyed and light-haired individuals, and no individuals with other combinations. In the second generation all possible combinations will appear, but the phenotypes of the original populations and first-generation hybrids will still be more numerous than expected at equilibrium. With every new successive generation, each combination will approach its equilibrium frequency more closely. Thus, a study of the frequencies of combinations of traits that depend on different genes can throw light on the past history of a population.

Population Genetics

This chapter has provided an introduction to a particularly important part of the study of human genetics: the study of the genetic composition of whole populations in contrast to that of individual families or kindreds. Both population genetics and pedigree genetics are significant, and both rest on the Mendelian analysis of inheritance.

We have seen that the Hardy-Weinberg Law is a basic guide to the understanding of population genetics. In the following chapters, the Hardy-Weinberg Law and such concepts as random mating and allele frequency will often prove useful in our study of the genetics of human populations.

Problems

72. Assume people of the three genotypes AA, Aa, and aa to occur in the proportions of $1/4:2/4:1/4$. If there is completely positive assortative mating between like genotypes: (a) What proportions of the whole would each of the three types represent in the next generation? (b) What proportions would result in the following generation?

73. In a given population, how would you determine the percentage frequency of the gene for: (a) Brachydactyly? (b) Nontasting?

74. Which of the following populations are in genetic equilibrium:

(a)	100% AA,	(d)	1% AA, 98% Aa, 1% aa,
(b)	100% aa,	(e)	32% AA, 64% Aa, 4% aa,
(c)	100% Aa,	(f)	4% AA, 32% Aa, 64% aa?

75. In a certain population, 16 per cent of all people belong to blood group N. Assuming panmixis, how many do you expect to be M and how many MN?

76. What can be concluded regarding a population of 1,000 people which has the following composition: M 33%, MN 34%, N 33%?

77. Direct observations of a very large population have shown that three phenotypes occur in the ratios of 70:21:9. Are these frequencies compatible with the theory that this is a case of simple single gene pair inheritance, the three phenotypes representing the genotypes AA, Aa, and aa?

78. Assume that an isolated population consists of people of blood group M only. At a certain time immigration occurs, the immigrants equalling the original population in number. Twenty-five per cent of the immigrants belong to group N. Since the immigrants were a thoroughly random-mated group, you can calculate the frequencies of the L^M and L^N genes among them. After the immigrants and the original population have married at random, what proportions of the blood groups will you expect in future generations?

79. Although panmictic population I contains, for gene *A*, only homozygous individuals, it contains, in regard to a different locus, *BB*, *Bb*, and *bb* individuals, the last in a frequency of 0.04. Another equally large and panmictic population II is homozygous for *BB*, but contains *AA*, *Aa*, and *aa* individuals, the last in a frequency of 0.01. If populations I and II intermarry completely and there is random mating in later generations, what frequencies, expressed in per cent, of *aa*, *bb*, and *aabb* people do you expect?

80. The frequency of the supposed recessive allele for inability to roll one's tongue lengthwise has been estimated as q = 0.6. (a) What are the frequencies of rollers and nonrollers? (b) In pooled data, what proportion of rollers to nonrollers are expected among the children from marriages of two roller parents? (c) What proportion are expected if one spouse is a nonroller and the other a roller?

81. Table 30 (p. 194) gives data on the offspring from marriages of Rh-positive and Rh-negative persons. Read the paragraph in which Table 30 is discussed and apply the allele frequency tests to the simple genetic interpretation given there.

References

Dahlberg, G., 1947. *Mathematical Methods for Population Genetics.* 182 pp. S. Karger, New York.

————, 1948. Genetics of human populations. *Adv. Genet.,* **2:** 67–98.

Hardy, G. H., 1908. Mendelian proportions in a mixed population. *Science,* **28:** 49–50.

Jones, Harold E., 1929. Homogamy in intellectual abilities. *Am. J. Sociol.,* **35:** 369–382.

Li, C. C., 1955. *Population Genetics.* 366 pp. University of Chicago Press, Chicago.

Neel, J. V., and Valentine, W. N., 1947. Further studies on the genetics of thalassemia. *Genetics, ***32:** 38–63.

Snyder, L. H., The inheritance of taste deficiency in man. *Ohio J. Sci.,* **32:** 436–440.

Steinberg, A. G., 1959. Methodology in human genetics. *J. Med. Ed.,* **34:** 315–334 (also *Am. J. Human Genet.,* **11,** 2 Part 2: 315–334), see pp. 323–326.

Weinberg, W., 1908. Über den Nachweis der Vererbung beim Menschen. *Jahreshefte Verein f. vaterl. Naturk. in Württemberg,* **64:** 368–382. (An important section of this paper is translated in C. Stern, 1943. The Hardy-Weinberg law. *Science,* **97:** 137–138.)

Wiener, A. S., 1943. *Blood Groups and Transfusion.* 3rd ed. Chapters 13 and 14, pp. 219–244. C. C. Thomas, Springfield, Ill.

CHAPTER **11**

MULTIPLE ALLELES AND
THE BLOOD GROUPS

Most of the examples of inheritance which have been given in the preceding chapters dealt with two alleles only, e.g., one for normal and the other for woolly hair, or one for pigmentation and the other for albinism. However, as stated earlier, many genes have more than two allelic forms. Such groups of alleles form the subject of the present chapter.

The individual alleles of a group are called *multiple alleles,* a term which does not mean that the alleles themselves are multiple in some way but only that they belong to a group of more than two. Since alleles are alternative varieties of a gene at a given locus, multiple alleles obey the same rules of transmission as alleles of which there are only two kinds. An individual may be homozygous for any one of the alleles or heterozygous for a combination of any two of them, and segregation, in meiosis, results in gametes which contain only a single allele.

How many different forms can an allele at a specific locus have? In order to answer this question, many individuals need to be studied, since, in a single person, each locus is only represented twice and no more than two different alleles can be found. If, on the other hand, 100 individuals are tested, their 200 homologous loci could theoretically be occupied by 200 different alleles. In reality, no such diversity can be expected within an interbreeding population in which many different individuals must have inherited the same alleles from common ancestors. A great diversity of alleles has, however, been found at many loci in numerous organisms.

The Phenotypic Effects of Multiple Alleles. Multiple alleles of a gene normally affect similar parts or processes in an organism. In rabbits, for instance, the C series of alleles affects the degree of pigmentation of the fur. Homozygotes for C (CC) are wild-type, or agouti, while those for c^{chi}, c^d,

174

c^m, c^h, and c are responsible for the increasingly lighter phenotypes—dark chinchilla, intermediate chinchilla, light chinchilla, Himalayan albino, and complete albino. Strictly speaking, such a series is almost never simply quantitative throughout. The Himalayan albinos differ from all other homozygotes, in that the pigment present is unevenly distributed; most parts of the body are colorless; but the tips of the feet, snout, ears, and tail are darkly pigmented. Some as yet unknown differences in the molecular structure of different alleles seem to cause quantitatively different effects, and some to cause qualitative ones.

If more than one phenotypic characteristic of an organism is influenced by a gene, its multiple alleles may often be distinguishable from each other by their dissimilar effects on one character, although their effects on others may be alike; other alleles may vary in their effect on more than one trait. For some multiple alleles, their arrangement in a series according to the strength of effect on one trait is identical with a series that shows strength of effect on another trait. For others, two or more series may be partly or wholly independent.

The best-known types of multiple allelism in man concern the blood groups. Here, the availability of very sensitive immunological tests has led to the recognition of numerous alleles at a variety of loci. The present chapter, therefore, will be concerned particularly with the genetics of blood groups. This is one of the most rapidly growing branches of the study of human heredity. Excellent summaries have been published by Race and Sanger, and Wiener and Wexler, all of whom are in the forefront of workers in immunogenetics.

Dominance Relations in Multiple Alleles.   The dominance relations among multiple alleles vary from one group of alleles to another. For some groups of alleles every homozygous and heterozygous genotype produces a different phenotype. In other groups the alleles may be arranged in a descending series in which every allele is dominant over all alleles below it. In this latter case, with the three alleles A^1, A^2, and A^3, the phenotypes produced by A^1A^1, A^1A^2, and A^1A^3 would be alike; A^2A^2 and A^2A^3 would be alike, but different from phenotypes with A^1; and A^3A^3 would differ from both.

Another kind of phenotypic expression of homo- and heterozygotes is that in which the top member of a series of alleles is dominant over all others, and intermediate expression is observed in heterozygotes of any two other alleles. In the coat-color series of alleles mentioned above, C homozygously or heterozygously leads to wild-type fur, but $c^{chi}c^d$, $c^{chi}c$, and most other heterozygotes are more or less intermediate in color between the corresponding homozygotes, that is, $c^{chi}c^{chi}$ and c^dc^d, $c^{chi}c^{chi}$ and cc.

Finally, in some groups of multiple alleles, certain heterozygotes show dominance or intermediacy, and other heterozygotes with alleles with qualitatively different effects show both effects simultaneously. The combination of dominance and codominance is found in the blood groups.

The Number of Possible Genotypes. When a gene has only two alleles, the total number of genotypes is three, namely, the two homozygotes and the heterozygote. The more alleles a gene possesses, the larger, of course, is the number of possible genotypes. Thus, with three alleles, A^1, A^2, and A^3, there are three homozygotes, A^1A^1, A^2A^2, A^3A^3; two heterozygotes of A^1 with the other alleles, A^1A^2 and A^1A^3; and one heterozygote, A^2A^3. With n alleles, A^1, A^2 ... A^n, the following genotypes may occur:

n homozygotes	A^1A^1	A^2A^2	...	...	...	... A^nA^n
(n − 1) heterozygotes with A^1	A^1A^2	A^1A^3	...	...	...	A^1A^n
(n − 2) heterozygotes with A^2	A^2A^3	A^2A^4	...	...	A^2A^n	
(n − 3) heterozygotes with A^3	A^3A^4	A^3A^5	...	A^3A^n		
....	...	...	...			
2 heterozygotes with A^{n-2}	$A^{n-2}A^{n-1}$	$A^{n-2}A^n$				
1 heterozygote with A^{n-1}	$A^{n-1}A^n$					

The sum of all these genotypes is $n + (n - 1) + (n - 2) + \dots 1$, which is equal to $1/2 \, [n \cdot (n + 1)]$. If there are five alleles, the number of genotypes is thus $5 + 4 + 3 + 2 + 1 = (1/2) \cdot (5 \cdot 6) = 15$; if n = 20, the number of genotypes increases to 210.

The ABO Blood Groups

The Four ABO Blood Groups. It has been known, since Landsteiner's discovery in 1901, that the blood of an individual may belong to one of several different types, according to the reactions observed in mixtures of blood of different persons. Essentially, these are reactions between the red blood cells of one individual and the fluid part, or *plasma,* of the blood of another.

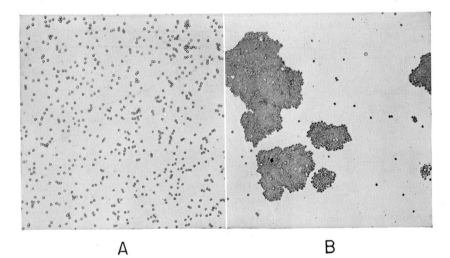

A   B

FIG. 81. Photographs of (A) nonagglutinated and (B) agglutinated red blood cells. 100× (Originals from Dr. C. L. Conley.)

GROUP	ANTIGENS IN RED BLOOD CELLS	ANTIBODY PRESENT IN SERUM	REACTION TO SERUM (LISTED TO LEFT) OF RED BLOOD CELLS FROM GROUP			
			O	A	B	A B
O	O	ANTI-A ANTI-B				
A	A	ANTI-B				
B	B	ANTI-A				
AB	AB	—				

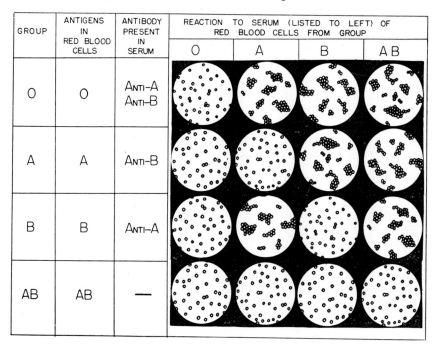

FIG. 82. Reactions of red blood cells of O, A, B, and AB individuals to antibodies anti-A and anti-B. (Adapted from Hardin, *Biology, Its Human Implications,* W. H. Freeman and Co., 1949.)

The fibrinogen, which is involved in blood clotting, can be removed from the plasma, and the remaining fluid is called the *serum.* By centrifugation, red blood cells may be removed from whole blood. Then, when red blood cells and serum from the same individual are brought together, the cells will become freely distributed in the fluid. If, however, red cells from one individual are mixed with serum from another, one of two different results will be observed. The cells may become normally distributed in the serum, or they may clump together (Fig. 81). These results are constant for any two individuals. Such observations divide mankind into at least two different groups. Further tests have established the existence of four main groups of human beings with respect to ABO *isoagglutination.* The term agglutination refers to the clumping of the blood cells, and the prefix iso (from the Greek *isos,* meaning equal) signifies that agglutination is caused by sera from the same species, man.

These four groups of persons are distinguished from one another by the immunological properties of both their red cells and their serum. The red cells of an individual possess either one or the other, both, or neither of two substances (or groups of substances) called *antigens,* or *agglutinogens,* A and B; and his serum possesses either one or the other, neither, or both of two substances (or groups of substances) called *antibodies,* or *agglutinins,* anti-B and anti-A (Fig. 82). Red cells containing antigen A are agglutinated by anti-A, cells containing antigen B by anti-B. The four groups of persons are named after their antigens: A, B, AB, and O. Not only does every kind of human blood lack the antibodies which would agglutinate its own red cells —a necessary condition, since any appreciable clumping would be fatal—but also every kind of human blood contains those antibodies which are compatible with the antigens of its cells. It may be added that some human sera agglutinate not only the cells of O individuals but also, though less thoroughly, those of the other groups. Such sera are called anti-O or anti-H, and the corresponding antigen, which is common to all groups, H.

The ABO Blood Groups in Transfusion. The importance of distinguishing the isoagglutinin blood groups for transfusion is obvious. Transfusion of whole blood is safe only between members of the same group. However, if necessary, it is possible to use certain other combinations of blood groups of donor and receiver. This can be done because the antibodies in the plasma of transfused blood are partly adsorbed by the tissues of an incompatible recipient before they can agglutinate appreciable numbers of his red cells, and the transfused blood is so diluted by the recipient's plasma that the concentration of the donor's antibodies may be below that causing a serious amount of agglutination. Such adsorption and dilution do not apply to antigens which are bound to the red blood cells of the donor. The properties of the cells are, therefore, of greater importance in determining the consequences of transfusions than are the properties of the sera. This fact has found expression in the terms "universal donor" and "universal recipient": the former applying to group O persons, whose red cells cannot be agglutinated by any recipient; the latter to group AB persons, whose serum cannot act on the cells of any donor (Fig. 82). Since, however, the effect of the donor's antibodies, if present, is not wholly negligible (Table 21), the terms universal donor and recipient are not fully correct and the use of any donor different in blood group from the recipient should be discouraged.

The problem is different when, instead of whole blood, plasma or serum is used in transfusion. Since it has been found that the mixing of sera or plasmas containing different isoantibodies results in their inactivation, the sera or

TABLE 21. *Possible Effects of Transfusions of Whole Blood.*

		Recipient			
		O	A	B	AB
Donor	O	−	+	+	+
	A	**+**	−	**+**+	+
	B	**+**	**+**+	−	+
	AB	**+**	**+**	**+**	−

NOTE: **+** heavy agglutination of donor's cells, + light agglutination of recipient's cells, − no agglutination.

TABLE 22.   *Data on ABO Blood Groups Among Children from All Types of Marriages.* (Wiener, *Blood Groups and Transfusion*, 3rd ed., Thomas, 1943.)

Marriage	No. of Families	No. of Children in Each Group*				
		O	A	B	AB	Total
O × O	1,563	3,772	(14)	(9)	0	3,795
O × A	2,903	2,707	3,749	(10)	(1)	6,467
O × B	1,456	1,418	(7)	1,831	(1)	3,257
A × A	1,385	556	2,538	0	(2)	3,096
A × B	1,400	605	957	771	848	3,181
B × B	554	203	(1)	1,009	0	1,213
O × AB	530	(8)	633	646	(3)	1,290
A × AB	455	0	533	247	312	1,092
B × AB	323	(2)	183	406	232	823
AB × AB	59	0	28	36	65	129
Total	10,628	9,271	8,643	4,965	1,464	24,343

* Numbers in parentheses represent "exceptions" (see text).

plasmas of a number of individuals are pooled and the inactivated mixture is used.

Genetics of the ABO Blood Groups

These facts are significant in studies of human genetics because the blood groups are inherited. Studies of pedigrees have shown that children do not have the A antigen unless at least one of their parents has it. Similarly, the B antigen is found only among the offspring of a parent who has B. This indicates dominance for A and B. On the other hand, O persons occur not only in the progeny of O parents, but also among the children of A and of B parents, thus indicating recessive inheritance for O. A summary of numerous data on children from all ten possible combinations of persons of the four blood groups is given in Table 22. It is seen that there are some exceptions to the rule that A and B antigens occur only among children of parents who carry A and B. These exceptions, as well as some others which are open to suspicion because of their rarity, will be discussed after we have dealt with the more common facts.

It is obvious that the existence of four blood groups means that the gene that controls them must have more than two allelic forms, since two alleles may, at most, give rise to three different phenotypes. The now well-established explanation that three multiple alleles govern the inheritance of the main blood groups was historically preceded by another hypothesis. It will be instructive to discuss this hypothesis and to show why it became untenable.

The Earlier Hypothesis of Two Gene Loci.   The earlier hypothesis was based on the assumption that an individual's blood group was determined by

TABLE 23. *Comparison of the Two Theories of the Inheritance of the ABO Blood Groups.* (Wiener, *Blood Groups and Transfusion,* 3rd ed., Thomas, 1943.)

	Groups of Children Expected According to Theory of:	
Groups of Parents	Two-gene Pairs*	Multiple Alleles
O × O	O	O
O × A	O, A	O, A
O × B	O, B	O, B
A × A	O, A	O, A
A × A	O, A, B, AB	O, A, B, AB
B × B	O, B	O, B
O × AB	(O), A, B, (AB)	A, B
A × AB	(O), A, B, AB	A, B, AB
B × AB	(O), A, B, AB	A, B, AB
AB × AB	(O), A, B, AB	A, B, AB

* Parentheses indicate absence of the group in actual data.

two genes at independent loci in two pairs of chromosomes. The scheme may be represented by the symbols *A, a* and *B, b*; allele *A* would be responsible for antigen A, and allele *B* for antigen B, so that the existence of the following genotypes characterizing the four blood groups would be deduced:

aabb . . . . group O
AAbb, Aabb . . . . group A
aaBB, aaBb . . . . group B
AABB, AaBB, AABb, AaBb . . . . . group AB

Analysis of Family Data. As shown in Table 23 (middle column), this genetic scheme is able to account for the kinds of children resulting from the first six of the ten types of marriages, but not for those from the four types of marriages in which at least one of the parents belongs to group AB. Thus, parents O × AB, should have AB children exclusively if the AB parent was *AABB*; B and AB children if the AB parent was *AaBB*; A and AB children if the AB parent was *AABb*; and children of all types (A, B, AB, and O) if the AB parent was heterozygous for both loci, namely, *AaBb*. In reality, neither AB nor O children occur, if we omit the 11 exceptions out of 1,290 individuals (Table 22). Similarly, contrary to observations, marriages A × AB, B × AB, and AB × AB should, on the basis of the two-gene hypothesis, give rise not only to children of groups A, B, and AB, as they actually do, but also to O children.

These contradictions of the theory were not apparent for many years because of several circumstances. Among these is the fact that people of group AB constitute less than 5 per cent of most white populations, so that in the great majority of marriages neither spouse is AB, and thus the overwhelming proportion of marriages are of one of the six types that have children of the expected groups only. A second reason was that the techniques of blood-group determination were imperfect, so that some children assigned to group O really belonged to another group. Such erroneous determination meant that group O children were listed among the offspring of AB persons, where they were expected according to the two-gene theory, although more correct determinations have since shown that such parents have no O children. Finally, a certain amount of illegitimacy must be reckoned with, even in carefully selected data, and this can explain the occurrence of AB children from O × AB marriages (Table 22), where, again, they were expected according to the two-gene theory, but where they do not occur among legitimate offspring.

Allele Frequency Analysis.   The replacement of the hypothesis of two genes with two alleles each by the theory of multiple alleles was not based on an analysis of family data and of the discrepancies in groups of children expected and observed, but on a consideration, by the mathematician Felix Bernstein (1878–1956) of the relative frequencies of the four types of individuals in various populations. The two-gene hypothesis can be subjected to the allele frequency analysis with which we became acquainted in the chapter on the Hardy-Weinberg Law. We shall assign the frequency p_A to the dominant allele *A* of the *A, a* pair, and the frequency p_B to the allele *B* of the *B, b* pair. The frequencies of the recessive alleles *a* and *b* are, therefore, $(1 - p_A)$ and $(1 - p_B)$, respectively. It is, then, a simple matter of multiplying the frequencies of genotypes *AA*, *aa*, and *Aa*, p_A^2, $(1 - p_A)^2$, and $2p_A(1 - p_A)$, by those of *BB*, *bb*, and *Bb*, p_B^2, $(1 - p_B)^2$ and $2p_B(1 - p_B)$, in order to obtain the frequencies of the different combinations of the genotypes at both loci (Table 24A). These calculations give us the expected frequencies of the four blood groups in the two-gene hypothesis (last column of Table 24A).

TABLE 24A.   *ABO Blood Group Composition of a Population According to the Two-gene-pair Hypothesis.*

Blood Group	Genotype	Frequency of: Genotype	Blood Group (Sum of Appropriate Genotypes)
O	*aa bb*	$(1 - p_A)^2(1 - p_B)^2$	$(1 - p_A)^2(1 - p_B)^2$
A	*AA bb* *Aa bb*	$p_A^2(1 - p_B)^2$ $2p_A(1 - p_A)(1 - p_B)^2$	$(2p_A - p_A^2)(1 - p_B)^2$
B	*aa BB* *aa Bb*	$(1 - p_A)^2 \cdot p_B^2$ $(1 - p_A)^2 \cdot 2p_B(1 - p_B)$	$(1 - p_A)^2(2p_B - p_B^2)$
AB	*AA BB* *Aa BB* *AA Bb* *Aa Bb*	$p_A^2 \cdot p_B^2$ $2p_A(1 - p_A) \cdot p_B^2$ $p_A^2 \cdot 2p_B(1 - p_B)$ $2p_A(1 - p_A) \cdot 2p_B(1 - p_B)$	$(2p_A - p_A^2)(2p_B - p_B^2)$

By adding the frequencies of all A and AB persons, we obtain the following relation, in which $\overline{A}$ and $\overline{AB}$ indicate the frequency of $\overline{A}$ and of $\overline{AB}$, respectively:

$$\overline{A} + \overline{AB} = 2p_A - p_A^2.$$

Similarly,

$$\overline{B} + \overline{AB} = 2p_B - p_B^2.$$

Since the frequency of AB persons is $(2p_A - p_A^2) \cdot (2p_B - p_B^2)$, the two preceding equations may be combined into the equation:

$$(\overline{A} + \overline{AB}) \cdot (\overline{B} + \overline{AB}) = \overline{AB}.$$

This equation and with it the two-gene hypothesis *can be tested*. All three terms, $\overline{A}$, $\overline{B}$, and $\overline{AB}$, indicate frequencies known from observation. If we add the percentage of A persons in any given population to the percentage of AB persons and multiply the sum by the sum of the percentages of B and AB persons, the resulting product should be the same as the percentage of AB persons.

This test of the hypothesis of two independent genes may be applied, not only to one population, but to a great number of populations, since it has been discovered that different racial groups show different frequencies of the four blood groups. Each racial group should fit the equation, since it should hold for any frequency of A, B, and AB.

However, the product $(\overline{A} + \overline{AB}) \cdot (\overline{B} + \overline{AB})$ is not equal to, but consistently larger than, $\overline{AB}$. This will be shown specifically for samples of two populations, American whites and Japanese. For the whites, the observed frequencies of the blood groups are

$$\overline{O} = 0.45, \overline{A} = 0.41, \overline{B} = 0.10, \overline{AB} = 0.04.$$

Entering these values in the equation, we obtain

$$(\overline{A} + \overline{AB}) \cdot (\overline{B} + \overline{AB}) = 0.45 \cdot 0.14 = 0.063,$$

which is more than 50 per cent greater than the observed frequency of AB, 0.04.

For the Japanese population, observation gave

$$\overline{O} = 0.294, \overline{A} = 0.422, \overline{B} = 0.206, \overline{AB} = 0.078.$$

Thus,

$$(\overline{A} + \overline{AB}) \cdot (\overline{B} + \overline{AB}) = 0.500 \cdot 0.284 = 0.142,$$

which is nearly twice as large as the observed frequency, 0.078. Similar discrepancies were found in many other populations. The disagreement between expected and observed frequencies means that either the underlying theory of two-gene pairs is false or that, of all different populations tested, none was the result of random mating. This latter possibility could clearly be excluded, since family data show that there is certainly not enough, if any, assortative

TABLE 24B.   *ABO Blood Group Composition of a Population According to the Theory of Three Multiple Alleles.*

Blood Group	Genotype	Frequency of: Genotype	Frequency of: Blood Group (Sum of Appropriate Genotypes)
O	$I^O I^O$	r_O^2	r_O^2
A	$I^A I^A$ $I^A I^O$	$\left. \begin{array}{c} p_A^2 \\ 2p_A r_O \end{array} \right\}$	$2p_A r_O + p_A^2$
B	$I^B I^B$ $I^B I^O$	$\left. \begin{array}{c} q_B^2 \\ 2q_B r_O \end{array} \right\}$	$2q_B r_O + q_B^2$
AB	$I^A I^B$	$2p_A q_B$	$2p_A q_B$

mating by blood groups to account for the observed deviation in frequencies. Therefore, the two-gene hypothesis had to be abandoned.

The Theory of Multiple Alleles.   Having thus proven the inadequacy of the two-gene hypothesis, Bernstein assumed the existence of three multiple alleles, best called I^A, I^B, and I^O (some writers use such symbols as A, B, and R, or A, B, and O). It was further assumed that the alleles I^A and I^B are codominant if combined in the genotype $I^A I^B$, but that either allele is dominant in heterozygous combination with I^O.

From these assumptions, the frequencies of the six possible genotypes can be calculated as shown in the third column of Table 24B. Then, by adding the frequencies of those genotypes that have identical phenotypes, the frequencies of the four blood groups are obtained (final column).

Allele Frequency Analysis.   The frequencies p_A, q_B, and r_O, which were assigned to the three alleles, must add up to 1 ($p_A + q_B + r_O = 1$), just as the sum of the frequencies of two alleles, p and q, equals 1. Our goal is to compare the theoretical expectation that $p_A + q_B + r_O = 1$ (an expectation which holds only if the theory of multiple alleles is correct) with data derived from actual observation.

The formulas in the last column of Table 24B enable us to express the allele frequencies p, q, and r in terms of observed frequencies of blood groups. Since the frequency of O individuals is r_O^2,

$$r_O = \sqrt{O}. \tag{1}$$

The frequency of O and A persons together is

$$\overline{O} + \overline{A} = r_O^2 + 2p_A r_O + p_A^2 = (r_O + p_A)^2,$$

or

$$p_A + r_O = \sqrt{\overline{O} + \overline{A}}. \tag{2}$$

Similarly,

$$\overline{O} + \overline{B} = r_o^2 + 2q_Br_o + q_B^2 = (r_o + q_B)^2,$$

or

$$q_B + r_o = \sqrt{\overline{O} + \overline{B}}. \qquad (3)$$

By substitution, according to (1), of $\sqrt{\overline{O}}$ for r_o in (2), we obtain

$$p_A = \sqrt{\overline{O} + \overline{A}} - \sqrt{\overline{O}}, \qquad (4)$$

and by the same substitution in (3),

$$q_B = \sqrt{\overline{O} + \overline{B}} - \sqrt{\overline{O}}. \qquad (5)$$

Adding the three allele frequencies as given by the three equations (5), (4), and (1), we find

$$p_A + q_B + r_o = \sqrt{\overline{O} + \overline{A}} - \sqrt{\overline{O}} + \sqrt{\overline{O} + \overline{B}} - \sqrt{\overline{O}} + \sqrt{\overline{O}},$$

which, since $p_A + q_B + r_o = 1$, may be expressed finally as

$$\sqrt{\overline{O} + \overline{A}} + \sqrt{\overline{O} + \overline{B}} - \sqrt{\overline{O}} = 1. \qquad (6)$$

This equation, (6), and with it the theory of multiple alleles may be tested by determining the frequencies of O, B, and A persons in different populations and entering these frequencies in the left side of the equation. If the theory of multiple alleles is correct the left side of the equation will always equal 1.

When we apply this procedure to the same two populations, American whites and Japanese, for which the two-gene hypothesis failed to give a satisfactory explanation, we find excellent agreement between observation and expectation, the difference between 1 and the calculated values being only about 1 per cent. This is shown in Table 25. This test for the theory of multiple alleles has been carried out for hundreds of different populations, always with close agreement between observed and expected values.

Instead of using the abstract terms listed in the headings of Table 25, it is customary to calculate, by means of formulas (4), (5), and (1), the actual frequencies p_A, q_B, and r_o of the three alleles I^A, I^B, and I^O. Addition of the three values for p_A, q_B, and r_o should, and does, give a value close to 1. In our two examples, p_A, q_B, and r_o are 0.258, 0.073, and 0.671 for whites,

TABLE 25. *ABO Blood Groups. Test of the Theory of Multiple Alleles by Means of Equation (6).*

Population	$\sqrt{\overline{O} + \overline{B}}$	$\sqrt{\overline{O} + \overline{A}}$	$\sqrt{\overline{O}}$	$\sqrt{\overline{O} + \overline{B}} + \sqrt{\overline{O} + \overline{A}} - \sqrt{\overline{O}}$
Whites	$\sqrt{0.45 + 0.10}$ $= 0.742$	$\sqrt{0.45 + 0.41}$ $= 0.927$	$\sqrt{0.45}$ $= 0.671$	0.998
Japanese	$\sqrt{0.294 + 0.206}$ $= 0.707$	$\sqrt{0.294 + 0.422}$ $= 0.846$	$\sqrt{0.294}$ $= 0.542$	1.011

TABLE 26.   *Allele Frequencies of I^A, I^B, and I^O in Six Different Populations.* (Wiener, *Blood Groups and Transfusion*, 3rd ed., Thomas, 1943.)

Population	p_A	q_B	r_O	$p_A + q_B + r_O$
English	0.268	0.052	0.681	1.001
French	0.262	0.074	0.657	0.993
Bulgarians	0.271	0.108	0.624	1.003
Arabs	0.209	0.129	0.660	0.998
Senegal Negroes	0.149	0.189	0.657	0.995
Hindus	0.149	0.291	0.560	1.000

and 0.293, 0.154, and 0.542 for Japanese, which add up, respectively, to 1.002 and 0.989. The results of some other calculations of p_A, q_B, and r_O from various populations are given in Table 26. (It may be noted that the derivation of the allele frequencies p, q, and r is not "fully efficient" in the statistical sense. Fisher and others have devised more efficient but also more complex formulas.)

Analysis of Family Data.   The theory of multiple alleles not only gives a satisfactory explanation for the relative proportions of the four blood groups in different populations but also, in contrast to the two-gene hypothesis, fits the results of all possible matings (Table 23, last column). It is interesting to note that when the theory of multiple alleles was first proposed, full agreement between the theory and the available family data was not obtained. Many discrepancies, such as those listed as "exceptions" in Table 22, were on record. Indeed, this table summarizes only more recent data, and "exceptions" were considerably more numerous in the earlier determinations. Thus, among 2,270 children from 973 families tested before 1924, the year of Bernstein's first publication, 1.32 per cent represented exceptions, but among 12,614 children from 5,559 families tested between 1927 and 1937, only 0.2 per cent were exceptions.

There were several reasons why the number of apparent exceptions decreased after the theory of multiple alleles was proposed. It has already been pointed out that "exceptions" may be a result of faulty technique in determining blood groups. In the past few decades, techniques have generally improved and fewer mistakes are made. Furthermore, special rechecks are usually made whenever an apparent exception to Bernstein's theory is encountered, and, in this way, some errors in blood-group determination are rectified.

That many seeming exceptions were really faulty determinations of blood groups has been shown in an ingenious way. Some "exceptions" are the result not of faulty determination but of illegitimacy. Such exceptions can be excluded if one selects data on blood groups of children and mothers only, leaving the fathers out of the picture. Suitable for such a study are AB mothers, who should not have O children; and O mothers, who should not have AB children. Among 946 children of 675 AB mothers, only 3 O children were found; and among 5,454 children from 4,370 O mothers, 5 AB children. These data came from fifteen different reports, and the 8 exceptions were not evenly distributed through these reports but came from only three of them. Since these three studies contain less than 5 per cent of the total number of cases examined and were all made without knowledge of the multiple allele theory—and hence were not rechecked—the exceptions may be regarded as due to errors of observation and not to inadequacy of the theory.

The Possible Occurrence of True Exceptions from Expected Genotypes. It is, of course, possible that true exceptions to the rules of inheritance of the ABO or other blood groups, or any other character, may occur. Extremely rare genes have been discovered which suppress the appearance of the ABO antigens even though the I genes are present (see p. 314). Or, although very unlikely, there is always the chance that a mutation will cause a child to have an allele which neither parent possessed. Furthermore, irregular chromosome distribution, as in nondisjunction, could account for true exceptions. If, in an AB individual, the two chromosomes which carry the I^A and I^B alleles do not segregate from each other in meiosis, gametes may be formed which carry both I^A and I^B alleles, or which lack both. If the mate of the AB individual belonged to group O, then fertilization with the abnormal gametes would result in AB and O children, either of which would be true exceptions.

This hypothetical explanation of exceptions implies that the resulting AB children would possess three instead of two chromosomes carrying I alleles ($I^A I^B I^O$) and that the O children possess only one (I^O). Since each chromosome has associated with it many more genes than the one considered here, it may be expected that the upset in genic balance caused by the abnormal number of chromosomes would lead to developmental abnormalities. Indeed, in experimental animals and plants, various abnormal traits are known to result from the presence of an extra chromosome or the absence of one of two homologous chromosomes. In some cases, only a very slight divergence from the normal phenotype is observed, but in others gross abnormalities in form and function of the individuals appear. It has even been observed that an abnormal number of chromosomes does not permit complete development but leads to death of the zygote during development. In man, one abnormal syndrome, mongolism, is caused by the presence of three, instead of the normal pair, of one of the small autosomes (p. 472). The fact that one of the very few carefully checked exceptions in a study of blood groups, an O child from an AB mother, was severely pathological—mentally deficient and nearly blind—suggests that a chromosomal abnormality was involved.

The Subgroups of A. Refined immunological tests have shown that blood group A consists of persons belonging to one or another of three different subgroups, called A_1, A_2, and A_3, and that group AB contains persons who are classed as A_1B, A_2B, and A_3B. Groups A_3 and A_3B are very small, comprising only a fraction of a per cent of all A or AB individuals. A_1 and A_1B, and A_2 and A_2B, make up about three-quarters and one-quarter, respectively, of all A or AB American whites. On the whole, pedigree studies indicate that the subgroups A_1, A_2, and A_3 depend on three alleles at the I locus, which might be called I^{A_1}, I^{A_2}, and I^{A_3}. The allele I^{A_1} is dominant over both I^{A_2} and I^{A_3}, and I^{A_2} is dominant over I^{A_3}.

The recognition of the four important alleles I^{A_1}, I^{A_2}, I^B, and I^O leads to the expectation of ten different genotypes and of six recognizable phenotypes. If one includes I^{A_3} and a fourth allele, I^{A_4}, which is even rarer than I^{A_3}, many more different genotypes and phenotypes are to be expected. It has been suggested that, like the I^A allele, the I^B allele exists in more than one form, but no definite information is available on this point.

Secretors and Nonsecretors

The ABO antigens occur in an alcohol-soluble form, not only on the red blood cells but also in many other tissues. The presence of ABO antigens in different tissues is perhaps not particularly remarkable, since the I genes of an individual are presumably present in all his cells. A more significant fact is that many persons have water-soluble forms of the ABO antigens in their *secretions,* particularly the saliva, while the secretions of other persons do not contain any ABO antigens. The "secretors" and "non-secretors" are differentiated by a pair of alleles: the former are *SeSe* and *Sese*; and the latter, *sese*. The ABO blood group of a secretor can be determined either by testing his blood or his saliva, but the saliva of a nonsecretor gives no clue. Secretion is restricted to the ABO antigens and to the so-called Lewis antigens, which will be discussed later: none of the antigens in the other blood groups are secreted.

The MN Blood Groups

Landsteiner and Levine, in 1927, found two new human antigens, which they called M and N. One or the other is found in all human blood: the red blood cells of some persons possess M; of others, N; and of still others, both M and N. Antibodies against M and N are not usually found in humans, but they can be obtained by injecting either M or N blood into rabbits or other animals, which induces the animal to produce the appropriate antibody. The serum of untreated rabbits does not agglutinate human blood cells, but that of a rabbit injected with M blood clumps both M and MN cells, and that of a rabbit injected with N blood clumps both N and MN cells (Fig. 83).

The inheritance of the M and N antigens through a codominant pair of alleles L^M and L^N has been described in the preceding chapter. That the L alleles, named L in honor of Landsteiner (1868–1943), are inherited in-

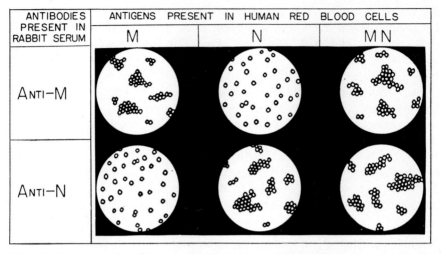

ANTIBODIES PRESENT IN RABBIT SERUM	ANTIGENS PRESENT IN HUMAN RED BLOOD CELLS		
	M	N	M N
Anti-M			
Anti-N			

FIG. 83. Reactions of red blood cells of M, N, and MN individuals to antibodies anti-M and anti-N. (Hardin, *Biology, Its Human Implications,* W. H. Freeman and Co., 1949.)

dependently of the *I* alleles can be shown by family data. Thus, marriages of OM to ABMN spouses produce four types of children, AM, BM, AMN, and BMN, in equal numbers. This shows that two separate recombining loci are involved, with the genotypes of the parents being $I^O I^O L^M L^M$ and $I^A I^B L^M L^N$. The same information can be obtained from a survey of a population. According to the Hardy-Weinberg Law, as applied simultaneously to two different loci, the frequencies of M, MN, and N individuals should be the same in each of the groups O, A, B, and AB. This is true, within chance limits, as shown in Table 27.

MN Subgroups. A number of subgroups, similar to the A_1, A_2, and other subgroups of the ABO system, have been found in the MN system. Among these is one consisting of persons who have the rare, weak antigen N_2, which depends on the presence of the allele L^{N_2}; another, of those who have the antigen M^g, transmitted by the very rare allele designated as L^{M_g}. The antigen M^g is remarkable in that it does not react with either antibody

TABLE 27. *Percentage Frequencies of the M, MN, and N Blood Groups among the O, A, B, and AB Groups.* (Wellisch, *Z. Rassenphys.,* **10,** p. 65, 1938.)

Group	Percentage		
	M	MN	N
O	32.5	46.5	21.0
A	32.6	48.0	19.4
B	31.8	47.7	20.5
AB	30.6	50.5	18.9

anti-M or anti-N. Only heterozygous $L^{Mg}L^M$ and $L^{Mg}L^N$ individuals have been found so far. A homozygous $L^{Mg}L^{Mg}$ person—who must be excessively rare—tested with anti-M and anti-N sera would be neither M nor N nor MN!

The Ss Antigens.   In 1947, twenty years after the discovery of the antigens M and N, a new antigen, S, was found. It differs serologically from M and N, occurs among individuals of all three MN blood types, and has an intimate genetic relation to them. Family studies made it clear that individuals who have S are homozygous or heterozygous for a dominant allele and that individuals without it are homozygous for a recessive allele. An antibody which agglutinates the blood cells of the homozygous recessives as well as those of the heterozygotes was soon discovered, thus indicating that there are two antigens, S and s, and three blood types, S, Ss, and s. (The nomenclature for antigens has grown up haphazardly. There is no good reason why one pair of antigens is designated by two different capital letters, namely M and N, and another pair by the capital and lower-case forms of a single letter, namely, S and s. Since heterozygotes have both antigens of a pair, it would perhaps be best to have a single letter for each pair and a subscript for each partner, e.g., M_1 and M_2, and S_1 and S_2. Since, however, MN and Ss are in general use, we shall continue to use these symbols.)

The Relation between MN and Ss.   If S and s were determined by genes different from those determining M and N, then the frequencies of M, MN, and N should be the same among both S and s individuals. As shown in Table 28, this is not true. There are appreciably more M individuals among those with S, and more N individuals among those with s. Family data also show an association between M and S, and N and s. Thus, the offspring of MNSs × Ms parents consists of only two types of children: in some families these are MSs and MNs; in others they are Ms and MNSs. Clearly, in the first group all the children received either M and S or N and s from their heterozygous parent; in the second group all the children received either M and s or N and S. Not a single sibship has ever been found which comprised more than two combinations or in which the two combinations observed were not complementary, either MS and Ns, or Ms and NS. This phenomenon has a simple explanation. There are in any population four different multiple alleles, which may be called L^{MS}, L^{Ms}, L^{NS}, and L^{Ns}. Each allele is responsible for the appearance of those two antigens noted in its

TABLE 28.   *Percentage Frequencies of the M, MN, and N Groups among 221 S– and 173 ss Individuals. (After Wiener and Wexler, 1958.)*

Individuals	M	MN	N
S–	22.3	26.9	7.0
ss	9.4	22.0	12.4

superscript. MNSs persons are of two different genotypes: $L^{MS}L^{Ns}$ and $L^{Ms}L^{NS}$.

The frequencies of the four alleles are not alike; M and S are more commonly found together than M and s, and N and s more commonly than N and S. Among whites about 25 per cent of the L alleles are L^{MS}; 28 per cent L^{Ms}; 8 per cent L^{NS}; and 39 per cent L^{Ns}. (Another hypothesis, instead of assuming the existence of four multiple alleles, assumes two pairs of closely linked genes, M and N, and S and s. See p. 191.)

There is a very rare kind of blood, called u, which does not react with either anti-S or anti-s serum—just as the rare antigen M^g does not react with either anti-M or anti-N. Genetic evidence indicates that u depends on one or the other of two very rare alleles at the L locus, L^{Mu} and L^{Nu}. Disregarding for the moment the rare antigens N^2, M^g, and others, we have thus six L alleles, namely, L^{MS}, L^{Ms}, L^{NS}, L^{Ns}, L^{Mu}, and L^{Nu}. There is a serum, called anti-U, which agglutinates the blood cells of all individuals who have at least one of the first four alleles, and thus indicates the presence of a very common antigen, U. Absence of agglutination, which indicates that the blood is type u, is characteristic for the genotypes $L^{Mu}L^{Mu}$, $L^{Nu}L^{Nu}$, and $L^{Mu}L^{Nu}$, which signifies that the alleles with u as a superscript are recessive, as far as u is concerned.

The Hunter (Hu) and Henshaw (He) Antigens. Still two other antigens —named after the two negroes, one from New York and the other from Nigeria, in whom they were discovered—are controlled by the L alleles. Both antigens are rare and the majority of persons tested do not have them. Family as well as population data show that heterozygotes for either Hu or He invariably transmit the ability to form these antigens together with a specific combination of M or N with S or s. The anti-Hu and anti-He sera have made it possible to distinguish further subtypes among the already known L alleles: L^{Ms} becomes L^{MsHu} and $L^{Ms\ not-Hu}$; and other alleles are L^{NSHu}, $L^{NS\ not-Hu}$, L^{NsHu}, $L^{Ns\ not-Hu}$, L^{NSHe}, $L^{NS\ not-He}$, L^{NsHe}, and $L^{Ns\ not-He}$. It is likely that alleles causing the appearance of still other combinations of antigenic properties of M, N, N_2, M^g, S, s, U, He, Hu, etc., will be discovered.

Genes, Antigens, and Antibodies

In recent years the concept of the gene as the unit of heredity has been subjected to critical scrutiny, particularly on the basis of experimental data from Drosophila, corn, and microorganisms. It is possible, in some cases, to distinguish between (a) the gene as a unit of transmission and recombination, which follows the Mendelian law of segregation, (b) the gene as a mutable unit, which may represent only one or another of many small regions or sites within the unit of recombination, and (c) the gene as a unit of chromosomal activity, which may be larger or smaller than either one of the units of recombination or mutation. These distinctions should be just as valid for human genes as they are for genes of flies and bacterial viruses, but in practice it is difficult to apply them. There is little doubt that the various L alleles behave as units of transmission as far as known data permit such a conclusion. This is shown by family data which indicate that heterozygous parents always segregate these alleles into two types of gametes only. That the L alleles are units of transmission is even more clearly shown by population data. If two different L alleles could be recombined by crossing over, or in some other way, to form new types of alleles—for instance, L^{MS} and L^{Ns} from the heterozygote $L^{Ms}L^{NS}$—then in a population at equilibrium all four alleles should occur in chance proportions. This would mean that $L^{MS}:L^{Ms} = L^{NS}:L^{Ns}$, but as we have seen, the proportions are not the same: namely, among whites, 25:28 and 8:39. (For a more detailed discussion, see page 258 ff. The expectation of chance proportions would not be valid if certain L alleles have a lower chance than do others of being transmitted to later generations, and if the frequency of the supposed recombination process is of the same order as, or less than, the selective difference.)

If we accept the L alleles as units of transmission, can we distinguish specific units of mutation within them? This problem would be studied directly if we could observe mutations that transform one kind of L allele into another, new or already known. It is difficult to make the necessary observations in humans, and the single likely mutation that has been described— from L^{MS} or L^{Ms} to L^{NS}—does not throw light on the topic of mutational sites.

It is tempting to think of the different antigens, M, N, S, s, U, etc., as characterizing different mutational sites on the L gene. If this assumption is made, M and N, being alternative antigens, could perhaps be thought of as defining one specific site, with N_2 and M^g characterizing still different alternative properties of the same site. S, s, and U would characterize a second site, and He and Hu either a third or a third and a fourth site. The designation of other sites would come from consideration of other antigenic properties at the L locus, some already known and others still to be discovered. How far such analysis might go is illustrated by the B blood groups in cattle, in which at least 24 pairs of alternative antigens have been recognized and more than 100 combinations of them, representing more than 100 B alleles, are known. Can one conclude from these observations that there are 24 established mutational sites at the B locus of cattle?

The assumption that different antigens are controlled by separate physiologically active sites within a blood-group gene that is transmitted as a single unit has adherents among outstanding geneticists and students of the blood groups, particularly R. A. Fisher, Race, and Sanger. Originally these investigators spoke of different but closely linked loci usually transmitted without recombination, and they predicted that crossing over between these loci would be found. When this prediction did not come true, "closely linked" was changed to "absolutely linked" loci (Fig. 84, A, B). Instead of a single gene symbol L with the allelic specification in a superscript, e.g., L^{MsHe}, the assumption of separately acting loci would be symbolized by *MSHe*, perhaps with

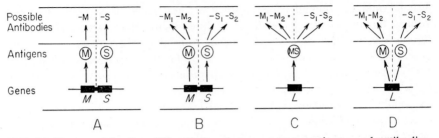

FIG. 84. Four models of possible relations between genes, antigens, and antibodies. A. Two absolutely linked genes M and S produce two separate specificities (antigens) M and S, each of which may cause, in another organism, the production of one antibody, $-M$ and $-S$. B. Gene-antigen relation as in A, but each antigen may produce more than one antibody, $-M_1$ and $-M_2$ and $-S_1$ and $-S_2$. C. A single gene produces a single antigen (MS) which may cause the production of several antibodies. D. A single gene produces two antigens, each of which may cause the production of more than one antibody.

superscripts to denote the specific allele, e.g., $M^M S^s He^{He}$ (M^M = M and not N; S^s = s and not S; He^{He} = He and not he).

The assumption of separate loci is not accepted by other outstanding immunogeneticists; for example, Wiener, Owen, and Stormont feel that there is no justification for assigning separate areas of activity to a genetic unit of recombination which controls several antigens, that is, has a multiple (pleiotropic) antigenic effect. These investigators cite Landsteiner's experiments, which contradict the idea of a specific site for each antigenic specificity. Landsteiner prepared chemicals with rather simple molecular structures and combined them with proteins. The ensuing substances acted as antigens that after injection into rabbits induced the production of antibodies. One of Landsteiner's remarkable findings was that an artificial antigen does not cause production of a single antibody but of a whole spectrum of antibodies that can be distinguished from one another. Moreover, artificial antigens that are different but closely related chemically may differ greatly in their production of antibodies.

The artificial antigens do not seem to induce a variety of antibodies by means of different molecular subsites, each of which reacts separately with the unspecific globulin molecules in the blood of the rabbit so as to transform them into specific antibodies. Rather, each antigen seems to act as a whole but with somewhat variable results—like a rubber stamp whose repeated imprints are not sharp and thus slightly different from one another. If a single, well-defined artificial antigen can induce several antibodies, why, it is asked, should this not hold for the natural blood antigens (Fig. 84, C, D)? Moreover, if several natural antigens depend on a single transmissible genetic unit, why should one conclude that these antigens are individually controlled by separately active, though linked gene sites? It is clear that the two questions are concerned with two different processes in the sequence of reactions, gene → antigen → antibody. The first process, from gene to antigen, was formerly believed by many to be relatively simple and direct, as if a gene transferred a unique antigenic specificity, perhaps a specific arrangement of the molecular surface, to a substance with which it came in contact (Fig. 84, C). It now seems clear that this transfer is less immediate and that the idea "1 gene—1 antigen" is therefore not necessarily valid. It may well have to be replaced by "1 gene—several antigens" (Fig. 84, D). The second process, from antigen to antibody, may then have to be defined by replacing "1 antigen —several antibodies" by "several antigens—several antibodies per antigen." Reactions to anti-M and anti-S sera mark either separate M and S antigens or a single antigen with multiple response (different "blood factors," C). As long as these alternatives exist, it would perhaps be best not to commit ourselves and to speak of antigenic properties of the blood rather than of antigens. However, "antigen" is usually used in a sense that covers both alternatives. At the present state of knowledge about the detailed structure of genes, antigens, and antibodies and the reaction, gene → antigen(s) → antibody(ies), it would perhaps be wisest to label different allelic units of transmission by simple superscripts, e.g., L^1, L^2, L^3, and to list in a table their antigenic properties as known by reactions to antibodies (Table 29). Although a symbol such as L^3 is, without consultation of the table, less informative than the symbol $L^{MsU \; not–Hu}$, it is less likely to imply, wrongly, that one is justified in projecting reactions to different antibodies onto hypothetical gene sites.

Regardless of the symbols used, genetic transmission is simple and is, of course, the same by any name—the symbols here are different interpretations of genic action and not of the generally agreed-on facts of transmission: any individual has two of the various kinds of existing units of segregation called alleles and transmits them in simple Mendelian fashion.

TABLE 29. *Six of the L Alleles As Defined by the Reactions of Antigenic Properties Controlled by Them.*

Alleles	Reactions with these Antisera:							
	M	N	M^g	S	s	U	Hu	He
L^1	+	−	−	+	−	+		
L^2	+	−	−	−	+	+	+	
L^3	+	−	−	−	+	+	−	
L^4	−	+	−	+	−	+		+
L^5	−	−	+	−	+			
L^6	−	+	−	−	−	−		

NOTE: Alternative designations of the alleles: $L^1 = L^{MSU}$; $L^2 = L^{MsUHu}$; $L^3 = L^{MsU \; not–Hu}$; and so on. Absence of a + or − sign indicates that no test with the respective antiserum has been made.

The Rh Blood Groups

Rh Positives and Rh Negatives. At the time of their discovery, the M and N groups seemed uncomplicated, but later studies showed the existence of a long series of finer divisions. The same applies to the Rh groups. In 1940, Landsteiner and Wiener injected blood from the Rhesus monkey into rabbits and guinea pigs. Serum containing the resulting antibodies agglutinated not only Rhesus blood cells, but also those of about 85 per cent of a population of white New Yorkers; the cells of the other 15 per cent of the population did not react with the *antiserum,* a term used to designate a serum containing antibodies.

Apparently, the blood of the majority of the humans tested contained an antigen, called Rh, which is identical with an antigen present in Rhesus monkeys or similar to it; that of a minority did not contain this antigen.

It was soon demonstrated that the presence or absence of the antigen is heritable (Table 30). Two Rh-negative parents yield only Rh-negative children, but marriages of two Rh positives or of an Rh positive and an Rh negative may produce children of both types. The proportions of the two types of offspring in the two latter marriages fit a simple single factor interpretation, according to which Rh positives are either homo- or heterozygous for a dominant allele (R) and Rh negatives are homozygous for a recessive allele (r). The reader can easily verify this statement by applying equations (5) and (6) on pages 168 and 169 to the data in Table 30. The frequency of the recessive allele in a large white population is obtained from the frequency of the recessive homozygote, which is $q_r^2 = 0.15$; thus, $q_r = 0.39$.

Since the discovery of the Rh groups, many different Rh antisera have been found, and these permit subdivision of what seemed at first to be simply two types of human blood. Most of these antisera have not been obtained from rabbits injected with monkey blood, but from humans who have produced antibodies against Rh antigens of other humans, either as a result of blood transfusions, the experimental injection of volunteers with the blood of others, or the passage of antigens from a fetus into the blood of the mother. It is this last process and its consequences for the health of the fetus that has made the Rh blood groups of unusual medical importance. The Rh interactions between mother and fetus will be dealt with in detail in Chapter 17.

TABLE 30. *Inheritance of Rh Blood Groups.* (Wiener, *Blood Groups and Transfusion,* 3rd ed., Thomas, 1943.)

Type of Marriage	No. of Families	Children: Rh-Positive	Children: Rh-Negative	Percentage Rh-Negative
Rh-positive × Rh-positive	73	248	16	6.1
Rh-positive × Rh-negative	20	54	23	29.9
Rh-negative × Rh-negative	7	—	34	100

Rh Nomenclature.   Two different styles of nomenclature are used to designate the phenotypes and genotypes of the Rh blood groups. Fisher, Race, Sanger, and others interpret the data on the assumption that there is a series of very closely, if not absolutely, linked genes, which they call C, D, E, etc., and that each of these genes has two or more allelic forms, e.g., C, c, and C^w; D and d; E and e. Correspondingly, they speak of C antigens and of anti-C antibodies, and so on. Any given gamete will contain a combination of alleles at the several loci or sites, such as CDe . . . , cDe . . . , Cde . . . , cde . . . , etc.

Wiener and others interpret the data on the assumption that a single locus has any one of numerous different alleles. These are given the base letters R and r and distinguishing superscripts, e.g., R^1, R^0, R', and r. The antigens are called Rh, rh, and hr, with super- or subscripts; the antibodies, anti-Rh, anti-rh, anti-hr, again with specifying super- or subscripts. It is obvious that the two different nomenclatures mirror two different concepts of the interrelation between gene, antigen, and antibody, concepts already discussed in connection with the L locus for blood groups M and N. In this book, preference will be given to the use of R, as opposed to CDE, but the latter will often be given also to facilitate comparisons.

The Eight R Alleles Distinguishable by Three Specific Antisera.   Three important and readily available antisera are anti-Rh_0, anti-rh', and anti-rh'' (anti-D, anti-C, and anti-E). They permit recognition of eight different alleles (Table 31; consider the first three columns of reactions only). The allele r does not control antigens that react with any one of the three sera; the alleles r', r'', and R^0 control only one antigen each; the alleles r^y, R^1, and R^2, two antigens; and R^z, all three. Each antiserum, it is seen from the table, divides the blood tested into two groups, one that reacts positively and one that reacts negatively, and the combinations of the two alternatives in sets of

TABLE 31.   *Eight of the Rh Alleles As Tested with the Three Antisera, Anti-Rh_0, Anti-rh', and Anti-rh''. (Last two columns refer to additional tests with anti-hr' and anti-hr''.)*

Alleles	Allele Frequency in Whites (%)	Reactions with Antisera				
		Anti-Rh_0(D)	Anti-rh'(C)	Anti-rh''(E)	Anti-hr'(c)	Anti-hr''(e)
r	38	−	−	−	+	+
r'	0.6	−	+	−	−	+
r''	0.5	−	−	+	+	−
r^y	0.01	−	+	+	−	−
R^0	2.7	+	−	−	+	+
R^1	41	+	+	−	−	+
R^2	15	+	−	+	+	−
R^z	0.2	+	+	+	−	−

three indicate the existence of eight different alleles. Their frequencies vary greatly, from 41 per cent to only 0.01 per cent.

Actually, blood tests do not provide a direct answer to the question: Which antigens are controlled by a specific allele? What such tests really determine are diploid genotypes, not single alleles. Genetic data show that the antigens produced by any one Rh heterozygote are the codominant sum of the antigens controlled by their two alleles or, viewed from a different angle, that the presence of an antigen reacting with any one of the three antisera is dominant over its absence. The homozygote rr is uniquely defined by its triple negative reaction, $- - -$, but more than one genotype can be assigned to all blood cells that give at least one positive reaction. Thus, blood cells which give the reaction $- + -$ are genetically either $r'r'$ or $r'r$, and individuals whose cells react $+ + +$ could belong to any one of the following genotypes: $R^z R^z$, $R^z R^2$, $R^z R^1$, $R^z R^0$, $R^z r^y$, $R^z r''$, $R^z r'$, $R^z r$, $R^2 R^1$, $R^2 r^y$, $R^2 r'$, $R^1 r^y$, $R^1 r''$, $R^0 r^y$. Some of these genotypes are very rare among whites, e.g., $R^z r^y$, and statistically, the most likely genotype for the $+ + +$ reaction is $R^1 R^2$. Pedigree data, of course, often make possible a clear decision about the specific genotype involved or narrow down the range of alternatives.

Some Further Attributes of the Eight Rh Alleles. Two antisera, besides the three named, are the readily available anti-hr' and the rare anti-hr'' (or anti-c and anti-e). No new alleles can be distinguished by the use of these sera, but they make it possible to distinguish various homozygotes from heterozygotes. Anti-hr' gives positive reactions when anti-rh' fails to do so, and anti-hr'' gives positive reactions when anti-rh'' does not (see Table 31, last columns). Anti-hr' and anti-hr'' give negative reactions when, respectively, anti-rh' and anti-rh'' give positive ones. In other words, rh' and hr', like M and N, are a pair of alternative antigens, and so are rh'' and hr''. Since heterozygotes have the antigens controlled by each of the two alleles, such genotypes as $r'r'$ and $r'r$ give different reactions to the battery of five antisera. For $r'r'$ they are $- + - - +$; and for $r'r$, $- + - + +$.

Much effort has been expended to find an antiserum to which the cells of Rh_0 negative bloods would react, but no anti-Hr_0 (anti-d) serum has yet been discovered. Although the symbols c (hr') and e (hr'') stand for specific antigenic properties, the symbol d does not stand for a recognizable antigen, but only for the absence of an antigen. From a practical point of view this was long regrettable, since in cases of possibly unfavorable mother-fetus interaction (see p. 342) it is often desirable to know whether an Rh_0-positive father carries two relevant $R^{...}$ alleles or whether he is $R^{...} r^{...}$. An anti-Hr_0 serum, if it exists, would be able to provide the answer. Fortunately, methods not involving an anti-Hr_0 serum have been worked out which permit distinction of Rh-positive homo- from heterozygotes (p. 674).

Additional R Alleles. The reader may have noticed that in Table 31 the sum of the allele frequencies of the eight alleles adds up to less than 100 per cent. The reason for this is that there are still other alleles. The most common of these is called R^{1w}; it has an allele frequency of nearly 2 per cent and is similar in its action to R^1. The two alleles can be distinguished from each other by a special anti-rh^w (anti-C^W) serum, which reacts with an antigenic product of R^{1w} but not with R^1. Both R^1 and R^{1w} control positive reactions with anti-rh′ (anti-C). The anti-rh^w serum has also led to the discovery of an exceedingly rare r'^w allele, which is similar to r' but different from it in controlling a positive reaction with anti-rh^w.

Another differentiating antiserum is called anti-hr^v (anti-V). It permits recognition of two kinds of R^o and two kinds of r alleles, but does not react with blood cells of genotypes which do not contain R^o or r. The alleles that control positive reactions with anti-hr are called R^{ov} and r^v, respectively, and those whose genotypes do not react are called R^o and r "proper." R^{ov} and R^v are frequent in negroes but rare in whites. Race and Sanger are inclined to interpret the V antigen as either a product of their postulated F site, or of a new site, G—sites additional to C, D, and E.

Only two more examples of additional R alleles will be cited. One comprises a whole group of alleles which have been called "variants of $R^{o''}$" (cD^ue) and which differ from the typical R^o by controlling antigens that give only weak reactions with anti-Rh$_o$, or reactions with anti-Rh$_o$ sera from some but not all bloods. These variant alleles are, in a way, intermediate between typical R^o, which controls strong reactions with all anti-Rh$_o$ sera, and typical r, which leads to no reaction with any anti-Rh$_o$ sera. Intermediate reactions to anti-Rh$_o$ sera are also found with variants of R^1 and other R alleles. Still other variant alleles of a corresponding intermediate type are known for reactions to anti-rh′ and other antisera.

A remarkable R allele is $\overline{R^o}$ (–D–). Blood of the very rare persons who are homozygous for this allele reacts positively with anti-Rh$_o$ but not with anti-rh′, anti-hr′, anti-rh″, or anti-hr″! Thus, the $\overline{R^o}$ allele is an exception to the otherwise nearly universal rule that an R allele controls one or the other of the two antigens rh′ or hr′ (C or c), and also either rh″ or hr″ (E or e). The symbol $\overline{R^o}$ denotes the existence of these unusual attributes without indicating how $\overline{R^o}$ differs from other R alleles. On the other hand, the notation –D– was devised in order to suggest that the C and E sites had actually been lost from the chromosome (*chromosome deficiency;* see also p. 198).

The Heterozygote R^1r'.   In heterozygotes the different R alleles usually act as codominants, leading to the production of all antigens controlled by each of the two alleles. According to Cepellini, the R^1r' heterozygote is exceptional in that its anti-Rh$_o$ reaction is not the reaction typical for R^1 in other genetic combinations. Rather, it reacts with anti-Rh$_o$ sera in an "intermediate" manner, like some of the variants of R^1 (CD^ue). Pedigree studies make it clear that the intermediate reactions of R^1r' are not caused by an actual R^1 variant, but only by the combination of typical R^1 with r'. A certain R^1r' man with the atypical intermediate reaction who was married to an

rr woman produced an R^1r daughter with the typical reaction to anti-Rh_o; and a typically reacting R^1r woman married to an $r'r$ man had, among her children, a typically reacting R^1r son and an atypically reacting R^1r' daughter.

The reason for the exception to typical dominance in the heterozygote R^1r' is not known. The C–D–E notation has suggested an explanation for this phenomenon. According to it, the genotype R^1r' is written as CDe/Cde; and R^1r, as CDe/cde. If we consider reactions to anti-Rh_o as expressions of D and d, we must then ascribe the normal reaction of R^1r to the fact that d is next to c, and the intermediate reaction of R^1r' to d being next to C. Such *position effects* are known in other organisms, in which they have been tested by comparison between the two double heterozygous combinations of linked loci A and B, namely, Ab/aB and AB/ab (the oblique line separates two genes in one chromosome from their alleles in the homologous chromosome). In these tests it was certain that the A, a and the B, b alleles in the two heterozygotes were the same, since AB and ab had been synthesized by crossing over from Ab and aB. In the R alleles no crossover syntheses have been possible, so that it remains unknown whether the supposed d site in the Cde combination is identical with the supposed d site in the cde combination. It is therefore not clear why R^1r' shows intermediate reactions against anti-Rh_o, even on the C–D–E interpretation.

The Hypothetical Gene Sequence D–C–E.   Fisher's original hypothesis of three linked loci envisages occasional crossing over between C and D and between D and E. Given the existence of the two common combinations Cde and cde in the English population, it attempts to explain the origin of the rarer combinations, such as cDe and Cde. If the sequence of the three loci is CDE, then the rare combinations could be produced from CDe/cde heterozygotes by double crossovers only, on either side of D or d. Since double crossovers seemed less probable than singles, it was assumed that the true sequence is DCE and that the heterozygotes should be written DCe/dce. From such heterozygotes single crossovers between D and C would result in dCe and Dce as desired by the creator of the theory.

Support for the D–C–E notation was seen in the fact that the $\overline{R^o}$, or $-D-$, allele described above could now be written $D/-/-$. In this way the supposed deficiencies for C and E would encompass adjoining loci and represent a single missing chromosomal segment instead of two missing segments separated from each other by the D locus.

Serious objections can be raised to the interpretation of the origin of rare Rh alleles from their frequent forms by crossing over, particularly since in some racial groups the rarer alleles cannot be derived by single crossing over from the more frequent alleles. There are other objections to the interpretation of $\overline{R^o}$ in terms of a chromosomal deficiency. Homozygous $\overline{R^o}\overline{R^o}$ persons are fully viable in contrast to other organisms in which homozygotes for deficiencies are lethal or sublethal. Although the C–D–E–F . . . interpretation is very ingenious, it does not explain some important phenomena, and those who support it have been forced to retreat and redesign it several times.

Differences in Allele Frequencies in Different Racial Groups. Most references to the frequencies of the Rh alleles are qualified by the statement that they relate either to whites or to negroes. This is necessary since there are striking differences in allele frequencies between different populations. We have mentioned this earlier in regard to the PTC taster alleles, and also in regard to the *I* alleles for the ABO blood groups, and the same applies to alleles at other blood-group loci discussed in this chapter. A general treatment of the anthropological significance of variations in allele frequencies and detailed examples will be found in Chapter 31.

A Brief Summary of the Genetics of Rh. The analysis of genic loci may be compared with that of atomic "species." For a long time it was believed that there was a single type of atom for each element—carbon, phosphorus, uranium, etc.—but we now know that each consists of a family of isotopes that have similar or nearly identical chemical properties and yet differ in atomic weight, nuclear composition, and other respects. Physicists and chemists are not expected to know by heart all isotopes and their properties. Instead, tables are provided in which they can look up these facts. Similarly, any one of the numerous Rh alleles that are defined by their reactions with a series of antisera will be known to most persons concerned only after consultation of appropriate tables.

For some general purposes it is still adequate to distinguish Rh-positive and Rh-negative individuals by the reaction of their blood to a single serum containing anti-Rh_o. Use of two additional sera, anti-rh' and anti-rh", permits recognition of a total of eight Rh alleles (Table 31). Two other sera define the same eight alleles in more detail and permit the recognition of distinctions between some homo- and heterozygous genotypes which otherwise appear phenotypically alike. The inheritance of the Rh alleles follows the simple rules of single factor transmission. Any one individual can be homozygous for a single allele or heterozygous for two alleles, but a great variety of different multiple alleles may be found in any population.

Other Blood-group Systems

At the time this book is being written, six other blood systems are known which are inherited independently of each other and of the ABO, MN, and Rh systems, and still other systems have not been studied intensively. The most closely studied systems are listed in Table 32. Apart from P, their names are derived from the persons who were either the first known carriers of the antibodies or of the antigen. Only two alleles have been recognized for the Lutheran, Duffy, and Kidd systems, but three or more for P and Kell. These alleles either determine the presence or absence of an antigen or a pair of

TABLE 32.   *Some Other Blood Group Systems and Their Alleles.*

Blood System	Designations of Alleles*
P (= Q of Furuhata)	P^1, P^2, p
Kell	K, k, k^P
Lutheran	Lu^a, Lu^b
Duffy	Fy^a, Fy^b
Kidd	Jk^a, Jk^b
Lewis	Le, le

* After either Race and Sanger, or Wiener and Wexler.

alternative antigens, or control more complex situations such as those described for the MN and Rh systems. It may be surmised that future work will reveal more involved genetic and immunological situations in each system. (The naming of the Duffy allele reflects the controversy concerning single *vs.* linked loci. Race and Sanger choose the symbol *Fy*, the last two letters of *Duffy,* in order to avoid the first letter *D*, which appears in the *CDEF* nomenclature which they support. Wiener, who is opposed to this nomenclature, dropped the letter y from *Fy*, to make the symbol *F*, which conflicts with the *F* symbol of the *CDEF* proponents.)

In every blood-group system, alleles which lead to the appearance of specific antigenic properties are always dominant over alleles which do not produce them. If two alleles each lead to different antigens, they are codominant in the heterozygotes.

The basic genetics of most blood groups is well understood even though many of the precise and theoretically intriguing details are still obscure. For some time the Lewis groups were the outstanding exceptions, but even the basic features of their genetics now seem to be understood. The difficulties to understanding were connected with a peculiar interaction between the gene *Le, le* in the control of the antigen Le^a and the secretor gene *Se, se* (see p. 187). Accordingly, one has to determine the presence or absence of Le^a separately for the saliva and the red blood cells. In the saliva the genotypes *LeLe* and *Lele* cause the appearance of Le^a regardless of the secretor genotype— be it *SeSe, Sese,* or *sese*—but on the red blood cells Le^a is present only when the dominant allele *Le*, homozygously or heterozygously, is accompanied by homozygous *sese*. No antigen is known which would be dependent on the recessive allele *le*. A special antigen, Le^b, which appears on the red blood cells of *Se–Le–* persons, does not seem to be controlled by a specific allele and its origin is not clear.

One of the genes connected with the Lewis group—namely, the secretor gene—is located in the same chromosome as the Lutheran gene. This is the only known linkage involving blood-group loci.

"Private" and "Public" Blood Antigens. A number of antigens have been found only in single kindreds; others are found in nearly all persons. It is difficult to investigate whether specific private, or family, antigens belong to any one of the well-established blood-group systems since they are so rare, but some have been found to be controlled by very rare alleles of a known system. The public antigens are hard to recognize because their existence becomes known only if the rare individuals in whom they are lacking are discovered.

In the past, some antigens that were originally believed to be private have later been found to be common in racial groups other than that in which they were discovered. A striking example is the Diego-antigen, Di^a, which is inherited as a dominant. It is very uncommon in whites, but abundant in American Indians, Chinese, and Japanese. The *Di* gene seems to occupy a locus different from those of all other known genes for blood groups.

The Number of Blood-group Combinations. Since there are at least nine blood-group systems, each represented by at least two blood groups and some by many, it is obvious that genetic recombination produces a great variety of combinations of blood types in any one person. Some of these combinations are rare and others common, but even relatively common combinations occur in only one out of several hundred persons. Race and Sanger point out that the commonest combination of groups in England—O, M, N, s, Rh_1, rh, P_1, Lu^a negative, K negative, Fy^a and Fy^b positive, Jk^a and Jk^b positive, and Le^a negative and Le^b positive—is found in only 1 out of 270 persons. They have also encountered a person with the combination B, M, N, S, Rh_{1w}, Rh_1, P_2, Lu^a negative, KK, Fy^a negative, Jk^a positive, and Le^a positive, which should have a calculated frequency of only 1.4 in 100,000,000.

It is possible to demonstrate the great diversity of human blood groups even without the complete battery of all available antisera. Some 475 Londoners were tested for blood reaction with antibodies against A_1, A_2, B; M, N, S; Rh_o, rh', rh^w, hr', rh'', hr''; K; Lu^a; and Le^a. They belonged to 296 different types. Of these, 211 were unique, each being represented by a single person. Forty-five types occurred alike in 2 persons, 17 others in 3 persons each, and the rest were distributed as follows: 9 types in 4 persons each, 7 in 5, 1 in 6, 4 in 7, 1 in 8, and 1 in 10. The 211 unique individuals constituted 44 per cent of the whole group; thus, given the result of the tests of a sample of blood, there were about 2 chances in 5 of identifying its donor. If a few more agglutination tests, and perhaps tests of hemoglobin constitution, of the newly discovered antigen groups of white blood cells, of the serum proteins (see p. 202), and others are added, it may soon be possible to identify a person from his blood alone—as is already done from fingerprints and other external features. Only identical twins, triplets, and so on, will remain indistinguishable by blood tests.

Multiple Allelism for Hemoglobin, Serum Protein Traits, and Red-Green Color Blindness

Proof of multiple allelism in man is most easily obtained from alleles that are present in such high frequencies that it is possible to make observations

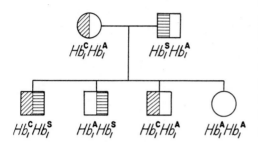

of numerous individuals heterozygous for the various allele combinations and of their segregations as studied in their offspring. It also makes it possible to apply allele frequency analyses to populations and thus to secure data for a comparison between observed ratios of phenotypes and the ratios predicted from theories of multiple allelism. As we have seen, such comparisons are possible for many blood-group systems. Based on pedigrees, evidence of multiple allelism has been obtained for at least three

FIG. 85. Pedigree of a family in which the three alleles for normal, sickle cell, and C hemoglobin segregate. Absence of shading = hemoglobin A, diagonal shading = hemoglobin C, horizontal shading = hemoglobin S. (After Smith and Krevans, *Bull. Johns Hopk. Hosp.*, **104**, 1959.)

codominant genes concerned with the molecular structure of hemoglobin (see p. 57). Normal hemoglobin, sickle-cell hemoglobin, and hemoglobin C are controlled by the alleles $Hb_1{}^A$, $Hb_1{}^S$, and $Hb_1{}^C$. A pedigree of a family in which all three alleles segregate is shown in Figure 85.

Three codominant alleles, β^B, β^C, and β^D, which divide a population into groups of individuals whose serum contains different proteins of the β-globu-

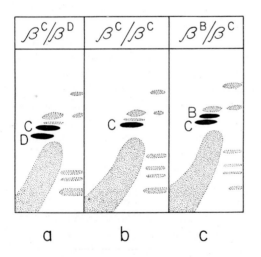

FIG. 86. The results of electrophoresis of β-globulins from the sera of three individuals. The β-globulins were initially placed in the left-hand corner of each area and the electric fields applied once in the upward direction and once from left to right. a, from a $\beta^C\beta^D$ heterozygote who possesses β-globulins C and D; b, from a $\beta^C\beta^C$ homozygote who possesses C and not D; and c, from a $\beta^B\beta^C$ heterozygote who possesses B and C. The stippled areas represent other β-globulin components, among them the small amounts of B found in individuals who do not carry the β^B allele. (After Smithies, *Nature*, **181**, 1958.)

lin type are known. These proteins are characterized by their specific speeds of migration under the influence of an electric current (electrophoresis; Fig. 86). Other serum proteins, the α_2-globulins, or haptoglobulins, are controlled by an independent locus. Two alleles in homo- and heterozygous combinations are responsible for the three known haptoglobin groups, but it is almost certain that variant forms of these alleles will have been discovered by the time this sentence appears in print (Fig. 54).

We turn now to a different type of trait. The genes controlling the different kinds of red-green color blindness provide outstanding examples of multiple alleles. There are at least five alleles whose phenotypic effects, in homo- and heterozygotes, present problems concerning the existence of a single locus or two closely linked loci that are similar to those encountered for the Rh and other blood-group genes. The alleles for color blindness are located in the X-chromosome, and will be discussed in Chapter 13, Sex Linkage.

The Fate of Tissue Grafts: Histo-incompatibility Genes

When pieces of skin taken from one person are grafted to another, as in severe burns, the transplant does not "take" permanently but sloughs off after a few weeks. Such *histo-incompatibility* can also be observed in transplants of other tissues, including tumors. The destruction of the foreign tissue by the host is the result of immunological reactions. The transplant possesses antigens not present in the host, these antigens cause the production of antibodies by the host, and the interaction between the antibodies and antigens leads to the death of the transplant's cells.

In mice, detailed evidence of a genetic basis of histo-incompatibility has been obtained. Transplants between two strains homozygous for different alleles of a histo-incompatibility locus, H^1H^1 and H^2H^2, are not successful, nor are transplants from H^1H^2 hybrids to either parental type. However, reciprocal transplants from either parent to the hybrid are permanent.

Why is this true? Apparently, the alleles H^1 and H^2 control the production of different antigens. The presence of an antigen within tissue transplanted to an animal which lacks this antigen causes the production of specific antibodies, but an animal whose tissues already carry the antigen will not produce the antibodies and will therefore tolerate the transplant. In the mouse, at least fourteen different histo-incompatibility loci are known, some with multiple alleles; most experiments can be explained on the basis of the assumption that in a heterozygote the two different alleles codominantly lead to the production of different antigens. The outcome of transplantation experiments in certain other hybrids requires the assumption that the heterozygote does not possess either of the antigens that are present separately in its parents, but that a new antigenic "hybrid substance" is formed under the influence of the heterozygous genotype.

It is a remarkable and obviously necessary phenomenon that an animal or man does not ordinarily form antibodies against his own antigens. This tolerance is established at an early embryonic stage. Indeed, tolerance even against foreign antigens can be attained if the foreign tissue is grafted on the embryo early enough. It has been known for some time that, in cattle twins of different genotypes, blood-forming cells can pass from one embryo to the other, and that this "foreign" tissue becomes permanently established in the host. Recently some human blood mosaics—defined as producers of a mixture of genetically different cells—have been discovered in which a similar embryonic "transplantation" had led to permanent tolerance.

Although a genetic analysis of histo-incompatibility in man is lacking, there is little doubt that the general situation is the same as in other mammals.

Difficulties in Proving Multiple Allelism

Evidence of multiple allelism is often difficult to obtain. Thus, for example, recessive albinism is known from many different kindreds. Within each kindred, albinos undoubtedly are homozygous for the same allele. It is difficult, however, to prove or disprove that the albino gene in one pedigree is the same as that in another, that is, that they are alleles of each other. Only when people from both kindreds, particularly albinos themselves, intermarry can this be decided. A few such intermarriages are on record, and in all but one the resulting albino children showed the allelism of the genes involved. One family in which two albino parents had three nonalbino children seems to demonstrate nonallelism in spite of like phenotypes (see p. 106; unfortunately no blood-group tests were made to exclude the possibility that a nonalbino, and not the albino husband, was the biological father of the children).

Proof of allelism for two rare dominant genes occurring in different kindreds, such as the gene for woolly hair, is even less frequently possible than for recessives, since it depends on the recognition of individuals who have obtained the dominant from each of the different kindreds. The phenotype of such an individual would not be decisive, since he may well show an extreme woolly phenotype regardless of whether he is homozygous for a dominant allele at a single locus or heterozygous for each of the dominants at separate loci. Only his offspring might reveal his genotype by being all woolly if he were the former, or segregating for woolly and nonwoolly if he were the latter. Considering the rarity of individuals with woolly hair, it is not surprising that no intermarriages between two different families are known. It remains undecided, therefore, whether the woolly-hair alleles that occur in different pedigrees are located at identical loci. The problem of the allelism of woolly hair shows how difficult it may be to discover whether like phenotypes are due to like genotypes.

In this discussion, we have assumed that all woolly-haired individuals in all pedigrees are phenotypically alike. No question of multiple allelism was involved, therefore, but only the question whether all woolly-hair genes were alleles of one another. In many cases, the situation is more involved, since variations can often be observed in the expression of a given character from individual to individual. It will be shown, in Chapter 16, that such variations may be caused by environmental influences or by differences in the "genetic background" in which the "main" gene acts. They may also be controlled by different genes responsible for similar phenotypes: genes which may be either different multiple alleles or occupy different loci. In the absence of recorded marriages between individuals whose differences in otherwise similar traits are due to their different genotypes, it is often impossible to decide definitely whether the difference is due to different genes at different loci or to multiple alleles. Under special circumstances, however, a decision is easy. If, for instance, one of the genes lies in a sex chromosome and the other in an autosome, multiple allelism cannot be involved. On the other hand, if all genes under consideration are autosomal, no conclusion can be drawn, since all may be at different loci in the 22 different autosomes, all may be alleles of a single locus, or some may be multiple alleles and others belong at different loci.

If several similar genetic traits are due to genes located in the same chromosome, it is still possible that they are at different loci. This has been established in other organisms: for example, in Drosophila, "singed" and "forked" bristles look very much alike and are both based on genes in the X-chromosome, but an accurate localization proves that they lie far away from each other. Such cases are less common, however, than those in which similar phenotypes based on genes in the same chromosome are really due to multiple alleles.

In man, with his large number of chromosome pairs, the chance that genes similar in effect and located in the same chromosome are allelic is greater than in organisms with a smaller number of chromosomes. If the oversimplified assumption is made that all four different chromosomes in Drosophila have an equal chance of containing a given gene, then the chance that two genes with similar effect lie in the same chromosome pair would be 1/4. This is a high probability, and finding that two genes are in the same chromosome pair would, therefore, not be surprising. In man, on the other hand, with his 23 chromosome pairs, the chance that two genes with similar effect will lie in the same chromosome pair would be only 1/23. This is a rather low probability, and finding that two genes with similar effect are in the same chromosome pair would, therefore, suggest that there was a special reason for this, namely, that the two genes are allelic to each other. In other words, localization of similar genes in the same human chromosome will usually be due to their allelic nature.

Further Examples of Multiple Alleles

On the basis of this reasoning concerning the localization of similar genes it is likely that there exists a set of at least three alleles for the so-called

Duchenne type of muscular degeneration: a dominant allele for normal health; a recessive for late onset of the disease; and a recessive for early onset. These genes are typically sex-linked, i.e., located in the X-chromosome (see Chap. 13).

Similarly, it is probable that there are several recessive alleles of the X-linked gene for hemophilia, or bleeder's disease. This at least has been the interpretation of the fact that the severity, the age of onset, or the part of the body in which internal bleeding occurs is often similar among the affected individuals of a given kindred, but different from one kindred to another. However, these families must be restudied, since it is now likely that at least two different loci in the X-chromosome can give rise to types of bleeder diseases.

If, in the future, it proves possible to locate rare alleles in the chromosomes accurately by means of well-established chromosome maps, the rarity of such alleles will no longer be a hindrance in deciding whether differences in a phenotype are a result of separate localization or multiple allelism. Understanding of the type of inheritance will enable the prediction of expected types of offspring and will be helpful in all considerations of the appearance of traits in pedigrees and populations.

Multiple Isoalleles.   In general, different alleles are recognized by clearly different phenotypic effects. If two or more alleles are very similar in their effects, it may often be difficult to discriminate between them—even to be aware of their separate existence. If, for instance, two alleles for hemophilia control blood-coagulation times that differ only slightly in length and if there is a variability in this time from one individual to another within each of the two genetically different groups, it may not easily become known that two alleles are actually present in the population. In such cases, one speaks of abnormal, or mutant, isoalleles.

Perhaps of more fundamental importance are normal isoalleles; that is, alleles that each control a phenotype within the range of normality but different phenotypes in that range. Much normal variation may have its basis in the presence of many normal isoalleles at many loci.

It is seldom possible to find specific evidence of normal isoalleles. One way of demonstrating their existence becomes available when heterozygotes for a dominant abnormal allele show somewhat different phenotypes if the allele is combined with different normal isoalleles. Cases suggestive of this have been found in pedigrees in which there is great similarity between the phenotypes of affected sibs but little similarity between phenotypes of affected parents and their affected children. In pedigrees of the type of muscular dystrophy, which is due to a dominant autosomal gene, there is a much lower correlation between the ages of onset of the affliction of parents and children ($r = 0.32$) than between the ages of onset of paired sibs ($r = 0.66$). Similarly, variabilities in expression of a dominant autosomal gene for congenital abnormalities of the nails and of the patellae (kneecaps) show no significant parent-child correlation but very significant sib-sib correlation (0.46 for nails; 0.58 for kneecaps). According to Penrose, a genetic explanation for this phenomenon might be as follows: In certain families the affected parent is heterozygous for the mutant allele D and a normal isoallele d^1, and this combination (Dd^1) causes early onset or strong expression of the trait. The nonaffected parent is homozygous for a different isoallele (d^2d^2). The affected children are all Dd^2, a genotype that leads to late onset or weak expression of the trait. The affected sibs therefore will be similar among themselves (positive correlation), but different from the affected parent (negative correlation). In other families, the affected parent may be Dd^2, resulting in late onset or weak expression of the trait, and the non-affected parent d^1d^1. The affected children will be Dd^1, with early onset or strong expression (again positive sib-sib and negative parent-sib correlation). Still other families will have other isoallelic combinations—$Dd^1 \times d^1d^1$, $Dd^1 \times d^1d^2$, etc.—some of which give positive correlations between parents and children as well as among sibs. Given high frequencies of both d^1 and d^2, or of additional isoalleles, the combined data will add up to absence of parent-child correlation but will retain positive sib-sib correlation.

This chapter has given various examples of multiple alleles in man. They are important in both family and population genetics. Their recognition has provided the genetic interpretation of the striking diversities of human blood types and of other human differences. In addition they play a role in the theoretical discussions of genes, gene structure, and gene action.

Problems

82. Six alleles (A^1, A^2, A^3, A^4, A^5, and A^6) occur at a certain gene locus. Enumerate, in two columns, all homozygous and all heterozygous combinations.

83. Give all possible genotypes for each of the following phenotypes relating to the blood groups:

(i) O	(iii) A_2	(v) A_1B
(ii) A	(iv) B	(vi) A_2B.

84. Given the alleles I^{A_1}, I^{A_2}, I^{A_3}, I^B, and I^O and the alleles L^{MS}, L^{Ms}, L^{NS}, and L^{Ns}, how many different genotypes are possible? How many phenotypes?

85. Assume the existence of 4 alleles of the I locus, 4 of L, 8 of R, 3 of P, 3 of K, and 2 each of Lu, Fy, Jk, Le, and Se. How many homozygous genotypes can be formed? How many genotypes, either homozygous or heterozygous?

86. From the allele frequencies given in Table 26, determine the frequencies of the four ABO blood groups among: (a) Bulgarians, (b) Arabs, (c) Hindus.

87. The frequencies of the ABO blood group alleles among Arabs and Hindus are given in Table 26. (a) If equal numbers of these two peoples intermarry at random, what will be the allele frequencies of the resulting population? (b) What will be the frequencies of the four blood groups?

88. In marriages of two $I^A I^O$ $L^M L^N$ people, what is the probability: (a) Of a child being A, M? (b) Of having one A, M child in a sibship of four? (c) Of having at least one (i.e., one or more) A, M child in a sibship of four?

89. With the use of Table 31, calculate the expected frequencies of the following genotypes in a population: rr, rr^y, $r^y r^y$, $R^1 r$, $R^1 R^1$.

90. The blood of a man gives positive reactions with all five antisera listed in Table 31. (a) What are his possible genotypes? (b) If it is found that his son has blood which reacts as $- - - + +$, what is the man's genotype?

91. List all possible types of transplantations, and their ultimate success or failure, between animals of the following histo-compatibility genotypes: $H^1 H^1$, $H^2 H^2$, $H^3 H^3$, $H^1 H^2$.

References

Bernstein, F., 1925. Zusammenfassende Betrachtungen über die erblichen Blutstrukturen des Menschen. *Zeitschr. Abstgs. u. Vererbgsl.,* **37:** 237–270.

Carlson, E. A., 1958. The bearing of a complex-locus in Drosophila on the interpretation of the Rh series. *Am. J. Human Genet.,* **10:** 465–473.

Fisher, R. A., 1947. The Rhesus factor. A study in scientific method. *Am. Scientist,* **35:** 95–103.

Owen, R. D., 1959. Genetic aspects of tissue transplantation and tolerance. *J. Med. Ed.,* **34:** 366–384 (also *Am. J. Human Genet.,* **11,** 2 Part 2: 366–384).

———, 1959. Immunogenetics. *Proc. Xth Intern. Congr. Genetics,* **1:** 364–374. University of Toronto Press, Toronto.

Penrose, L. S., 1948. The problem of anticipation in pedigrees of dystrophia myotonica. *Ann. Eugen.,* **14:** 125–132.

Race, R. R., and Sanger, R., 1959. *Blood Groups in Man.* 3rd ed. 377 pp. C. C. Thomas, Springfield, Ill.

Renwick, J. H., 1956. Nail-patella syndrome: evidence for modification by alleles at the main locus. *Ann. Human Genet.,* **21:** 159–169.

Stormont, C., 1955. Linked genes, pseudoalleles and blood groups. *Am. Naturalist,* **89:** 105–116.

Wiener, A. S., 1943. *Blood Groups and Transfusion.* 3rd ed. 438 pp. C. C. Thomas, Springfield, Ill.

———, 1954. *An Rh-Hr Syllabus.* 82 pp. Gruen & Stratton, New York.

———, and Wexler, I. B., 1958. *Heredity of the Blood Groups.* 150 pp. Gruen & Stratton, New York.

CHAPTER 12

MEDICOLEGAL
APPLICATIONS
OF GENETICS

The genetic parent, or parents, of a given individual are not always known with certainty. It has happened, though very rarely, that newly born babies in a hospital have been assigned to the wrong mothers. A person may claim to be the long-lost child of a couple (usually a wealthy one!). War and social upheaval may separate children and parents for years, so that it is difficult to establish their relationship. Occasionally, the claims of individuals born outside the United States that they are citizens by American parentage have been doubted.

By far the most common cause of uncertain relationship is illegitimacy; in such cases, the paternity of the child is often in doubt. More than 40 of every 1,000 live births in the United States are registered as illegitimate; specifically, in 1956, there were approximately 193,500 illegitimate births out of a total 4,163,090. In reality, these figures for illegitimacy are inaccurate. They refer only to children of women not legally married and do not include children from extramarital relations. Conversely, many so-called cases of illegitimacy are derived from purely monogamic associations in which only social custom or poverty has kept the couple from entering their marriage into an official register and paying the required fee. There are, also, several states in which births are registered without reference to the married or unmarried state of the mother: for these states, only estimates are available.

Many thousands of cases of disputed paternity and a few of disputed maternity come before the courts each year, mainly to decide whether a "suspected father" should support his supposed offspring. Hereditary characters are useful in helping to decide whether or not a person could be the

209

parent of a specific child. Traits which depend on simple single factor inheritance, including multiple alleles, are particularly suitable for medicolegal
analysis, since the relation between presence of the trait and presence of its
determining allele is clear cut.

Exclusion of Paternity

There is no question that genetic evidence often shows conclusively that
a specific man can *not* be the father of a given child: he is clearly not the
father if the child carries a gene which is not carried either by him or the
mother. However, genetic evidence that is compatible with the possibility
that a specific man is the father of a given child does not constitute proof
of his actual paternity. Almost always, other men have genotypes that are
also compatible with their possible parenthood of the child. In general,
exclusion of paternity is decisive; nonexclusion is not. In some situations,
however, exclusion of one individual may be sufficient for positive designation
of another. There may be nongenetic, social evidence that one of a known
group of individuals must be the parent of a child. For example, a married
woman may be suspected of adultery with a specific man, and it is desired
to determine whether the husband or the suspect is the father of a child.
If genetic evidence excludes the suspect, the husband will be judged to be
the father, and vice versa. Such a judgment depends on showing that one
of the two men could not be the father.

In many countries or states where genetic evidence is acceptable in
court procedures, only decisions based on exclusion of paternity (or maternity) are considered valid. In some countries positive evidence of paternity
that is based on genetic facts is also accepted. The justification for positive
assignment that is not based on exclusion of another person will be discussed at the end of this chapter. First, genetic methods of exclusion will
be presented. These methods depend on the analysis of the genotypes of
certain traits of mother, child, and putative father. The most widely used
traits are the blood groups.

Evidence Using the ABO Blood Groups. If evidence of paternity is
derived from a study of the ABO blood groups of the individuals concerned, it is obvious that in many instances no decision can be reached. This
is true not only when all three individuals belong to the same blood group,
but even when the child and the putative father both have the same *I* allele
and that allele is not present in the mother. Thus, an A child from an O
mother can have an A father, but no specific A man can be so designated
in the absence of other evidence; if the putative father is O or B, however, there
is no possibility that the child is his.

When it can be assumed that only one or the other of two men is the
father of a child, a first prerequisite to a genetic determination of parenthood is that the genotypes of the two men be different. Both of them,

TABLE 33. *An Example in Which It Is Equally Possible Genetically That Either One of Two Men May Be the Father of a Certain Child.*

Individual	Group	Possible Genotypes	Possible Matings Mother	Father (I or II)	Genotype of A Child
Mother	A	$I^A I^A$, $I^A I^O$	$I^A I^A$ ×	$I^O I^O$	$I^A I^O$
Child	A	$I^A I^A$, $I^A I^O$	$I^A I^A$ ×	$I^A I^B$	$I^A I^A$
Possible Father I	O	$I^O I^O$	$I^A I^O$ ×	$I^O I^O$	$I^A I^O$
Possible Father II	AB	$I^A I^B$	$I^A I^O$ ×	$I^A I^B$	$I^A I^A$, $I^A I^O$

therefore, must not belong to groups O or AB. If both belong to either group A or group B, it will seldom be known whether they are homozygous or heterozygous for the I^A or I^B allele, but knowledge of the blood groups of one or both parents of the two men may permit recognition of their genotypes. Even if the genotypes of the two men are known to be different, an assignment of genetic paternity will depend also on knowing the genotype of the mother as well as that of the child. Assuming that one of the men is $I^O I^O$ and the other $I^A I^B$ and that the child and its mother both belong to group A, then no decision can be made. As shown in Table 33, all four genotypically different kinds of matings can give rise to a group A child. On the contrary, a clear conclusion as to paternity can be reached if the mother belongs to group O. In this case the father of an A child would be the AB man; any children derived from the O man could only be O.

Genetic information is more frequently used to exclude the possibility that a suspected man is the father of the child in question. Clearly, regardless of the group of mother, an O man cannot be the father of an AB child, or an AB man of an O child. If the man belongs to group A or B and it is not known whether he is homozygous, or heterozygous for I^O, an exclusion of paternity depends on the genotype of the mother; if neither she nor the man carry a gene present in the child, paternity of the suspect is excluded. The reader will find it instructive to compile a table showing the 16 combinations of the four ABO blood groups of alleged father and known mother and listing both the possible and the impossible blood groups of children from these unions. Additional exclusions can be arrived at if the subgroups dependent on I^{A_1} and I^{A_2} are taken into account.

Evidence Using the MN Blood Groups. The ABO blood groups were the first genetic traits employed on a large scale in cases of doubtful parenthood. Since the discovery of the existence and kind of inheritance of the MN groups, extensive use has also been made of these.

Use of the antibodies for M and N make exclusion of paternity, if possible at all, particularly easy, since the three genotypes $L^M L^M$, $L^M L^N$, and $L^N L^N$ are all phenotypically recognizable. A child who possesses an M or

N antigen not present in the putative parent cannot be his offspring. However, this test is not able to exclude paternity for a putative father who is MN, since such a man could be the father of any of the three types of children, M, MN, or N. Tests employing the antibodies against the S and s antigens of the L alleles allow still further exclusions.

Evidence Using the Rh Blood Groups.   Numerous Rh alleles provide additional possibilities for exclusion of parentage. Because of the rarity of some of the sera containing specific antibodies, medicolegal tests are usually restricted to the use of the more common of them—namely, anti-Rh_0 (anti-D), anti-rh′ (anti-C), anti-rh″ (anti-E), and perhaps anti-hr′ (anti-c).

Other Evidence.   Any of the other genetically well-understood systems of blood groups can be employed to exclude paternity. Nor is there a necessary restriction to blood groups. Any set of genotypes that are regularly expressed as specific phenotypes may serve the same purpose. Preference in tests for characteristics of the blood is primarily due to their easy recognition. Future paternity tests will, if necessary, almost certainly involve not only various blood groups but also hemoglobin and serum protein traits. Apart from blood, determination of the secretion of ABO antigens is useful. Less satisfactory, if taken by themselves, are traits in which there is variability in expression. Thus, the presence of hair on the middle digit of one or more of the four fingers is indicative of the presence of specific alleles which are dominant over alleles causing absence of such hair, and a man who lacks this hair may therefore be presumed not to be the father of a child with mid-digital hair from a mother without it. Although the genetic hypothesis accounting for this trait is not definitive, its use may, in otherwise undecided cases, add to the probability of exclusion or nonexclusion.

The Probabilities of Exclusion.   The usefulness in paternity cases of any test based on a pair or group of alleles depends on the frequencies of the alleles in the population. In most aboriginal American Indian populations the frequency of the I^0 allele is 1: all individuals belong to blood group O. Obviously, in such populations the ABO blood groups supply no information on paternity. Formulas which give the probability that a man who is not the father can be excluded, based on allele frequencies, have been worked out by Wiener and Boyd.

For the ABO groups the maximum probability of exclusion of a wrongly accused man is about 20 per cent, but in most populations the allele frequencies permit only a lower percentage of exclusions. For the MN groups exclusion has a maximum probability of 18.75 per cent, this maximum probably being actually approached in many populations. For the Rh groups the chance of exclusion in Caucasoid populations is approximately 25 per cent.

TABLE 34. *An Example in Which Exclusion of Paternity Is Based on Both ABO and MN Blood Groups.*

Mother	Putative Father	Children			
		First	Second	Third	Fourth
O, MN	AB, N	O, MN	A, M	O, M	A, MN
Parentship of putative father excluded on basis of child being:		O	M	O, M	?

Evidence Using More than One Blood-group System. In many cases in which knowledge of the ABO phenotypes of the individuals under investigation does not permit exclusion, analysis of the MN blood groups may do so. Conversely, the ABO groups may supply an answer where the MN groups fail to do so. An example would be the case of an O, MN woman and an AB, N man who is alleged to be the father of one or more of her four children —the children being O, MN; A, M; O, M; and A, MN (Table 34). The man cannot be the father of the first child because of the lack of genetic relation between the AB group and the O group, though there is genetic compatibility of the MN constitutions. For the second child, no decision is possible on the basis of the ABO relation, but the N man cannot be the father because of the lack of N antigen in the child. The third child cannot be his on the double score of genetic incompatibility between ABO and MN blood groups. Finally, no decision is possible about the fourth child, since neither his A nor MN phenotypes contradict the constitution of the putative father. In general, it is obviously desirable, in medicolegal cases, to base a verdict on the results of tests for both ABO and MN antigens, since the probability of exclusion is greatly increased if both sets of data are available.

On the same grounds, information on the Rh groups may lead to exclusion when ABO and MN tests fail to do so. If, in the example presented in Table 34, both the mother and the putative father had been Rh negative but the last two children Rh positive, then the man would also be excluded as the father of the fourth child. The third child, who had been shown not to be the man's child by the ABO and MN groupings, would now be excluded in triplicate by his ABO, MN, and Rh constitution.

Although the probabilities of exclusion of wrongly accused men increase with a multiple use of blood groups, the increase becomes smaller with each additional test. If two blood groups each provide a 20 per cent probability of exclusion, then using the second after the first has been tried will lead to exclusion of 20 per cent of the 80 per cent for whom the first was not decisive; i.e., it will add only 16 per cent. Multiple use of the ABO, MN, and Rh groups in a white population may provide about 50 per cent exclusion, and additional evidence based on other known groups will raise the chances to slightly more than 75 per cent.

Among a sample of several thousand court cases the frequency of actual exclusions fell far short of the theoretical expectation, and the discrepancy suggests that perhaps 2 out of 3 men imputed to be the fathers of illegitimate children are indeed correctly designated.

Positive Assignment of Paternity

Mohr reports a case in Norway in which the normal mother of a brachyphalangic child designated a specific man as the father. The man denied his involvement; but when requested by the court to show his hands, he was seen to be short-fingered. Consequently, he was adjudged to be the father and ordered to support the child. This decision was made because brachyphalangy is caused by a dominant gene and so rare that the probability of another individual with the same genotype being the father was most remote. The brachyphalangic man must have been heterozygous for the rare dominant gene and hence have had a 50 per cent chance of begetting a normal child. The absence of the abnormality in the child would not have absolved him from possible paternity, but would have left the case undecided unless other evidence had been forthcoming.

A similar basis for assignment of paternity exists in other cases, where the putative father and the child both carry a very rare allele that is not present in the mother. Thus, a child heterozygous for an r^y allele of the Rh blood-group system born to a mother who does not possess r^y can only have been sired by an r^y- man. The frequency of such men in a white population is considerably less than 1 in 1,000, so that if a man accused of being the father of an r^y- child proves to be r^y- himself, the likelihood that he is the father is very high. It is clear, however, that in a large population there are many other men who have the r^y allele. A positive assignment of paternity could not be based solely on the "suitable" genotype of the man in question, but would depend also on the strength of the nongenetic evidence that led to his being named as the possible parent.

If a child carries a very rare allele, at more than one locus, that he must have inherited from his male parent and if a designated man is shown to carry all of them, then, of course, it is highly probable on purely genetic grounds that he is the father. Such genetic situations, however, are rare by definition.

A more generally applicable method than that of basing positive assignment of paternity on rare alleles is to base the assignment on combinations of several genes, none of which by itself is particularly rare. Assume that a child has the genotype $A'-$, $B'-$, $C'-$, $D'-$, $E'-$ (where the dashes stand for the alleles received from the mother, which are assumed to be different from the A', B', C', D', E' alleles received from the father). If the allele frequencies (p) of the paternal genes are, for instance, 0.3, 0.2, 0.6, 0.05, and 0.4, respectively, then the probability that a man will have a genotype that enables one of his sperm to be $A'B'C'D'E'$ can be calculated as follows.

In order to be able to transmit A', he must be either homo- or heterozygous for this allele. The probability that he does not have A' is $q^2 = 0.7^2$, and that of his having it is $(1 - 0.7^2)$. Similarly the probability that he carries B' is $(1 - 0.8^2)$, and that of his carrying $A'B'C'D'E'$ together is the product of the separate probabilities $(1 - 0.7^2) \cdot (1 - 0.8^2) \cdot \ldots = 0.0096$. The smaller the probability of finding a given combination of genes, the greater the probability that a man who carries it is the father of a child who has it too.

It must be emphasized that positive assignment of paternity is based on probability and thus can never be entirely certain, no matter how great the probability; whereas genetically justified exclusions are certain. In many countries, therefore, the law does not recognize positive assignment of paternity. In Germany—one of the countries where positive assignments are acceptable—expert testimony is couched in terms of probability. Designations of the degree of the possibility of paternity that are used in the German courts are (1) not determinable, (2) more probable than not, (3) probable, (4) very probable, (5) probable to a degree bordering on certainty, (6) more improbable than not, (7) improbable, (8) very improbable, and (9) improbable to a degree bordering on certainty.

These conclusions are normally based not on a determination of genetic constitutions but on a comparison of physical similarities. Facial appearance and other traits of the mother, child, and putative father are compared in great detail, and the degree of similarity between the father and child is one of the bases for the probability designations. Even though such procedures cannot fail to involve subjective evaluation, they may, in expert hands, reach a fair level of validity. This has been tested on a sample of 100 children of known paternity and their parents. In no case was a man mistakenly declared not to be the father of his child: none of the conclusions was of improbability of the degrees (6) to (9) above. For 7 father-child pairs the similarity evaluation led to the verdict "not determinable," but for the remaining 93 children different degrees of positive probability assignments were possible.

Formulas have been worked out which would permit an exact numerical evaluation of the probability of correctness of a paternity judgment if exact figures on the relative frequencies with which individual traits of children are found in their true fathers and in men of the general population were known. But such figures are only rarely known.

Superfecundation.   The use of genes as markers of paternity has provided an answer to the question of whether it is possible for twins to have different fathers. A case is on record in which an O, M mother bore as twins a boy who was B, M and a girl who was A, MN. Two men were considered, on non-genetic evidence, to be the only possible fathers of the children. One of the men was A, MN; the other, B, M. The first man was thus excluded from being the father of the boy and the second man from being the father of the girl. If it is granted that the twins were not the offspring of a third man who was AB, MN, this case may be regarded as proof of "superfecundation."

Telegony.   An elementary knowledge of genetics shows that it is not possible for one male to influence the genotype of the child of another male. Among breeders of dogs, there was a widespread superstition that mating of a purebred bitch with a dog of another breed not only leads to an immediate litter of mongrels (which is true), but also gives rise to mongrel traits in puppies that are later sired by males of the same breed as the bitch. This erroneous belief in *telegony* (influence of one sire on the "distant offspring" of a later sire) is also held by some to be true of man: the procreation of a child by a man and woman who belong to different anthropological groups is thought to have an effect on the appearance of a child from a later union between the woman and a man who belongs to the same group as she. Some opponents of racial intermixture have spread falsehoods of this kind deliberately.

Problems

92. For a given year, find the following data, if available, in U. S. National Office of Vital Statistics, *Vital Statistics of the United States,* Washington, D. C., 1937– date:

   (a) Total number of births for the United States Birth Registration Area.
   (b) Total birth rate per 1,000 population.
   (c) Total number of illegitimate births for the United States.
   (d) Total illegitimate birth rate per 1,000 live births.
   (e) Illegitimate birth rate per 1,000 live births in Louisiana, New York, Ohio, Vermont for (i) Whites, (ii) All other races.

93. Construct a table listing all combinations of putative father, mother, and child which would allow a falsely designated man to establish nonpaternity by MN types.

94. Four babies were born in a hospital on the same night and their blood groups were later found to be O, A, B, and AB. The four pairs of parents were: (i) O and O, (ii) AB and O, (iii) A and B, (iv) B and B. All four babies can be definitely assigned to their parents. How?

95. For all of the following six mother-child combinations, list: (a) The phenotypes of men who could be the father of the child in each case. (b) The phenotypes of men who could not be the father in each case.

Combination	1	2	3	4	5	6
Mother	O, M	O, N	O, MN	AB, MN	A, N	B, MN
Child	O, M	A, MN	O, MN	AB, MN	AB, MN	O, N

96. Assume a case of disputed paternity involving a woman X, two men Y and Z, and four children, 1, 2, 3, and 4. On the basis of the blood properties, assign each child to his father, whenever possible. Let the constitutions be:

Individuals involved	Blood properties	
♀ X	A	MN
♂ Y	B	MN
♂ Z	AB	N
1	AB	N
2	B	MN
3	O	N
4	AB	M

97. A woman of the blood properties A, M has a child B, MN. Her husband, who is A, N, accuses a certain man of being the father of the child. If the accused man turns out to be B, N, how would you judge the case?

98. Exclusion of alleged paternity is relatively more frequent for AB men than for O men. Why?

99. Analyze the possibility of exclusion of paternity in the following cases:

Case	Putative father	Mother	Child
(a)	$I^O I^O, L^M L^N, R^1 r$	$I^O I^O, L^M L^N, R^1 R^2$	$I^O I^O, L^M L^N, R^1 r$
(b)	$I^{A_2} I^{A_2}$ or $I^{A_2} I^O, L^M L^M, rr$	$I^{A_1} I^{A_1}$ or $I^{A_1} I^O, L^N L^N, R^1 R^1$	$I^{A_1} I^{A_1}$ or $I^{A_1} I^O, L^M L^N, R^1 R^2$
(c)	$I^{A_2} I^{A_2}$ or $I^{A_2} I^O. L^N L^N R^1 R^1$	$I^O I^O, L^N L^N, r'' r$	$I^B I^B$ or $I^B I^O, L^M L^N, rr$

References

Essen-Möller, E., and Quensel, C.-E., 1938. Die Beweiskraft der Ähnlichkeit im Vaterschaftsnachweis.—Theoretische Grundlagen. *Mitt. Anthrop. Ges. Wien,* **68:** 9–53.

Geyer, E., 1940. Ein Zwillingspärchen mit zwei Vätern. *Arch. Rassenbiol.,* **34:** 226–236.

Schade, H., 1954. *Vaterschaftsbegutachtung.* 250 pp. Schweizerbart'sche Verlagsbuchhandlung (Erwin Nägele), Stuttgart.

Schatkin, S. B., 1953. *Disputed Paternity Proceedings.* 3rd ed. 823 pp. Bender, New York.

Schwidetzky, I., 1954. Forensic anthropology in Germany. *Hum. Biol.,* **26:** 1–20.

U. S. National Office of Vital Statistics, 1937–date. *Vital Statistics of the United States.* Washington, D. C.

Wiener, A. S., 1943. *Blood Groups and Blood Transfusion.* 3rd ed. Chapter 21, 380–398. Thomas, Springfield, Ill.

————, Owen, R. D., Stormont, C., and Wexler, I. B., 1957. Medicolegal applications of blood grouping tests. *J. Am. Med. Assn.,* **164:** 2036–2044.

CHAPTER 13

SEX LINKAGE

The examples of simple dominant and recessive inheritance discussed in the preceding parts of this book do not show any association with sex. Individuals of one sex are no more frequently affected than those of the other, and there is only a random relation between the sex of the affected parent and the sex of affected offspring. This is to be expected if the gene responsible for a given trait is carried in any one of the 22 pairs of autosomes. Since men and women alike possess these autosomes, the hereditary roles of the two sexes should be equivalent.

The ordinary rules of inheritance, however, are not valid for all human traits. For some, the frequencies of affected individuals are very different in the two sexes, and the reappearance of the trait in children depends upon whether it is handed down by the father or the mother. Some of these traits are now recognized as being due to ordinary autosomal alleles that have different phenotypic expressions in the two sexes; examples of these will be discussed in Chapter 16, Variations in the Expression of Genes. The present chapter deals with traits which are due to alleles whose transmission is specifically related to sex.

Our understanding of these has been made possible only by the discovery of the sex chromosomes (see p. 21). The twenty-third pair of chromosomes is not the same in both sexes, for the female has two X-chromosomes in her nuclei and the male one X- and one Y-chromosome. Therefore, it can be expected that the two sexes are not equivalent in respect to genes located in the sex chromosomes. Traits based on such genes are called sex linked; their mode of transmission, sex-linked inheritance.

Obviously, two main types of sex-linked inheritance are possible, depending upon whether the sex-linked genes are located in the X-chromosome or the Y-chromosome. Many X-linked genes are known, but, except for sex determiners, the existence of Y-linked genes is still problematical.

In addition to genes restricted to either the X- or the Y-chromosome, i.e., absolutely or completely X- or Y-linked, it has been suspected that there are others which by crossing over in the male are able to change their localization in successive generations: to go back and forth from the X- to the Y-chromosome and from the Y- to the X-chromosome. Such genes have been called partially or incompletely sex linked. The unresolved question of the existence of such genes will be discussed in Chapter 14. In general, the terms X-linkage and Y-linkage will only be used to designate complete linkage of the respective types.

A female, with her two X-chromosomes, has two alleles of all X-linked genes and may be either homozygous or heterozygous for them. A male, who has only one X-chromosome, is called *hemizygous* for the single allele of his X-linked genes, since the terms homo- and heterozygous imply the presence of two alleles.

Y-linkage

The inheritance of a gene which is permanently located in the Y-chromosome is exceedingly simple: (1) Only men possess a Y-chromosome, and the gene should, therefore, be found in the male sex only; (2) since all sons, and no daughters, receive a Y-chromosome from their father (Fig. 87), only the sons receive the gene, which they in turn transmit to all of their sons but to none of their daughters (holandric inheritance). If the gene expresses itself phenotypically whenever it is present in an individual, the inherited trait will be strictly limited to the male sex.

Restriction of a trait to males is not, however, sufficient evidence for the presence of a Y-linked gene. Some traits that occur only in the male sex, such as tenor, baritone, and bass voices, do not depend on Y-linked but on autosomal alleles that are present in both men and

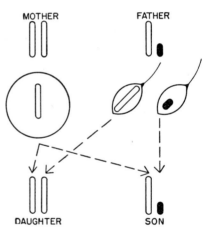

FIG. 87. Transmission of the Y-chromosome from one generation to the next.

women, but which express themselves differently in the two sexes. Male sex-limited autosomal and male sex-limited Y-linked inheritance are distinguished by the fact that the autosomal traits depend equally on alleles transmitted by both parents, while Y-linked traits neither appear in women nor are transmitted by them.

"Porcupine Men."   Only a few of the many hundreds of inherited characteristics in man have been reported to be transmitted in Y-linked fashion. The most remarkable case of this nature was that of the so-called porcupine men who lived in England during the eighteenth and nineteenth centuries. In 1716, a normal-appearing baby, Edward Lambert, was born to two normal parents. They had many other children, all of whom remained normal throughout life. Edward's skin, however, began to yellow when he was seven or eight weeks old. It gradually became black, and then began to thicken until his whole body—except palms, soles, head, and face—was covered with rough, bristly scales and cylindrical bristle-like outgrowths nearly an inch long.

Edward Lambert was reported to have had 6 sons, all afflicted with the same condition. The trait was said to have appeared in four later generations and was said to have been present in every son of an affected father, absent in every daughter, and never transmitted by any daughter. A pedigree, reprinted in numerous publications, including the original edition of the present book, showed 12 affected males and 7 unaffected female sibs in six generations (Fig. 88, A).

It is hardly possible for an author to verify each statement that he finds in earlier, presumably careful publications. The pedigree of the porcupine men, however, seemed to deserve some special inquiry. By going back to the contemporary accounts of the affected Lamberts, who were exhibited for

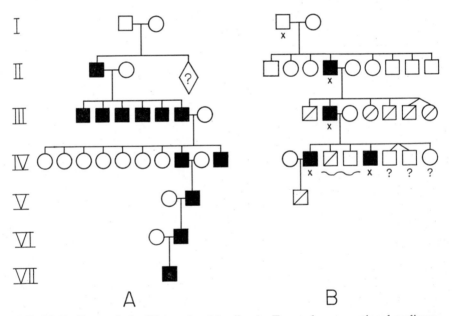

FIG. 88. Pedigree of the "Porcupine Men." A. Formerly conventional pedigree. B. Revised pedigree. Symbols with an oblique line indicate that these individuals were reported to have been affected but have not been seen by independent witnesses. The wavy line in IV indicates that it is not known whether IV-3 or IV-4 is the older. The zygosity of the twins in IV is unknown. The question marks signify absence of information concerning the trait. (Stern, *Am. J. Human Genet.,* **9,** 1957.)

money in Great Britain, Germany, France, Italy, and possibly Russia, and by consulting parish registers of births, baptisms, marriages, and burials, it was ascertained that important parts of the supposed family tree do not correspond to the facts. The most reliable evidence available indicates that there were only three instead of six generations of affected males, and that 5 instead of 12 persons were affected. The 6 children of the first affected male were not all sons but included 2 daughters. If their father, who had reported correctly the presence of both sexes, was also right in his statement that all 6 children were affected, then the existence of 2 affected daughters immediately rules out Y-linkage (Fig. 88, B). If we disbelieve his report of the presence of the skin disease in all his children, then we must disregard all but the one son who was carefully described by several contemporary observers. Similar considerations apply to the next generation (IV), the last in which affected individuals are definitely known to have appeared. We now are certain that there were at least 6 sons and probably 1 (and not 7) daughters in this generation, and it is nearly certain that only 3 of these sons were affected (Fig. 88, B). Altogether, this reappraisal leads to the conclusion that the porcupine men cannot be used as an example of Y-linkage. Presumably they owed their abnormality to an extremely rare dominant autosomal gene. This interpretation is not invalidated by the fact that all individuals definitely known to be affected were males. If there were really only 5 affected persons, then chance could easily account for a distribution of 5 males and no females instead of the expected near equality. It is more likely, however, that there may have actually been affected females, as the statement of the original porcupine man seems to indicate.

Webbed Toes.   Another record often quoted to substantiate Y-linked inheritance concerns a web-like connection between the second and third toes of the 14 male members of a Schofield family in the United States. None, it was stated, lacked the trait, and none of the 11 daughters of the affected men were said to possess it. At the time the pedigree was published, only 3 of the daughters had married, and their 7 children were all normal.

Before accepting the sex association of webbed toes in this pedigree as proof for Y-linkage, it must be stated that there are numerous pedigrees for webbing between toes that do not show this type of inheritance, since both men and women possess and transmit webbed toes. Most of these pedigrees, however, show a higher incidence of the trait in males than in females, which makes them somewhat similar to the Schofield pedigree. The relatively high frequency of inherited webbed toes raises the question of "selection for curiosity's sake" in singling out the Schofield pedigree, and the observed preponderance of affected males over females in other pedigrees must be taken into account in any consideration of the expected probability of the appearance of the trait.

The higher incidence of webbed toes in males is probably due to variable expression of a dominant autosomal allele during the development of the two sexes. In order to calculate the chance of finding a pedigree like that of the Schofield family if inheritance were of the dominant autosomal type, the probabilities of phenotypic expression in all 13 male descendants of affected men and of phenotypic absence in all 11 female descendants must be determined. If it is assumed, for example, that the webbed-toe allele is always expressed visibly in the male but in only 1/10 of all females, then the probability that a son of an affected father will be affected is 1/2; however, the probability of a daughter being normal is not only 1/2 (the chance that she does not inherit the allele) but in addition, $1/2 \times 9/10$ (the chance that she does inherit the allele but that it does not show in her phenotype). The total chance that a woman would not have webbed toes would then be

$$1/2 + (9/10 \times 1/2) = 19/20.$$

Under these various assumptions, and omitting from consideration the marriages of 3 normal women who had 7 normal children, the probability of a deviation in the observed direction from an expected sex distribution of affected and nonaffected individuals as large as that found in the Schofield family is

$$(\tfrac{1}{2})^{13}(\male)^{13} \times (\tfrac{19}{20})^{11}(\female)^{11},$$

which is equal to about 1 chance in 14,000. Such a small probability makes it seem very unlikely that the trait can be attributed to an autosomal dominant gene. On the other hand, some questions remain unanswered. Webbing of toes is a variable trait—clearly discernible in some persons, less discernible in others. How reliable was the classification in this family? Was there an unconscious inclination to regard borderline cases which barely suggested webbing as positive in males, but as negative in females? Only a restudy of the still-living individuals in the original Schofield family and of their descendants could resolve these doubts. In the meantime this pedigree of webbed toes cannot be considered evidence of Y-linkage.

A few other kindreds have been described in which some trait has been transmitted in a fashion that seems to indicate Y-linkage, but in each the evidence for this mode of inheritance is incomplete. There is no reason why the human Y-chromosome should not carry typical genes, but comparison with other organisms does not necessarily lead to such an expectation. Some fish have Y-linked genes, but the Y-chromosome in Drosophila is nearly devoid of them. In no mammal is the role of the Y-chromosome in inheritance known, except for its function in sex determination (see Chap. 20).

X-linkage

Color Blindness.   If red, green, and blue lights are projected on a screen so that they overlap, the triple mixture of these primaries will make a white light. A person with normal vision will require a particular intensity ratio of red:green:blue to "see" white—he is a *normal trichromate* (requiring three primaries to match white). Some persons, however, need more of one of the primary colors and less of the other two—these are *anomalous trichromates.* Nearly as many persons need only two primaries to see "white"—these are *dichromates* (requiring two primaries). A very few people can match a white light with just one primary color (any one); these *monochromates,* or *achromates* (requiring one primary), perceive no hues and see only white or gray.

Most of these conditions have a genetic basis. They are all called "color blindness," but here we must distinguish at once between total color blindness (*achromasia*) and the partial color blindnesses, *dichromasia* and *anomalous trichromasia,* often popularly referred to jointly as red-green color blindnesses. In each of the last two categories, there are four subtypes. We shall concern ourselves here with only the two commonest subtypes of dichromasia and the two commonest subtypes of anomalous trichromasia. Something will be said about each of these four kinds of deficiency, but, for the present, the four will be treated as if they constituted a single genetic entity called color blindness, and as if there were no other (much rarer) kinds of color-vision deficiency.

During the late eighteenth and the nineteenth century, it became known that color blindness is inherited. Observations showed a number of regularities. Thus, if a color-blind man marries a normal woman, all of their children are usually normal. If a color-blind woman marries a normal man, a peculiar "crisscross" type of inheritance takes place: all sons are color blind, like the mother; and all daughters are normal, like the father. The phenotypically normal daughters of a color-blind parent are, however, able to transmit the defect to their sons. In spite of other observations on the transmission of color blindness which added to the already complicated picture, there seemed to be certain simple rules which were formulated under such names as "Nasse's Law" and "Horner's Law."

A true understanding of the empirical findings was obtained only after similar rules had been formulated for the inheritance of quite different traits (e.g., pigmentation in birds, moths, and flies), and after theoretical geneticists and cytologists had applied to these the knowledge gained from microscopic studies of chromosomes. It became clear, about 1910, that the peculiar features of the inheritance of color blindness could be understood if it were assumed that (1) the genes concerned are located in the X-chromosomes, and that (2) normal color vision is dominant over color blindness. Assuming that the Y-chromosome plays no role in the determination of color vision, men are hemizygous for either the normal or the color-blindness allele (located in their one X-chromosome), while women (who have two X-chromosomes) may be of any of three types: homozygous normal, homozygous color blind, or heterozygous.

Every man receives his X-chromosome from his mother and does not transmit it to his sons (Fig. 89). Every woman receives an X-chromosome from each of her parents. Her sons inherit either one or the other of her X-chromosomes, as do her daughters, who, in addition, receive a second X-chromosome from their father. From these facts, it follows that the sons of a color-blind man do not inherit their father's defect (Fig. 90). All daughters, however, are heterozygous carriers who, on the average, will produce normal and color-blind sons regardless of the color-vision status of their husbands (Fig. 92). Should the husband be color blind, then half of the daughters will be carriers and half will be color-blind homozygotes. Finally, all the sons of a normal man and a color-blind woman will be color blind, like the mother, and all the daughters will be heterozygotes, though phenotypically normal, like the father (Fig. 91). Pedigrees showing various types of marriages are reproduced in Figure 93. In general, genes which are transmitted in the fashion outlined for color blindness are thereby recognized as X-linked. Since most sex-linked genes are located on the X-chromosome (and not on the Y-chromosome), the terms X-linked and sex-linked are often used as synonyms.

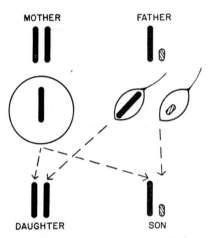

MOTHER   FATHER

DAUGHTER   SON

FIG. 89. Transmission of the X-chromosomes from one generation to the next.

Frequencies of Affected Men and Women. The male is more frequently affected by X-linked recessive traits than is the female. This is readily under-

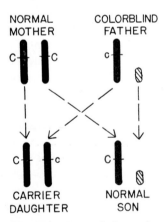

NORMAL MOTHER   COLORBLIND FATHER

CARRIER DAUGHTER   NORMAL SON

FIG. 90. Transmission of color blindness. Normal woman×color-blind man.

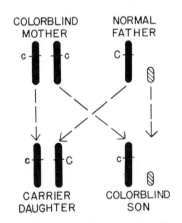

COLORBLIND MOTHER   NORMAL FATHER

CARRIER DAUGHTER   COLORBLIND SON

FIG. 91. Transmission of color blindness. Color-blind woman× normal man.

stood both from a consideration of individual marriages and from population genetics. All couples in which the female is heterozygous or homozygous for the X-linked abnormal allele may have affected sons, but only in
the rare cases where the husband is affected and the wife is also affected or
is a carrier can there be affected
daughters. If q is the frequency
of the abnormal X-linked
allele, and $p = (1 - q)$ is that
of the normal allele, then a
man in the general population
will have the probability q of
having an X-chromosome with
the abnormal allele and the
probability p of having the normal allele. The frequency of
the two kinds of men is, therefore, identical with the allele
frequencies. For women, the
proportions of the homozygous
normal, heterozygous, and homozygous affected individuals
are like those for autosomal

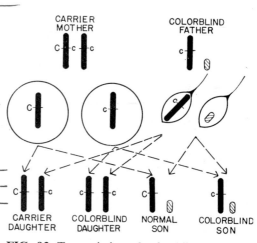

FIG. 92. Transmission of color blindness. Carrier woman×color-blind man.

genes. There is a probability of p^2 that both X-chromosomes will carry the
normal allele, of 2pq that one X-chromosome will have the normal and the
other will have the abnormal allele, and of q^2 that both X-chromosomes will
carry the abnormal allele.

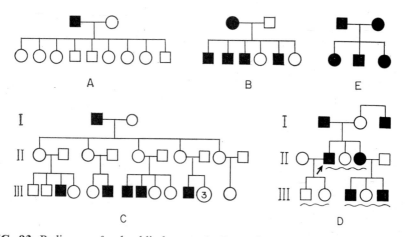

FIG. 93. Pedigrees of color blindness.   A. Part of Pedigree No. 406, Nettleship.
B. Pedigree No. 584.   C. Part of Horner's pedigree.   D. Pedigree, Whisson,
1778.   This is the first known pedigree of color blindness.   E. Pedigree, Vogt.
(A, B, after Bell, *Treas. Hum. Inher.*, **II**, 2, 1926; C, after Gates, *Human Genetics,*
Macmillan; E, after Baur, Fischer, Lenz.)

[handwritten annotation in top margin:] affected women = q^2 men = q

These considerations show an interesting relation between the relative frequencies of men and women affected with X-linked recessive traits. The frequency of the affected women, q^2, should be the square of the frequency of affected men, q. In different white populations, from 5 to 9 per cent of all men are color blind; i.e., q varies from 0.05 to 0.09. If there are 0.05 color-blind men, there should be only 0.0025 color-blind women; or, if 0.09 color-blind men, 0.0081 color-blind women. Thus, in a population in which 9 per cent of the men are color blind, color-blind women should be 11 times as rare as color-blind men. If 5 per cent of the men are color blind, affected women should be 20 times as rare.

Actual figures lie close to these expected ones, but the agreement is not perfect. One reason it is not is that some women who are heterozygous for color blindness have "poor color aptitude." Moreover, an occasional heterozygous women is color blind because of imperfect recessiveness of the gene concerned, and certain rare abnormalities of sex determination introduce slight deviations from expectation (see p. 430 and Chap. 20). Finally, not all kinds of color blindness are caused by the same genotype, as we have assumed in our discussion.

Homozygous color-blind women are rare, but heterozygous carriers are relatively frequent. In a population in which the incidence of color blindness among men is 0.08 (q) that of carrier women is 0.15 ($2pq$).

The Chief Kinds of Color Blindness. All, or possibly all but one, of the X-linked partial color blindnesses fall into two different groups, called *protanoid* and *deuteranoid*. Physiologically these two groups seem to be fundamentally distinct. In each group there are three subtypes that may be regarded as variations of the same kind of defect. The two most common subtypes in the protanoid group are the anomalous trichromatic (ordinary *protanomaly*) and the dichromatic (*protanopia*). The two most common subtypes in the deuteranoid group are the anomalous trichromatic (ordinary *deuteranomaly*) and the dichromatic (*deuteranopia*) (in these four terms the accent is on the syllable "no"). The popular names for all these conditions are misleading, since they were coined before the physiology of the defects began to be understood.

A very extensive study of the incidence of these four conditions that was published by Waaler in 1927 was based on tests given to secondary-school children in Oslo, Norway. In all, 9,049 boys and 9,072 girls were available, and parents and other relatives were studied whenever this seemed important. Waaler found that about 5 per cent of the males were deuteranomalous, and that each of the other three defects was present in about 1 per cent of the males. Since all four of these abnormalities are transmitted in an X-linked fashion, the percentages of affected males indicate corresponding allele frequencies of 0.05 and 0.01. Females homozygous for the different genes are expected at frequencies equal to the squares of 0.05 and 0.01, or 0.0025 and 0.0001, respectively. Thus, homozygous deuteranomaly should be more common in women than any other homozygous type of color blindness, and Waaler's observations confirmed this.

The Number of Loci for X-linked Color Blindnesses.

The question arises: Do four different genes at two or more different loci in the X-chromosome control the common types of color blindness, or are they controlled by different alleles at a single locus? This question could most easily be answered if there were numerous women (with sons available for study) known to carry one of the four genes in one X-chromosome and another of the four in the other X-chromosome. Six different combinations of two X-chromosomes carrying different genes are possible. They would usually originate from marriages of men affected by any one type of color blindness to women heterozygous for normal color vision and some type of color blindness different from that of their husbands.

Women who possess two X-chromosomes with different genes for color blindness can be ascertained through close relatives. Thus, if a woman has two or more sons and if two types of color blindness occur among them, it may be concluded that she is heterozygous for two different color-blindness genes. The same conclusion applies if her father exhibits one type of color blindness, and a son another. Such women have been discovered. When heterozygous for protanomaly and protanopia, they are phenotypically protanomalous. This suggests that protanomaly and protanopia are allelic to each other, with the former (the "lesser" deviation from normality) dominant (Fig. 94, A). Women who are heterozygous for deuteranomaly and deuteranopia are phenotypically deuteranomalous. This suggests that these two conditions are also allelic to each other, and that the minor deviation from normality is again dominant over the major one (Fig. 94, B). Thus, there are two sets of three alleles, the first with increasing dominance in the order protanopia-protanomaly-normality, and the second in the order deuteranopia-deuteranomaly-normality. Although it has been suggested that each of the two sets has at least one more allele, which is intermediate in effect between the two abnormal alleles, this need not concern us here.

A rigorous demonstration of the allelic nature of protanomaly and protanopia or of deuteranomaly and deuteranopia would have to come from evi-

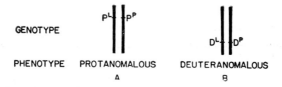

GENOTYPE P^L P^P D^L D^P

PHENOTYPE   PROTANOMALOUS   DEUTERANOMALOUS
                    A   B

FIG. 94. A. Dominance of protanomaly in heterozygous women of the genotype protanomaly/protanopia. Interpretation in terms of one pair of loci with two abnormal alleles, P^L and P^P. B. Dominance of deuteranomaly in heterozygous women of the genotype deuteranomaly/deuteranopia. Interpretation in terms of a different pair of loci with two abnormal alleles, D^L and D^P.

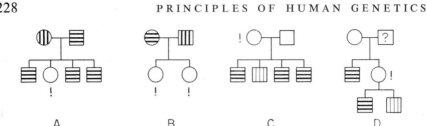

FIG. 95. Pedigrees involving women (marked "!") who are compounds of two different X-linked alleles for defective color vision. Heavy horizontal lines = protanopia; heavy vertical lines = deuteranopia; light vertical lines = deuteranomaly. (A, B, after Franceschetti, *Bull. Acad. Suisse Sc. Médic.*, **5**, 1949, and Franceschetti and Klein, *Acta Genet.*, **7**, 1957; C, after Komai, 1947; D, after Waaler.)

dence of segregation, based on a study of numerous sons of women heterozygous for both "prot" or for both "deuter" genes. If they are alleles, segregation should be absolute, and all sons of such mothers should be affected with either one or the other of the two defects. In the very limited number of suitable pedigrees known, this has been found to be true.

The question whether the prot and deuter genes occupy two separate loci in the X-chromosome or whether they all belong to one single allelic group at one locus has been the subject of much thought. One method of approach is to study women who have one X-chromosome with a prot defect and another with a deuter defect. All four possible combinations—(1) protanomalous/deuteranomalous; (2) protanopic/deuteranopic; (3) protanopic/deuteranomalous; and (4) protanomalous/deuteranopic—have been identified with reasonable certainty. The identification was, in two cases, based upon the direct knowledge that one parent of the "compound" women was protanopic and the other parent deuteranopic (Fig. 95, A, B) and, in other cases, on the fact that the sons were of two color-defective types (Fig. 95, C, D). In the fourth pedigree reproduced in Figure 95, the phenotypes of other members of the family add to the evidence (from her sons) that the woman II-2 was a protanopic/deuteranomalous heterozygote.

A remarkable fact about prot-deuter compound women (Fig. 95) is that they have *normal* color vision (a few do not, but their abnormal vision seems not to be connected with their compound genotype). A simple calculation lends support to the belief that women heterozygous for both a protanoid and a deuteranoid allele should have normal color vision. If the frequencies of the four atypical genes are designated r, s, t, and u, then the expected frequencies of the mixed prot-deuter heterozygotes are 2rt, 2ru, 2st, and 2su, respectively, provided that all four genes are allelic to one another, so that no single X-chromosome can carry more than one of them. (If the color-blindness genes are on two separate loci, the expected frequencies are different, but not strikingly so.) Since r, s, t, and u are known to be approximately 0.01 (protanomaly), 0.01 (protanopia), 0.05 (deuteranomaly), and 0.01 (deuteranopia), respectively, the frequencies of the expected mixed heterozygotes are around 0.001 each for protanomalous/deuteranomalous and protanopic/deuteranomalous, and around 0.0002 each for protanomalous/deuteranopic and protanopic/deuteranopic. The sum of these four values is 0.0024, or 24 per 10,000. Among the more than 9,000 Oslo schoolgirls, about 20 should have shown one or another of the four compound conditions. Actually, however, none of the 40 color-blind girls belonged to any one of these types, but some were homozygous for a single kind of defect and others heterozygous for protanomaly/protanopia or for deuteranomaly/deuteranopia (being, in either of the latter two cases, phenotypically anomalously trichromatic). The frequencies were in good agreement with expectations calculated on the basis of the allele frequencies. The fact that no girls exhibited any sort of prot-deuter combination of color blindnesses is interpreted to mean that typical prot-deuter heterozygotes have normal color vision.

The normal color vision of women who are heterozygous for one abnormal prot allele and one abnormal deuter allele, in contrast to the defective color vision of compounds of two abnormal prot alleles or of two abnormal deuter alleles (Fig. 96) has some bearing on the question raised earlier of whether the prot and deuter genes occupy two separate loci or only a single one (Fig. 97, A, B). In general, if two nonallelic recessive genes are both present heterozygously, they permit the development of the double dominant phenotype; i.e., they complement each other. Thus, a person who is heterozygous for phenylketonuria as well as alkaptonuria would be neither a phenylketonuric nor an alkaptonuric, since the dominant normal allele at the first locus permits the transformation of phenylalanine to tyrosine and the dominant normal allele at the second locus that of homogentisic acid to acetoacetic acid (see Fig. 32, p. 58).

It does not follow from this that only nonallelic genes complement each

	normal	protanom.	protanop.	deuteranom.	deuteranop.
normal	normal 1	normal 2	normal 3	normal 4	normal 5
protanom.		protanom. 6	protanom. 7	normal 12	probably normal 13
protanop.			protanop. 8	normal 14	normal 15
deuteranom.				deuteranom. 9	deuteranom. 10
deuteranop.					deuteranop. 11

FIG. 96. The phenotypes of women possessing various combinations of X-chromosomes with a genotype for normal vision and with any one of the four chief genotypes for partial color blindness.

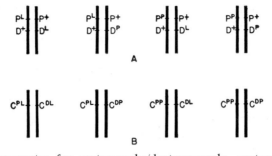

FIG. 97. Heterozygotes for protanomaly/deuteranomaly, protanomaly/deuteranopia, protanopia/deuteranomaly, and protanopia/deuteranopia. A. Interpretation in terms of two pairs of loci with three alleles each: P^L (protanomaly), P^P (protanopia), and P^+ (normal); and D^L (deuteranomaly), D^P (deuteranopia), and D^+ (normal). B. Interpretation in terms of one pair of loci with four alleles: C^{PL} (protanomaly), C^{DL} (deuteranomaly), C^{DP} (deuteranopia), and C^{PP} (protanopia).

other in a compound and thus lead to the dominant phenotype. An organism that possesses two different recessive alleles at the same locus may, nevertheless, exhibit the dominant phenotype, although this is not common. In Drosophila, for example, the recessive mutant allele "spineless" (ss) shortens or eliminates many bristle organs, and the recessive mutant allele "aristapedia" (ss^{ap}) transforms the feather-like arista of the antenna into an extra foot. The compound heterozygote $ss\ ss^{ap}$ has normal bristles as well as normal antennae. The normal effect of the ss allele on the arista and the normal effect of the ss^{ap} allele on the bristles are each dominant in the compound. Related examples in man are provided by the Rh alleles. R^1, for instance, does not lead to the appearance of the E antigen, and R^2 forms no C antigen, but the compound R^1R^2 causes formation of both C and E antigens.

Returning to color blindness, it is clear that the normal phenotype of the combinations of prot and deuter genes is compatible with—but of course does not validate—the assumption that the four genes that cause defects are allelic to one another (see Fig. 97, B) and occupy the same locus as a fifth allele for normal color vision.

It should be possible to decide between the one- and two-locus hypotheses. A clear-cut decision could be reached through a study of the sons of many mothers who are heterozygous for those combinations of atypical genes that result in normal color vision. If two alleles at one locus are involved, rather than heterozygosity at two separate loci, then only color-blind sons should appear. The occurrence of any normal sons would show that there was crossing over and would, thus, establish the existence of two recombinable loci controlling the four common types of color blindness.

Considerations of Population Genetics. There is an independent approach to the problem of one or two loci for color blindness which makes use of population genetics. If two separate loci are involved, one would expect to find four main types of X-chromosomes in the population: those with nor-

mal alleles at both loci, those with one normal allele at one locus and either a
prot or deuter allele at the other, and those with both a prot and deuter allele.
As will be shown in the next chapter (see p. 258 ff.), the frequency of the last
type of chromosome, regardless of the distance between the two loci, would
be the product of the frequencies of the prot and deuter alleles in the population. To be specific, men with an X-chromosome which carries both protanopia and deuteranopia should occur with a frequency of 0.01 × 0.01, or
1 in 10,000. Similarly, combinations of the relatively common deuteranomaly
allele with one of the protanoid alleles should occur in 5 out of 10,000 men,
and the sum of the four combinations of the two prot and two deuter alleles
would be 12 in 10,000, or 1 in 833. Among color-blind men about 1 in 80
would be a compound. If there are indeed two separate loci, one would thus
expect to find X-chromosomes in which each locus is occupied by an abnormal allele.

It is not certain whether the four types of compound men postulated on
the basis of the two-locus hypothesis could all be distinguished phenotypically from men with an abnormal gene at one locus and a normal gene at
the other. Only one of the four types has been described. Walls and Matthews
have discovered two brothers whose color vision combined the characteristics
of protanopia and deuteranopia. Their mother exhibited neither defect. Such
a situation may be interpreted as meaning that the mother had one X-chromosome containing normal alleles at both loci and another X-chromosome containing abnormal alleles at both loci: the two brothers inherited the latter
X-chromosome and thus were doubly hemizygous recessive. An alternative
interpretation is possible, however. If only one locus for color blindness exists,
then the presence of the compound phenotype in this family may be due to
the existence of a very rare, hitherto unknown allele at this locus—an allele
that causes simultaneously defects of the protanopic and deuteranopic type.
Such an allele would be analogous to the R^o allele of the Rh blood groups,
the allele responsible for absence of both C and E antigens. It is not possible
to decide between the one- and two-locus hypotheses on the basis of the single
family in which males with a compound defect have appeared. But their
rarity would suggest that the expectation, based on the two-locus hypothesis,
of an appreciable frequency of males with a compound effect is not fulfilled
unless two special assumptions are made: (a) the two loci are so close to
each other that the frequency of recombination is very low; and (b) the
doubly color-defective combinations of the two loci in the same chromosome
have a lower chance of being transmitted to later generations than the other
combinations, the degree of disadvantage of the doubly defective combination
being at least of the same order of magnitude as the frequency of recombination. Under these conditions the frequencies of the doubly color-defective
combinations in the population will be kept very low, since they will be eliminated soon after they have been produced by rare crossing over.

A hypothesis which postulates two very closely linked loci but which cannot point to evidence for crossing over is in some ways identical with a hypothe-

TABLE 35.   *The Inheritance of Ability To Smell HCN.* (After Kirk and Sten-house, *Nature,* **171,** 1953; and Fukumoto, Nakajima, Uetake, Matsuyama, and Yoshida, *Jap. J. Human Genet.,* **2,** 1957.)

Parents		No. of Families	Daughters		Sons	
Mother	Father		Smeller	Nonsmeller	Smeller	Nonsmeller
Smeller	Smeller	83	99	(1)	92	6
Smeller	Nonsmeller	27	26	6	22	5
Nonsmeller	Smeller	14	14	0	(2)	13
Nonsmeller	Nonsmeller	4	0	4	0	4

NOTE: The numbers in parentheses represent individuals not expected in X-linkage. It appears from other data that the degree of recognition of HCN by smell may vary. This may account for the exceptions.

sis which postulates a single locus. A similar view was expressed earlier in regard to the Rh and *L* alleles. It may also apply to the Drosophila example of the spineless and aristapedia alleles (p. 230). At present, the difference between the two hypotheses is of little practical importance; but the facts established regarding the effects of the different gene combinations for color blindness are of considerable interest.

Other X-linked Traits.   Many other traits which follow the transmission of the X-chromosomes are known in man. Only a few differences within the range of normality are known to be controlled by X-linked genes. A recently described case concerns sensitivity to the smell of hydrogen cyanide (HCN), an extremely toxic gas (Table 35). In an Australian sample, 18.2 per cent of 132 white males, but only 4.5 per cent of 112 females, could not smell this substance at the concentration used. These two percentages fit, within chance limits, the expectation for the frequencies of an X-linked trait in males (q) and females (q^2), and family data support the assumption of X-linkage. Very similar frequencies of nonsmellers were found among 433 Japanese, namely, 18.2 per cent among males and 5.5 per cent among females. The results of a Swiss study, however, are not in agreement with expectations for X-linkage. It would be interesting to study other populations for this trait, but the great toxicity of the substance makes the test dangerous.

Many abnormal traits are due to abnormal X-linked alleles, and the corresponding normal traits are thus known to be controlled by normal alleles in the X-chromosomes. Among the abnormal traits may be mentioned certain types of congenital night blindness; atrophy of the optic nerve (X-linked type of Leber's disease); the toothlessness and hairlessness among the men of a certain community in India ("toothless men of Sind") and in American kindreds; X-linked ichthyosis, a rough, scaly condition of the skin; hypogam-maglobulinemia, the strange inability of the body to produce sufficient gamma globulin in the blood, which is thus unable adequately to produce antibodies against bacterial infections; brown teeth; rickets due to vitamin D resistance;

X-linked (Duchenne) type of muscular dystrophy; hemophilia; two different types of diabetes insipidus, a condition in which the patient may void as many as 10 quarts of urine daily and require a similarly large intake of fluid—one type of the trait being caused by deficiency of a pituitary hormone (pitressin), the other by abnormal properties of the kidney; and ocular albinism, the nearly complete absence of pigmentation in the eyes of affected males, a trait with slight but recognizable expression in heterozygous females. In general, the inheritance of these traits is basically like that of color blindness, but a few of them will be used to demonstrate some special phenomena.

Dosage Compensation in X-linked Traits.   Before a discussion of individual traits, a fascinating general peculiarity of X-linked traits should be mentioned. Normal development of an organism depends on a harmonious coordination of the effects of numerous genes. Autosomal genes are always present in pairs, and it is known from experimental organisms that the loss of one of a pair often has unfavorable effects on development. The balance of normal development obviously depends on a double dose of each autosomal gene, and a single dose of one in the presence of a double dose of the others produces an imbalance of processes. This, however, does not hold for X-linked genes. They are present as pairs in females but singly in males, and yet their effects are similar if not identical. The color blindness of a hemizygous male is the same as that of a homozygous female, and the same is true of other traits transmitted by X-linked genes, whether recessive or dominant, mutant or normal. In some subtle way, the X-chromosomes compensate for the kind of effects which would otherwise arise from the 1 dose–2 doses relations.

X-linked Dominants.   Defective enamel leading to brown teeth is inherited in many families as an autosomal dominant. Some pedigrees exist, however, in which the defect seems to be due to an X-linked gene. (Fig. 98). Unlike color blindness and most of the other abnormal X-linked traits, it behaves as a dominant. Consequently, all the daughters of an affected man, to whom he transmits his X-chromosome, will be affected, but his sons will

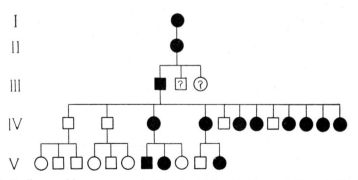

FIG. 98. Pedigree of brown enamel of teeth. (After Haldane, *J. Hered.*, **28**, 1937.)

not. This fits generation IV of the pedigree with its 8 affected daughters and 4 unaffected sons. The outcome of the reciprocal marriage, that of an affected woman and a normal man, will not betray the possible X-linked nature of the defect, since all affected women known are heterozygous for the rare dominant allele. Consequently, half of their sons will be hemizygous for the abnormal allele and half normal. Similarly, half of the daughters will receive from the mother the X-chromosome with the dominant atypical allele and the other half the normal allele. In other words, an affected woman will transmit the trait to half of her offspring, regardless of sex, exactly as in autosomal dominant inheritance.

Thus, the presumption that the dominant gene for brown enamel in the kindred depicted in Figure 98 is X-linked rests solely on the 12 children of generation IV. If the gene were an autosomal one, there would only be $(1/2)^{12}$, or 1 chance in 4,096, of obtaining the specific sex distribution of the trait. This speaks in favor of its X-linked nature, which is supported by other pedigrees that have recently been described.

A still stronger case can be made for X-linked transmission of a dominant gene that leads to deficiency of inorganic phosphorus in the blood and often results in rickets resistant to normal doses of Vitamin D (see p. 292 and Fig. 122). In an extensive kindred, 7 affected males married to normal females had 11 daughters, all affected, and 10 sons, all normal. The reciprocal marriages of 9 affected females and normal males produced affected and normal children of both sexes in a ratio compatible with a 1:1:1:1 expectation. Although the latter ratio from affected mothers could be due to transmission of either an autosomal or an X-linked dominant gene, the ratio of 11:0:0:10 from affected fathers rules out autosomal inheritance and fits X-linkage perfectly.

The close similarity in expression of X-linked genes in the two sexes that is due to dosage compensation, as described in the preceding section, does not extend to a comparison of males carrying a dominant allele, D, with females heterozygous for it. Here the genotypes to be compared are D and Dd, instead of D and DD. The heterozygotes (Dd) would be expected to be intermediate in phenotype between dd and DD. If the allele D is rare, DD individuals are even rarer and usually unknown, so that a direct comparison between the three phenotypes cannot be made. However, if, because of dosage compensation, D and DD produce like effects, then the phenotype of D males could serve for that of DD females, and Dd females should be intermediate between dd and D. It is in line with this expectation, which is based on the concept of dosage compensation for dominant alleles, that females heterozygous for the dominant allele for rickets resistant to vitamin D are on the average less strikingly affected than hemizygous males.

The distinction between a "normal" and an "abnormal" trait is not always clear cut. A striking illustration of this is provided by an X-linked trait characterized by an enzymatic defect in the red blood cells. Somewhat less than 10 per cent of all American Negroes show a greatly reduced activity of glucose-6-phosphate dehydrogenase, an enzyme concerned with the sulfur-containing tripeptide compound, glutathione, which plays a role in cellular respiration. The deficiency is rare in whites, but has been encountered, particularly in individuals of Mediterranean stock. Persons with the enzyme deficiency are completely normal, and so are most properties of their red blood cells. The low activity of the enzyme is usually apparent only in laboratory tests, but under special circumstances persons with the defect suffer from sudden destruction of many of their red blood cells and resulting severe anemia. The "special circumstances" are the inhalation of the pollen of broad beans (*Vicia fava*) or the ingestion of the raw bean, or the ingestion of certain drugs such as sulfanilamide, naphthalene (used in moth balls), and primaquine, an antimalarial agent. The illness brought about by the pollen or the eating of the bean is known as favism. An afflicted person recovers when the offending substances are eliminated. Many more males than females have the deficiency, and most of the females have an enzyme activity intermediate between normal and the low activity in affected males.

Pedigree studies show that an X-linked gene is responsible for the trait. The hemizygous males are strongly affected. The enzyme activity in heterozygous females varies from low to intermediate, dependent on unknown modifying genes somewhere else in the chromosomes. Homozygous females have not yet been recognized with certainty. The X-linked allele which is responsible for the deficiency is dominant in the sense that it often produces a defect in the heterozygote. *primaquine sensitive hemolytic anemia*

X-linked Muscular Dystrophy. Wasting of muscles may be caused by an abnormality of the nervous system, or the degeneration may be independent of the nervous system. The term muscular dystrophy is usually applied to the latter type of defect. A number of different kinds of muscular dystrophy can be distinguished; partly on the basis of their different phenotypes, including time of onset, and partly by their different modes of inheritance—namely, recessive X-linked or dominant or recessive autosomal.

The X-linked type of muscular dystrophy, which most so-called Duchenne-

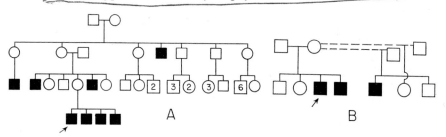

FIG. 99. Two pedigrees showing inheritance of Duchenne-type muscular dystrophy. A. Three successive generations in which the disease occurred. B. "A complicated family" showing the disease in three males who have a common mother but two different fathers (see Problem 109, p. 243). (A, after Stevenson, *Ann. Eugen.* **18,** 1953; B, after Walton, *Ann. Human Genet.,* **21,** 1956.)

type patients have, usually shows its first symptoms in early childhood and progressively leads to invalidism and death, the afflicted persons seldom surviving to the age of twenty. Since affected males almost never have offspring, the allele responsible for the disease is considered sublethal. It is a recessive, since women who are heterozygous for it are normal (Fig. 99). Homozygous affected women are not to be expected, since they would typically be the daughters of carrier women and affected men; but the sublethal nature of the defect almost entirely excludes such marriages. Nevertheless, there are a few records of affected females, but with normal fathers. Some of these females were probably misclassified as Duchenne-type muscular dystrophics, but at least one girl, who had 9 affected male relatives (grand-uncle, uncles, cousins), seems to have been affected with the Duchenne type of the disease.

There are several ways to account for the occurrence of the affected females. It is possible, for instance, that as a result of mutation a sperm of a normal father actually carries an abnormal allele. If this sperm fertilizes an egg which has received an abnormal allele from a heterozygous mother, a homozygous affected daughter would be produced. Another possibility rests on a rare but well-established abnormality of sex determination. In certain circumstances, fertilized eggs with only one X-chromosome may develop into females (see p. 412). If the allele for X-linked muscular dystrophy were present on the single X-chromosome, these females would be affected. A third possibility will be mentioned later in this chapter under "nondisjunction" (p. 239), and still other hypotheses could be advanced. Any of these occurrences is a rare event, but, fundamentally, this does not speak against them. Although one must attempt to explain all observations on the most likely assumptions, it is obvious that even the most unlikely of all possible events may be encountered when, as in human genetics, very large numbers of events are recorded.

X-linked Hemophilia.   One of the most famous inherited abnormalities in man is the bleeder disease, hemophilia. It is one of several genetic conditions which may result in excessive bleeding at points of injury or stress, usually as a result of delayed clotting which is due to a deficiency of certain components of the blood. Different abnormal genes, some autosomal and others X-linked, are responsible for the deficiency of different components. In classical X-linked hemophilia, hemophilia A, "anti-hemophilic globulin" is lacking or present only in small quantities. In another recently discovered X-linked bleeder disease, called hemophilia B, or Christmas disease (after a kindred which contained several affected persons), there is a deficiency for another substance, the "plasma thromboplastin component." Only recently has it become possible to distinguish the two X-linked hemophilias, and it has not yet been decided whether the corresponding genes occupy one or two loci. Hemophilia is well known, even among laymen, because of its seriousness and of the mystical feelings which are still commonly associated with true or imagined properties of blood, and because, during the past hundred years, it has occurred in many members of the royal families of Europe (Fig. 188, p. 449).

The inheritance of hemophilia has been partly known, though, of course, not understood, for a long time. The Talmud, in the second century A.D., contained rules regarding circumcision of boys in families in which death had occurred as a result of excessive bleeding following the operation. Not only was it stated that the later-born sons of a woman who lost two boys due to bleeding should not be circumcised, but even the sons of her sisters were to be exempted from the ritual. Half-brothers of the dead children, by the same father and a different mother, were treated as normal individuals. These regulations imply that the Jews knew that the tendency was inherited from the mother, that the sisters of a known carrier could also be carriers, and that the occurrence of the disease among the sons is independent of the father.

In 1820, a more definite rule for the inheritance of the trait was given by Nasse, which, somewhat freely translated from the German, reads: "Women whose fathers were bleeders transmit the trait to their children, even if married to normal men. In these women themselves, and, in general, in all females, the trait is never expressed." A final formulation of the transmission of hemophilia, based on the discovery of sex chromosomes and their recognition as carriers of sex-linked genes, became possible only in the twentieth century (Fig. 100).

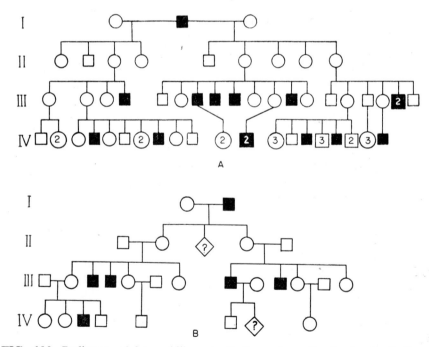

FIG. 100. Pedigrees of hemophilia. A. Pedigree from Scotland. B. Pedigree from Germany. (A, after Bulloch and Fildes, *Treas. Hum. Inher.,* **1,** 1911; pedigree No. 490; B, part of the Schloessmann pedigree, after Baur, Fischer, Lenz.)

It has often been wondered whether female bleeders actually exist, even though some women of this type have been listed in the rare autosomal pedigrees of bleeder diseases. Until 1951, no X-linked hemophilic female had been diagnosed, a fact which led to the suggestion that *hh* females either die before birth or that they live but are phenotypically normal nonbleeders. Geneticists were not inclined to accept either hypothesis, but pointed out that *hh* females would only occur among the offspring of heterozygous (*Hh*) women and affected *h* men and that the very small number of such marriages had, by chance, not produced *hh* daughters. This view was strengthened when typical X-linked hemophilia was discovered in a kindred of dogs and when matings between the heterozygous female and affected male dogs produced hemophilic females as well as males. Studies of the blood of these dogs contributed greatly to the understanding of hemophilia in man.

Soon after the hemophilic dogs had become known, human females were described who were *hh* homozygous and exhibited, according to careful tests, all symptoms of true X-linked hemophilia. The best-established case is that of a woman who had had a history of easy bruising and free bleeding but who had successfully given birth to a child. She probably escaped serious bleeding at the time of delivery because, as is generally thought, the control of hemorrhage from the placental site is by muscular contraction of the uterine wall and not by coagulation of blood. This hemophilic woman's father had died of hemophilia, as had one of her mother's brothers (Fig. 101). Her mother may therefore be classified as a carrier, and the genotypes of the parents as *Hh* and *h*.

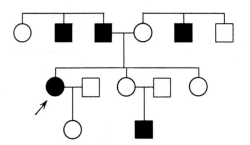

FIG. 101. Pedigree of hemophilia containing a hemophilic woman. (After Israels, Lempert, and Gilbertson, *Lancet,* **260,** 1951.)

X-linked genes are generally regarded as having no allele in the Y-chromosome, and this chromosome can consequently be neglected in the discussion of X-linked transmission. It would, however, be possible to assume that the Y-chromosome contains recessive alleles for all X-linked genes. If this were true, a nonhemophilic man, for example, would not be hemizygous for normality, but heterozygous for the normal allele in the X-chromosome and the recessive hemophilia allele in the Y-chromosome; and a hemophilic man would be homozygous for the abnormal allele because of its presence in both sex chromosomes. It is unlikely that such a view of the localization and nature of X-linked genes is correct. It does not seem to explain anything that the simpler interpretation of the hemizygous nature of X-linked genes in the male cannot, and, in any case, it can at present neither be proven nor disproven.

Nondisjunction.   In the extensive investigations made by experimental geneticists and cytologists, many cases have been uncovered in which apparent exceptions from normal hereditary behavior can be explained by exceptional behavior of chromosomes.

A well-known kind of "abnormal" transmission is that involving non-disjunction of the X-chromosomes in Drosophila. In rare cases the two separate X-chromosomes of a female may be included in one daughter nucleus at a meiotic division, instead of going to opposite spindle poles. Such non-disjunction leads to two types of mature but unfertilized eggs: XX, when the two chromosomes remain in the egg nucleus; no-X, when they go jointly into the polar nucleus. Either may be fertilized by X or Y sperm, so that four types of zygotes are possible: XXX, XXY, X, and Y. In Drosophila, type XXX rarely and type Y never develop into adults, but types XXY and X become females and males, respectively. The males, which lack a Y-chromosome, are sterile (XO) males. If the two X-chromosomes of the original female parent are homozygous for a recessive sex-linked gene, and the X-chromosome of the male parent contains a dominant allele of this gene, then the nondisjunctional daughters are phenotypically like their mother, and the nondisjunctional sons are like their father (noncrisscross exceptions).

Nondisjunction of the X-chromosomes is now known to occur occasionally in man. Therefore, occasional exceptions from X-linked inheritance are to be expected, though under slightly different genetic situations than in Drosophila. It has been shown that in man XXY zygotes may develop into males, and XO zygotes into females (pp. 412–414). If sperm of a color-blind man that carries a Y-chromosome should fertilize a nondisjunctional XX egg of a normal woman, the resulting XXY son would be as normal as an XY son. If, however, sperm of a color-blind man carrying an X-chromosome should fertilize a nondisjunctional O egg, then the resulting XO daughter would be color blind, like her father, contrary to regular expectations.

Nondisjunction of sex chromosomes can also occur in the testis, resulting in XY and O sperm. Fertilization of an X egg by an XY sperm will result in an XXY son who may constitute an exception to regular X-linked in-heritance. If, for instance, the parents were a color-blind female and a normal male, the XXY son would not be color blind, contrary to usual expectation. Conversely, fertilization of an X egg by an O sperm may result in an XO daughter who, given a color-blind mother and a normal father, would be color blind, again contrary to usual expectation: this kind of exception has actually been discovered (see p. 412).

It is probable that nondisjunctional human zygotes without an X-chromosome will not be viable, as in Drosophila, but zygotes with three X-chromosome can develop into viable women (see p. 414).

In some Drosophila strains, the two rod-shaped X-chromosomes have become permanently attached to each other, forming a large **V**-shaped body. These $\widehat{X}X$ females also carry a Y-chromosome ($\widehat{X}XY$). The attached X-chromosomes behave as a single unit in meiosis, so that nondisjunction always occurs in the females that possess them. A female Drosophila homozygous for a recessive allele in her attached X-chromosomes mated with a normal male will have only X̂X̂Y daughters (like herself) and XY sons (like her mate), since the daughters receive both of the mother's X-chromosomes and the sons the father's single X-chromosome. In man, a few pedigrees are known in which all daughters in successive generations have the phenotype of their mothers and all sons that of their fathers. Such "hologynic" transmission could conceivably be based on attached X-chromosomes, but other explanations, such as chance transmission of an autosomal dominant gene to all daughters and to no sons, or nonexpression in sons, are perhaps more likely to be true (see also p. 316 ff. on so-called sex limitation and p. 109 on extranuclear inheritance).

X-linked and Autosomal Genes and Differences in Sex Incidence of Traits. Many inherited human traits occur more frequently among males than among females. This phenomenon is, of course, fully understandable when an X-linked locus is responsible; for example, in partial color blindness. When, however, autosomal inheritance is involved, a higher frequency of affected males than females requires a special explanation. Two alternative explanations have been proposed: one, developmental; the other, genetic. The former assumes that a higher incidence of some inherited conditions among males is a result of developmental reactions induced by the specific genotypes, taking a different course in males than they do in females. The genetic explanation assumes that a given trait becomes apparent only when, in addition to an autosomal genotype, a recessive X-linked allele is present homozygously in the female or hemizygously in the male. Thus, if an abnormal autosomal genotype is recessive (aa) and the X-linked allele is designated by s, then, only s aa males and ss aa females will be affected; but S aa males and Ss aa or SS aa females will be normal. (All AA or Aa would also be normal regardless of whether they are S or s males, or SS, Ss, or ss females.) Since the ratio of s males to ss females is $q:q^2$ (where q equals the frequency of the allele s) s aa males and ss aa females should occur in the proportion $q:q^2$. Thus the genetic hypothesis fulfills the basic requirement; namely, it explains the surplus of affected males.

The hypothesis entails further genetic considerations, however, and these have been tested for four kinds of inherited abnormalities that have a higher male than female incidence: the Laurence-Moon-Biedl syndrome, harelip and cleft palate, allergy, and mental deficiency. The method of testing, suggested by R. A. Fisher and applied by Csik and Mather, requires determination of the mode of transmission of these traits. If an X-linked gene participates in causing them, X-linked inheritance should be involved; but if no evidence for X-linked inheritance is found, then the genetic hypothesis is untenable. Specifically, the expectations that would accord with the genetic theory were derived in the following way: The presence of the autosomal allele *a* in the parents, either homozygously or heterozygously, and homo-zygously in the children, is a prerequisite for the possible appearance of the trait. Since transmission of *a* has no relation to sex, it does not need to be considered further. Therefore, only the hypothetical X-linked allele pair *S* and *s* must be studied.

1. If a father had a normal X-linked allele *S*, then all his daughters would be normal, but his sons could be affected if the mother carried *s* homozygously or heterozygously.

2. If, on the contrary, the father transmitted *s*, then both his daughters and his sons could show the abnormal trait if the mother was *Ss* or *ss*. The frequency of affected daughters should be the same as that of affected sons, since a homozygous *ss* woman and a hemizygous *s* man will have *ss* daugh-ters and *s* sons only; and a heterozygous *Ss* woman and hemizygous *s* man will have *Ss* and *ss* daughters and *S* and *s* sons in equal proportions.

Thus, two kinds of sibships would be expected: one having affected boys only, and the other having equal numbers of affected girls and boys.

A test for this simple expectation must take into account the variability of genetic ratios in small families: sibships of the second type will not always contain equal numbers of affected girls and boys. Moreover, ascertainment by means of affected sibs requires correction of the data before they may be compared with expectation (see pp. 133–139). These secondary difficulties were overcome in the tests by determining the proportions of affected girls to boys among the sibs of affected individuals. If a trait is sex linked, the expectation is an equal number of affected girls and boys among the sibs of affected girls, but more affected boys than girls among the sibs of affected boys.

An examination of data from numerous pedigrees shows that a surplus of affected males occurs among the sibs of *both* affected girls and boys. Conse-quently, the genetic hypothesis, which assumes an X-linked component, is disproved, and it may be concluded that the developmental interpretation is correct: i.e., the higher frequency of affected males is due to a more pro-nounced action of certain autosomal genotypes in the male sex. This con-clusion applies also to traits other than those tested by Csik and Mather, including baldness.

X-linkage and Counseling.   The recognition of X-linkage of human traits provides an important tool for the genetic adviser. Predictions can be made with certainty about the phenotypes and genotypes of the sons and daughters of men affected with an X-linked trait, provided his wife can be assumed to be homozygously normal. Absolute predictions can also be made about the types of offspring of affected women who are homozygous for a recessive allele. The progeny of a heterozygous woman married to a normal man can be foretold in terms of probabilities only, her sons having an even chance of being normal or affected, and her daughters an even chance of being homozygous normal or carriers.

The presence of a recessive X-linked allele in a heterozygous mother may be cause for reasonable concern; whereas presence of a recessive autosomal allele may not. A woman heterozygous for an uncommon autosomal gene will very rarely happen to marry a man who is also heterozygous for it—unless the spouses are closely related to each other—and only if both parents transmit the atypical gene to the same zygote will an affected child be born. But if the gene is X-linked, half of the sons of a heterozygous mother are likely to be affected, regardless of the genotype of the father.

A woman whose father was affected by a recessive sex-linked allele or who has an affected son is a carrier. The probability that daughters of such a woman will be carriers is 1/2. That probability is often a sufficient cause for abstaining from marriage if the abnormality is severe. If methods were available to diagnose, by medical tests, the presence or absence of heterozygosity, advice on the desirability of having children could be based not on probability but on determinate evidence. In hemophilia, such a diagnosis, which makes use of the slightly prolonged clotting time of the blood of carrier women, is sometimes available. Another approach to more specific counseling in connection with X-linked genes will be described in Chapter 15.

The Relative Frequency of Sex-linked Traits. The phenomenon of sex linkage has some dramatic features. The usual "disappearance" of sex-linked traits in the children of affected men and the reappearance among some of their daughters' sons, the rarity of affected women as compared to men or even their virtual absence, are causes for wonder to the uninitiated. Knowledge of the chromosomal basis of inheritance provides clear insight into such facts, and also explains why there are relatively so many more known examples of sex-linked than of autosomal inheritance. Statistically, the sex-chromosome pair should not be expected to carry more than about 1/23 of all genes, since it is only one of 23 pairs of chromosomes, yet the proportion of known sex-linked genes is much higher than 1 in 23. This is a result of greater ease of detection: a rare, recessive X-linked gene with an allele frequency q will show its phenotype in a fraction q of all males, while an equally rare autosomal recessive will become apparent in only q^2 of all individuals.

Problems

100. For a Y-linked trait, what phenotypes do you expect in the following descendants of an affected man?

(a) His sons.
(b) His daughters.
(c) The sons of his sons.
(d) The daughters of his daughters.
(e) The daughters of his sons.
(f) The sons of his daughters.

101. List the genotypes of color blindness for all individuals in the pedigrees in Figure 93. If more than one genotype is possible, list the alternatives and state their probabilities.

102. A woman has normal parents and a color-blind brother. What is the probability that her first son will be color blind?

103. A normal woman whose father was color blind marries a man with normal vision. (a) What proportion of her sons is expected to be color blind? (b) If her husband had been color blind, what would have been the expectation for the sons?

104. List the genotypes of hemophilia for all individuals in the pedigrees in Figure 100. If more than one genotype is possible, list the alternatives and state their probabilities.

105. (a) Determine the genotypes of all individuals shown in the pedigree in Figure 101. (b) If the proposita had had a son, what would have been the probability of his being normal? If her daughter marries a normal man, what kinds of children can they expect?

106. In a certain population, the frequency of women affected with a harmless X-linked recessive trait is 1 in 10,000. What is the frequency of affected men?

107. In a considerable number of pedigrees, color-blind fathers have color-blind sons. Is this evidence for genetic transmission of color blindness?

108. In the first known pedigree of red-green color blindness in several generations, illustrated in Figure 93D, J. Scott (II–2) was affected and had an affected father and a normal mother. What is the probability of a color-blind man having parents such as those of J. Scott?

109. In several sibships, such as that shown in Figure 99, B, two or more sons affected with Duchenne-type muscular dystrophy have the same mother but different fathers. The parents are unrelated to each other. Why are these sibships strong indications for X-linked recessive, and against autosomal recessive, inheritance of the disease?

110. In population I, the frequency of a sex-linked recessive gene is 20 per cent. In population II, the frequency of the same sex-linked recessive is 4 per cent. After panmixis, established as a result of several generations of random mating of equal numbers of the two initial populations, what will be the frequency of all possible genotypes?

111. A man is affected with a dominant X-linked trait. His wife is not affected. Give the possible genotypes of their sons and daughters and of their sons' and daughters' children.

112. Can the pedigree of Leber's disease, shown in Figure 67 be explained on the basis of X-linked inheritance?

References

Bell, J., 1926. Colour blindness. *Treas. Hum. Inher.*, II, **2:** 125–267.

Brunner, W., 1930. Über den Vererbungsmodus der verschiedenen Typen der angeborenen Rotgrünblindheit. V. Graefe's *Arch. Ophthalmol.,* **124:** 1–52.

Childs, B., Zinkham, W. H., Browne, E. A., Kimbro, E. L., and Torbert, J. V., 1958. A genetic study of a defect in glutathione metabolism of the erythrocyte. *Bull. Johns Hopk. Hosp.,* **102:** 21–37.

Csik, L., and Mather, K., 1938. The sex incidence of certain hereditary traits in man. *Ann. Eugen.,* **8:** 126–145.

Forssmann, H., 1955. Two different mutations of the X-chromosome causing diabetes insipidus. *Am. J. Human Genet.,* **7:** 21–27.

Graham, J. B., 1956. Biochemical genetics of blood coagulation. *Am. J. Human Genet.,* **8:** 63–79.

Gross, R. T., Hurwitz, R. E., and Marks, P. A., 1958. An hereditary enzymatic defect in erythrocyte metabolism: glucose-6-phosphate dehydrogenase deficiency. *J. Clin. Invest.,* **37:** 1176–1184.

Jaeger, W., 1952. Beitrag zur Frage der Genlokalisation der Farbsinnstörungen. Graefe's *Arch. Ophthalmol.,* **152:** 385–388.

Kherumian, R., and Pickford, R. W., 1959. *Hérédité et Fréquence des Dyschromatopsies.* 109 pp. Vigot Frères, Paris.

Penrose, L. S., and Stern, C., 1958. Reconsideration of the Lambert pedigree (Ichthyosis hystrix gravior). *Ann. Human Genet.,* **22:** 258–283.

Stern, C., 1958. Le Daltonisme lié au chromosome X a-t-il une localisation unique ou double? *J. Génét. Hum.,* **7:** 302–307.

Waaler, G. H. M., 1927. Über die Erblichkeitsverhältnisse der verschiedenen Arten von angeborener Rotgrünblindheit. *Zeitschr. Abstgs. u. Vererbgsl.,* **45:** 279–333.

Walls, G. L., and Mathews, R. W., 1952. New means of studying color blindness and normal foveal color vision. *Univ. of Calif. Public. in Psychol.,* **7:** 1–172.

Winters, R. W., Graham, J. B., Williams, T. F., McFalls, V. W., and Burnett, C. H., 1958. A genetic study of familial hypophosphatemia and vitamin D resistant rickets with a review of the literature. *Medicine,* **37:** 97–142.

CHAPTER 14

LINKAGE AND CROSSING OVER

I. TYPES OF LINKAGE AND ASSOCIATION

In earlier chapters on the biological basis of inheritance and on meiosis (Chaps. 2 and 4), we discussed the fact that two different nonallelic genes in man may either be located in two different chromosomes or at different loci in the same chromosome. If in different chromosomes, they are transmitted independently of each other. An individual who receives the alleles A^1 and B^1 in two different chromosomes from his mother and A^2 and B^2 in the homologous chromosomes from his father forms four different kinds of gametes in equal numbers: A^1B^1, A^1B^2, A^2B^1, and A^2B^2. Thus, among the gametes, the "new" combinations, A^1B^2 and A^2B^1, are as common as the "old" combinations, A^1B^1 and A^2B^2. We have seen that independent recombination of the maternal and paternal alleles at the two pairs of loci results from the independent arrangement of different chromosome pairs on the meiotic spindles (Fig. 35, p. 66).

If the genes A and B are in the same chromosome, segregation in an individual who receives A^1B^1 from his mother and A^2B^2 from his father might or might not result in equal numbers of gametes with old and new combinations. The old combinations, A^1B^1 and A^2B^2, are formed by meiotic chromosome strands which do not cross over in the section between A and B; the new combinations, A^1B^2 and A^2B^1, are formed by crossover chromosome strands (see Fig. 36, p. 67; the less common multiple crossovers will be disregarded). Since the frequency of crossing over in the section between two loci is positively correlated with the distance between them, new, crossover combinations of two closely linked loci are much rarer than the old, noncrossover combinations; but crossover combinations of two distantly linked loci may be as common as the noncrossover combinations.

It follows that chromosomal linkage of two genes can be easily recognized if an individual heterozygous for two pairs of loci forms gametes in unequal numbers, that is, if the two noncrossover gametes are more common than the two crossovers. If, however, the four kinds of gametes are equally common, it is not obvious whether the two gene pairs are located in different chromosome pairs, or whether they are in the same pair, but distant from each other.

Crossover Frequency and Recombination Frequency.   The frequency of crossing over in the section between two loci in a pair of homologous chromosomes is not always identical with the frequency of new combinations of the loci. When the two loci are so close to each other that only single crossovers occur, then each crossover results in new genic combinations (e.g., A^1B^2 and A^2B^1 from A^1B^1 and A^2B^2). When, however, the distance between the two loci is great enough to permit double (or higher multiple) crossing over in the section between them, the frequency of new combinations is lower than the frequency of crossovers. This is so because a double crossover may lead to the exchange of a section between the loci of A and B without separating A^1 from B^1 or A^2 from B^2.

In genetic studies one cannot determine the actual frequency of crossing over but only the frequency of crossovers that result in recombination of genes. In other words, the frequency of new combinations gives us the *recombination frequency* but not the *crossover frequency*. A low frequency of recombination is a close measure of the crossover frequency, but high recombination frequencies indicate only that crossover frequencies are still higher.

Recombination frequencies seldom rise above 50 per cent, even if the two loci considered lie very far apart. Two genes at widely separated loci will therefore be present as frequently in old as in new combinations, just as if the loci were in different chromosome pairs.

In experimental organisms it is often possible to decide whether genes are in different chromosomes or in the same chromosome but far apart. In man it is at present rarely possible to decide between these alternatives.

X-linked and Autosomal Genes.   Such a decision is simple if one of two genes which recombine freely with each other is sex linked but the other is transmitted autosomally. These conditions are met by partial color blindness and the dominant brittle-bone defect blue sclerotics (p. 291), both of which occur together in the pedigree in Figure 102. The transmission of one is X-linked and that of the other autosomal. This marks their location in different chromosomes.

Autosomal Genes.   If both genes are autosomal, the problem of possible chromosomal linkage between two freely combining genes A and B must be attacked in a different way. If each of these genes can be shown to be linked with a third gene, C, then it is obvious that A and B are in the same chromosome. However, failure to find a third gene linked with both A and B does not prove that these genes are in different chromosomes: the negative result

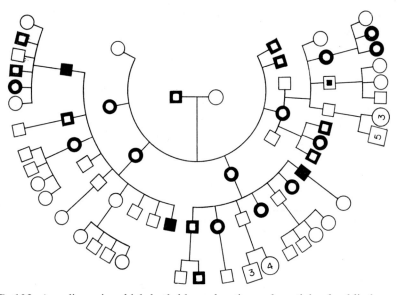

FIG. 102. A pedigree in which both blue sclerotics and partial color blindness are transmitted. Symbols with heavy border and light center = blue sclerotics; with black center and light border = color blind; solid symbols = blue sclerotics and color blind. (After Riddell, *Ann. Eugen.,* **10**, 1940.)

may be due to an insufficient number of known genes, or it may even be that the distance between the loci *A* and *B* is so great that no intermediate locus is close enough to both to be linked with each of them. If the latter is true, it may require two intermediately located genes, *C* and *D*, which show (1) genetic linkage with each other, (2) linkage of *C* with *A*, and (3) linkage of *D* with *B*, to demonstrate that *A* and *B* lie in the same chromosome.

In summary, genetic linkage, if once established, definitely assigns certain genes to a chromosome; but free combination of different genes does not establish their location in different chromosomes. New information will often show that such freely recombining genes are very loosely linked. Even two groups of linked genes, one group segregating independently of the other, may become recognized as widely separated members of one linkage group (that is, genes in the same chromosome) if a gene is found to be linked with both groups. In time, it may be expected that twenty-three human linkage groups will be known.

Linkage of Completely X-linked Genes. Linkage and crossing over may be studied most directly in pedigrees in which two completely X-linked genes can be followed simultaneously. If gene *A* is shown by means of typical X-linked inheritance to be in the X-chromosomes, and if the same can be shown for gene *B*, then, obviously, *A* and *B* must be located in the same chromosome. Information on the distance between different loci can be obtained if more than one X-linked gene can be followed simultaneously in the same pedigree. Most traits known to depend on X-linked genes are rare, so that the chance of finding more than one in the same kindred is extremely small. An exception is partial color blindness, the various alleles for which, as we saw, can be found in nearly 10 per cent of all X-chromosomes. A search for color blindness in those families in which some other X-linked trait occurs should uncover pedigrees in which the two traits appear together. Several such searches have been successful.

Hemophilia and Color Blindness. Nearly twenty different pedigrees are now available in which both hemophilia and color blindness occur. Unfortunately, neither the type of red-green color blindness nor that of hemophilia is known for most of these pedigrees. The absence of information on the type of color blindness is perhaps not too serious, since it may be assumed that a single locus is involved in all types, but we do not know whether a single locus or separate loci are involved in the two types of X-linked hemophilia, *A* and *B*, which only recently have been recognized as distinct. Since information on the types of the two defects is not given in most relevant pedigrees, we shall, reluctantly, follow the example of students of this linkage, particularly Haldane, and treat X-linked color blindness and X-linked hemophilia as though they were each controlled by genes at a single locus.

Figure 103 gives a pedigree in which both hemophilia and color blindness are transmitted. The earliest known male ancestor, I–1, was affected with both traits, *h* and *c*, which were therefore both controlled by genes in his one X-chromosome. His daughter, II–1, who was normal, must have received this double recessive X-chromosome and a double dominant one from her mother. She became the mother of 5 children. Two of her sons, III–3 and III–5, received both recessive alleles, *h* and *c*, and one, III–6, the alleles *H* and *C*. In other words, the three gametes of this woman that gave rise to sons retained the original linkages, either *h* and *c* (2 sons) or *H* and *C* (1 son). Her first daughter, III–2, of normal phenotype, had 2 sons, IV–1 and IV–2, the first *H* and *C* and the other *h* and *c*. She had received a noncrossover

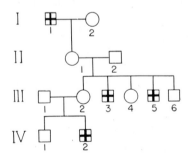

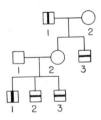

FIG. 103. Part of a pedigree showing transmission of color blindness and hemophilia together. Symbols with cross inside = color blind and hemophilic. (After Madlener, *Arch. Rassenbiol.,* **20**, 1928.)

FIG. 104. A pedigree showing transmission of color blindness and hemophilia alternatively. Vertical bar inside symbol = hemophilic; horizontal bar = color blind. (After Birch, *Illinois Medic. Dental Monogr.,* **4**, 1937.)

FIG. 105. Pedigrees with more than two combinations of color blindness and hemophilia. A. All four possible combinations. B. Three of the four possible combinations. For explanation of symbols, see Figures 103, 104. Broken bar in I-1 means uncertainty regarding this person's color vision. (A, after Rath, *Arch. Rassenbiol.*, **32**, 1938; B, after Hoogvliet, *Genetica*, **23**, 1942.)

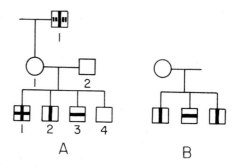

A   B

X-chromosome, containing *h* and *c*, from her mother and a normal X-chromosome, with *H* and *C*, from her father. Her 2 sons had been given noncrossover X-chromosomes. The constitution of six gametes from two double heterozygous women can thus be deduced from this pedigree. The two women were *hc/HC* (the diagonal line separates the genotypes of their two X-chromosomes) and the gametes were of two kinds only, namely, four *hc* and two *HC*. Therefore, the two loci are so closely linked that no crossovers occurred among the six gametes.

Three phenotypes from another family (Fig. 104) were also the result of noncrossover gametes. Unlike the first pedigree, where *h* and *c* were found together in the X-chromosome of a male ancestor, the second pedigree shows the descendants of a male, I–1, who was hemophilic but not color blind: his normal-appearing wife must have brought in the allele for color blindness. The female, II–2, was, therefore, *hC/Hc*; and her 3 sons, III–1, III–2, and III–3, received noncrossover X-chromosomes, *hC* and *Hc*, respectively. The original pedigree contained other individuals who were not tested for color vision and therefore have been omitted here.

A third pedigree in which both traits occur together, with examples of both noncrossover and crossover gametes, was historically the first of its kind (Fig. 105, A). A normal-appearing woman, II–1, whose father was hemophilic, had four sons, among whom both hemophilia and color blindness occurred. Her own ancestors had not been tested for color vision, so that it is not known whether her hemophilic father also carried *c* in his X-chromosome or whether she received this allele from her mother. If the first alternative was true, her constitution was *hc/HC*; if the second, *Hc/hC*. The 4 sons were all different: one was both hemophilic and color blind; the next, only hemophilic; the third, only color blind; and the last, normal in both respects. Thus, two of the four X-chromosomes which the woman transmitted to these sons were noncrossovers between the loci of *H* and *C*, and two were crossovers. Which of the two were noncrossovers and which crossovers cannot be stated, since the decision depends on the unknown item in the constitution of the mother, II–1. If she was *hc/HC*, then her first and last sons were the noncrossovers, and the second and third the crossovers. If she was *Hc/hC*, the relations would be reversed. The 2 color-blind males in this classical pedigree were reinvestigated in 1952 by Jaeger, who found that III–1 was protanopic but III–3 protanomalous. Since the mother (II–1) was clearly not color-defective, it has been surmised that, in contrast to other well-established findings, the two kinds of color defect in this family are alternative expressions of a single allele that depend on the presence or absence of a specific allele at another locus.

One more pedigree, consisting of only a normal-appearing mother and her 3 sons, presents us with another uncertainty (Fig. 105, B). Segregation among the sons shows that the mother was heterozygous for both hemophilia and color blindness, but, lacking knowledge of her ancestry, it cannot be decided whether she was hc/HC or hC/Hc. If she was the former, then all 3 sons came from crossover gametes; but if she was the latter, all 3 sons came from noncrossover gametes.

The frequency of recombination of the genes for hemophilia and color blindness was zero among nine gametes in the first two pedigrees, 2 out of 4 in the third, and either 3 or zero out of 3 in the last pedigree. Further relevant pedigrees are known, and a pooling of all information by the method of likelihood ratio described on pages 273–276 gave Haldane and C. A. B. Smith an estimate of 9.8 per cent as the most likely frequency for recombination of the two loci.

Color Blindness and Myopic Night Blindness. A less close linkage has been found between deuteranopic color blindness and another X-linked gene, that for myopic night blindness. They appeared together in a kindred that was, consequently, well investigated for linkage and crossing over (Fig. 106). An analysis of the data shows that the genes for color blindness and myopic night blindness recombine so freely that the frequency of crossovers is as

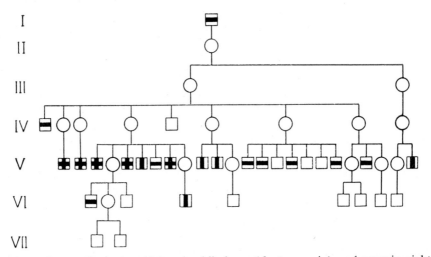

FIG. 106. A pedigree in which color blindness (deuteranopia) and myopic night blindness occur in all possible combinations and without numerical indications of linkage between the two X-linked traits. Horizontal bar inside symbols = night blind, vertical bar = color blind. (After White, *J. Genet.*, **40**, 1940.)

high as that of noncrossovers. The verdict of linkage is based only on the knowledge that both are completely X-linked.

Color Blindness and X-linked Muscular Dystrophy.   A third linkage between two X-linked loci is that of protanopic color blindness and Duchenne-type muscular dystrophy. In a kindred afflicted with the disease, color blindness also occurred. It was possible to determine whether 8 sons from mothers who were heterozygous for both loci originated from noncrossover or crossover eggs. Six were from the former, 2 from the latter. This yields a recombination frequency of 25 per cent; but, in view of the small number of individuals on which it is based, additional data may be expected to change it considerably.

The Problem of Partial Sex Linkage

Until 1936, autosomal inheritance and complete sex linkage were the only types of chromosomal inheritance expected in man, although in 1921 a third type of inheritance had been discovered in Japan by Aida in experiments with a small fresh-water fish (*Aplocheilus latipes*). Fifteen years later, the possible significance of this discovery for human genetics became apparent.

The traits studied in the fish consisted of various color patterns on its body, and these were found to be transmitted in a modified sex-linked fashion. The genetic behavior of these traits was explicable on the theory that a pair of alleles is located at a pair of homologous loci in the sex chromosomes of both females and males. In the female, with its two X-chromosomes, these are no different from X-linked genes in other organisms. In the male, however, the theory stipulates that both the X- and Y-chromosomes contain alleles of the same gene. Moreover, the facts of transmission could be explained only by the assumption that the X- and Y-chromosomes in the male can exchange their alleles, so that the X-linked allele may become Y-linked, and the Y-linked allele X-linked.

Homologous Sections of X- and Y-chromosomes.   Later, cytological observations of a mammal, the rat, seemed to show the following about the two sex chromosomes of the males: During meiosis, the X- and Y-chromosomes become paired, but only in a limited section of each. Since pairing of chromosomes is apparently caused by specific attraction of homologous parts, this cytological finding was interpreted to mean that the pairing sections in the X- and Y-chromosomes were genetically homologous and the nonpairing sections genetically nonhomologous. Obviously, the existence of homologous sections of the X- and Y-chromosomes could mean the existence of homologous loci in these chromosomes. The nonhomologous sections, also called the *differential segments,* were regarded as the seat of those genes which were either completely X-linked or, if such exist, completely Y-linked.

The microscopic details of sex-chromosomal behavior in mammals are difficult to study. In the female, the two X-chromosomes show cytological

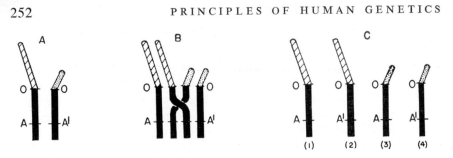

FIG. 107. Diagram of hypothetical crossing over between the homologous segments of the sex chromosomes. A. X-chromosome to the left, Y-chromosome to the right. Black = homologous segment; diagonal lines = differential segment of the X-chromosome; stippled = differential segment of the Y-chromosome; O = differential end point: A, A' = a pair of alleles. B. Four-strand stage with crossover. C. The four chromosomes resulting from crossing over at the four-strand stage.

configurations like those in the autosomes that are usually interpreted as indicators of crossing over (see pp. 67–72). In the male, the X- and Y-chromosomes are less intimately associated, and some recent investigators doubt that there is any opportunity for crossing over. Nevertheless, as long as the cellular details do not exclude the possibility of this process, it is appropriate to consider what its genetic consequences would be.

Crossing over between the X- and Y-chromosomes, if it occurs regularly, would involve exchanges within homologous parts (Fig. 107). Assume that the homologous section of the X-chromosome contains an allele A, and that of the Y-chromosome an allele A'. If no crossing over took place in the parts between the A and A' locus and the ends of the homologous sections to which the differential segments are joined (the differential end point O), A would remain in the X-chromosome and A' would remain in the Y [Fig. 107, C (1) and (4)]. If, on the other hand, a crossover took place in the region located between the A and A' locus and the differential end point O, the A allele would be transferred from the X- to the Y-chromosome, and A' from the Y- to the X-chromosome [Fig. 107, C (2) and (3)]. The over-all result would be a partial or incomplete sex linkage of the A and A' alleles.

Partial Sex Linkage in Man. Stimulated by the genetic studies on partial sex linkage in the fish and by the interpretations of chromosome behavior in the rat, J. B. S. Haldane assumed that the cytology and genetics of the X- and the Y-chromosomes in man were essentially like those in the rat. He therefore searched for evidence of incomplete sex linkage among published human pedigrees, in a manner which will now be described.

Partial sex linkage is, by definition, easily differentiated from complete X- or Y-linkage, but is more difficult to distinguish from ordinary autosomal inheritance. The search for partial sex linkage was, accordingly, made among those traits which had heretofore been considered autosomal. If A represents a rare dominant gene located in an autosome, then the offspring from marriages of the type $Aa \times aa$ will yield equal numbers of Aa and aa children with random distribution of the two genotypes among sons and daughters. This will be so regardless of whether the mother is Aa and the father aa, or whether the mother is aa and the father Aa. If A is an incompletely sex-linked gene and the marriages are $Aa\ ♀ \times aa\ ♂$, the expectation of equality among daughters and sons remains unchanged, since the X-chromosomes of the mothers that carry A and those that carry a each have an equal chance of segregating into eggs that after fertilization may become either a female or a male (Fig. 108). If, however, the Aa parents are the males ($aa\ ♀ \times Aa\ ♂$), different fre-

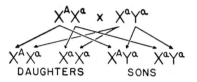
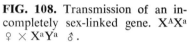

FIG. 108. Transmission of an incompletely sex-linked gene. X^AX^a ♀ $\times X^aY^a$ ♂.

quencies of the genotypes Aa and aa are to be expected in the two sexes (Fig. 109). These frequencies should vary inversely with the frequency with which a crossover interchanges the A and a alleles between the homologous segments of the X- and Y-chromosome of the fathers. If, in a group of such male parents, A is in the X-chromosome and a in the Y-chromosome (X^AY^a; Fig. 109, A), and if, in 90 per cent of the sperm cells, A remains in the X-chromosome (X^A) and a in the Y (Y^a), then 90 per cent of all daughters would inherit A and 90 per cent of all sons a from their father. The remaining 10 per cent of the sperm cells would carry, as a result of crossing over, either an X^a or a Y^A chromosome, so that 10 per cent of all daughters would inherit a and 10 per cent of all sons A from their father. If the frequency of crossing over is less than 10 per cent, a still higher number of daughters and lower number of sons would inherit A, thus approaching the limiting case of complete X-linkage of A. If the frequency is more than 10 per cent, a lower number of daughters and a higher number of sons will inherit A. Since general experience has shown that the frequency of recombinations between any two loci is not higher than 50 per cent, it may be

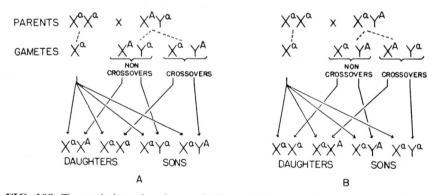

FIG. 109. Transmission of an incompletely sex-linked gene from one generation to the next. A. X^aX^a ♀ $\times X^AY^a$ ♂. B. X^aX^a ♀ $\times X^aY^A$ ♂.

assumed that 50 per cent is the upper limit of the frequency of recombinations between a gene A and the differential end point of the homologous segment. At this limit, equal numbers of X^A and X^a, Y^A and Y^a sperm would be formed, resulting in equal numbers of Aa and aa daughters and sons. Without additional data, such a case would be indistinguishable from autosomal inheritance, even though the A and a alleles were in the sex chromosomes.

Males heterozygous for a partially sex-linked gene have two different genotypes. One of these, X^AY^a, has been dealt with in the preceding paragraph. The other genotype is X^aY^A, with the recessive allele in the X-chromosome and the dominant allele in the Y-chromosome (Fig. 109, B). If we assume, as before, 10 per cent crossing over, the X^aY^A genotype would produce 90 per cent X^a and Y^A sperm and 10 per cent X^A and Y^a sperm, resulting in 90 per cent aa daughters and Aa sons and in 10 per cent Aa daughters and aa sons—a distribution with frequency relations directly opposite those expected from the X^AY^a male genotype.

An X^AY^a man inherits the dominant gene from his mother and transmits it, as we have seen, to the majority of his daughters and to a minority of his sons. Therefore, the crossover individuals among his progeny are those females who are unlike their paternal grandmother and those males who are like her. An X^aY^A man inherits the dominant gene from his father, and his own crossover offspring are the daughters who are like their paternal grandfather and the sons who are not. Generalizing, it may be said that crossover individuals are those who are unaffected and of the same sex as the affected grandparent and those who are affected and not of the same sex as the affected grandparent.

A Dominant Partially Sex-linked Trait?   A peculiar disease of the kidneys, chronic pyelonephritis, has been observed in a large kindred and analyzed genetically by Stephens. It consists of a syndrome which includes a bacterial infection of the kidneys that is often fatal; most persons who are seriously affected also develop nerve deafness. The kidney disease was found in 74 individuals in four successive generations, and is much more severe in the male. Most affected females are healthy despite the presence of the urinary disorder, and no females become seriously ill. Affected males, however, do become seriously ill and die of the disease. The pedigree begins with a couple whose state of health could not be investigated. They had 9 daughters and 1 son. The son and 3 of his sisters were affected. All but 2 (both nonaffected) of the 9 sisters had affected children or grandchildren, or both. Among the 49 children of the 12 affected males who had offspring, nearly all sons are normal and nearly all daughters affected. Since every affected father seems to have inherited the condition from his mother, one might conclude that it depends on a dominant, completely X-linked gene, were it not for seven exceptions among the 49 children: 2 affected males and 5 normal females. The normality of the females is of only minor significance for the interpretation of the type of inheritance involved. As will be shown in Chapter 16, dominant genes whose effects remain phenotypically unexpressed in some persons are not uncommon; thus, it would be possible that the 5 females, although appearing normal, still carry the gene which in other individuals is responsible for the disease. More significant is the presence of the 2 affected sons of an affected father—which contradicts the hypothesis of an absolutely X-linked gene. It suggests the possibility that a partially sex-linked gene was transmitted to each of the affected fathers in the X-chromosome that he received from his mother. The fathers in turn transmitted the gene in their X-chromosomes to at least 24 of their 29 daughters, while 18 of their 20 sons received the normal Y-chromosome, which carried the normal allele of the defect-causing gene. The 2 affected sons, and perhaps some or all of the 5 normal daughters, resulted from crossing over between the X- and the Y-chromosomes of the affected fathers. In the affected sons the Y-chromosome became the carrier of the defect-causing allele, and in the normal daughters the paternal X-chromosome could have carried the normal allele, obtained by crossing over from the Y-chromosome.

The existence of all four possible combinations—presence or absence of the disease in both sexes—clearly excludes complete X-linkage of the gene concerned. It must be determined, however, before we can go further, whether the facts are compatible with the view that the gene is a dominant autosomal one.

A chi-square test, which compares the observed distribution of 24 affected daughters and 5 normal daughters and 2 affected sons and 18 normal sons with the 1:1:1:1 distribution expected on the hypothesis of autosomal dominance, shows that there is less than one chance in many thousands of obtaining a deviation from expectation as great as, or greater than, that found. Thus there is hardly justification for assuming simple autosomal inheritance.

Doubts, however, still remain regarding an assignment to partial sex linkage. The trait, chronic pyelonephritis, is a peculiar one. Its genetic interpretation requires that the postulated abnormal allele be such that it regularly permits certain bacteria to attack the urinary tract, and that the normal allele of the gene nearly always precludes an infection. Furthermore, the expression of the trait in females is often so slight or of such short duration that the 5 seemingly normal daughters could all be in perfect health and yet have the abnormal allele. Thus the interpretation rests primarily on the 2 affected sons of one affected father. Could they possibly be affected by a condition similar to the pyelonephritis in the rest of the family but really of independent origin? Only additional evidence from future generations in this kindred or from other kindreds can clarify the situation. The present evidence of partial sex linkage would be strengthened by examples of sibships whose affected fathers had obtained their defect-causing allele from their own fathers instead of their mothers—i.e., who presumably had the defect-causing allele on their Y-chromosome. In such sibships affected daughters and normal sons should be rare, and normal daughters and affected sons should be common.

Recessive Partial Sex Linkage. The genetic analysis of pedigrees in order to detect the presence of dominant, incompletely sex-linked genes is fundamentally simple, since it is easy to discriminate between the two possible "phases" of the genotype of an affected heterozygous father, X^AY^a and X^aY^A, if one knows which of his parents was affected. Rare recessive genes, however, usually do not affect parents or earlier ancestors, and it is often impossible to determine the genotypic phase of the father in a specific sibship.

The methods of analysis are basically similar to those in autosomal linkage studies, in which two ordinary loci that control certain traits in kindreds or sibships are studied to determine their nonrecombinant and recombinant associations. In partial sex linkage, one of the two loci studied is that for the specific trait under scrutiny. The other is represented by the differential segments of both the X- and Y-chromosomes, which, since they do not exchange genes, behave as typical segregating units. The differential segment of the X-chromosome as opposed to that of the Y-chromosome is responsible for female versus male determination. The sexes of the offspring, therefore, are the second trait to be considered, so that the task is to determine which associations of the first trait with the male or female sex of the offspring are nonrecombinants and which are recombinants, as was already demonstrated for the dominant pyelonephritis. In recessive partial sex linkage, both parents would usually be heterozygous. According to the phase of the genotype of the male parent, matings would be of two types: $X^AX^a \; \female \times X^AY^a \; \male$ and $X^AX^a \; \female \times X^aY^A \; \male$. The children of the first mating (Fig. 110, left, generations III, IV) would be as follows, and their frequencies as indicated, where

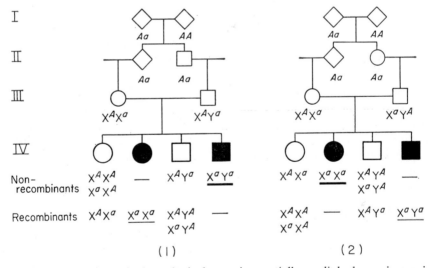

FIG. 110. Inheritance of a hypothetical recessive partially sex-linked gene in cousin marriages. (1) Genotypes of cousins (III): $X^AX^a \; \female \times X^AY^a \; \male$. (2) $X^AX^a \; \female \times X^aY^A \; \male$.

x = frequency of recombination and $(1 - x)$ = frequency of nonrecombination.

$\frac{1}{2}(1 - x)$	nonrecombinant	X^AX^A, X^aX^A	normal daughters
$\frac{1}{4}(1 - x)$	nonrecombinant	X^AY^a	normal sons
$\frac{1}{4}(1 - x)$	nonrecombinant	X^aY^a	affected sons
$\frac{1}{4}x$	recombinant	X^AX^a	normal daughters
$\frac{1}{4}x$	recombinant	X^aX^a	affected daughters
$\frac{1}{2}x$	recombinant	X^AY^A, X^aY^A	normal sons

Unless A and a were very distant from the differential segment, the recombinants would be less common than the nonrecombinants. This type of mating would therefore produce more affected sons than affected daughters and more normal daughters than normal sons.

The frequencies of the types of children expected from the second type of mating (Fig. 110 right, generations III, IV) would be the direct opposite.

$\frac{1}{4}(1 - x)$	nonrecombinant	X^AX^a	normal daughters
$\frac{1}{4}(1 - x)$	nonrecombinant	X^aX^a	affected daughters
$\frac{1}{2}(1 - x)$	nonrecombinant	X^AY^A, X^aY^A	normal sons
$\frac{1}{2}x$	recombinant	X^AX^A, X^aX^A	normal daughters
$\frac{1}{4}x$	recombinant	X^AY^a	normal sons
$\frac{1}{4}x$	recombinant	X^aY^a	affected sons

There would be more affected daughters than affected sons, and more normal sons than normal daughters.

If the genotypic phase of a father of such a family were known, then the sibship could be unequivocally assigned to either type. It is sometimes possible to determine this when close relatives of either the father's father or his mother are affected, thus suggesting that the father himself obtained his a allele either from his father, that is, in the Y-chromosome, or from his mother, that is, in the X-chromosome.

A close blood relationship of the two parents of affected persons may be indicative of the phase of the father's genotype, even if no relatives are affected. If the parents (Fig. 110, generation III) are first cousins, their heterozygosity for the a allele may usually be assumed to be due to their having received it from a common grandparent (generation I). If the male cousin's father was a brother of one of the female cousin's parents, then it is most likely that the Y-chromosome of the male cousin is the carrier of a (Fig. 110, left); but if the relationship was through the male cousin's mother, the X-chromosome would be the carrier of a (Fig. 110, right). Thus, in cousin marriages, the X^AY^a or X^aY^A constitution of the husband can be inferred when it is known whether the relationship of the spouses was through the husband's father or his mother. Many published pedigrees that show only a cousin marriage, without specifying the type, lose much of their value for an analysis of this as well as of other genetic phenomena.

When, as is usual, there is no reasonable certainty about the genotypic phase of the heterozygous male parent, modifications of the various methods of determining linkage in general must be applied to the data (see Chap. 15). One of the most conclusive indications of partial sex linkage would be the discovery of a particular trait in two types of sibships: one with more affected males than affected females and more normal females than normal males; and one in which the opposite was true.

At first the search for recessive partially sex-linked genes seemed to be highly successful. A large number of traits which did not follow the rules for complete X-linked inheritance seemed to deviate sufficiently from those of autosomal inheritance to make their assignment to partially sex-linked recessive genes a reasonable hypothesis. Gradually, ambiguities in the data and their interpretation came to the foreground, and at present, as shown particularly by Morton, no decisive case of either recessive or dominant partial sex linkage can be recognized. There are several reasons for the present rejection of earlier accepted assignments of certain traits to partial sex linkage. One of the most important is the fact that many genes are not "simple" in the sense defined earlier (p. 88), which specified clear and more or less identical expression in all individuals endowed with them. There are many genes that express themselves in varying fashion, and some of these produce a recognizable phenotype more frequently in one sex than in the other. This may sometimes be due to other, unrelated genes in the genotype which modify the expression of the gene under scrutiny. If modifying genes that suppress the expression of an *aa* genotype preferentially in the female segregate in some sibships, then the result will be more affected males than females; if in other sibships there is segregation of different modifying genes, which suppress the manifestation of *aa* preferentially in the male, the opposite will be true. Such "familial sex limitation" of the expression of *aa* in different sibships would simulate to some degree the results expected from partial sex linkage. Other reasons for false indication of partial sex linkage are special bias in the recording of atypical sibships and inconsistencies in the pedigree data used for analysis. All this does not exclude the possibility that partial sex linkage in man may exist, but proof that it does—or does not—lies in the future.

The Random Occurrence of Different Allelic Associations in Linkage

Two different constitutions of females heterozygous for both hemophilia and color blindness were seen to exist, namely, hc/Hc and hC/Hc. Their presence presupposes that all four possible kinds of chromosomes, namely, hc, HC, hC, and Hc, occur in the population. What are their frequencies? This question has often been answered incorrectly. The correct statement "hemophilia and color blindness are linked," was interpreted to mean that the combinations *hc* (hemophilic and color blind) and *HC* (not hemophilic, not color blind) are both more common than the combinations *hC* (hemophilic, not color blind) and *Hc* (not hemophilic, color blind). That this is not so may be seen from the following considerations: Assume a population in which the alleles *H* and *h* are equally common ($p_1 = q_1 = 0.5$) and in which the alleles *C* and *c* are equally common ($p_2 = q_2 = 0.5$). If this population, at one time, contained only two types of chromosomes, *HC* and *hc,* in equal numbers, then, as a result of random mating, there would be three types of females, *HC/HC, hc/hc,* and *HC/hc,* and two types of males, *HC* and *hc.* This population would not be in equilibrium but would change from generation to generation. The homozygous females and the males would form gametes containing the original *HC* and *hc* chromosomes only. The heterozygous *HC/hc* females, however, would form gametes with not only the original chromosomes, *HC* and *hc,* but also new, crossover chromosomes, *Hc* and *hC.*

Some females in the next generation will be *Hc/HC* and *hC/HC,* and some males *Hc* and *hC.* Mating between these will lead, one generation later, to some *Hc/hC* females. Thus, the population will now contain both *HC/hc* and *Hc/hC* heterozygotes. The majority will be *HC/hc* women, derived from noncrossover gametes, who will continue to segregate *Hc* and *hC* crossover chromosomes, and the minority *Hc/hC* women who, as noncrossovers, will propagate mainly the same two kinds of chromosomes, *Hc* and *hC.* As long as the *HC/hc* combination is more common than its *Hc/hC* counterpart, it will diminish, and the latter will increase, until an equilibrium is reached at which there are equal numbers of all four chromosome types: *hc, Hc, hC,* and *HC.*

It is noteworthy that this equality of all combinations is independent of the degree of linkage between the two loci. If the linkage is so close that relatively few crossovers take place between the two loci, it will require more generations until equilibrium is reached than if linkage is loose. Equilibrium is reached only when the two heterozygotes *HC/hc* and *Hc/hC* are equally common, so that one recreates, by crossing over, those combinations that the other loses by crossing over.

The initial assumption that the alleles *h* and *H,* and *c* and *C* are equally common was introduced in order to simplify the discussion. In reality, the allele frequencies are very unlike and, perhaps, roughly: p_1 (of *H*) = 0.9999, q_1 (of *h*) = 0.0001, p_2 (of *C*) = 0.9, and q_2 (of *c*) = 0.1. In such a population, equilibrium is reached when the four combinations occur at random frequencies; that is, chromosomes which carry *H* and *C* and those which carry *H* and *c* occur in proportion to the frequencies of *C* and *c,* and chromosomes which carry *h* and *C* and those which carry *h* and *c* also occur in proportion to the frequencies of *C* and *c.* Using the allelic frequencies given above, we obtain the following chromosomal frequencies:

$$HC = p_1 \cdot p_2 = 0.89991$$
$$hc = q_1 \cdot q_2 = 0.00001$$
$$Hc = p_1 \cdot q_2 = 0.09999$$
$$hC = q_1 \cdot p_2 = 0.00009$$

It is seen that the combination of the alleles for hemophilia and color blindness (hc) is *not* more common than those of the alleles for hemophilia and normal vision, and nonhemophilia and color blindness; but, on the contrary, is by far the least common chromosome.

That the random association of the H and h with the C and c alleles does indeed represent equilibrium may be seen if any other frequencies of association are considered. Let us assume, for instance, that at a given time, more hc chromosomes are present than in a population at equilibrium. They would cross over with HC chromosomes in HC/hc women and give rise to new Hc and hC chromosomes, so that, after some generations, the number of these chromosomes will have increased, and the number of the hc chromosomes decreased, until Hc/hC women produce as many HC and hc chromosomes as are lost by crossing over in HC/hc women. This condition is fulfilled when the population contains equal numbers of HC/hc and Hc/hC heterozygotes, the former having the equilibrium frequency $2 \cdot (p_1 \cdot p_2) \cdot (q_1 \cdot q_2)$, the latter $2 \cdot (p_1 \cdot q_2) \cdot (q_1 \cdot p_2)$, the two products being identical.

The statement that the four chromosomal constitutions of two pairs of linked genes occur at random frequencies is valid not only for X-linked genes but for any pair of linked genes. But it is also evident that even if the two genes were not linked, but located in different chromosome pairs, the same

TABLE 36.   *Types of Association between Two Inherited Traits.*

	Correlation in	
Genetic Basis	General Population	Segregating Sibships
(1) Multiple effects of a gene	+	+
(2) Allelism	−	−
(3) Group differences in gene frequencies		
(a) Genes not linked	+	0
(b) Genes linked	+	+ or −
(4) Inbreeding		
(a) Genes not linked	+	0
(b) Genes linked	+	+ or −
(5) Panmictic population		
(a) Genes not linked	0	0
(b) Genes linked	0	+ or −

TABLE 37.   *Random Association of Traits Based on Two Linked Loci, ABO Blood Group and Nail-patella Syndrome.* (After Renwick and Lawler, 1955.)

Nail-Patella Syndrome	O		Not O	
	Obs.	Exp.	Obs.	Exp.
Affected	35	(32.9)	50	(52.1)
Nonaffected	39	(41.1)	67	(64.9)
	$\chi^2 = 0.37$		$P \sim 0.55$	

NOTE: The table compares the associations in blood group O individuals with those in not O ($= A + B + AB$) individuals. A more detailed tabulation shows random association of the syndrome with any one of the four blood groups individually.

random frequencies would apply to the four genic combinations. Because of this, the existence of linkage cannot be established from a consideration of the frequencies of combinations of traits in a long-established panmictic population (Table 36:5, a, b, middle column). This may be shown for the distribution of two traits: the ABO blood groups, and an abnormality of the nails and the patella. The genes for the two traits—blood group and nail-patella—are rather closely linked; yet the frequency with which any of the blood groups was associated with the nail-patella abnormality was no different than the frequency of the blood group in the general population (Table 37).

Bernstein has offered an amusing simile of the principle of random association between the alleles of two linked genes:

> Imagine a number of ladies and gentlemen in a dance hall, who possess exactly equal attraction toward each other. Assume further the peculiarity, which corresponds to the linkage hypothesis, that a gentleman while he is dancing with a certain lady has a greater inclination to dance the next dance with her than with another one. Also be it the property of the ladies, to make their partner forget with whom he had danced earlier so that while he favors his momentary partner, he faces all other ladies indiscriminately. In this case, even if the attractive force is very great, but not infinitely so, then—provided the party lasts long enough—each gentleman would get together with each lady with equal frequency. This then would be the same result as if the momentary partner had not offered a special attraction. The only difference would be in the time required.

To the naïve observer, it seems plausible that traits based on linked genes should more often be associated than separate. Often enough, two characters which show a frequent or even absolute association have been described as new examples of linkage. In reality, however, such a finding is, in itself, likely to be evidence against linkage, since in a population mating at random chance governs the association of genes responsible for two traits: if the traits are associated more frequently than may be expected by chance, the reason must be sought in causes other than chromosomal linkage. To these we will now turn.

Causes of Nonrandom Association of Different Traits

Multiple Effects of a Gene.   A high frequency of association between different traits is often simply due to multiple effects of one and the same gene (Table 36:1). This is clearly so when the association is absolute, that is, when the two traits are always found together as, for instance, excretion of phenylpyruvic acid and absence of phenylalanine oxidase. If the two traits were caused by two separate closely linked genes, crossing over in former generations should have led to their separation, so that excretion of phenylpyruvic acid unaccompanied by the enzyme deficiency, and the enzyme deficiency unaccompanied by abnormal excretion, would occur.

The known multiple effects of a gene may not always be seen in the same person. In Marfan's syndrome, for example, long-fingeredness, misplaced eye lens, and heart defects are frequently, but not invariably, found together in the same individual. Each of these traits, separately, is so rare that a chance association of two or three of them would be most exceptional. A study of pedigrees indicates that a long-fingered person who does not have a misplaced lens is as likely to have the latter defect appear in his long-fingered progeny as one who is both long-fingered and has an abnormal lens. This shows that the same dominant gene is responsible for both traits in this syndrome, but that, developmentally, sometimes only one trait is expressed. The incomplete association of the different traits is therefore not caused by linked genes whose abnormal allelic varieties may or may not be present together in the same chromosome, but by a single gene with irregularly expressed multiple effects (a partly expressed, "frustrated" syndrome is called a *forme fruste*).

Some pedigrees contain individuals with misplaced lenses, none of whom is arachnodactylous. In these families, misplaced lenses are inherited in strictly dominant fashion, in contrast to the irregular appearance of the trait when it is associated with long-fingeredness. The different type of inheritance is a strong indication that misplaced lenses without arachnodactyly do not depend on the same locus, or at least not on the same allele, that controls arachnodactyly. This eliminates the possibility that misplaced lenses without long-fingeredness are the result of crossing over between two linked genes. There is, however, a possible objection to this argument: it could be true that two separate genes, one for misplaced lenses and another for long-fingeredness, so interact with each other in development that the effect of the lens gene is irregular when they are present in the same individual but regularly dominant if they are not. The main, decisive argument against interpreting frequent association of traits as evidence of linkage is the statistical one given above.

It is possible to look at the problem in still a different way. If we assume the existence of a separate atypical gene for each trait of a syndrome, it is also necessary to assume that, originally, mutations from normal to abnormal took place simultaneously at the different linked loci. It is most unlikely, from what we know about mutations, that simultaneous mutations of separate genes occur with sufficient frequency—if at all—to account for the origin of syndromes.

Allelism. The influence of allelism on association of different traits is the converse of that of a gene with multiple effects. In a population in which three-quarters of the individuals have the M antigen and one-quarter lacks it, and in which three-quarters have the N antigen and one-quarter lacks it, inheritance through two separate pairs of loci, either on different chromosome pairs or linked within one pair, would lead to an expectation of individuals of four types—MN, notMnotN, M, and N—in the proportions $9/16:1/16:3/16:3/16$. Actually, there are only three types—MN, M, and N —and they occur in the proportions $1/2:1/4:1/4$. This shows a negative correlation between M and N (only $1/2$ MN observed as compared to $9/16$ expected, and no notMnotN observed as compared to $1/16$ expected). The reason for the discrepancy is, of course, that M and N do not depend on different pairs of loci but on a single pair of alleles, L^M and L^N, which combine in only three genotypes: $L^M L^N$, $L^M L^M$, and $L^N L^N$. Allelism thus leads to a negative correlation of the phenotypic traits involved (Table 36:2).

Heterogeneous Populations. We have seen that, in a population which mates at random and is at equilibrium, associations of traits due to separate linked genes occur at random. If a population does not fulfill these conditions, such traits may not be associated at random frequencies. In the population of the United States there is a high association between straight hair and light skin, and between kinky hair and dark skin. This, of course, is because whites have genes for both straight hair and light skin in their chromosomal set, and negroes have genes for kinky hair and dark skin. That these traits are controlled by separate genes and not by multiple effects of one gene is shown by the segregation of hair and skin traits in the immediate and subsequent progeny of hybrids. Whether such segregation is the result of free recombination of genes in different chromosome pairs or of crossovers between loci of linked genes is not known. Investigation may someday show which of these alternatives is correct, since the speed of obtaining random association after generations of intermarriage would depend on whether recombination took place freely or was restricted by linkage (Table 36:3, a, b). Rife has pointed out that nonrandom association of two genetic traits and the presence of random association of either with a third, within a hybrid population of relatively recent origin, may under certain conditions be indicative of linkage. In a hybrid population, presence of some random associations of traits that are nonrandomly associated in the unmixed groups might indicate that enough generations had elapsed to have resulted in full recombination of independently inherited or loosely linked genes; nonrandom association of other traits might be the expression of linkages, which had not yet had time to become randomized. In Sudanese and American negroes, who are both of mixed Negro-Caucasian descent, Rife found nonrandom association between degree of pigmentation and specific patterns of lines on the palms of hands. Both of these traits showed random association with ability to taste PTC. There is thus a suggestion that the genes involved in pigmentation and palm pattern are linked, but because, among other difficulties, the genetics of both traits is complex, it is no more than a suggestion.

Inbreeding.   Still another cause of a frequency of association of traits that exceeds random expectations in a population is inbreeding, that is, more marriages between relatives than in panmixis (Table 36:4, a, b). Assume that two different recessive traits, due to the genotypes aa and bb respectively, each have a frequency of 1 in 10,000. If the population is panmictic, then only one person in 100,000,000 should have both of them. Most of these double recessive $aabb$ individuals will have two apparently normal double heterozygous $AaBb$ parents. Since $AaBb$ individuals are rare, marriages between two such individuals in populations with random mating will be rare indeed. If, however, an $AaBb$ individual marries a relative—for instance, a first cousin—then the probability is relatively high that both spouses are $AaBb,$ since they may well have inherited the a and the b allele from their one or two common ancestors. As a consequence, an inbred population will contain more children in which the aa and the bb trait are associated than will a panmictic one.

This chapter has dealt with some of the general problems of linkage, some aspects of complete sex linkage, the possibility of partial sex linkage, and the relation between linkage of genes and association of traits. The next chapter deals with two further features of the study of linkage, namely, the methods of detecting it and the construction of maps of human chromosomes.

Problems

113. (a) If a woman has three sons, one hemophilic and two color blind, what, most likely, is her genetic constitution? (b) If another woman also has three sons, two normal and one both hemophilic and color blind, what, most likely, is her genetic constitution?

114. A woman's father is color blind. Two of her brothers, as well as an uncle on her mother's side, are hemophilic. (a) What are the possible genotypes of all individuals mentioned? (b) If the woman has a hemophilic son, what must be her genotype? (c) What is the probability that a sister of the hemophilic son is a carrier for hemophilia? (d) If the woman's husband is color blind, what is the probability that a color-blind sister of her hemophilic son is a carrier for hemophilia? (e) What is the probability that a noncolor-blind sister does not carry hemophilia?

115. Among whites the frequency of the dominant secretor allele Se is 0.5 that of the Lutheran blood-group allele Lu^a, 0.35. The two genes are linked with a re-

combination frequency of 10 per cent. (a) What is the frequency of $Se\ Lu^a/se\ Lu^b$ people in a panmictic population? (b) Of $Se\ Lu^b/se\ Lu^a$ people? (c) What would these frequencies be if the recombination frequency were (i) only 1 per cent, or (ii) 50 per cent?

116. People with blue sclerae frequently have brittle bones. Is this due to linkage?

References

Aida, T., 1921. On the inheritance of color in a fresh-water fish *Aplocheilus latipes* Temmick and Schlegel, with special reference to sex-linked inheritance. *Genetics,* **6:** 554–573.

Bernstein, F., 1925. Zusammenfassende Betrachtungen über die erblichen Blutstrukturen des Menschen. *Zeitschr. Abstgs. u. Vererbgsl.,* **37:** 237–270.

Haldane, J. B. S., 1936. A search for incomplete sex-linkage in man. *Ann. Eugen.,* **7:** 28–57.

———, and Smith, C. A. B., 1947. A new estimate of the linkage between the genes for colour blindness and hemophilia in man. *Ann. Eugen.,* **14:** 10–31.

Harris, H., 1948. On sex limitation in human genetics. *Eugen. Rev.,* **40:** 70–76.

Perkoff, G. T., Nugent, C. A., Dolowitz, D. A., Stephens, F. E., Carnes, W. H., and Tyler, F. H., 1958. A follow-up study of hereditary chronic nephritis. *Arch. Intern. Med.,* **102:** 733–746.

Renwick, J. H., and Lawler, S. D., 1955. Genetical linkage between the ABO and nail-patella loci. *Ann. Human Genet.,* **19:** 312–331.

Rife, D. C., 1954. Populations of hybrid origin as source material for the detection of linkage. *Am. J. Human Genet.,* **6:** 26–33.

CHAPTER 15

LINKAGE AND
CROSSING OVER

II. THE DETECTION OF LINKAGE;
CHROMOSOME MAPS

In studying possible genetic linkage, it is first necessary to exclude the various other causes of positive or negative nonrandom association of different traits. After this is done, it may seem an easy matter to decide whether two genes recombine freely or with the limited frequency of crossovers. This is indeed true in most organisms but only rarely true in man, largely because of the relatively small size of human families. If the number of children in a sibship is less than 4, it is impossible for all four phenotypes, *A-B-*, *A-bb, aaB-*, and *aabb,* to appear. If, in a larger sibship, all four phenotypes do appear, the number of each may well be statistically compatible with the assumption of either independent recombination or moderate, if not close, linkage.

Some of these difficulties are similar to those pertaining to expected ratios in single factor recessive inheritance. There, many marriages of two heterozygotes do not come to the attention of the investigator because many sibships with such parents do not include recessive children, and the mark by which marriages of two heterozygotes are recognized is the production of at least one homozygous recessive child. In single factor inheritance, these difficulties can be overcome by adding together data from many sibships with at least one homozygous recessive child and by applying appropriate statistical corrections to these pooled data. In determining possible linkage, pooling of data by simple addition of sibships is of no help. If a parent is heterozygous for each of two linked pairs of genes, *A* and *a* and *B* and *b,* he may have either of two different genotypes: the two alleles *A* and *B* may be in one chromosome and *a* and *b* in the other (*AB/ab*)—this is called the *coupling,* or *cis,* phase—or *A* and *b* may be in one and *a* and *B* in the other

TABLE 38. *Gametes Produced by Parents Heterozygous for Two Linked Gene Pairs A, a and B, b.* (The frequency of recombination is x.)

	Gametes			
Parents	*AB*	*Ab*	*aB*	*ab*
AB/ab	$\frac{1}{2}(1-x)$	$\frac{1}{2}x$	$\frac{1}{2}x$	$\frac{1}{2}(1-x)$
Ab/aB	$\frac{1}{2}x$	$\frac{1}{2}(1-x)$	$\frac{1}{2}(1-x)$	$\frac{1}{2}x$
Sum of gametes of both parents	$\frac{1}{2}$	$\frac{1}{2}$	$\frac{1}{2}$	$\frac{1}{2}$

(*Ab/aB*)—this is called the *repulsion,* or *trans,* phase. The proportions of the four combinations *AB, Ab, aB,* and *ab* in the gametes of the two kinds of parents are quite different. An *AB/ab* parent will form more *AB* and *ab* noncrossover gametes and fewer *Ab* and *aB* crossover gametes, resulting in positive correlation of *A* and *B* and of *a* and *b*. On the contrary, in the gametes of an *Ab/aB* parent, the more common noncrossover combinations will be *Ab* and *aB,* and the less common crossover combinations *AB* and *ab,* resulting in a negative correlation of *A* and *B* and of *a* and *b*. If x is the frequency of recombination of *A* and *B,* then the proportions of gametes produced by the two kinds of parents are as listed in the first two lines of Table 38.

As we have seen, in a population mating at random the two kinds of parents are equally common. Consequently, by adding the gametes from many parents (more accurately, by adding the phenotypes of sibships derived from the gametes), we obtain the result, given in the last line of Table 38: equality of all kinds of gametes, no matter what the strength of linkage!

There are, however, several different ways in which the difficulties inherent in the exploration of human linkage can be met. A simple direct study is possible if the genotypic phase of a double heterozygous parent is known. Indirect approaches make use of statistical phenomena that are consequences of linkage, and can be found even in collections of pedigrees where the genotypes of parents are incompletely known.

Direct Analysis for Linkage.   The genotypes of the parents of sibships that provide information on linkage can sometimes be deduced with certainty from (1) genetic information on the sib's grandparents, (2) investigation of the kinds of children in large sibships, and (3) inspection of the parental phenotypes. Sometimes all these sources have to be tapped. To illustrate this by an example, let us consider a group of parents, each of normal pigmentation and belonging to blood group A and all having children with the following phenotypes: normally pigmented, group A; normally pigmented, group O; albino, group A; and albino, group O. From this, we can derive that the parents were all *Aa* for pigmentation and $I^A I^O$ for blood group. If the genes for pigmentation and blood group were linked, these pairs of parents could be of four different kinds, namely,

Females		Males
AI^A/aI^O	$\times$	AI^A/aI^O
AI^A/aI^O	$\times$	AI^O/aI^A
AI^O/aI^A	$\times$	AI^A/aI^O
AI^O/aI^A	$\times$	AI^O/aI^A

Unless it is known to which of these kinds a specific pair belongs, it is not clear which children are noncrossovers and which crossovers. Knowledge of the grandparents can sometimes provide the necessary information. If, for instance, the maternal grandmother were an albino and group O, then her normally pigmented daughter would receive from her the combination aI^O and would, therefore, be AI^A/aI^O. If the paternal grandfather belonged to group O and, although he was normally pigmented, was known to be a carrier of albinism, his son would most likely owe his genes aI^O to this parent and would, therefore, be AI^A/aI^O like his wife, so that the mating would be $AI^A/aI^O \times AI^A/aI^O$. On the basis of this information, assuming linkage was involved, the albino, group O children (aI^O/aI^O) from this couple could be diagnosed as noncrossovers, and the albino, group A children as crossovers. The nonalbino children could be of various genotypes, some representing noncrossovers and others crossover gametes.

Circumstances are not always as unfavorable as in the example given, where both parents were heterozygous for both allelic pairs. Sometimes, one parent may be known to be homozygous double recessive (ab/ab), or at least a homozygous recessive for one of the two gene pairs (aB/ab or Ab/ab). Or, in cases involving X-chromosomal genes, it is necessary to know only the genotype of the mother to analyze linkage among her sons, since the father does not contribute an X-chromosome to them. Moreover, the genotype of the mother may be relatively easy to determine if that of her father is known. Examples of such pedigrees were shown in Figures 103 and 104 (p. 248).

Usually, however, there will be even less information than in the example of albinism and blood groups. If, for instance, the pigmentation and the blood group of the maternal grandmother were unknown, or if she was normally pigmented and belonged to blood group A, and if the paternal grandfather's genotype was less clearly defined, then it would be impossible to proceed by the direct method.

Indirect Analysis for Linkage.   A number of different methods of obtaining information on linkage from incompletely known genotypes have been devised. It is not the purpose of the following pages to describe these methods in detail. Rather, an attempt will be made to give some insight into the ingenious thinking which has been applied to the problems of human linkage.

The y and u Statistics.   The earliest approach used data from two generations. Restricting ourselves to one of the simplest cases, we consider again families with one parent heterozygous for two different recessive genes and the other homozygous for them. In a random sample of such families the two types of marriages $AB/ab \times ab/ab$ and $Ab/aB \times ab/ab$ can be expected to be equally common, but given typically small human families the frequencies of the different types of offspring do not tell us the type of any particular parental pair. It is therefore impossible to separate the sibships with an AB/ab parent from those with an Ab/aB parent, and without such separation no information on linkage seems to be obtainable (*see* Table 38).

It was this situation which led Bernstein to a "new thought." In the absence of linkage—that is, in independent assortment—the four types of gametes AB, Ab, aB, and ab are equally common, but with linkage either AB and ab are more common than Ab and aB, or the reverse is true, depending on whether a parent was AB/ab or Ab/aB. The recognition that, from either of the two linkage phases, two more-common and less-common types of gametes were to be expected, opened a way to distinguish between independent assortment and linkage. If we obtain for each sibship the product y of the sum of gametes AB and ab and the sum of gametes Ab and aB, so that

$$y = (AB + ab) \cdot (Ab + aB),$$

the value of y, which depends on the frequency of recombination, is the same whether the parent was AB/ab or Ab/aB. This may be shown by a very simple example. Consider families of 4 sibs. If there is no linkage (recombination value x = 0.5), the most probable sibship from either type of parent would consist of one individual of each gametic type, so that

$$y = (1 + 1) \cdot (1 + 1) = 4.$$

If, on the other hand, linkage is present and if, say, x = 0.25, then the most probable sibships from an AB/ab parent would contain 3 nonrecombinant individuals from gametes AB or ab, and 1 recombinant individual of type Ab or aB, making

$$y = (3) \cdot (1) = 3.$$

Conversely, from an Ab/aB parent, the 3 nonrecombinants would be Ab or aB and the 1 recombinant AB or ab. This would give the same result, namely,

$$y = (1) \cdot (3) = 3.$$

Not all 4-child sibships from gametes of independently assorted A and B pairs will have y = 4, since chance may lead to many sibships less probable than the 1:1:1:1 type. Likewise, when x = 0.25, many sibships of 4 will not yield y = 3. On the average, however, the value of y will be higher for x = 0.5 than for x = 0.25.

One can construct a table in which the mean values of y are given for the whole range of recombination values from x = 0.0 (complete linkage) to x = 0.5 (independence) adjusted for any number of sibs in each sibship (Table 39). Such a table can then be consulted for the detection and estimation of linkage. Assume, for instance, that among a total of 16 sibships

TABLE 39. *Product Method for Detection of Linkage (y statistics). Mean Values of the Product* $y = (AB + ab) \cdot (Ab + aB)$ *for Sibships of from 2 to 4 Individuals from Parents of the Genotypes* $AB/ab \times ab/ab$ *and* $Ab/aB \times ab/ab$. (Excerpt from Bernstein, 1931.)

Recombination Value (x)	Mean Values of y for Different Numbers of Sibs		
	2	3	4
0.1	0.18	0.54	1.08
0.2	0.32	0.96	1.92
0.5	0.5	1.5	3.0

the sum of y for 6 sibships of 2 children is 2, for 7 sibships of 3 is 8, and for 3 sibships of 4 is 6. The observed mean values of y are thus 0.33, 1.14, and 2.0 for the three types of sibships. Table 39 shows that for x = 0.5 (absence of linkage) the expected mean value of y for sibships containing 2 children is 0.5, 3 children 1.5, and 4 children 3.0—values from which the observed mean values deviate considerably. The disagreement becomes even more obvious when one compares the sum of the observed y values 2 + 8 + 6 = 16 with the sum of the expected ones, $(6 \cdot 0.5) + (7 \cdot 1.5) + (3 \cdot 3.0) = 22.5$.

Since the y values for our families do not fit those expected for independently transmitted genes, they should be compared with y values characteristic of linkage; and the table shows that they fit rather well those for a recombination frequency of x = 0.2. For this frequency the table gives y values of 0.32 for sibships of 2, 0.96 for those of 3, and 1.92 for those of 4; and these give a sum of 14.4 for all sibships, close to the observed sum of 16. It is concluded, therefore, that the families under discussion are compatible with the hypothesis that the two traits are controlled by linked loci. The recombination value seems to be about 20 per cent, but no definite statement about linkage or nonlinkage can be made without studying more families.

The mating of a double heterozygote with a double recessive homozygote is, of course, only one of many different possible unions. Each type of mating requires a separate treatment and separate tables. Several of these were supplied in Bernstein's original paper.

Independently of Bernstein, another method for the detection of linkage was proposed by Wiener. Important extensions of the basic principle of Bernstein's "y statistic," which is now mainly of historical interest, have been made by R. A. Fisher and by Finney, among others. These authors introduced an improved scoring method based on a "u statistic," which is in part equivalent to the y statistic. Extensive tables have been provided to facilitate the use of u statistics in linkage studies.

The Sib-Pair Method. Penrose and Burks conceived the striking idea that evidence of human linkage can be obtained from data on a single generation. Let us again consider matings $AB/ab \times ab/ab$ and $Ab/aB \times ab/ab$.

In 2-child sibships, the following ten types of sib pairs would be found (the capital letters A and B stand for the phenotypes of AA or $Aa,$ and BB or Bb; and the lower-case letters a and b for aa and bb, respectively):

Type 1	AB, AB	Type 6	AB, aB
Type 2	Ab, Ab	Type 7	AB, ab
Type 3	aB, aB	Type 8	Ab, aB
Type 4	ab, ab	Type 9	Ab, ab
Type 5	AB, Ab	Type 10	aB, ab

These ten types can be easily classified in four groups:

Group 1. Sibs alike in both traits (types 1, 2, 3, and 4—both sibs being either A and B, A and b, a and B, or a and b).

Group 2. Sibs alike in the first but unlike in the second trait (types 5 and 10—both sibs A or both a, but one B and the other b).

Group 3. Sibs unlike in the first but alike in the second trait (types 6 and 9—one sib A and the other a, but both B or both b).

Group 4. Sibs unlike in both traits (types 7 and 8—one sib AB and the other ab, or one Ab and the other aB).

If the genes A and B are not linked, then the four groups are equally common, since the pairs formed by unlike partners, types 5 to 10, are each alike in frequency but twice as frequent as the pairs formed by like partners, types 1 to 4. An entry of the numbers of sib pairs of the four groups in a "fourfold" table (see Table 40) should therefore result in equality of its four cells. If, however, the genes A and B are linked, some combinations will be more common than others regardless of the linkage phase in the heterozygous parent. Consider the extreme case of a linkage so close that, in a sample of families, only the original, noncrossover combinations of the parent appear among the sibs. The sib pairs will be

AB/ab Parents		Ab/aB Parents	
Type 1	AB, AB	Type 2	Ab, Ab
Type 4	ab, ab	Type 3	aB, aB
Type 7	AB, ab	Type 8	Ab, aB

In the fourfold table, only the upper-left and lower-right cell will be filled, the former with types 1 to 4, the latter with 7 and 8.

TABLE 40.   *Tabulating the Results of Paired Sibship Analysis. Similarity within Pairs of Sibs.*

		Phenotype A *or* a	
		Sibs Like	Sibs Unlike
Phenotype	Sibs Like	(1)	(3)
B *or* b	Sibs Unlike	(2)	(4)

TABLE 41. *The Sib-pair Method Applied to the Loci for the Nail-patella Syndrome and the MNS Blood Groups.* (Renwick and Lawler, 1955.)

Type of Pair		Syndrome			
		Sibs Like		Sibs Unlike	
		Obs	Random Exp.	Obs.	Random Exp.
MNS {	Sibs Like	29	(30.5)	76	(74.5)
	Sibs Unlike	35	(33.5)	80	(81.5)
		$\chi^2 = 0.2$	$P = 0.9$	No linkage!	

If the genes *A* and *B* are less closely linked, so that all possible types of offspring are produced, types 5, 6, 9, and 10, which consist of one non-crossover and one crossover sib, will also occur. These sib pairs will provide entries for the upper-right and lower-left cells of the fourfold table, but, since crossovers are less frequent than noncrossovers, only a minority of all sib pairs will go in these cells.

It is seen that the sib-pair method provides a means of distinguishing between independent recombination and linkage of different genes without knowing whether the parental genotype is *AB/ab* or *Ab/aB*. The entries of paired sibs in a fourfold table will show a random distribution when there is no linkage but, when linkage exists, an excess of sib pairs in those cells where the two sibs are alike in both traits or unlike in both.

There are, of course, in any population, many more genotypes relating to the *A* and *a* and *B* and *b* loci than the three (*AB/ab, Ab/aB* and *ab/ab*) which formed the basis of our discussion of the sib-pair method. Some types of parental pairs, for example, *AB/AB* × *ab/ab,* will not give any evidence on linkage or its absence, and other types, such as *AB/ab* × *Ab/aB,* will provide only partial evidence. But it can be shown that, taking all types of parents together, those sib pairs which do not contribute decisive information fall into the four cells in a random manner in contrast to those which do contribute such information and which fall into the doubly like or doubly unlike classes. The net result is that the sib-pair method, although essentially valid, is not very efficient, since, by disregarding the parents, it fills the fourfold table with much useless information. Whenever possible it is therefore preferable to use other methods for the analysis of linkage.

Two actual examples of the use of the sib-pair method are given in Tables 41 and 42, where linkage between the genes for the nail-patella syndrome and those for either the MNS or the ABO blood groups is tested. It is seen that the entries in the fourfold table for the syndrome and MNS do not deviate significantly from random distribution. There is, therefore, no evidence of linkage. But in the table concerned with the syndrome and ABO groups, the entries for pairs alike in possessing or lacking the syndrome and in ABO blood group and for pairs unlike for both traits are significantly greater

TABLE 42.   *The Sib-pair Method Applied to the Loci for the Nail-patella Syndrome and the ABO Blood Groups.* (Renwick and Lawler, 1955.)

Type of Pair		Syndrome			
		Sibs Like		Sibs Unlike	
		Obs.	Random Exp.	Obs.	Random Exp.
ABO	Sibs Like	78	(55.8)	44	(66.2)
	Sibs Unlike	30	(52.2)	84	(61.8)
	$\chi^2 = 33.7$		P $<$ 0.0001	Linkage!	

than would accord with random expectation. The genes for these two traits are obviously linked. Special methods permit estimation of the frequency of recombination from the amount of deviation from random expectation. In the present example, the estimate suggests a frequency of recombination of about 7 per cent—a figure that is admittedly only an approximation.

It is not always easy to evaluate the possibility that a surplus of sib pairs alike and unlike for both traits is not due to factors other than linkage. The sib-pair method is, therefore, likely to give false positives, that is, "evidence" for linkage when it does not really exist.

Odds: The Method of Likelihood Ratio.   A third method for the detection and estimation of the strength of linkage is conceptually the simplest. Devised by J. B. S. Haldane and C. A. B. Smith, it consists of determining the amount of information available in a collection of data on two loci and comparing the probability of obtaining such data if the two loci are linked with the probability if they are not. The ratio of these two probabilities gives the odds for or against linkage. If, for example, the probability of obtaining the observed distribution of two traits in a pedigree is much higher if the genes are linked than if they are not, then the odds are obviously in favor of linkage. Conversely, if the probability of obtaining the information given by a pedigree is much higher if the genes are not linked than if they are, then the odds are against linkage. This method of likelihood ratio, which is also known as the *lod* (log odds) method, since the necessary calculations make use of tables of logarithms of odds ("z scores," Morton), will probably become the method of general choice in linkage studies.

Linkage itself may be strong or weak: strong if the recombination value x is low (0.0 indicates complete linkage); weak if it is high (0.5 indicates no linkage). The probability of obtaining the particular distribution of traits shown by a given pedigree or collection of pedigrees is therefore expressed as a function of x, different degrees of probability corresponding to different degrees of linkage. The recombination value that gives the highest probability that the observed distribution would be obtained is also the best estimate of the degree of linkage between the two loci.

The nail-patella syndrome and the ABO blood groups may once more serve as a simplified example illustrating the method of likelihood ratio. Figure 111, A, gives a small part of the extensive pedigree of one of the kindreds which were classified for the syndrome and the blood groups. The

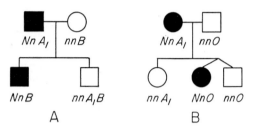

FIG. 111. Two families in which one of the parents was heterozygous for the nail-patella syndrome N, and for an allele of the ABO blood-group locus. (After Renwick and Lawler.)

father of the family shown was heterozygous for the syndrome-producing allele, N, and for the I^{A_1} allele, as seen from the fact that the two children indicate segregation for both loci. He was therefore either NI^{A_1}/nI^O or NI^O/nI^{A_1}. The first son obviously received an NI^O sperm from his father, and the second son an nI^{A_1} sperm. What is the probability of having two such sons if N and I are linked and the recombination value is x? If the father is NI^{A_1}/nI^O, then the probability of producing an NI^O crossover gamete is $\frac{1}{2}x$ and that of forming an nI^{A_1} crossover gamete is also $\frac{1}{2}x$ (the sum of the two probabilities, $\frac{1}{2}x + \frac{1}{2}x = x$, represents the total probability of a recombinant gamete). The probability of obtaining the particular sibship of two sons would therefore be $(\frac{1}{2}x)^2$. On the other hand, if the father was NI^O/nI^{A_1}, then the probability of producing an NI^O or an nI^{A_1} noncrossover gamete was $\frac{1}{2}(1-x)$ each (the sum of the two probabilities, $\frac{1}{2}(1-x) + \frac{1}{2}(1-x) = 1-x$, represents the total probability of a noncrossover gamete). The probability of obtaining the sibship would thus be $[\frac{1}{2}(1-x)]^2$. The probability of obtaining the sibship from either an NI^{A_1}/nI^O or an NI^O/nI^{A_1} father is the sum of the two probabilities, namely,

$$P = (\tfrac{1}{2}x)^2 + [\tfrac{1}{2}(1-x)]^2 = \tfrac{1}{4}(1 - 2x + x^2).$$

In order to determine the numerical probability of obtaining the sibship if there were no linkage, we make x = 0.5, and thus obtain P = 2/16. If now we make x = 0.0, we can determine the probability of obtaining the sibship if there were complete linkage: P = 4/16. The odds in favor of complete linkage as against no linkage are therefore two to one. In a similar manner the odds can be determined for any intermediate value of x. The odds for six values of x are listed under sibship 1 in Table 43. It can be seen that it is most likely that the sibship resulted from the behavior of two completely linked loci, but it is also apparent that the lesser likelihood that the sibship resulted from looser linkage, or even no linkage, cannot be excluded on the basis of this small sibship.

Let us therefore consider another family with data on the same syndrome and the same blood groups (Fig. 111, B). This time it was the mother who was heterozygous for both loci, her genotype being either NI^O/nI^{A_1} (Case 1)

TABLE 43. *Linkage between the Loci for the Nail-patella Syndrome and the ABO Blood Groups.* (The table lists the odds in favor of linkage, as compared to free assortment, for various recombination values.) (After Renwick and Lawler, 1955.)

Recombination Value x	Odds			
	Sibship 1	Sibship 2	Sibship 1 + 2	All Data
0	2.00	0	0	0
0.1	1.64	0.36	0.59	4,000,000,000
0.2	1.36	0.64	0.87	200,000,000
0.3	1.16	0.84	0.97	600,000
0.4	1.04	0.96	0.998	500
0.5	1.00	1.00	1.00	1

or NI^{A_1}/nI^O (Case 2). The probabilities that she would produce eggs resulting in the 3 children listed were

Case 1: $\frac{1}{2}(1 - x)$, $\frac{1}{2}(1 - x)$, and $\frac{1}{2}x$
Case 2: $\frac{1}{2}x$, $\frac{1}{2}x$, and $\frac{1}{2}(1 - x)$.

The joint probabilities of the sibships from either phase were

$$P = [\tfrac{1}{2}(1 - x)]^2 \cdot \tfrac{1}{2}x + (\tfrac{1}{2}x)^2 \cdot \tfrac{1}{2}(1 - x) = \tfrac{1}{8}(x - x^2).$$

Making $x = 0.5$, to find the probability of no linkage, $P = 1/32$; whereas if $x = 0.0$ (complete linkage), $P = 0$. The odds on complete linkage are thus zero; that is, complete linkage of the two genes is excluded. The odds for intermediate values of x entered under sibship 2 in Table 43 show that it is most likely that in the second family the two loci are independent, although the lesser likelihood of any degree of partial linkage cannot be excluded.

To obtain a joint estimate of the situation, it is necessary only to find the product of the odds for each of the families for each value of x. The results, given in the fourth column of the table, show that there is a maximum likelihood of obtaining the two sibships if the two loci are not linked, but the odds against linkage of even close degree are not high.

Obviously, with so few data, no reliable estimate of the value of x can be made. However, the totality of the data of which those on our two families constitute only a small fraction yields undeniable evidence for rather close linkage. By combining the individual odds for all families, we find that the over-all odds in favor of various degrees of linkage as against no linkage have the values listed in the final column of Table 43 and shown graphically in Figure 112. This final column shows once more that there is no possibility of explaining the data by assuming that the syndrome and the ABO blood groups are completely linked. The distribution of odds shows a very high peak in the neighborhood of the recombination value 0.1; in fact, the odds are four billion to one in favor of such linkage as against independence (x =

0.5), and the odds in favor of more frequent recombination (x = 0.2, 0.3, or 0.4) are also high. The most likely recombination value, that which gives the highest odds against absence of linkage, has been estimated as 0.104, or 10.4 per cent. This estimate may still be subject to considerable revision when new pedigrees become available. In order to show how carefully one should express oneself when presenting such an estimate, we mention that the authors of this linkage study imply that, although the most likely value is close to 10 per cent, there may be a chance of 5 in 100 that the true value is less than 5 per cent or more than 14 per cent.

The methods for the detection of linkage that have been described here involve the analysis of given sets of pooled observations. Morton has adapted the "sequential analysis method" to the study of problems of linkage—a statistical method whose importance for problems of human genetics was first pointed out by Macklin. This method makes use of the fact that information on possible linkage is accumulated as a succession of samples, each of which is quite small relative to the amount of data required to detect even moder-

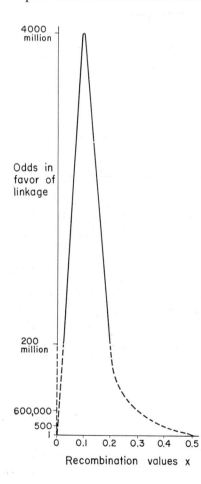

ately close linkage. It consists of determining, at successive stages during the collection of data, whether enough information has been collected to make it possible to decide that there is no linkage (H_0), that there is linkage of a specified degree (H_1), or that such a decision cannot be made one way or the other. The decision itself is given in terms of probability and makes use of lods, the logarithms of likelihood ratios.

It should not be surprising that only a few autosomal linkages have been established in man. Whenever two loci are tested for linkage, the a priori probability is small that they are in the same chromosome; it is much more likely that if one locus is in a certain autosome, the other will be in any one of the other 21. In addition, two loci in the same chromosome may be so

FIG. 112. Linkage between the loci for the nail-patella syndrome and ABO blood groups. The probability ratio in favor of linkage represented by different recombination values as compared to free assortment (=0.5). This figure is a graphic representation of the last column of Table 43.

far apart that they assort freely and thus appear unlinked. Conversely, apparent cases of linkage must be treated very critically, since such extraneous circumstances as interaction between different alleles of the two loci that reduce the viability of their bearers may simulate linkage ratios (for instance, if A^1B^1 and A^2B^2 confer on their bearers higher viabilities than A^1B^2 and A^2B^1). Acceptance of supposed linkages in man must be based on a very high level of confidence. In this connection it should be reiterated that information about three or more generations in a pedigree may often establish the exact genotypes of relevant parents and thus lead to clearly significant findings.

Crossing Over in Males and Females. In Drosophila, crossing over occurs only in the female, and in the silkworm Bombyx, it is restricted to the male; but in man, as in mice, rats, and other mammals, crossing over has been found in both sexes. All three known examples of linkage between two pairs of absolutely X-linked genes are, of course, evidence of crossing over between the two X-chromosomes in females. Crossing over of autosomal genes has been recorded for both females and males in the three best-established cases of autosomal linkage.

As yet, there are not enough data to show whether the strength of linkage is the same in both sexes. All calculations of recombination values make the assumption that it is—an assumption which, judging from other organisms, may not be valid.

Heterogeneity in Linkage Data. One of the well-established autosomal linkages is that between the loci that determine the Rh blood groups and either the usual round or the rare oval shape of red blood cells (Fig. 113). Elliptocytosis or ovalocytosis is caused by a dominant gene *El*. By the combining of data from numerous pedigrees, it has been shown that the recombination value is approximately 20 per cent. A study of the individual pedigrees indicates that they fall into at least two different groups: one of kindreds with linkage closer than 20 per cent, and one of kindreds with apparently free assortment. Statistical tests confirm the impression that the recombination values in the different pedigrees differ from one another more than chance alone can account for—in other words, that

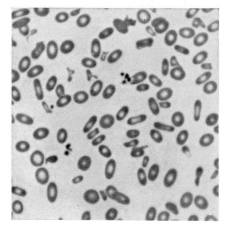

FIG. 113. Hereditary elliptocytosis: 500×. (Originals from Dr. C. L. Conley.)

the data are heterogeneous. On the other hand, no significant heterogeneity for linkage has been encountered in the fourteen known nail-patella syndrome kindreds or in the Lutheran-secretor kindreds (p. 280).

Indications of heterogeneity will probably be found in various future studies. There are two principal, but not mutually exclusive, explanations of such—at first—disconcerting findings. One is based on the knowledge that similar or seemingly identical phenotypes may be caused by action of entirely unrelated genes. If there were two different loci, El_1 and El_2, for elliptocytosis, and if one of these was in the same chromosome as the Rh locus while the other was in a different chromosome, then clearly some kindreds would show linkage and others free assortment. The finding of heterogeneity in linkage studies may thus serve as an incentive to search for biochemical, physiological, or morphological differences between apparently identical phenotypes from different pedigrees.

Another explanation of heterogeneity in linkage data assumes that in all families one and the same locus controls a given phenotype, but considers the possibility of variations in the chromosomal constitutions of different persons. It is well known that more than one kind of arrangement of genetic material is found in different populations of many animals and plants. Thus, one group of individuals may have a chromosome pair containing the two linked loci, A and B, and another pair in which two other loci, C and D, are linked (Fig. 114, 1). In another group, A and C may be together in one chromosome pair, and B and D in another (Fig. 114, 2). Still a third group may have an "arrangement-heterozygote" consisting of four different chromosomes (Fig. 114, 3). Such situations are the result of an exchange of segments between nonhomologous chromosomes, a rare process which results in a *translocation*. Once having been produced, translocation chromosomes reproduce their own kind. It is obvious that individuals of the first type would show linkage between A and B and between C and D, but that individuals of the second type would show independence of the loci for A and B and of the loci for C and D, but linkage between A and C and between B and D. The third type would behave in an unexpected way. Gametes with various combinations of the four chromosomes would be formed, but only those gametes in which all four loci are present would contribute to viable zygotes; in other

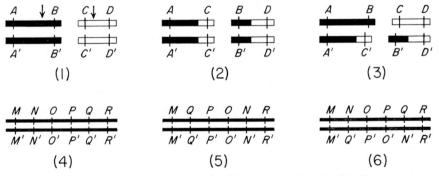

FIG. 114. Chromosome translocation (1–3) and inversion (4–6). See text.

words, only the chromosome combinations with *AB* and *CD* or with *A'C'* and *B'D'* would be recovered in the offspring, thus simulating a single group of four linked loci.

Translocation between different pairs of chromosomes is only one kind of the different known causes of chromosomal heterogeneity in plants and ani-- mals. Another common variation concerns a single chromosome pair. Some individuals may have in a certain pair of chromosomes a linear sequence of loci *M–N–O–P–Q–R*; others may be homozygous for the partly "inverted" sequence *M–Q–P–O–N–R*; and still others may be inversion heterozygotes with one chromosome of each kind (Fig. 114, 4, 5, 6). If the loci *M* and *Q* in individuals with a regular sequence of loci are located very far from each other, they may assort so freely that they appear not to be linked. In those with an inverted sequence, the same two loci may show rather close linkage. Finally, in inversion heterozygotes, crossing over at the four-strand stage (see pp. 67–69) will frequently result in two chromosomes which have undergone no crossing over and two crossover chromosomes. The crossover chromosomes are usually so abnormal that if they are transmitted by a gamete, they do not lead to a viable zygote (Fig. 208, B, p. 513); hence, the loci *M* and *Q* seem to be almost absolutely linked. We see, then, that according to the sequences of loci in chromosomes which are inverted in relation to each other and the homo- or heterozygosity for such sequences, two gene pairs may assort freely, be linked to some degree, or seem to be absolutely linked. *now we do*

We have no certain knowledge yet that chromosomal translocations or inversions exist in man, but configurations suggestive of inversions have been seen. It seems reasonable to predict that future studies will discover evidence of human chromosomal polymorphism.

Maps of Human Chromosomes.   The strengths of various linkages are measured by the frequency of recombination—a frequency that depends on the physical distance between the linked loci in the chromosomes. This makes it possible to construct chromosome maps in which the loci of known genes are represented by points on a line whose distances from one another are proportional to their recombination percentages. Detailed chromosome maps have been made for microorganisms and many higher plants, insects, chickens, mice, rats, and a few other mammals, but the mapping of man's chromosomes in terms of genic loci has only begun.

The tools for the detection of human linkages are now applied routinely in studies in which more than one locus can be followed simultaneously. It is natural that such well-established loci as those for blood groups are fore- most among those tested, for linkage among themselves and between any one of them and loci governing other traits. The authors of reports giving "Data on Linkage in Man" often come to the conclusion that the traits studied are not linked. Analysis sometimes demonstrates that seemingly established link- ages must now be considered spurious or at least doubtful either because the assignment of linkage was never fully warranted or because new facts or more

refined methods lead to new interpretations. Still other studies give suggestions for the existence of linkages that are incentives to future efforts that
may well lead to conclusive evidence.

A few certain linkages have become known. Linkage of two autosomal loci
probably define three of the autosomes: one carries the loci for ABO blood
groups and the nail-patella syndrome
(N); a second, those for Rh and elliptocytosis (El); and a third, the loci for
the Lutheran blood group and the ABH
secretor trait. Using present estimates
to obtain the recombination frequencies in these three chromosomes, we
obtain the maps drawn in Figure 115.
It will probably not be long until these
"2-point maps" become 3-point, 4-
point, and many-point maps, by the
discovery of linkage of additional loci
with those at present recognized as
linked. Some of the additional loci will
undoubtedly lie between those now located and others on either side of the
chromosome region now delimited by them. It is also possible that a locus
X may be found which is linked with the ABO locus and the Rh locus. These
two loci segregate independently and are therefore now regarded as being in
different chromosomes, although their freeness of recombination is compatible
with location on the same chromosome, but far enough from each other that
crossing over separates them as frequently as if they were not linked. The
hypothetical discovery of a locus X that is linked to both would require the
construction of a single new chromosome map, incorporating perhaps the
sequence $N–I–X–R–El$.

At present, useful linkage maps can be constructed only for well-defined
pairs of single loci. Suggestions for the existence of further linkages can also
come from studies of traits that may be less well defined genetically. We have
referred to data on linkage between hand patterns and skin pigmentation in
northern Sudanese and American negro populations. In another investigation 300 whites from New England have been tested, by the sib-pair method,
for linkage between body build and 9 other phenotypes: the data point to an
autosomal linkage of loci involved in body build and in freckling. In a somewhat similar study of 75 pairs of white brothers, 37 physical traits were tested
in 666 paired comparisons, one of which was highly suggestive of linkage
between genes for "nose-tip thickness" and "Darwin's point" of the external
ear. One more autosomal linkage is suggested by one of the earliest applications of the sib-pair method: between loci concerned with a tooth deficiency
and hair color.

In addition to the three well-defined maps of sections of autosomes, a partial map of the X-chromosome can be constructed. All X-linked loci are, of

FIG. 115. Maps of three autosomal linkages in man. (1) Lutheran blood group and secretor ($Lu–Se$), (2) Rhesus and elliptocytosis ($R–El$), (3) Nail-patella syndrome, and ABO ($N–I$).

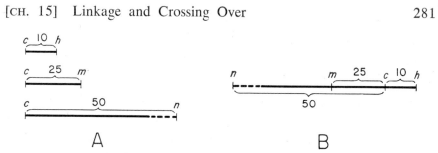

FIG. 116.   A. Three sections of the map of the X-chromosome each containing the locus for X-linked partial color blindness. B. A map of one of six possible sequences of the four loci. The sequence chosen for representation has no greater likelihood of being correct than the other five.

course, in this chromosome, but the recombination values that represent relative distances are known only for color blindness (treated as a single locus, c) in combination with hemophilia A or B (also treated as a single locus, h), X-linked muscular dystrophy (m), and myopic night blindness (n). The first two loci have a recombination value of about 10 per cent; the second (with considerable uncertainty), of about 25 per cent; and the third, of about 50 per cent (Fig. 116, A). This suggests that the loci for color blindness and hemophilia are nearer each other than those for color blindness and dystrophy, and that those for color blindness and night blindness so distant that crossing over leads to recombinants as often as to nonrecombinants. (In addition to these X-chromosome linkages a large pedigree with a combination of color blindness and an X-linked eye tremor—nystagmus—suggests that the loci for these are a considerable distance apart.)

Despite this positive but still uncertain information, we lack knowledge of the sequence of the four loci (Fig. 116, B). Considering first only three of them, we may ask whether the sequence is (1) hemophilia–color blindness–night blindness, (2) hemophilia–night blindness–color blindness, or (3) color blindness–hemophilia–night blindness. An answer might be obtained if pedigrees could be found in which hemophilia and night blindness occurred together and in which the strength of linkage of these two loci could be determined. No such kindreds have been found. Additional information would be required to place the fourth locus, that for muscular dystrophy, in its correct position in the sequence.

If partial sex linkage actually exists in man, a further advance could be made in mapping the X-chromosome. If pedigrees became known in which there were heterozygosity for a partially sex-linked gene, ps, and for one or the other of the absolutely X-linked genes—for example, color blindness in one group, hemophilia in another—it might be possible to determine the distance between the loci for ps and the color-blindness gene and between ps and the gene for hemophilia. If these relative distances were 40 and 30, respectively, a map like that in Figure 117 could be drawn, which would give the sequence of the loci for color blindness and hemophilia in relation to the differential end point O.

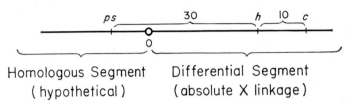

Homologous Segment   Differential Segment
    (hypothetical)   (absolute X linkage)

FIG. 117. Hypothetical map of part of the X-chromosome based on recombination of an assumed partly sex-linked locus *ps* with the loci for color blindness and hemophilia.

It may even be possible to derive the relative positions of completely X-linked genes from data involving only one locus at a time. If a woman is heterozygous for the alleles *A* and *a*, then, in meiosis, two chromosome strands carrying *A* and two carrying *a* will be present in her eggs (Fig. 118, A). If there has been a single crossover involving two strands between the kinetochores and the locus of *A, a*, each kinetochore will have a strand attached to it that carries *A* and another that carries *a* (Fig. 118, B). If nondisjunction of the chromosomes occurs at the first meiotic division, the egg nucleus may receive both kinetochores and their four strands. The second meiotic division may then separate the four strands in such a way that the mature egg nucleus receives the two chromosomes carrying *a* (Fig. 118, C). If fertilized by a spermatozoon that carries a Y-chromosome, such an egg

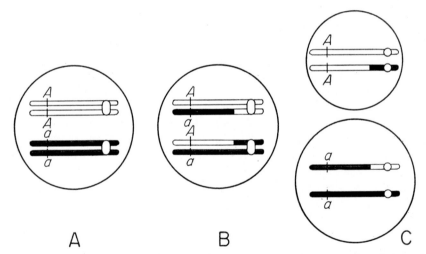

A   B   C

FIG. 118. Nondisjunction and the origin of a homozygous *aa* nucleus in an *Aa* heterozygote. A. Two homologous chromosomes reduplicated into two strands each. The oval bodies are the kinetochores. B. The same chromosomes after crossing over between the kinetochore and the locus of *A,a*. Nondisjunction of the chromosomes at the first meiotic division has retained them in a single nucleus. C. Division and separation of the kinetochores at the second meiotic division has resulted in a polar-body nucleus of the genotype *AA*, and an egg nucleus of the genotype *aa*.

will give rise to an XXY individual (Klinefelter type, see pp. 413–414), who is homozygous for the allele *a* from his mother, although she herself was heterozygous for it. According to the mechanism outlined, the frequency of homozygosity for an X-linked gene in XXY individuals is positively correlated with the frequency with which crossing over takes place between the kinetochore and its locus, that is, with the map distance from the kinetochore to the locus. Data on the frequency of color blindness in XXY individuals suggest that the locus controlling the trait is relatively far from the kinetochore.

The "mapping" of human chromosomes is an example of the present status of age-old efforts to gain an understanding of the structure of organisms. Even before recorded history, man presumably endeavored to gain knowledge of his own body. The science of anatomy gradually grew up from incidental and isolated observations until the locations and interrelations of the various organs, the bones and tendons, the muscles and nerves, became ever better known. When the skill of the anatomist became inadequate for the elucidation of the finer structures of the body, the microscope, the electron microscope, methods of differential staining, and microchemical methods led to further advances. Outrunning these delicate probes, the subtle tools of the mind now lay bare the topography of molecular entities within the chromosomes—the genes whose allelic forms so differentiate the individual's development that he may turn out to be dark- or light-skinned, endowed with normal limbs or misshapen ones, able to see the beauty and ugliness of the physical world or assigned to lifelong darkness.

Linkage and Genetic Counseling

Linkage Involving Two Loci.   When extensive linkage maps of all human chromosomes are at last available, more than just an intimate knowledge of man's biological make-up will have been achieved. The maps will also help determine the genotypes of individuals and thus remove some of the great difficulties confronting genetic advisers. These are the inability to distinguish carriers of recessive atypical genes from homozygous normal individuals; to recognize, at an early stage, atypical dominant or homozygous recessive genotypes for genetically conditioned abnormal traits which do not become apparent before a certain age; or to differentiate between genetically normal and abnormal individuals in those cases in which atypical genes may not be expressed phenotypically. It is of relatively little help to tell a healthy young man or woman with a parent who carried the dominant gene for Huntington's chorea that he has 1 chance in 2 of having inherited the gene and of becoming afflicted in later life. If it were known, however, that this gene, *Ht*, is located in the same chromosome as some other gene and is close to it, and if the presence or absence of the other gene could be recognized more easily than that of *Ht*, then the diagnosis of the desirable genotype *ht/ht* or the ominous genotype *Ht/ht* could be made with greater certainty.

We may clarify this statement by a hypothetical example. Assume that a deleterious dominant gene *V'*, whose effect does not appear until middle age, is linked to the blood-group gene *I* and that *V* and *I* are crossovers 5 per cent of the time. A man without the allele *V'* and in blood group O marries a woman in blood group A who later develops the defect. Their young son is in group A. What are his chances of being a carrier of *V'*? The accuracy of the answer will depend upon knowledge of the blood-group genotype of the mother. If it were known that her father was in blood group O and had the abnormal trait caused by *V'*, then she must be $V'I^O/VI^A$. Her son, who received his I^A allele from his mother, has therefore a chance of 95 per cent of not having the allele *V'*, since this is the frequency with which *V* is linked with I^A in the mother's gametes. Differently expressed, there is only 1 chance in 20 that he is a carrier.

This example assumed linkage between the gene *V* and a gene *I* whose alleles I^O and I^A are both common. To serve as a useful marker for the presence or absence of an allele at another locus, an allele must occur frequently in heterozygous combinations. Had the mother of the young son been homozygous for I^A, I^B, or I^O, no marker for the *V* allele would have been available.

There are already a few cases on record in which a knowledge of linkage has been employed in counseling. Hoogvliet, in his studies of hemophilia and color blindness, concluded that a certain mother was heterozygous for genes for these two traits and that her genotype almost certainly was of the cis phase, *HC/hc* (the *c* gene was one of the deuteranoid alleles). Her husband was a deuteranope, and the mating was thus *HC/hc* × *Hc*. One of the daughters was color blind, but four others appeared to have normal color vision. Accepting the recombination value for the linkage of *h* and *c* as about 10 per cent, we can conclude that the color-blind daughter had a 90 per cent chance of having received from her mother a nonrecombinant X-chromosome, *hc,* making her *hc/Hc*; if so, the probability that any son she might have would be hemophilic would be 50 per cent. Against this distressing report to the color-blind daughter may be placed the more reassuring one to her normal-visioned sisters. They have a 90 per cent chance of having received from their mother the other nonrecombinant X-chromosome, *HC*, and thus of being *HC/Hc*; hence there is only a slight chance that they would have any hemophilic offspring. Similar counsel was given families in which the mother was also doubly heterozygous for hemophilia and color blindness but, probably, in the trans phase, *Hc/hC*.

Linkage Involving Three Loci. Improvement of the method of determining the genotype of an individual by means of linked marker genes will result from detailed human chromosome maps. In the example involving *V* and *I*, it was assumed that *V* and *I* would be crossovers 5 per cent of the time; so the uncertainty of predicting the presence or absence of *V* on the basis of the *I* marker was still 5 per cent. If *two* marker genes were known, located not too far to the right and left of the *V* locus, the accuracy of prediction would approach certainty. This follows from the knowledge that double crossovers are so rare within short map distances that they can practically be ignored. Consequently, if the marker alleles retain their original linkage relations, there is a very high probability that the test gene has remained between them.

The utilization of marker genes on both sides of the test gene has its limitations. It depends, of course, on heterozygosity for all loci concerned, since recombination is discoverable only in heterozygotes. Moreover, if a crossover has occurred between the two marker genes, then there may be no clear indication whether the test gene is present or absent in the recombined chromosome. These limitations could be overcome if enough loci in each chromosome were known, so that it was possible to select those that gave maximum information. Although we are far from having the requisite knowledge, the search for new marker genes will continue to provide new loci for future chromosome maps. When enough marker genes are known to make the method feasible for general use, information on several generations preceding the individuals under consideration will be desirable. It is not too early to begin collecting such information in each family, and one may foresee that, at some future date, genealogical records containing the greatest possible amount of data on every common, easily determinable genetic property will be available.

Linkage and the Direct Evidence on Genotypes.   It is, of course, possible that other methods of recognizing hidden genotypes will develop faster than the linkage method. It is likely that most, if not all, heterozygotes for recessive genes will be found to be different from the dominant homozygote in some slight, detectable way, and that every genotype will someday become phenotypically distinguishable from every other. If this should be true, direct methods of ascertaining the presence or absence of any given allele would be available, and no recourse to marker genes would be necessary. Whatever methods may finally be employed, it should not be forgotten that they will apply not only to unfavorable alleles but also to the less obvious favorables ones.

The value of linkage studies in man is not limited to the construction of maps of human chromosomes and to their application in counseling. Data on linkage can throw light on such questions as whether there is only one locus, or several loci, able to produce a given phenotype, or whether sex linkage or autosomal linkage exists in inherited traits that involve nonreproduction of affected males and absence of affected females (see male pseudohermaphroditism, p. 416). An answer to the first question would have particular significance. If the frequency with which a given trait arises by mutation is determined, it is obviously important to know whether mutation has occurred at the same single locus each time or whether a variety of loci—one at a time —are involved, so that the frequency of mutation per locus is only a fraction of the total rate of mutation for the trait. Another value of linkage studies, already mentioned in connection with elliptocytosis, is their potentiality of revealing genetic heterogeneity of seemingly uniform traits. Such findings may stimulate biochemical and developmental exploration to differentiate between the different genetic pathways which lead to the trait and then to design appropriate methods of control.

The Possible Control of Linkage.   The frequency with which a given pair of genes cross over is not constant. In many experimental organisms, such variables as temperature, sex, age, and nutrition are known to influence it. In many, crossover frequencies are higher in females than in males; and the relation between the age of an animal and the number of crossover gametes it produces may be a complex one, falling and rising several times as the organism grows older. Nothing is known about such variations in man, though it cannot be doubted that they occur. A time may come in which it may seem desirable to transmit unchanged a certain linked arrangement of alleles present in a parent to his or her offspring, or, on the contrary, to have such an association broken by crossing over. Knowledge of controllable factors that influence the frequency of crossovers would then become a practical tool. Such a speculation may appear farfetched, but even more unexpected developments have arisen from small beginnings.

Problems

117. Why can even a large number of one-child sibships give no information on linkage when it is unknown whether the parental genotypes are in the coupling or repulsion phase? Why can two-child sibships provide such information?

118. Assume that 2 autosomal genes are linked with a recombination value of 20 per cent. Among 100 sibships of 2 sibs each, from a random sample of 100 marriages of the genotypes $AaBb \times aabb$, what are the expected numbers of all possible types of sibships? (Proceed in the following sequence: First, list all possible combinations of two sibs. Second, determine which of these combinations consist of (a) identical crossovers or non-crossovers, (b) complementary crossovers or non-crossovers, (c) crossovers and non-crossovers. Third, determine the frequencies of a, b, and c. Fourth, assign to each combination of two sibs its frequency among 100 sibships.) Note: assume that $p_A = p_B = 0.5$.

119. (a) By means of the method of likelihood ratio, calculate the odds in favor of linkage between hemophilia and color blindness for recombination values of $x = 0, 0.1, 0.2, 0.3, 0.4$, and 0.5 for each of the pedigrees shown in Figure 105, A and B. (b) Combine the odds for the two pedigrees. If these two pedigrees were the only basis for your decision, which one of the x values in your table is closest to the most likely recombination value?

120. (a) If recombination data on hemophilia and night blindness were to indicate a recombination frequency of 40 per cent, how would you place these loci in relation to the locus for color blindness (make use of the information given in Fig. 116). (b) If hemophilia and night blindness gave 50 per cent recombination, how would you place the three loci?

121. Draw alternative maps of the sequence of the four X-linked loci given in Figure 116.

122. Assume: that a gene F has two alleles F^1 and F^2 which control the presence of antigens F_1 and F_2; that a gene G has two alleles G^1 and G^2 which control the presence of antigens G_1 and G_2; that the loci of F and G are in the X-chromosome and close to each other; and that y, a recessive X-linked gene causing a serious affliction, lies between F and G. A woman with the antigenic properties F_1, G_1, and G_2 has several brothers afflicted with the y trait. The following genotypes of her ancestors are known:

  (i) maternal grandmother F^1yG^2/F^1YG^2;
  (ii) maternal grandfather F^2YG^1;
  (iii) father F^1YG^1.

(a) Draw a pedigree of the kindred. (b) What is the chance that the woman is a carrier for the atypical allele y which would lead to the production of affected sons? (Assume absence of double crossovers.) (c) What would have been the answer to Part b if the woman had been of the phenotype F_1, F_2, G_1?

References

Bernstein, F., 1931. Zur Grundlegung der Chromosomentheorie der Vererbung beim Menschen. *Zeitschr. Abstgs. u. Vererbgsl.* **57**: 113–138 (also **63**: 181–184, 1932).

Burks, B., 1938. Autosomal linkage in man. The recombination ratio between congenital tooth deficiency and hair color. *Proc. Nat. Acad. Sci.,* **24**: 512–519.

Finney, D. J., 1940–43. The detection of linkage. I–III, V–VII. *Ann. Eugen.,* **10**: 171–214; **11**: 10–30, 115–135, 224–232, 233–244; **12**: 31–43. IV. *J. Hered.,* **33**: 157–160.

Fisher, R. A., 1935. The detection of linkage. *Ann. Eugen.,* **6**: 187–201; 339–357.

Gates, R. R., 1954. *Genetic Linkage in Man.* 46 pp. Junk, The Hague.

Haldane, J. B. S., and Smith, C. A. B., 1947. A new estimate of the linkage between the genes for colour-blindness and haemophilia in man. *Ann. Eugen.,* **14**: 10–31.

Hoogvliet, B., 1942. Genetische en klinische beschouwing naar aanleiding van bloederziekte en kleurenblindheit in dezelfde familie. *Genetica,* **23**: 93–220.

Howells, W. W., and Slowey, A. P., 1956. "Linkage studies" in morphological traits. *Am. J. Human Genet.,* **8**: 154–161.

Kloepfer, H. W., 1946. An investigation of 171 possible linkage relationships in man. *Ann. Eugen.,* **13**: 35–71.

Lawler, S. D., and Sandler, M., 1954. Data on linkage in man: elliptocytosis and blood groups. IV. Families 5, 6 and 7. *Ann. Eugen.,* **18**: 328–334.

Macklin, M. T., 1954. The use of sequential analysis method in problems in human genetics. *Am. J. Human Genet.,* **6**: 346–353.

Mohr, J., 1954. *A Study of Linkage in Man.* 119 pp. Munksgaard, Copenhagen.

Morton, N. E., 1955. Sequential tests for the detection of linkage. *Am. J. Human Genet.,* **7**: 277–318.

————, 1956. The detection and estimation of linkage between genes for elliptocytosis and the Rh blood type. *Am. J. Human Genet.,* **8**: 80–96.

————, 1957. Further scoring types in sequential linkage tests, with a critical review of autosomal and partial sex linkage in man. *Am. J. Human Genet.,* **9**: 55–75.

Penrose, L. S., 1935. The detection of autosomal linkage in data which consist of pairs of brothers and sisters of unspecified parentage. *Ann. Eugen.,* **6:** 133–138.

Renwick, J. H., and Lawler, S. D., 1955. Genetical linkage between the ABO and nail-patella loci. *Ann. Human Genet.,* **19:** 312–331.

Sanger, R., and Race, R. R., 1958. The Lutheran-secretor linkage in man: support for Mohr's findings. *Heredity,* **12:** 513–520.

Smith, C. A. B., 1953. The detection of linkage in human genetics. *J. Roy. Stat. Soc., B,* **15:** 153–192.

Taillard, W., 1951. Le linkage autosomique chez l'homme. *Acta Genet. Stat. Med.,* **2:** 193–219.

CHAPTER 16

VARIATIONS
IN THE EXPRESSION
OF GENES

The study of inheritance would be simpler than it is if a given genotype always expressed itself in exactly the same way in all individuals. Although there are many genes whose effect on development seems to be constant under all known circumstances, there are many others of which this is not true. Examples of unequivocal expression like albinism or woolly hair best demonstrate the regularities of gene transmission, but it is obviously equally important to consider genes whose effects are variable.

There is no inherent difficulty in understanding variable gene effects if we remember the concept of a network of developmental reactions. If gene and effect are not related to each other directly, but through numerous interconnecting steps, it is easy to realize that a change anywhere along the network of interconnections may lead to a change in the expression of the gene.

It may be wondered whether variable expression of a gene may not be caused by variability of the gene itself—that is, mutation—rather than by variability in the network of reactions. This is not impossible, but the probability that it is true is very small. Stability or instability of genes has been ascertained by study of their transmission through germ cells from generation to generation. Such studies have established that genes at any given locus are transmitted unchanged in the overwhelming majority of all gametes, a mutation occurring in usually less than one of 50,000 cells. We have little justification for believing that the genes in body cells are less stable than those in germ cells. It is therefore not reasonable to explain the high variability of certain phenotypic effects by a low stability of the genes that control them.

The concept of interacting developmental processes, on the other hand,

289

gives us an interpretation of variable phenotypes that accords with our knowledge of invariable genes. Until we have proof to the contrary, we regard it as
a sound premise that *differences in genic expression are variable consequences of constant genes.*

Incomplete Penetrance of Genes (7 Complete)

Stiff Little Finger. We have defined a dominant gene as one whose effect
is recognizable in the heterozygous condition. A pedigree involving a domi-

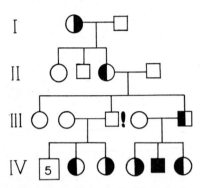

nant gene (*D*) that causes a permanently bent and stiff little finger (camptodactyly) is reproduced in Figure 119.
The condition is due not to an abnormal joint but to defects in the attach-
ments of some of the muscles controlling
this joint. Obviously, it is not a serious
aberration, although it may cause slight
inconvenience. Most of the individuals
in this pedigree have a bent finger
on one hand only, and the trait seems
to appear equally on the right and the

FIG. 119. Pedigree of stiff little finger (camptodactyly). Solid left or
right half of symbol = left or right
hand affected only; ! = no penetrance. (After Moore and Messina,
J. Hered., **27,** 1936.)

left hand. The appearance of the trait
on one hand only is the result of a
variable effect of the *Dd* genotype on
different parts of the same person. As
these individuals developed from the
fertilized *Dd* eggs, a stiff little finger

was formed on one hand of the embryo and a normal finger on the other,
because the action of the gene *D* failed to "penetrate" the developmental
network on the normal side and to create the abnormal phenotype. A genotype which may or may not produce a given trait is said to be *incompletely
penetrant.*

The reasons for unilateral penetrance of the gene *D* for camptodactyly
presumably lie in some delicately balanced embryological events that may
tip the scale toward abnormal expression in one hand but toward normality
in the other. It is to be expected that in some individuals the balance will
be such as to lead to the formation of stiff little fingers on both hands, and
in others to normal fingers on both. The pedigree contains 1 bilaterally affected
male in generation IV and 1 who is not affected in either hand in generation
III. The latter, although normal himself, has 2 affected children. We conclude
that he had the same *Dd* constitution as his mother and his 2 affected children, but that the gene *D* failed to express itself during the development of his
hands.

The penetrance of such a gene may be quantitatively expressed in terms of
the percentage of all those who have the gene who show the trait. A dominant

gene with phenotypic expression in all individuals who carry it has 100 per cent penetrance; one expressed in only half the individuals, 50 per cent. To determine the penetrance of a specific gene, we must know the number of carriers who do not show its effect as well as the number who do. A method for such determination consists of counting the numbers of affected and un-affected parental pairs in whose progeny the incompletely penetrant gene expresses itself. In Figure 119, there are four sibships with affected individuals. Three of the four parental pairs contained an affected member, but both of one pair (III–2 and III–3) were normal. The normal father, III–3, was a carrier, as proven by his affected offspring. Therefore, the penetrance of stiff little finger was 3 out of 4, or 75 per cent. The statistical uncertainty of this value is, of course, high, since it is based on a sample of four parental pairs only.

Blue Sclerotics. A slightly different kind of example in which an abnormality is due to a dominant gene with incomplete penetrance is supplied by blue sclerotics (van der Hoeve's syndrome). Persons with this trait have an unusually thin, bluish outer wall of the eye instead of the white sclerotic (or sclera) of normals. The eye condition itself is harmless but is commonly associated with serious defects in other parts of the body. Among these are otosclerosis which leads to deafness, and excessive fragility of the bones (osteogenesis imperfecta), causing frequent fractures (Fig. 120).

FIG. 120. Skeleton of a man who was affected with blue sclerotics and brittle bones. (Bell, *Treas. Hum. Inher.*, II, **3**, 1928.)

The medical literature contains many descriptions of inherited brittle bones, among them the following: "In Oslo, a young heterogygous man, turning around suddenly in the street in order to look at the legs of a pretty girl, fractured his leg bone. Another time, when he took his fiancee on his lap, his thigh-bone broke" (Mohr).

It is not clear how the three abnormalities are developmentally related to one another, whether by some general metabolic condition that involves the mineral content of the blood or by control of fundamentally different proc-

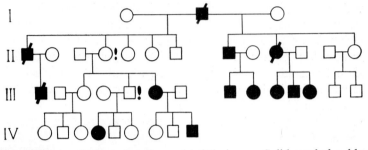

FIG. 121. Pedigree of blue sclerotics and brittle bones. Solid symbol = blue sclerotics; diagonal bar = brittle bones; ! = no penetrance. (Bell, *Treas. Hum. Inher.*,
II, **3**, 1928; pedigree No. 621.)

esses in different parts of the body by the gene for blue scleras. The gene
effect on the sclera itself has a very high, but not complete, penetrance, but
fractures due to bone fragility were met with in only 63 per cent of a sample
of 400 persons carrying the gene (see Fig. 121). A similarly lower degree
of pentrance of 60 per cent seems to apply to the effect on deafness caused
by the gene. The three defects were found together in 44 per cent of all
individuals known to carry the gene. Actually, these percentages vary in different groups. Thus, in two large Japanese kindreds the frequency of fragile
bones among persons with blue scleras was 60 per cent in one kindred, 29
per cent in the other; of deafness, 36 and 26 per cent; and simultaneous
presence of all these traits, 28 and 7 per cent.

Vitamin-D-resistant Rickets.   A type of rickets which was very common
before the need of vitamin D for bone development was recognized has now
practically disappeared in many parts of the world. Some children, however,
develop rickets even though provided with a normally adequate diet containing from 400 to 1,000 international units of vitamin D daily, and do not
improve when given several times the normal amount of vitamin D. Only
when very large doses of the vitamin, up to 150,000 units per day, are administered do the rickets disappear.

In a large pedigree from North Carolina, with at least 28 affected individuals in five generations, a pattern of inheritance is discernible which suggests
presence of a dominant gene with incomplete penetrance (Fig. 122, A: note
nonpenetrance in the normal woman II–2 as evidenced by her affected son).

A careful clinical study of this kindred brought out the fact that all individuals with bone defects had an abnormally low concentration of inorganic
phosphorus in their blood serum (hypophosphatemia)—a condition which is
in part responsible for rickets. The low concentration of phosphorus was also
found in some individuals with normal bone development, but all these "normal" individuals had both an affected parent and affected offspring. Part B
of Figure 122 consists of the same pedigree as part A, but in it the affected

persons are those who have a low phosphorus concentration. Clearly, the gene transmits hypophosphatemia in a fully penetrant dominant fashion.

In this pedigree the gene has incomplete penetrance so far as rickets is concerned, and this is clearly due to a variation in some secondary process in the network of development. The gene invariably causes a low phosphorus concentration; but the processes of bone formation, which are also ultimately dependent on the gene, may sometimes lead to normality, sometimes to defectiveness.

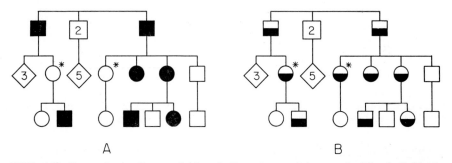

A   B

FIG. 122. Part of a pedigree of vitamin-D-resistant rickets.   A. The individuals indicated as affected show active rickets or deformities.   B. The same part of the pedigree, showing as affected individuals those having an abnormally low concentration of inorganic phosphorus in their serum. The low phosphorus concentration in the two individuals marked with an asterisk signifies that they carry the gene responsible for it although it did not lead to bone defects. (After Winters, Graham, Williams, McFalls, and Barnett, *Medicine,* **37,** 1958.)

Variable Age of Onset of Genetically Caused Diseases

Most of the phenotypes we have discussed were determined during prenatal life or were clearly present within a few days after birth. The fragility of the bones of blue-sclerotic individuals is a partial exception. The bones of normal babies are poorly ossified but highly cartilaginous. Gradually, during childhood, the mineral content of the bones increases, the minerals replacing the soft cartilage. In many blue-sclerotic individuals, therefore, the bone fragility becomes apparent only when the process of ossification nears completion. Since the time it takes bones to harden varies somewhat from child to child, the fragility of bones in affected individuals is not apparent at the same age in all. This variation in age of onset of the disease is so great that, in some families, the bones are defective before birth and the condition may lead to stillbirth or death in early infancy.

Many other inherited conditions become apparent only in an adult, particularly certain nervous diseases, most kinds of cancer, diseases of the heart, some eye abnormalities, and, obviously, all specific afflictions of old age. The speed of aging itself is variable, and it is not to be wondered that the onset of the expression of these characters varies over a wide range of years in different persons.

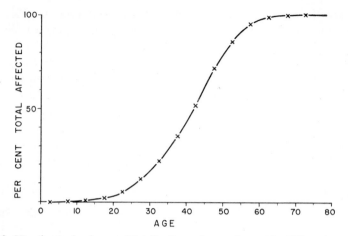

FIG. 123. Huntington's chorea. Distribution of age of onset in 762 patients. (After Landzettel, Unterreiner, and Wendt, *Acta Genet. Stat. Med.,* **9,** 1959.)

Huntington's Chorea. Huntington's chorea, a disease characterized by involuntary jerking movements of body and limbs, well illustrates differences in age of onset of a genetically caused affliction. The disease consists of a progressive degeneration of the nervous system, and leads to gradual physical and mental impairment of affected individuals and eventually to death. The mean age of onset of this affliction lies between forty and forty-five, but Figure 123, based on a survey of age of onset of many cases, shows that the disease sometimes appears in the first years of life and sometimes after sixty. The trait is clearly hereditary, occurring only in certain families and usually being transmitted from an affected parent to half of the children. This simple picture of a dominant trait is disturbed by the variable age of onset. Choreic children may be born to parents who appear normal, although one of them must be heterozygous for the allele *Ht* which causes the disease. If this parent dies before having shown choreic symptoms, and any of the children develop the disease, an exception to typical dominance may be recorded in a pedigree. The older the parents at death, the less pronounced this incomplete penetrance becomes.

If one wants to study the inheritance of Huntington's chorea in detail, data such as those given in Figure 123 are useful, since they enable one to adjust one's observations to account for seemingly normal persons who may be carriers although they do not yet show it. Obviously, in determining the type of inheritance of traits with a variable age of onset, it is necessary to know the age of persons in a pedigree at the time it is recorded and the age of death of persons who appeared normal.

Relatively few individuals who have an affliction with a rather early mean age of onset—like Huntington's chorea—die of natural causes before they show signs of their affliction. But those hereditary diseases that usually do not appear until later—such as certain defects of the heart or the general circulatory system, and particularly many afflictions of old age—will remain undiscovered in a large number of persons, since these persons will die of other causes before symptoms of the disease in question can be noticed. In order to investigate the inheritance of such a condition, several corrections must be applied to raw data on its frequency in families with affected members. These corrections are based on tables which give the probabilities of survival of an individual in the general population, and also the percentages of individuals that can be identified as affected in each age class. A pioneer study on the inheritance of sugar diabetes, made in 1933 by Pincus and White, may serve as a model to show the refinements needed in an analysis of a disease of variable and often late onset.

Further Aspects of Penetrance. The term penetrance is applicable not only to heterozygously dominant genes but also to either dominant or recessive homozygous genotypes. This use expresses the fact that not only the phenotypes of heterozygotes but also those of homozygotes may vary. An example of incomplete penetrance of a homozygous recessive gene is provided by diabetes mellitus, the metabolic disease which leads to excretion of sugar in the urine. Certain data suggest that this condition may very likely be based on homozygosity for a relatively common recessive allele. If this is correct, about 5 per cent of all Americans have the genotype. However, only one-fifth of those who have it are diagnosed as diabetic; some of the other four-fifths are not so diagnosed because they are weakly affected and the rest are not affected because they have not yet reached the age of onset of the disease. In diabetes the degree of ascertained penetrance is itself variable: among other factors it depends on the mean longevity of the population, since the higher the age of death, the higher the ultimately ascertained penetrance.

Variability in the expression of genotypes is undoubtedly an important factor in the ability to taste phenylthiocarbamide (PTC) or related chemicals —a trait discussed earlier as an example of "simple" inheritance (p. 167). Careful tests show that persons who can taste PTC differ widely in their sen-

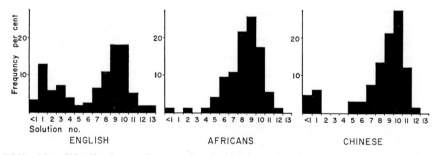

FIG. 124. Distributions of taste thresholds for phenylthiourea in 155 English males, 74 African Negroes, and 66 Chinese. The strongest solution (1) had a concentration of 0.13 per cent in water, the next (2) half this strength, and so on through 13. (Barnicot, *Ann. Eugen.,* **15,** 1950.)

sitivity to it: some can taste highly diluted solutions of the substance; others can recognize it only in strong solutions. Plots of the frequency distribution of tasters and their response to various concentrations may be either continuous, with two peaks, or discontinuous (Fig. 124). The two ends of such distributions may be regarded as corresponding to the genotypes tt (left) and TT and Tt (right), but it is not possible to decide exactly where to place the dividing line. The causes of the variability in the taster reaction are manifold: there are racial differences; the same person will give different responses in different tests; responses differ in different age groups; and women are more sensitive tasters than men. In other words, the penetrance of one or all three T and t genotypes is variable, but details are still to be worked out.

Because of low penetrance, some abnormal genotypes may result in abnormal phenotypes so rarely that proof of their inherited nature may be impossible. Many abnormalities that occur singly in human pedigrees are probably genetically conditioned, although it seems strange to apply the term "inherited" to traits which were absent in all known ancestors and, in all likelihood, will not reappear in future generations.

Although the existence of incomplete penetrance is well established, it should not be invoked to explain specific cases without caution. We have seen earlier that albino children of an albino married to a nonalbino could theoretically be due either to a dominant or a recessive gene for albinism. If a dominant gene is involved, no further assumption is needed to explain the appearance of albinos in successive generations; but if a recessive gene is assumed to be present in the affected parent, then the additional assumption that the normal parent is a heterozygous carrier is required. Sometimes it is hard to decide whether dominant or recessive inheritance is involved, particularly for a trait common enough that heterozygotes for recessive alleles are relatively frequent. The difficulties are increased if there is reason to suspect incomplete penetrance. In albinism, which is fully penetrant, affected children from normal parents are clearly due to heterozygosity of both parents for a recessive allele. To explain the appearance of other traits in children of unaffected parents, an alternative explanation to that involving a recessive gene would be to assume that one of the unaffected parents carries a dominant abnormal gene that is incompletely penetrant. A still greater range of explanations is available if it can be assumed that a trait may be based on an incompletely penetrant dominant gene that is present heterozygously in some persons and homozygously in others. It is reasonable to expect these two genotypes to have different degrees of penetrance. An analysis of inheritance of the mental illness schizophrenia as found in a Swedish population makes use of this explanation. The hypothesis which well fits the Swedish data assumes that the disease is caused by a gene which is 20 per cent penetrant in heterozygotes and practically 100 per cent penetrant in homozygotes, but rigorous proof of such a hypothesis is difficult even though it may be correct (see pp. 583–584).

Notwithstanding the pitfalls in interpretation when penetrance is low, a simple consideration often helps to decide whether dominance or recessive-ness is involved in specific uncommon traits. In dominance, most affected chil-dren, *Dd* will come from *Dd* × *dd* marriages, and the sibs will be *Dd* and *dd* in a ratio of 1:1. It follows that whatever the degree of penetrance, the frequency of affected sibs should be the same as that of affected parents. In recessiveness, most affected propositi *aa* will come from *Aa* × *Aa* marriages and the sibs will be *AA*, *Aa*, and *aa*. This means that the frequency of affected sibs should be higher than that of affected parents.

Expressivity of Gene Effects

In a very large Norwegian pedigree compiled by Mohr and Wriedt, a short index finger (minor brachydactyly) was inherited in simple dominant fashion. However, there were two degrees of shortness of the second phalange: some individuals had a very short bone; but others, only a slightly shortened one (Fig. 125). It was shown that the short-fingeredness, regardless of the strength of its expression, was caused by the same dominant allele. Such production of different abnormal phenotypes by the same gene is called *variable expressivity*. The different degrees of expressivity may often form a continuous series grading from extreme expression to "no penetrance." *Penetrance* thus refers to the expression—presence or absence—of a gene, regardless of degree of expression; *expressivity* applies to the variability of the expression. The two terms were coined by the neurologist and biologist O. Vogt.

Variable expressivity is a very common attribute of genes, as demonstrated by innumerable examples among experimental animals and plants. However, it should not be assumed that similar phenotypes, different only in degree, are always due to variable expressivity of the same gene. Different genes at a variety of loci may result in similar phenotypes that are different in degree of expression. Similarly, multiple alleles of a single gene may differ in their degree of expression. Only when the expression of a rare trait varies in the same pedigree can we be reasonably certain that we are dealing with variable expressivity of a single gene.

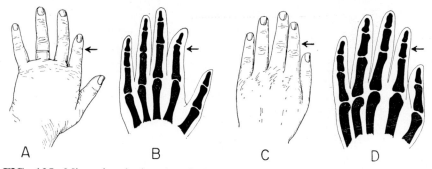

FIG. 125. Minor brachydactyly of the index finger.   A, B. Strong expression. C, D. Weak expression. (After Mohr and Wriedt.)

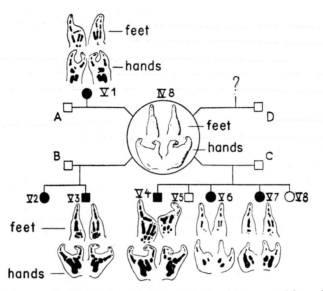

FIG. 126. Pedigree of cleft hand involving an affected woman and her offspring by three different fathers. The feet and hands, and associated skeletal structures, of affected individuals are shown. The feet have from one to about four metatarsals and one or two rows of phalanges. The large bones in the hands were probably formed by fusion of carpals and metacarpals. The skeletal structure of each extremity is unique. (Müller, after Ströer.)

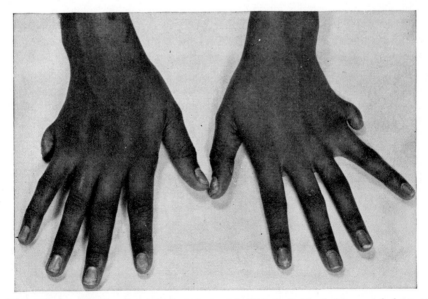

FIG. 127. The hands of a polydactylous girl. This individual does not belong to the polydactylous kindred presented in Figure 128. (Original from Dr. V. McKusick.)

A trait, cleft hand or lobster claw, which fulfills this requirement is illustrated in Figure 126. It is inherited as a dominant. The hands and feet of
affected persons show severe defects of the skeletal system and abnormal
external form. The six affected individuals about whom detailed information
is available—i.e., the mother, IV–8, and five of her affected children from
three different husbands, A, B, and C—all differ in degree of malformation.

Both incomplete penetrance and variable expressivity may be illustrated
in a pedigree of polydactyly (Figs. 127, 128). Clearly, a dominant gene (D)
controls the numbers of bony rays formed in the embryonic buds of hands
and feet. In normal dd genotypes five rays of metacarpals or metatarsals and
phalangeal bones lead to the formation of the normal number of digits. The
Dd genotype varies in its penetrance and expressivity in different extremities
and in different individuals. Thus, in III–2 there was no penetrance at all,
and in the last individual of generation IV no penetrance for one hand but
penetrance with different degrees of expressivity in the other extremities: six
fingers on the hand and six and seven toes, respectively, on the feet. If all
four extremities are considered the pedigree shows four different degrees of
expressivity: 5,5–6,6; 6,6–5,5; 5,6–6,7; and 6,6–6,6. Many more degrees
would probably have been discernible had the kindred not been described
before the discovery of X-rays.

One more example of variable expressivity is provided by schizophrenia.
If a genetic basis for this mental illness is granted (p. 581 ff.), then it appears that the same basic genotype, if penetrant, may cause not only a whole

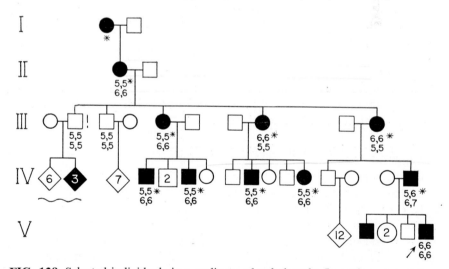

FIG. 128. Selected individuals in a pedigree of polydactyly. In each group of four
numbers, the upper two represent the numbers of fingers on the left and right
hand, respectively, and the lower two the numbers of toes. An asterisk indicates that
the type of polydactyly was not stated unequivocally in the original report. (After
Lucas, *Guy's Hosp. Rpts.* 3rd ser. **25**, 1881.)

array of symptoms that range from mild to severe, but also types of abnormal behavior so strikingly different that psychiatrists have given them different names.

Causal Factors in Variations of Genic Expression

The type of expression of a gene is dependent on its interaction with the other genes of the two genic sets with which it is associated in the nucleus of the cell of a developing and aging individual, as well as on the cytoplasm and on the environment in which the development and aging proceed. The term environment is here used in its widest meaning to designate every factor, except the genic content of the individual, that may influence the phenotype. Environment thus consists of not only the external physical world which surrounds a human being from birth to death, but also the maternal body which encloses the developing embryo. Through the placental connection, the physiologic state of the mother and the hormones, minerals, and other substances circulating in her blood may influence the expression of the embryo's genes. Even the position of the embryo within the uterus, or the presence of a twin, is an aspect of the embryonic environment. Finally, environment includes the intellectual, emotional, and cultural atmosphere that is provided by family, school, church, nation, social class, and the historically changing "climate of opinion."

Penetrance and expressivity are thus not intrinsic properties of a given gene but results of its interaction with other genes and of nongenetic factors. In order to avoid misconceptions, some students of human genetics do not use the term penetrance and prefer to speak of "probability or rate of manifestation" of a gene or genotype.

Penetrance and expressivity as consequences of developmental events in gene action are interrelated. Many genes with a low degree of penetrance express themselves weakly when they are penetrant, and high penetrance and strong expressivity often go together. Harelip and cleft palate will be cited later as examples of these interrelations.

Internal Environmental Factors

Internal Environment. In many cases, it is clear that extragenic influences —i.e., environmental factors—are responsible for the variability of gene effects, even though it may not be possible to define these factors specifically. Examples of this can be seen in the cases of the stiff little finger, the cleft hand and feet, and the polydactyly discussed above. One peculiarity of these conditions is the inequality of expression on the two hands or feet of an affected individual. Since we assume that all cells of the same individual contain the same genes, his two hands should be genetically identical. Therefore, we consider that differences in their phenotypes are caused by environment, although we cannot yet state what kind of environmental factors are at work. The determination of the characters of hands and feet occurs very early during development, and the factors involved are probably intrinsic to the embryo itself. The individual, so to speak, provides an "internal environment" for the genes acting within him.

Multiple Effects of Blebs in the Mouse. Embryological studies of an inherited syndrome of abnormalities in the mouse by Bagg, Kristine Bonnevie, and others have shed considerable light on some aspects of variable penetrance and expressivity. It has been suggested by analogy that a syndrome in man is similarly conditioned. In this human "Bonnevie-Ullrich" syndrome, fusion and shortening of fingers, paralysis of certain muscles, defects of breast muscles and of nipples, shortening of arms, and other malformations appear in various combinations on one or both sides of the body. In the mouse syndrome, a recessive gene, *mb*, causes abnormal development of the eyes, ears, limbs, and coat, as well as a variety of other defects.

The variable effects on eyes and feet only will be considered. The eye defects may be completely absent, present in one eye only, or present bilaterally. If present, they may vary from slight atrophy of the eyelids to missing eyelids, and from slight to marked atrophy of the whole eye. The feet also vary from normal to such diverse phenotypes as syndactylism (joined toes), hypodactylism (absence of toes), and polydactylism (presence of extra toes) (Fig. 129). As with the eye effects, penetrance and expressivity may vary on the two sides of the body.

The bewildering multitude of phenotypes, their incomplete penetrance and variable expressivity, may be largely explained by a single developmental peculiarity of *mb mb* embryos. At a stage of development corresponding approximately to that of five-week-old human embryos, blisters (or blebs) filled with fluid appear under the epidermis. Sometime later, blood clots may form beneath the blebs and blood may escape into many of the blebs. The maldevelopment of eyes and feet is caused by the presence of blebs and blood clots (Fig. 130).

The essential point, so far as penetrance and expressivity are concerned, is that the location, size, and time of appearance (and later disappearance)

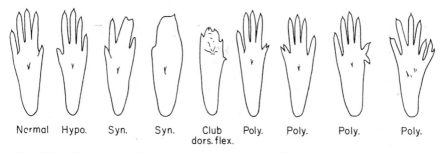

| Normal | Hypo. | Syn. | Syn. | Club dors. flex. | Poly. | Poly. | Poly. | Poly. |

FIG. 129. Myelencephalic blebs in mice. Normal hind foot (plantar view) and eight different defective types. (From Bagg, *Am. J. Anat.*, **43**, 1929.)

of the blebs are variable from animal to animal and from one side to the other of a single animal. The points at which fluid accumulates under the skin seem to be largely determined by chance.

The variability of the blebs is the direct cause of variability in the later phenotype. If the blister happens to be near a developing eye or limb bud, the effect of *mb mb* will be penetrant and its degree of expression will depend on the size of the bleb, its nearness to the eye or limb area, and the developmental stage of embryo at the time the bleb forms. If no bleb forms near an eye or limb area, normal development—i.e., no penetrance of *mb mb*— results.

The symbol *mb*, it may be remarked, was originally chosen to fit the theory that the blebs (b) were derived from cerebrospinal fluid that was extruded by a part of the brain, the myelencephalon (m), and migrated to the regions of the eyes, limbs, and other parts. This theory was abandoned when it was found that the blebs seem to originate directly under the skin in the positions where they are observed. That similar blebs in human embryos lead to the variable defects characteristic of the Bonnevie-Ullrich syndrome is no more than a surmise.

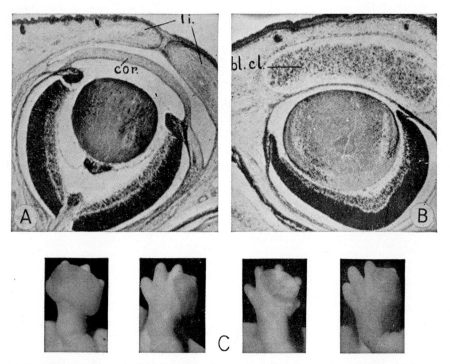

FIG. 130. Myelencephalic blebs in mice. A. Normal eye in a 15mm embryo; li = lid-forming tissue; cor = cornea. B. Abnormal eye in a 15mm embryo. The eye is covered with a blood clot (bl. cl.). C. Abnormalities of hind feet in four embryos. Note the swollen appearance caused by large blebs. (Bonnevie, 1934.)

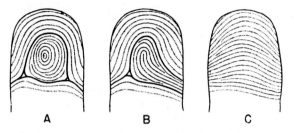

FIG. 131. The three main types of finger pattern: A. Whorl.   B. Loop.   C. Arch. (Cummins and Midlo, *Finger Prints, Palms and Soles.* Blakiston, 1943.)

Finger Pattern.   A normal character that shows variable expression on homologous parts of the same individual is the pattern of finger ridges. Although each individual has a unique pattern, it is possible to group the many different patterns in a few classes, three of which are shown in Figure 131. Individuals belonging to these different classes are genetically different, but the exact genotypes are not known. Superimposed on the genetic variability is a developmental, environmental one. In no person are the patterns of like fingers on the left and right hands identical in detail, even though they usually belong to the same general class.

We have some knowledge of the causes of this nongenetic variability. Some features of the finger pattern are apparently determined early in embryonic life by the arrangement of nerve fibers that grow from the spinal cord toward the surface of the finger rudiments. Although the growth and branching of these nerves, on the whole, is genetically determined, the details are sufficiently flexible to be subject to nongenetic influences. The growth of these nerves may be compared to the formation of the course of a small stream caused by a sudden downpour in the desert. The general outline of the course is determined by the arrangement and shape of mountains and valleys, but it is also dependent on small "accidental" conditions, such as the position of a rock or a tree, or previous weathering of the surface structure of the landscape.

Individual differences in nerve growth are due to differences in the environment of the growing structures, though this environment is part of the developing organism itself. These examples may serve to clarify the concept of "internal environment."

Changing Phenotypes.   Many phenotypes are fixed for life once embryonic processes have taken their course. The expression of other genetically determined characters is conditioned by the specific internal environment that the individual provides at a later stage. One of these characters is hair color. Although many very dark-haired persons are born with fully developed pigmentation, it is well known that others start with light hair that becomes darker as they grow older. The specific genotype of such individuals does not express itself by a static phenotype but, rather, by a phenotype dependent on time: at first, the genotype produces a different, lighter hair color than it does later; or, stated differently, the genes for pigmentation express themselves differently in the bodily environment of a young person than in that of an older one.

Change of Dominance.   This dependence of the phenotype on the age of the individual may give rise to the phenomenon called "change of dominance." Often, a child of a dark- and a light-haired parental pair will first show dominance of the genes derived from the light-haired parent. However, as he grows older, the genes from his dark-haired parent become dominant and his hair darkens. Similar changes in dominance may be observed in the phenotypes of other features, for example, shape of face or nose. Such traits are not fixed at birth but change all through life. Even if one assumes that genic action does not change, the action takes place in a different internal environment at different developmental stages, thus resulting in different phenotypes.

The picture of continuous, unchanging genic action in a changing environment is, of course, far too simple. A gene may be an agent which itself causes changes in its own environment. Any effect at a late stage of development may be due to an accumulation of the products of genic action in the preceding stages. In many cases, it may be impossible to define this relation with certainty. Is the onset of Huntington's chorea at the age of forty due to genic action that has not changed since birth, the difference between earlier health and later affliction resulting from changes in the nervous system, independent of the genotype $Ht\ ht$, that have made the nerve cells susceptible to damage? Or has the action of $Ht\ ht$ itself caused continuous, slight damage, which, after forty years, is great enough to result in manifestation of the disease?

Changes at Puberty.   In some instances the changes in internal environment that cause changes in the expression of a genotype can be specified. One of these is the change in the male voice that occurs at puberty. The voices of boys before puberty seem to be genetically determined. At puberty, each type of voice becomes lower. The changes as such are independent of genotype but dependent on the internal production of male sex hormones at this time. This is known from the fact that castrated boys, in whom no male hormones are secreted, retain their child-like voices, and from the fact that women who produce abnormally high amounts of male sex hormones—as those with diseases of the adrenal glands may do—develop deep, male voices.

A similar relation between the expression of genetically determined traits and the internal environment has been claimed for allergies. Although the mode of inheritance of these sensitivities to foreign substances is far from clear, the following theory, proposed by Wiener, Zieve, and Fries, is perhaps an approximation of the truth. Individuals without allergies are regarded as homozygous for an allele A; individuals affected early in life, as homozygous for the allele A'; and those affected after puberty, as AA' heterozygotes. This relation between allergic phenotype and puberty suggests influence of sex hormones. It is obvious, however, that other factors play a role in the variable penetrance of the genotypes responsible for allergies, since the traits may appear and disappear independent of puberty.

External Environmental Factors

External Environment.   If we pass to external environmental factors—i.e., those not located within the individual himself—that influence penetrance or expressivity, we enter the large field of the general interrelation of heredity and environment. We shall consider these problems at length later (Chaps. 25–27). Here, only a few examples will be given.

It was stated above that diabetes mellitus has a genetic basis, but that the penetrance of the genotype is incomplete. The following example, provided by a pair of genetically identical adult male twins, shows how a genotype may express itself differently according to different external circumstances. One of the twins was slightly diabetic; the other was healthy. However, a clinical test showed that the healthy brother reacted abnormally to a high sugar diet. The reason for the presence of diabetes in one twin and its near absence in the other was easily explained by their different modes of life. One had been a restaurant owner who had subjected his diabetically inclined body to an additional strain by heavy beer drinking, and thus made his genotype penetrant. The other twin, who had lived a more temperate life, had been spared the illness.

Differences in the frequency of diabetes have been observed in different populations. Some of these populations are from racially different groups, others from socioeconomic subgroups of racially similar people. The differences in the frequencies of the disease may be partly due to different frequencies of the responsible alleles, but it is certain that they are also partly due to differences in penetrance controlled by factors in the external environment—poverty or wealth, type of occupation, quantity and quality of diet.

Differences in human stature have a genetic basis but are also a result of the external environment. It is well known that the average height of many populations in the United States, Europe, and Japan has increased steadily during the past sixty or more years. Such an increase does not seem to be due primarily to changes in genic composition (see p. 700): it must be largely due to alterations in the external environment. Undoubtedly, these external influences consist mainly of the nutritional advantages which large groups of mankind have enjoyed during those sixty years. The same genotypes which gave certain heights during an earlier historical period now result in greater stature.

Right- and Left-sidedness.   The striking separation of mankind into right-handed and left-handed individuals seems to be a result of an interaction between genotype and environment—both internal and external—that results in variable penetrance and expressivity. An analysis of these two types is made difficult by the variety of criteria which can be used to define them: hand preferred in using tools, applauding, throwing, brushing teeth, and many other activities. The different criteria do not all measure the same underlying trait, and a person who uses his left hand in most tasks may carry out some with his right. There are other behavioral functions which are carried out by one or the other side of the body, among them standing with most of one's weight on a specific leg and using a specific (dominant) eye to determine the position of objects. There are significant positive correlations between the occurrence of different traits on the same side, so that it is possible within limits to speak of right- and left-sidedness in general.

Certainly, handedness is at least partly conditioned by the external environment. Social pressure, varying in strength in different countries or periods, may force a child to write with the right hand regardless of personal inclination, and the way of offering objects to a grasping infant may direct future development of sidedness. Nevertheless, the question remains whether all individuals are initially ambidextrous or, perhaps, right handed, so that the later handedness is solely determined by the environment, or whether different genotypes with variable penetrance and expressivity tend to right- or left-handedness.

Various facts favor the hypothesis of innate differences. Thus, in one study the frequency of left-handed individuals among the relatives of identical

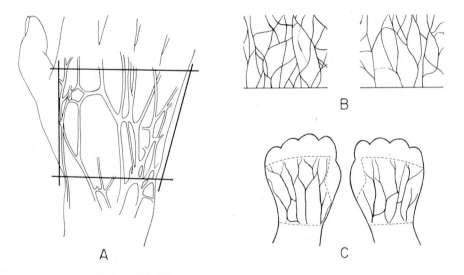

FIG. 132. A. Net of veins in the dorsal level of an adult hand. B. An extreme case of differences in the vein net of the two hands of a left-handed person with a dominant left eye. The left vein net contained 60 branches, had 21 ends entering and leaving the area, and a total length of 103 (in arbitrary units). The right vein net had 31 branches, 16 ends, and a length of 80 units. C. The veins in the two hands of a stillborn infant. (Strangmann-Koehler and Ludwig, 1954.)

TABLE 44. *Relations between Dominant Eye and Handedness, between Vein Value and Dominant Eye, and between Vein Value and Handedness.* (After Strangmann-Koehler and Ludwig.)

Trait		Right	Left	Correlation Coefficient
		Dominant eye		
Handedness	right	559	281	0.41
	left	22	149	
		Higher vein value		
Dominant eye	right	515	66	0.69
	left	84	346	
		Higher vein value		
Handedness	right	568	272	0.38
	left	31	140	

twins one or both of whom were left handed was 41 per cent, as against only 16 per cent among relatives of right-handed twins. Nevertheless, such data are open to an interpretation which stresses possible differences in the social environments of the two groups. More-convincing evidence of genetic components in handedness comes from anatomical features determined in the early embryo. One such feature is the pattern of ridges in special areas of the palm and finger tips. The average frequencies of loops and whorls and their combinations, as opposed to simple arched ridges, is significantly higher among left-handers than right-handers. Another relevant trait is the network of veins under the dorsal surface of the hands (Fig. 132). The number and types of branches of these veins vary from person to person and from one side to the other in the same individual. Three criteria have been selected by means of which the vein nets can be characterized quantitatively: numbers of branches within a defined area, numbers of veins entering and leaving the area, and total length of the network. When combined, these values made it possible to designate one of the hands of each of more than a thousand individuals as having a higher vein value than the other. The same individuals were also tested for dominant eye and handedness, and highly significant positive correlations were found not only between dominant eye and handedness but, what is more important, between dominant eye and higher vein value on the same side and between handedness and higher vein value (Table 44).

The correlations between type of vein net, which is laid down before birth, and sidedness, which becomes manifest only after birth, prove that sidedness is not solely due to influence of the postnatal environment. Consequently, prenatally acting causes must be involved. Although it is likely that prenatal internal environment plays a role in the development of details of the vein net, the findings on relatives of right- and left-handed propositi clearly point to the participation of genetic determiners.

Family data analyzed by Strangmann-Koehler and Ludwig are compatible with simple single factor inheritance of a gene pair R and r, with r recessive for left-sidedness and some of the rr individuals environmentally induced to behave right-handedly. Trankell's analysis of population data leads to the same result. Rife also assumes the existence of a single gene pair, which may be called R and R', but postulates that RR and $R'R'$ are highly penetrant for right- and left-handedness, respectively, and the heterozygote RR' is ambidextrously inclined with a chance of acquiring either functional right- or left-handedness. It is difficult to obtain decisive evidence which would discriminate between the two similar hypotheses or other possible ones. In any case it seems certain that there is a genotype that makes most of the children of two left-handed parents left handed and that there are other genotypes that may produce both left- and right-handed children if one or both parents are right handed.

The Genetic Background

The preceding section dealt with environmental circumstances that result in different expressions of a given genotype. In the examples discussed, we have sometimes used the term genotype to refer to a genetic situation controlled by a single pair of alleles, as in cleft hands, and at other times to refer to a more complex case involving a group of loci, not known in detail, as exemplified by finger pattern or stature. In either case, the concept of a network of genetically controlled reactions leads to the conclusion that the rest of the genotype, that overwhelming majority other than the one or few genes under primary consideration, may have an effect on the expression of the trait. It is customary to speak of the specific gene or genes that are primarily responsible for the appearance of a trait as the *main* gene or genes, and of the rest as their *genetic background*. Since the genetic background of the main gene differs from individual to individual, we can expect that individuals alike for a given pair of main loci may often show differences in the manifestation of the trait that they control.

Whenever gene effects are variable, it may be assumed that both environment and genetic background have important influences on penetrance and expressivity. In experimental animals or plants it is not too difficult to separate these genetic and environmental factors. The simplest experimental procedures are (1) to stabilize the genotype—main gene or genes, plus genetic background—and to investigate the influence of different environments, and (2) to keep the environment constant and vary the genetic background. Stabilization of the genotype is achieved by establishing a strain or colony of experimental organisms which are as alike as possible in their total genetic constitution.

Isogenicity.   A group of individuals that are identical genetically is called _isogenic._ In general, the ideal isogenic strain or population is one in which all individuals are homozygous for all loci. The term isogenic is, however, applicable also to a population of heterozygotes in which all individuals are genetically alike.

One of the most important ways of creating an isogenic strain is _close inbreeding,_ repeated for numerous generations. Individuals of common ancestry share many alleles. Matings between sibs, therefore, provide an opportunity for the production of individuals homozygous for the same alleles at many loci. After many generations of inbreeding, the probability of isogeneity at any one locus becomes very high. It is true, however, that there remains an appreciable probability that some loci may not have become isogenic and that complete stabilization of the genotype of a strain is only approached asymptotically.

The success of inbreeding for isogeneity can be judged in various ways. One method consists of evaluating phenotypic variability. When the establishment of an isogenic strain is begun the heterozygosity of many loci is expressed in a wide range of differences among sibs and between parents and offspring. The more isogenic the strain becomes, the more all individuals resemble each other.

Another test of high isogeneity is the ability of tissues transplanted from one animal to another to survive. In mammals, transplants generally do not persist in the host if the donor is genetically different, although the same tissues or organs grow readily if transplanted to another part of the same individual. In an isogenic strain, the tissues of one animal are genetically like those of any other, and no donor-host incompatibilities are encountered.

Much of our knowledge of human inheritance has to be based on the more accurately determinable facts derived from studies of laboratory animals. This is why long-inbred strains of mice, rats, guinea pigs, and various other organisms have been established in certain laboratories with considerable cost and made available to other investigators. In order that their results may be comparable, students in the United States, in England, on the Continent, and elsewhere do not work with any available nonstandardized mouse (formerly often referred to as "the" mouse), but with such animals as the "dbA" mouse from the Bar Harbor Laboratory in Maine or the inbred "Wistar" rat from the Wistar Institute in Philadelphia. The importance of such standardization may be illustrated by a report that showed that treatment of four different strains of mice with cancer-producing chemicals gave the following widely divergent percentages of animals showing effects of the treatment during a given period: strain I, 88 per cent; strain II, 48 per cent; strain III, 34 per cent; and strain IV, 15 per cent.

In man, isogenic individuals exist only in pairs or in small multiples. Identical twins, triplets, etc., are derived from single eggs, and the partners in such multiple births are therefore isogenic among themselves. The isogeneity, of course, is for genotypes which are heterozygous at many loci.

The five Dionne sisters were the largest isogenic group of humans ever to survive earliest infancy.

Genetic Modifiers

In the study of the genetics of experimental organisms, so-called modifying genes have been encountered. In Drosophila, the typical wild-type variety has a group of four bristles on the back of its thorax, while the variety "Dichaete" has fewer. The name of this variety suggests that only two (di-) out of the four bristles (chaetae) are present, but this was true only for the original Dichaete fly from which the strain was derived. A detailed analysis has shown that the condition is due to a dominant gene (D) present heterozygously (it is lethal if homozygous). The specific expression of the heterozygous genotype Dd may vary from apparent normality—that is, presence of four bristles—to absence of all four.

This variability is to some degree due to controllable environmental conditions. Dichaetes which develop at high temperatures or under crowded conditions have fewer bristles than those which develop at low temperatures or with less larval crowding. Part of the variability is uncontrollable and resembles the differences in expression of polydactyly on the hands of the same person. Even in highly constant environments, left and right halves of the same fly will often have different bristle patterns; there may, for instance, be two bristles on the left side and one on the right.

Finally, different isogenic strains of heterozygous Dichaetes have shown differences dependent on the genetic background. The average bristle number of Dd flies varies significantly from strain to strain even if the environment has been standardized for all of them. Genetic analysis has shown that in these strains different genes, which do not affect the four bristles of the normal type, are powerful determinants of the penetrance and expressivity of the D gene. The genetic background of two strains may differ only in a single modifying gene—so they may have different alleles at only one modifying locus—or they may differ in a few or many loci. Such different loci may have similar or different effects—some increasing penetrance or expressivity, others decreasing them. It may often be difficult, if not impossible, to disentangle, by genetic analysis, all the numerous "plus and minus modifiers" which can shift the expression of a main gene toward or away from an extreme phenotype.

The full nature of the interaction between D, the main gene, and the other modifying genes is not known. It has been speculated that the formation of bristles may require the presence of a substance at some decisive stage in development and that the normal d allele assures the production of a large amount of this substance, but that D so affects its production that the amount is usually insufficient for formation of four bristles. Within this hypothesis, modifying genes are considered to cause a slight increase or decrease in the amount of the critical substance. This slight variability is of no phenotypic consequence in normal, dd individuals because of the large amount of the

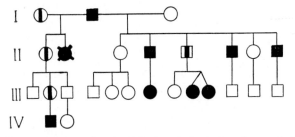

FIG. 133. Pedigree of minor brachydactyly of the index finger. Solid symbols = strongly affected; vertical bar in symbols = weakly affected; diagonally crossed symbol of II-2 = sublethal crippled child, presumably homozygous for the allele *B* for brachydactyly. (After Mohr and Wriedt.)

substance they form, but it may have striking phenotypic expression if the presence of *D* lowers the amount of the substance to a level close to the minimum for bristle formation. Presence of plus modifiers may assure enough of the substance to form bristles, and presence of minus modifiers may tend to keep the substance below the minimum level. It is immaterial in our context how true this specific hypothesis of the effect of modifying factors is. In any case, it provides a useful picture for their action.

Minor Brachydactyly.   An example of a modifying allele in man is provided by minor brachydactyly in a Norwegian kindred (Figs. 125, 133). As described earlier, this character has two clearly different forms of expression: one in which the second finger is very short; and another in which only careful inspection of the hands reveals the slightly expressed brachydactyly. Disregarding for a moment the variability in expression, the pedigree shows that the trait follows simple, dominant inheritance. Since the trait is rare, most affected individuals are heterozygous for its gene, *Bb.* It is possible to account for the trait's two sharply different phenotypes by assuming the presence of a single modifying locus at which there may be either of two common alleles, one dominant over the other in the heterozygote. If, for instance, the dominant allele *M* is necessary for full expression of brachydactyly, then all strongly affected individuals have the genotype *Bb MM* or *Bb Mm,* and the slightly affected ones have *Bb mm.* On this basis, the affected persons in the pedigree may be assigned their appropriate genetic constitutions.

The normal individuals also belong to different genotypes, namely, *bb MM, bb Mm,* and *bb mm.* They cannot be distinguished phenotypically, but the affected offspring of normal parents sometimes enable the geneticist to judge the parents' constitutions. The normal husband of II–1, for instance, could not have been *bb MM,* since if he had, there would have been no offspring with weak expression of *B,* such as III–2. The data are not sufficient, however, to enable us to distinguish between the possible genotypes *bb Mm* and *bb mm* for this husband.

An examination of the pedigree will show that its peculiarities may be explained equally well by the assumption of a homozygous recessive allele *n*, a modifier responsible for extreme expression, and a dominant allele *N* as the agent of slight expression. If this hypothesis were true, then the strongly brachydactylous individuals would be *Bb nn,* and the slightly affected ones would be either *Bb Nn* or *Bb NN*. Normal persons, again, would comprise three indistinguishable types, namely, *bb NN, bb Nn,* and *bb nn.*

It is very difficult to determine the modifiers that constitute the genetic background in man. Therefore, recognizing the presence of modifiers is of no positive help in predicting the specific type of a trait that will appear in individuals of future generations. Rather, it is important to be aware of the complications that can be caused by possible modifiers, both as a deterrent to rushing to conclusions and as a concept that helps us understand variability in inheritance.

Cataract. In Chapter 8, reference was made to an extensive pedigree of early cataract (Fig .73, p. 122). It was shown that the trait followed the rules of simple dominant inheritance. It may now be added that the expressivity of the condition was extremely variable. Examinations of the eye lenses of different affected individuals showed three general types of cataract, each of which varied and changed with age. The two most important

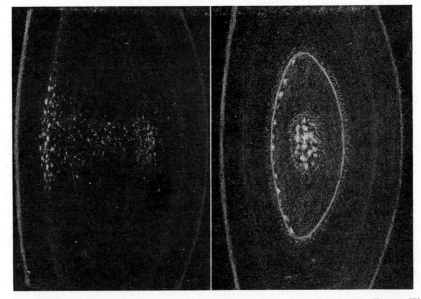

FIG. 134. Two types of expression in hereditary juvenile cataract (Pedigree, Fig. 73). Schematic cross sections through the lenses. *Left:* Anterior opacities mainly (see left part of figure). *Right:* Central opacity. (Lutman and Neel, *Arch. Ophthalmol.,* **33,** 1945.)

categories of cataract were that in which opacities developed mainly in the anterior region of the center of the lens and that in which the opacities were in the interior of the lens (Fig. 134, A, B). Both eyes of the same person were always alike. The different modes of expressivity are significant for the affected individuals, since the interior type causes more interference with vision, and at an earlier age, than the anterior type.

There is evidence that the type of expressivity is inherited. The anterior type of cataract was present in one woman, her 2 affected sons, and 1 affected grandchild. The interior type of cataract was found in a niece of this woman, 5 out of 6 of the niece's affected children, and all 5 affected grandchildren. (One of the 6 affected children had a feather-like lens opacity unlike either of the two categories described.)

It thus seems that the dominant gene responsible for the development of cataracts determines the occurrence of the affliction without specifying the particular type of opacity. The variations in type are probably due to simple modifiers. If the niece and her descendants were homozygous for a recessive allele m in addition to having the genotype for cataract, and her aunt was heterozygous for the dominant allele M (Mn), then it would be understandable why the 3 affected descendants of the aunt might show her specific type of cataract and her niece's descendants another type. There is a probability of $1/2$ that any of the affected descendants of the aunt would inherit M, and not m, from her. Assuming that neither her husband nor her grandchild's father carried an M allele, the probability of all 3 affected individuals inheriting M is 1 in 8—a figure well within the bounds of likelihood. There are other ways of postulating that genetic modifiers are responsible for a particular type of cataract. The existence of such modifiers seems proved, even if no conclusive formulation of their genotypes can be made.

Cleft Hand.   We may return here to the striking abnormality cleft hand, which was used earlier as an illustration of differences in expressivity in the hands and feet of the same person. Such differences were clearly environmental in origin and uncontrollable. It was also pointed out that the trait showed different degrees of expressivity in different affected individuals. In the remarkable pedigree (Fig. 126, p. 298) that lists an affected woman who had normal and affected children by four different normal husbands, a greater variation is found among the different children than in each child. The daughter V-6 has the fewest bones in hands and feet; her sister V-7 has the next greatest deviation from normality; their brother V-4 has the largest number of bones; and their half-sibs V-1 and V-3 are somewhere in between. This greater variability among sibs as compared with the lesser variability of hands or feet in a single person may have been brought about partly because the differences in the environments of embryos that develop at different times are greater than those on the two sides of the same embryo. It is probably also true that at least part of the variability among sibs is due to differences in their genetic backgrounds. Even though some have the same parents and all have one parent in common, normal heterozygosity will produce a great variety of different genotypes among them.

Different Types of Genic Interaction. Genetic modifiers are usually thought of as producing phenotypic effects not by themselves but as modifying traits dependent on a specific allele of a main gene. Although this view is useful as a first approximation, it is more likely that a modifying genotype, *MM* or *Mm,* will have effects different from those of *mm* not only when there is a specific allele at the main locus, but in general. Thus, it is possible that the *M* and *m* modifiers of the minor brachydactyly genotype *Bb* influence finger size in normal *bb* individuals, although the differences may be too small to be noticed. Or, even if *M* and *m* do not affect the size of normal fingers, a biochemical study of *MM, Mm* and *mm* persons might reveal differences.

Modification of genic effects by other genes may be of many kinds. In Drosophila, as we have seen, the gene *D* may reduce the number of certain bristles on the back of the thorax, but only of these bristles. Another dominant gene, *H,* reduces the number of certain other bristles. A fly which carries both *D* and *H* lacks not only the bristles affected by the two different genes but also other bristles not affected by either *D* or *H* alone. In man, an analogous example is that of the interaction of the separate genes for thalassemia and sickle-cell anemia. Heterozygotes with either one or the other abnormal gene are fundamentally healthy, though tests of their blood cells demonstrate the effect of the gene. In an individual heterozygous for both genes they may so interact as to produce a disease difficult to distinguish from that caused by homozygosity for the sickle-cell gene alone.

Another type of genic interaction seems to be the basis of a very rare, "atypical" type of total color blindness, characterized by normal or supernormal visual acuity. It is really the result of the summation of two different kinds of defects in color vision: Individuals of this type have been interpreted as being (1) homo- or heterozygous for an autosomal gene for congenital "tritanopia," which by itself causes defects in blue and yellow vision, and also (2) homo-, hetero-, or hemizygous for the X-linked protanopia or deuteranopia, which by themselves cause defects in red-green vision.

Suppressor Genes. Another striking interaction in man, discovered by Grubb and Cepellini, concerns certain blood-group properties. The dominant gene *Le* causes production of the Lewis-a blood-group substance, and the nonallelic dominant gene *Se* leads to secretion of the ABH antigens into the saliva. Persons with the genotypes *LeLesese* or *Lelesese* possess the Lewis-a antigen in their saliva and on their red blood cells, but in combination with *Le* the presence of at least one *Se* allele reduces the amount of the Lewis-a substance in the saliva and completely eliminates it on the red blood cells. The latter phenomenon represents a suppression of the effect of one gene by another.

A gene has also been found which suppresses the effect of the I^B blood allele. In an American family an O women married to an A_1 man gave birth to an A_1B child. The unexpected appearance of both A and B antigens in the child of an O mother cannot be explained by illegitimacy since no regular genotype of the father could cause this. Detailed blood tests showed that the mother possessed not only the anti-A and anti-B antibodies normally present in O individuals but also the anti-H antibody, which is not found in typical O persons. She had older identical twin sisters who had the same unusual blood properties, which had been discovered earlier in a few people from Bombay and had been thought to be due to a new "Bombay allele" of the I^A, I^B, I^O system. The appearance of the B antigen in the A_1B child of the woman with antibodies against A, B, and H led to a reinterpretation of the new type of blood. The woman herself must have carried the I^B allele in spite of lacking the B antigen. Her father was a typical O, her mother B. Both these parents, who were cousins, carried heterozygously a recessive gene x, which became homozygous in the $I^B I^O$ woman. The xx genotype suppressed B antigen formation, but not that of anti-H antibody: it was also shown to suppress the action of the dominant secretor gene. Phenotypically, both parents of the A_1B child were nonsecretors and would therefore normally have been se se. The A_1B child was a nonsecretor, as expected, but a younger sister, of true O type, was a secretor. The genotypes of the two children and their parents thus were as follows:

$$P \qquad I^B I^O; \; xx; \; Se \; se \; ♀ \times I^{A_1}I^O; \; XX; \; se \; se \; ♂$$
$$F_1 \quad (1) \; I^{A_1}I^B; \; Xx; \; se \; se \quad (2) \; I^O I^O; \; Xx; \; Se \; se$$

The genotype xx is a very rare one and its failure to suppress the formation of anti-H serves to distinguish xx individuals from true O individuals. It is clear, however, that suppressor genes can produce genetic situations which may easily seem contrary to established facts. The physiology of the suppressor action of xx is still to be studied. In the mold Neurospora as well as in Drosophila, careful analyses have partly mapped the biochemical pathways along which one gene may tend to undo the action another gene would otherwise accomplish.

Interaction between Alleles.   The genetic background of a main gene or genes is usually defined in terms of genes at other loci. In its widest sense the background may also be regarded as including, in heterozygotes, the allele with which a specific gene is paired. Nothing needs to be said here about a population that contains only two different alleles in a relation of complete dominance and recessiveness, intermediateness, or codominance. Sometimes, however, special interactions have been observed, and the existence of multiple alleles may also introduce modifying effects.

One special interaction between two I alleles was mentioned in an earlier chapter (p. 53). The anti-B antibodies produced in homozygous $I^{A_1}I^{A_1}$ and I^OI^O genotypes are smaller molecular compounds than the anti-B antibodies of $I^{A_1}I^O$ heterozygotes. The formation in the heterozygote of an antibody that is different from that produced by either homozygote is an example of single locus *heterosis*. This term is used to designate two kinds of phenomena. One is that just discussed: namely, the production by a heterozygote of a phenotypic effect essentially different from those produced by either homozygote. The other is a peculiar quantitative relation of the heterozygous phenotype to the two homozygotes: the quantitative effect of the heterozygote, be it on the amount of an enzyme produced, or on the height of an individual, is outside the range of the quantitative effect of the homozygotes, being greater or smaller than either of them.

An example of the second type of heterosis in man, to be treated in detail later, is supplied by persons heterozygous for the alleles for normal and sickle-cell hemoglobin, Hb_1^S and Hb_1^A. Under certain environmental conditions, $Hb_1^SHb_1^A$ has greater viability than either $Hb_1^SHb_1^S$ or $Hb_1^AHb_1^A$.

When more than two alleles of a single gene exist in a population, any one of them can be in heterozygous combination with any one of the others. Thus, in the rabbit, the allele c^{chi} for dark chinchilla hair may be paired in heterozygotes with the allele c^d for intermediate chinchilla, c^m for light chinchilla, or c for albinism. All heterozygotes have a chinchilla phenotype, but the degree of pigmentation depends not only on c^{chi} but also on the other allele. It is obvious that the variability in color of rabbits from populations not homozygous for the c^{chi} locus is in part due to the specific allele with which c^{chi} is combined.

Homozygotes for the c^d, c^m, and c alleles are all phenotypically distinguishable from one another. In contrast to these, multiple alleles are also known, in various organisms, which homozygously produce identical phenotypes but, in heterozygous combination with some other allele, produce different phenotypes. The discovery of such isoalleles often depends on their allelic interactions in heterozygotes.

One other example of allelic interaction was described earlier (p. 197). The R^1 allele, homozygously or paired with r, causes a typically strong reaction with anti-Rh$_0$; but when it is paired with r', only a weak reaction takes place. The expressivity of the R^1 allele is thus dependent on the type of allele with which it forms a heterozygote.

Sex-limited Traits

A very important part of the genetic background is the sexual constitution. Although penetrance and expressivity of many genes are alike in males and females, there is a great difference in the action of others in the two sexes, even though the genes in question are not themselves concerned with the determination of sex. Some such genes are *sex limited* in their effect; that is, they are expressed phenotypically in one sex only. In strict sex limitation, we may formulate the situation as follows: If S and s are two alleles with sex-limited expression, the three genotypes, SS, Ss, and ss, are indistinguishable in one sex but give rise to two or three different phenotypes in the other sex, depending on whether the heterozygote is like one of the homozygotes or different from both. Knowledge of sex limitation is of great practical importance in breeding dairy cattle. It is known that the yield and quality of milk are under the control of many genes, and that the genes are, on the whole, contributed equally by both parents. Since these genes are located in the autosomes, bulls and cows may have identical milk-yield genes. Obviously, the phenotype "milk yield and quality" is limited in expression to females, although, experimentally, it could be made to appear in males. No such experiments have been attempted in cattle, but male guinea pigs have secreted milk after they had been deprived of their testes, which produce the male hormones, and had been treated with a female sex hormone. The type and quantity of this milk would undoubtedly have shown indications of hereditary differences.

In man, no genetic analysis of sex-limited expression of genes has been made, but from general considerations, it seems certain that yield and quantity of milk of the human female are influenced by genes present in both sexes. Undoubtedly, genes contributed by both parents control various anatomical and physiological properties of the female sex, such as width of pelvis or age of onset of menstruation. Similarly, sex-limited male characters, such as type of beard growth or amount and distribution of body hair, probably depend on genes common to both sexes.

This is indicated by the results of interracial matings. Caucasoid males, on the average, are more hairy than Mongoloids, but the sons from marriages between members of the two races are often intermediate in hairiness—proof that the mother has contributed genes which find their expression in the male sex only. In other organisms, many genes are known which cause sterility of only one sex. In dairy cattle, for example, a recessive gene makes the cows infertile which are homozygous for it, but does not affect the bulls.

It must be emphasized that sex limitation is not the same as sex linkage. The latter term refers to the localization of genes in a sex chromosome; the former, to the developmental expression of the genes in only one of the two sexes. Most sex-limited genes are autosomal, but a few are known which are X-linked: both females and males may carry these genes, and simple inspection can show their sex-limited effect. It would be more difficult to judge the situation if Y-linked genes became known. Such genes would be linked with the determiner of maleness, which is itself located in the Y-chromosome. Normally, therefore, it would not be possible to decide whether a Y-linked gene is limited in expression to the male because it is Y-linked, or whether it is developmentally sex limited regardless of its chromosomal location.

Sex-controlled Traits

Sex limitation is only the extreme example of control of the expression of certain genotypes by sex. When a genotype is expressed in both sexes but in a different manner in each, we speak of *sex-controlled,* or *sex-modified,* genic expression. The earliest study of a sex-controlled character in man is that of Bernstein on the inheritance of singing voices in adult Europeans. A single pair of alleles was regarded as responsible for the six different singing voices: bass, baritone, tenor, soprano, mezzo-soprano and alto. Strangely enough, the low bass voice in males and the high soprano in females seemed to be determined by the same genotype, A^1A^1, and the high tenor in males and the low alto in females by A^2A^2, the heterozygote A^1A^2 leading to baritone and mezzo-soprano. However, Bernstein's specific interpretation has not withstood the test of time. While studies of twins, pedigrees, and populations point to genetic factors in the determination of singing voices, many independently variable properties are involved in type of voice. Some of these are indeed controlled by the sexual constitution of the individual: the development of the voice box in the divergent male and female direction of the adult takes place at puberty under the influence of the sex hormones. However, a single pair of alleles with simple expression in the two sexes is not sufficient to explain the facts, which still await detailed analysis.

A somewhat different type of sex control affects the penetrance and expressivity of many genotypes. Harelip and cleft palate are developmental abnormalities with a genetic basis. Penetrance is incomplete (Fig. 135), and expressivity varies from very slight external clefts to very severe clefts of the soft, and even the hard, palate. Sex control is apparent in the fact that penetrance is higher in males than in females (about 60 per cent of affected individuals are males), and that severe types of expression occur more frequently in males.

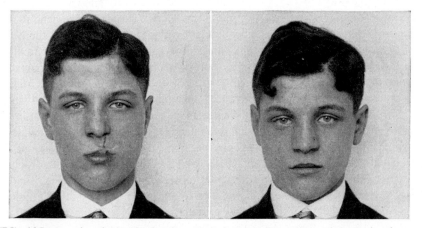

FIG. 135. A pair of identical twins. Penetrance of harelip at left, lack of penetrance at right. (Claussen, *Zeitschr. Abstgs. u. Vererbgsl.,* **76,** 1939.)

Even more extreme is the sex control of penetrance of gout. The metabolic abnormality which is the basis of this painful affliction, an excess of uric acid in the blood (hyperuricemia) seems to be caused by a dominant autosomal gene, but other genetic hypotheses are not excluded. Penetrance of the hyperuricemic genotypes that cause gout has been estimated as more than 80 per cent in males but less than 12 per cent in females, resulting in many more affected men than women.

A greater frequency of affected males than females is typical for many other abnormal traits which are under the control of autosomal genes. As shown earlier (pp. 240–241), a study of four such traits proved that the higher incidence of affected males is not due to X-linked modifying genes, but to developmental control of phenotypic expression. This is probably true of the majority of traits that are more common in one sex than the other.

Sex control may also lead to higher frequencies of affected females. Some congenital malformations with a genetic basis such as anencephaly (absence of the brain) or spina bifida (cleft vertebral column) are more often found in female than male zygotes.

Even a trait that has been used in an earlier chapter to demonstrate simple single factor inheritance, ability to taste PTC, is not always free from sex control. Without such control, one would expect equal percentages of male and female tasters. In reality, some samples of various populations deviate significantly from equality. Usually the percentage of female tasters is slightly higher than that of males.

Sex control of the expression of alternative genotypes sometimes affects the dominance relation of two alleles. This has been thoroughly analyzed in crosses between breeds of sheep. In some breeds, both sexes have horns, but in others both males and females are hornless. A pair of autosomal alleles, H^1 and H^2, is responsible for this difference, the horned breeds being homozygous H^1H^1, and the hornless H^2H^2. All hybrid males are horned, but all hybrid females hornless. Since their genotypes are alike, H^1H^2, it follows that the allele for horns H^1, is dominant in males, but recessive in females; or, if we view it differently, that the allele for absence of horns, H^2, is recessive in males but dominant in females. In this case the male and female hormones in the growing animals provide two different internal environments, which interact with the H^1H^2 genotype and control its expression.

Baldness. Sex-controlled dominance has been suggested as an explanation of the pattern of inheritance of baldness in man. The investigation of this, as of many other human characters, is made difficult by the fact that the phenotype "baldness" has variable expressivity. Baldness may be slight or extreme, occur first on the crown or on the forehead, and appear early or late in life; moreover, some baldness seems to be due to specific abnormalities in thyroid metabolism or to infectious diseases. But most types of typical "pattern baldness" occur in healthy individuals, and many pedigrees exhibit a succession of affected individuals or show numerous affected sibs and other

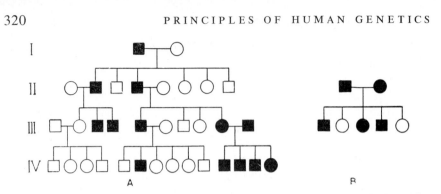

FIG. 136. Pedigrees of baldness. (After Snyder and Yingling, *Hum. Biol.*, **7**, 1935.)

relatives (Fig. 136). A hereditary basis for baldness is therefore probable.

Both sexes may be affected, but the high relative frequency of affected males is notable. That this is not due, as in color blindness, to the presence of a sex-linked gene is obvious from the fact that bald men often transmit the trait to about half of their sons but to very few of their daughters. If both parents are affected, either all their children are affected or all sons and some daughters are affected. Finally, most bald women have a bald father. In explanation, it has been suggested that an allele B^1 in homozygous state, B^1B^1, permits normal adult hair growth in both men and women; that the homozygotes B^2B^2 are bald regardless of sex; and that male B^1B^2 heterozygotes are bald, but females are not. This theory implies that the threshold for the baldness effect of the B^2 allele in heterozygotes is more easily reached in the male than in the female.

Like hornedness in sheep, hair growth in man is controlled by sex hormones. Few eunuchs become bald, but women with a tumor of the suprarenal cortex, which results in a high production of male-type sex hormones, not only may develop such typical sex-limited traits as beards and mustaches but also may become bald. Upon removal of the tumor, both the sex-limited and sex-controlled traits disappear. According to Conway Zirkle, the sex control of baldness was known to Hippocrates and Aristotle. "Eunuchs neither get gout nor grow bald," noted the former; and "No boy ever gets bald, no woman, and no castrated man," wrote the latter.

Snyder and Yingling tested the hypothesis that baldness is governed by a single pair of alleles whose expression in heterozygotes is sex controlled, by means of the allele frequency method. The theory designates men who are not bald as homozygous B^1B^1. Consequently, as with any autosomal gene in a random-mating population, the gene frequency of B^1 is obtained by extracting the square root of the frequency of B^1B^1 individuals:

$$p_{B^1} = \sqrt{\text{nonbald men.}} \tag{1}$$

Conversely, the theory designates bald women as homozygous B^2B^2. It follows, therefore, that

$$q_{B^2} = \sqrt{\text{bald women.}} \tag{2}$$

Since the sum of the two frequencies p and q is unity, the theory predicts

$$\sqrt{\overline{\text{nonbald men}}} + \sqrt{\overline{\text{bald women}}} = 1. \tag{3}$$

How do the observed data fit this expectation? Approximately 40 per cent of all men in the general population were found to be bald. (Since this figure was based on men of thirty-five and over, the criterion by which a person was judged to be bald must have been severe.) Given the percentage of bald men, the theory should predict the percentage of bald women. In order to obtain data on the frequency of baldness in women, it was necessary to determine the presence or absence of the trait in a fairly large sample of the population. This was difficult to accomplish in a general population so that data on the inmates of state hospitals for the insane in Ohio and Illinois were used. The frequency of bald women, based on a total of 1,883, was found to be 7.75 per cent (0.0775). This is regarded as a typical frequency, not in any way correlated with the mental condition of the women, since it was found that the frequency of bald men who were inmates of the same hospitals was not significantly different from that of mentally normal men in the general population. The specific percentage for the institutionalized men was 42.96 per cent, based on a total of nearly 4,000. The frequency of nonbald men, therefore, was 0.5704. Using this figure for nonbald men and 0.0775 for bald women, we obtain, by means of equations (1) and (2),

$$p_{B^1} = 0.755$$
$$q_{B^2} = 0.278$$

and testing equation (3), we find that

$$\sqrt{\overline{\text{nonbald men}}} + \sqrt{\overline{\text{bald women}}} = 1.033.$$

This is very close to the value of 1.000 required by the theory.

In spite of this agreement between expectation and observed data, some doubts regarding the correctness of the theory remain. The proof would be more convincing if different populations with different frequencies of baldness could be shown to conform to the theoretical requirements given in equation (3). Such multiple tests of the relevant theories were provided for various blood groups. It should likewise be possible to extend the test of the theory for baldness to various ethnic groups in which the incidence of the trait is known to be lower than in Snyder and Yingling's material.

There are recorded exceptions to the theory, such as a bald woman whose constitution, as judged by her parent's phenotype, must have been B^1B^2 and not B^2B^2, and men and women with very thin hair in a pedigree containing typical baldness who may have carried B^2 but did not show its typical effect.

The most serious objections to the theory are that the phenotypic class, baldness, seems to include several differently inherited types of lack of hair and that very little is known about baldness in women. Harris collected data that he divided into two groups: one of persons in whom baldness sets in before the age of thirty and is strong before forty; and another of persons in whom it begins later. Genetic examination shows that the two groups are hereditarily different. There is a suggestion that premature baldness may be due to an allele which is dominant in heterozygous men but not in heterozygous women, and is so rare that homozygous women are not yet known. It has also been suggested that no hormonally typical women are bald and that baldness is not really sex controlled but sex limited. According to this view, baldness in women would be a result of the interaction of a genotype normally unexpressed in females with a male-like hormonal condition. Further investigations are needed to clarify the genetics of baldness.

Anticipation

We have seen that the age of onset of Huntington's chorea varies from one affected individual to another. Such variability is typical of many inherited diseases whose symptoms appear late in life. An opinion widely held among medical men—and some statistics seem to support it—is that the age of onset of these diseases becomes earlier and earlier in successive generations (Table 45). The phenomenon is called *anticipation*, or *antedating*. Furthermore, it is held that diseases whose severity varies increase in severity from one generation to the next. This presumed phenomenon might exist independently of anticipation or could be a consequence of it, since many of these diseases involve progressive degeneration of the affected organs, and a disease that begins early in life will have more time to run its course than a disease with later onset.

The concept of anticipation does not readily fit in the system of genetic facts and interpretations that has proven so fruitful in the study of man and of a variety of experimental organisms. Geneticists have therefore carefully analyzed the data which suggest anticipation. That there are pedigrees which show an earlier and more severe onset of a disease in a younger generation than in a preceding one is not surprising. If the age of onset varies, one should expect such pedigrees, just as one should expect others

TABLE 45.   *Age of Onset of Various Hereditary Diseases.* (Penrose.)

Disease	No. of Parent-Child Pairs	Age of Onset, Mean Values (in Years)		
		Parent	Child	Difference
Peroneal atrophy (dominant)	86	24.30	19.36	4.94
Muscular dystrophy (dominant)	90	27.44	21.00	6.44
Hereditary glaucoma	113	42.08	30.66	11.42
Huntington's chorea	153	40.80	31.98	8.82
Diabetes mellitus	216	60.29	43.06	17.22
Mental illness (all diagnoses)	1,728	50.50	34.20	16.30
Dystrophia myotonica	51	38.48	15.24	23.24

in which onset is earlier in the older generation. These two types of pedigrees should be equally frequent, and it must therefore be explained why, for some diseases, pedigrees with earlier onset in older generations seem to be rarer than those with earlier onset in younger ones.

In some pedigrees this phenomenon is perhaps due to unknown environmental conditions which have changed with the times, and bring about earlier onset of the diseases in more recent generations. Or it may well be that the published data are not random samples of all cases, but represent a selected group. Probably the most common cause of selection stems from the fact that a serious disease that affects a person early in life greatly reduces his chances of leaving offspring. Therefore, only the individuals in the older generation with late onset will have children and thus become available for the records. If the average age of onset in their children were the same as that in an *unselected* preceding generation, it would be earlier than that in the *selected* group, who became known only because the disease began late.

Another source of selection in pedigrees showing anticipation may be that the early and more severe cases of the generation living at the time of the study have a greater chance of becoming known than the late and less severe ones. Hence, the average age of onset in the ascertained sample of the living generation may be earlier than if the whole unselected population were studied. If the age of onset in the affected parents of such propositi is determined it will tend to show a normal unselected distribution, and the average age of onset will be greater than that of their offspring.

Still other factors may contribute to an appearance of anticipation. It is likely, for instance, that individuals of the present generation do not know about, or have forgotten, the existence of ancestors who have had a particularly early onset of the disease: this may be the reason that data on the age of onset of diseases in affected persons show anticipation when compared with data on their aunts and uncles. Here, the argument based on selection for parents with late age of onset cannot be applied, since the relation between the ages of aunts or uncles and their nieces or nephews is not the same as that of parents and offspring.

Julia Bell, who collected extensive data on the age of onset of Huntington's chorea and other progressive diseases, has come to the conclusion that no anticipation can be demonstrated if allowances are made for the bias introduced into the data by methods of ascertainment. Although this does not necessarily mean that anticipation never occurs, it seems justified, until the contrary is proven, to consider anticipation as a statistical phenomenon which will disappear from the records when methods of ascertainment have been perfected.

Correlation between Ages of Onset among Relatives.   Ages of onset in parents and children and in sibs often show a high degree of correlation. This suggests that within families, similar agents determine the age of onset —agents that may be either genetic or environmental. If the similarity in age of onset within one family was genetically determined, the differences found in different pedigrees could be due to the existence of different genes, each of which was responsible for the disease; or of different alleles of the same gene; or of modifying genes in the genetic background against which some single main gene acts. If, on the other hand, the similarity in age of onset within one family was environmentally conditioned, then the differences between different families would signify that the external agents affecting the age of outbreak of the hereditary disease are those that are similar within families but not from one family to another.

Haldane has found evidence that in some diseases—for example, peroneal atrophy (wasting of the calf muscles)—age of onset in different kindreds is determined by different main genes. In other diseases, for instance, Huntington's chorea, the main gene seems to be the same in all pedigrees, and the difference among individuals appears to be due to modifying genes.

An interesting situation has been discovered in dominant muscular distrophy. There is much less similarity between the ages of onset in affected parents and children (correlation coefficient $+ 0.32$) than between pairs of sibs ($+0.66$). As described in Chapter 11 (p. 207), Penrose suggested that the age of onset is partly dependent on the type of normal isoallele, d^1, d^2, etc., with which the defect-carrying allele D is combined. If a parent with late onset of the disease were of the genotype Dd^2 and his normal spouse d^1d^1 and if Dd^1 led to early onset, then all affected offspring would be Dd^1, and all would have a similar age of onset of the disease, lower than in their affected parent.

There is still another way in which striking differences in age of onset of a disease may be genetically controlled. Figure 137 shows a pedigree of a type of spastic paraplegia (a degenerative condition of the nervous system). The individual I–3 remained healthy until the age of sixty-five, when his gait became uncertain. At the age of eighty-six, the failure of muscular coordination was marked; nevertheless, he lived to be ninety-one. His daughter (II–2) and her husband, who were double first cousins, were not affected, but 3 of their 5 children developed paraplegia at the age of ten. Haldane suggests, plausibly, that the affected grandfather of the children and his sister (I–2) or her husband (I–1) were both heterozygous for an abnormal allele of very low penetrance which either causes no defective phenotype or causes one only late in life. The normal parents II–1 and II–2, according to this interpretation, were also heterozygotes, but their first 3 children were homozygous for the abnormal allele. Thus, homozygosity for the allele is believed to be responsible for the very early age of onset in the youngest generation.

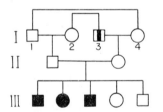

FIG. 137. Pedigree of spastic paraplegia. Vertical bar in symbol = late onset; solid symbol = early onset. (After Haldane, *J. Genet.*, **41**, 1941.)

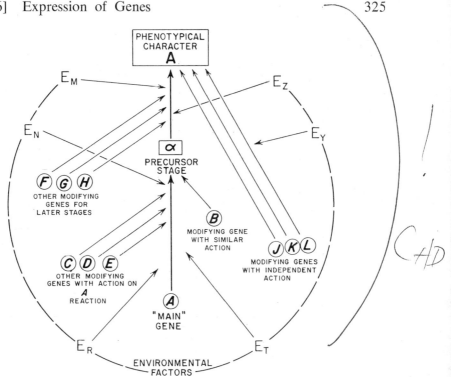

FIG. 138. Diagram of interaction of a "main" gene, with different kinds of modifying genes, and with environmental factors in the production of a trait. (After Timoféeff-Ressovsky, *Nachr. Ges. Wissensch., Göttingen,* **1,** 1934.)

When an abnormal condition is caused by a dominant allele, a heterozygote may be less severely affected than a homozygote. In several Swedish pedigrees a dominantly inherited muscular degeneration (distal myopathy) has a greatly variable age of onset, from thirty-four to eighty-two. In one family both spouses were affected. They had 16 children, of whom 7 were affected, 2 much more severely than the others. If these 2 were homozygous for the defect-causing gene, their children should all be carriers of the dominant gene. There are 8 of them, but most are still too young to show the effect of their genotype.

This chapter has provided a basis for understanding how the interplay of different components of the genotype affects phenotypic expression. It has also given examples that show the great significance of the various environmental factors that influence the appearance of genetic traits. Figure 138 may serve to summarize the general facts which studies on variation in the expression of genes have supplied, and the concepts by means of which these facts become intelligible.

Problems

123. Construct a typical pedigree of blue scleras comprising, altogether, fifteen individuals in three generations.

124. Give the genotypes of all individuals in the pedigree on blue scleras in Figure 121. If more than one genotype is possible, give alternatives.

125. From the data in Figure 123, what is the chance that an individual heterozygous for Huntington's chorea will remain unaffected at (a) 27.5 years of age? (b) At 47.5? (c) At. 67.5?

126. The 42.5-year-old daughter of a man who is affected with Huntington's chorea is not affected. What is the probability of her carrying the allele for Huntington's chorea?

127. Assume that M is a dominant modifier for strong expression of minor brachydactyly. Give the genotypes of all individuals in the pedigree in Figure 133. When more than one genotype is possible, give alternatives.

128. If the difference in expressivity of minor brachydactyly were due to a dominant modifier N for weak expression, what would be the genotypes of all individuals in the pedigree in Figure 133? When more than one genotype is possible, give alternatives.

129. Two parents were $I^B I^O$ and $I^A I^B$, respectively. They had three $I^B I^O$ or $I^B I^B$ children, one $I^A I^O$, two $I^A I^B$, and one more $I^A I^B$. The genotype of the last child was determined by means of the properties of her saliva, into which the antigens A and B had been secreted. Her red blood cells, however, carried antigen B only—that is, they lacked A. It has been assumed that the parents were heterozygous for genotype Yy, and that yy supresses the expression of the A antigen in the red blood cells. What are the possible Y,y genotypes of the children?

In Problems 130 and 131, assume the correctness of Bernstein's theory of inheritance of singing voices.

130. List all possible marriages in relation to types of singing voices. What types of offspring and in what proportions are expected in each type of marriage?

131. In a population, 25 per cent of all women are sopranos. What are the frequencies of all other types of female or male voices?

In Problems 132–135, assume the correctness of Snyder's theory of inheritance of baldness.

132. Give the genotypes of all individuals in the two pedigrees in Figure 136. Whenever appropriate, list alternative genotypes.

133. If a nonaffected woman in the sibship of Figure 136, B, married the individual IV–6 of Figure 136, A, what types of offspring, and in what proprtions, could they expect?

134. In a certain population, 1 per cent of all women are bald. (a) How many women are heterozygous? (b) How many men are bald?

135. In a certain population, 51 per cent of all men are bald. (a) How many women are bald? (b) What is the frequency of marriages between bald men and nonbald women?

References

Bell, Julia, 1928. Blue sclerotics and fragility of bone. *Treas. Hum. Inher.,* **II, 3:** 269–324.

————, 1934. Huntington's chorea. *Treas. Hum. Inher.,* **IV, 1:** 1–67.

————, 1942. On the age of onset and age of death in muscular dystrophy. *Ann. Eugen.,* **11:** 272–289.

Bonnevie, K., 1934. Embryological analysis of gene manifestation in Little and Bagg's abnormal mouse tribe. *J. Exp. Zool.,* **67:** 443–520.

Das, S. R., 1958. Inheritance of the P.T.C. taste character in man: an analysis of 126 Rárhi Bráhmin families of West Bengal. *Ann. Human Genet.,* **22:** 200–212.

Fogh-Andersen, P., 1943. Inheritance of harelip and cleft palate. *Opera Copenhagen Univers.,* **4:** 266 pp.

Grüneberg, H., 1952. *The Genetics of the Mouse.* 2nd ed. 650 pp. M. Nyhoff, The Hague.

Hamilton, J. B., 1958. Age, sex and genetic factors in the regulation of hair growth in man: a comparison of Caucasian and Japanese populations. In W. Montagna and R. A. Ellis (Ed.). *The Biology of Hair Growth.* pp. 399–433. Academic Press, New York.

Harris, H., 1946. Heredity and premature baldness in men. *Ann. Eugen.,* **13:** 172–181.

Hoyme, L. E., 1955. Genetics, physiology and phenylthiocarbamide. *J. Hered.,* **46:** 167–175.

Komai, T., Kunii, H., and Ozaki, Y., 1956. A note on the genetics of van der Hoeve's syndrome. *Am. J. Human Genet.,* **8:** 110–119.

Levine, P., Robinson, E., Celano, M., Briggs, O., and Falkinburg, L., 1955. Gene interaction resulting in suppression of blood group substance B. *Blood,* **10:** 1100–1108.

Levit, S. G., 1936. The problem of dominance in man. *J. Genet.,* **33:** 411–434.

Mohr, O. L., and Wriedt, Chr., 1919. A new type of hereditary brachyphalangy. *Carnegie Inst. Wash. Publ.,* **295:** 65 pp.

Müller, W., 1937. *Die angeborenen Fehlbildungen der menschlichen Hand.* 170 pp. Thieme, Leipzig.

Mundinger, F., 1951. Zum Vererbungsproblem der menschlichen Singstimme. *Folia Phoniatrica,* **3:** 191–223.

Penrose, L. S., 1948. The problem of anticipation in pedigrees of dystrophia myotonica. *Ann. Eugen.,* **14:** 125–132.

Pincus, G., and White, P., 1933. On the inheritance of diabetes mellitus. *Am. J. Med. Sci.,* **186:** 1–14.

Race, R. R., and Sanger, R., 1958. Some modifications of the ABO groups. *Am. J. Clin. Pathol.,* **29:** 515–524.

Reed, S. C., 1936. Harelip in the house mouse. I. Effects of the external and internal environments. II. Mendelian units concerned with harelip and application of the data to the human harelip problem. *Genetics,* **21:** 339–374.

Rife, D. C., 1951. Heredity and handedness. *Scient. Monthly,* **73:** 188–191.

Steinberg, A. G., and Wilder, R. M., 1952. A study of the genetics of diabetes mellitus. *Am. J. Human Genet.,* **4:** 113–135.

————, 1952. An analysis of the phenomenon of "anticipation" in diabetes mellitus. *Ann. Internal Med.,* **36:** 1285–1296.

Strangmann-Koehler, J., and Ludwig, W., 1954. Untersuchungen über die Komponenten der Seitigkeit des Menschen, insbesondere die Venigkeit. Zeitschr. Mensch. *Vererb. u. Konstitutionslehre,* **32:** 219–258.

Trankell, A., 1956. Penetrance calculus in population genetics. *Am. J. Human Genet.,* **8:** 44–48.

Ullrich, O., 1949. Turner's syndrome and status Bonnevie-Ullrich; a synthesis of animal phenogenetics and clinical observations on a typical complex of developmental anomalies. *Am. J. Human Genet.,* **1:** 179–202.

Zirkle, C., 1945. The discovery of sex-influenced, sex-limited and sex-linked heredity. In M. F. Ashley Montague (Ed.). *Studies and Essays in the History of Science and Learning in Honor of George Sarton.* pp. 169–194. H. Schuman, New York.

CHAPTER 17

PRENATAL
INTERACTIONS

In general, the genotypes of children are independent of any variation in the physiology of the parents caused by such factors as age, number of preceding births, or health. Thus, a person heterozygous for a pair of alleles forms equal numbers of the two possible kinds of gametes regardless of his physiological condition. Likewise, the independent assortment of genes in the different chromosome pairs is a basic process of normal meiosis and is not influenced by parental condition. However, two genetically significant processes, mutation and crossing over, are known to be affected by the physiology of an individual. For mutation, this will be shown in Chapter 23; for crossing over, a brief discussion will be given here.

In experimental organisms, including Drosophila and mice, the frequency of crossing over has been shown to be dependent, in complex ways, on age as well as on various metabolic conditions. In man, nothing is yet known about variability in the frequency of crossing over, but it may well be found that gametes from parents of certain ages will show higher cross-over frequencies than gametes from parents of other ages. Should this be true, the gametes produced by individuals during the period when the frequency of crossing over is low would more often contain blocks of alleles still linked in the same chromosomes in which they were received from the parents, than the gametes produced by the same individuals during the period when the frequency of crossing over is high. In the latter period, more new combinations of the alleles of a chromosome pair would be formed. As a consequence of this still hypothetical situation, children produced during the period when there was a low rate of crossing over in a parent would be likely to possess an association of linked characters present in one of the grandparents, whose chromosomes they would receive with

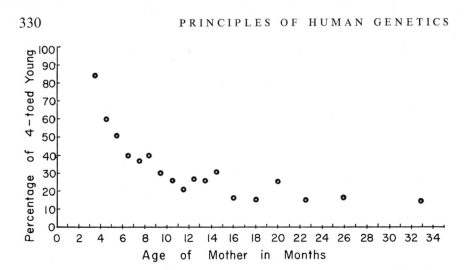

FIG. 139. Influence of age of mother on number of extra toes in 416 polydactylous guinea pigs. (After Wright, *Am. Naturalist,* **60,** 1926.)

relatively little change, and would lack the alternative block of characters of the other grandparent, whose chromosomes they would not receive. On the contrary, children produced when the rate of crossing over was high would be likely to present a finer mosaic of grandparental characters, since many of the chromosomes the children would receive would comprise segments derived from both grandparents.

In pooled data from many sibships, no correlation would be expected between characters and the high or low crossover periods of the parents. This follows from considerations similar to those presented in Chapter 14 (pp. 258–262) regarding the lack of correlation in a population between different traits that are controlled by linked genes. Thus, in no population could segregation and recombination or linkage and crossing over lead one to expect correlations between the ages of parents and the genotypes of offspring.

Maternal Physiology and Phenotypes of Children

In spite of the general expectation, the occurrence of a number of inherited congenital characteristics of offspring has been found to be correlated with physiological variables of the mothers, particularly with her age.

It is not surprising that no clearly established example of a paternal influence of this type is known. The father's contribution, the sperm, consists almost entirely of the genes that are contained in its head and hence of little that could exert extragenic influence. The mother, on the contrary, not only supplies the egg, which contains a large volume of extragenic substance, primarily the cytoplasm; but in addition provides, in her uterus, the environment in which the embryo develops. It would seem reasonable that the physiological condition of a woman should affect the cytoplasmic content of the egg cells ripening in her ovaries, and that differing uterine environments might have variable effects on the phenotype of the child.

In snails and insects, maternal influences which affect the phenotype of the offspring by way of the egg's cytoplasm have been discovered. In a few laboratory mammals, too, the physiological condition of the mother has been shown to affect the expression of the offspring's genotype. Thus, in a strain of polydactylous guinea pigs, Wright found that penetrance and expressivity are partly controlled by the age of the mother. The older the mother, the more young with the normal number of toes (Fig. 139). The same tendency has been found for a variety of skeletal abnormalities in certain strains of mice: polydactyly, absence of a third molar tooth, unusual position of a vertebral spine, and of an opening in a vertebral arch. Prenatal influence is also manifested in the size of white areas on the coat of the young in a piebald strain of guinea pigs, the areas becoming larger with increasing age of the mother.

Vertebrae in Mice.   Mice normally have either twenty-six or twenty-seven presacral—that is, thoracic and lumbar—vertebrae. Significantly more mice from young mothers have twenty-seven vertebrae than do mice from older mothers. Russell has carried out experiments which, although not concerned directly with the age of the mother, show that differences in number of vertebrae can be the result of differences in uterine environment, which does, of course, vary with age. These experiments with mice will be described in detail in order to make clear what the problems are if one tries to understand how the physiological condition of a human mother can influence the phenotype of her child.

Russell worked with two strains of mice in which the percentage of animals having five rather than six lumbar vertebrae varied greatly. In strain C57-black only 1.4 per cent, but in strain C3H 96.9 per cent, had five lumbar vertebrae. In crosses between these strains, the frequency of those with five was only about half as high when the mother was C57-black and the father C3H as when the mother was C3H and the father C57-black (Table 46).

TABLE 46.   *Percentage Frequency, in Two Strains, of Mice with Five Lumbar Vertebrae, and in the Offspring of Reciprocal Crosses.* (After Russell and Green, *Genetics*, **28**, 1943.)

	Per Cent with 5 Lumbar Vertebrae		
Type of Mice from:	Female	Male and Female	Male
C57 black		1.4	
C3H		96.9	
C57 black ♀ × C3H ♂	24.1		33.4
C3H ♀ × C57 black ♂	45.8		68.1

Such a difference in reciprocal crosses, in which the genetic constitution of the hybrids should be alike, could be due to any one of four factors. It is possible, first, that the cytoplasm in each strain contains different self-reproducing properties—similar in this respect to the genes in the nucleus—which lead to different kinds of cytoplasm in the eggs. Second, it could be that the cytoplasm of the eggs is different, not because it was derived from different kinds of maternal cytoplasm, but, rather, because it was built up in the ovaries of the mothers under the influence of different genes in the cells of the ovaries—those in the C57-black or those in the C3H strain (maternal prefertilization influence). A third possibility is that genes of the mother in cells outside the ovaries could influence the cytoplasm of the eggs while they grow in the ovaries (another type of maternal prefertilization influence). And the fourth possibility is that the difference in number of vertebrae is the result of the uterine environment in which the hybrid embryos develop —an environment which may vary in the two types of mothers (maternal postfertilization influence).

A test eliminated the hypothesis of self-reproducing cytoplasmic differences. If they existed, hybrid daughters of C57-black mothers should form eggs with the cytoplasm characteristic of the C57-black strain, and hybrid daughters of C3H mothers should form eggs with the cytoplasm characteristic of the C3H strain. Therefore, the offspring from the two types of hybrid daughters should again differ in mean number of vertebrae. This, however, proved not to be the case: The daughters from reciprocal crosses had progeny with the same mean number of vertebrae.

In order to determine whether genes in the mother's ovarian cells affected the egg cytoplasm, ovaries from a strain, "129," with high mean numbers of lumbar vertebrae were transplanted into females of a strain, "L," with low numbers whose own ovaries had been removed.

The "L" females with "129" ovaries were then mated to "129" males, so that young with the "129" genotype developed in the uteri of "L" mothers. In another experimental group, young with the "129" genotype were raised in "129" mothers, either as a result of mating "129" males to unoperated "129" females, or to "129" females whose ovaries had been removed and replaced by ovaries from other "129" females. (This latter procedure served as a control to safeguard against the possibility that transplantation itself might be responsible for differences in number of vertebrae; it turned out to have no influence.)

Comparison of young who had developed in "L" females with those who had developed in "129" females showed a significantly lower average of vertebrae in the former group.

Thus it was concluded that the skeletal effect observed in the experiments is caused by a difference either in the influence of the mother's extraovarian genes on the egg cytoplasm or in the uterine environments as furnished by the different mothers.

To decide between these last two alternatives, one more experiment was

TABLE 47. *Effect of the Uterine Environment on Skeletal Morphology in the Mouse.* (After McLaren and Michie, *Nature*, **181**, 1958.)

Cross		No. of Lumbar Vertebrae		
Females	Males	5	5 one side, 6 other side	6
C57BL × C3H		16	11	34
C3H × C57BL		30	11	8
C3H × C57BL*		7	4	19

* Fertilized eggs transferred to C57BL uteri.

carried out. Eggs from matings of C3H females (low mean number of lumbar vertebrae) with C57-black males (high number) were transplanted soon after fertilization into the uteri of C57-black "mothers." The young were carried to term and the number of their vertebrae determined. As shown in Table 47, the vertebral frequencies were characteristic of the C57-black strain and not of the C3H strain. This, then, leads to the conclusion that in this instance it is the uterine environment and not gene-dependent properties of the egg cytoplasm that causes the variation. In a similar transplantation experiment with different strains, E. L. and M. C. Green have demonstrated that differences in numbers of vertebrae were only partly caused by uterine differences and that the cytoplasm of the eggs formed in different mothers also exerted a differential effect.

In man, similar differences in the number of vertebrae of specific regions of different individuals are also common. There is evidence for genetic differences causing variability of the vertebral column, as well as of variable manifestation of the genotypes involved. It may well be that part of this nongenetic variability is due to prenatal influences. Obviously, such influences, which vary with the condition of the mother, are not due to inherited self-reproducing properties of the cytoplasm. Such self-reproducing properties, in any case, are not known in most animals, including man (for a possible exception, see p. 440f.). Whenever maternal influences are observed, it should be remembered that they may have a variable basis: namely, pre-fertilization effects exerted during the formation of the cytoplasm of the egg, or postfertilization effects exerted by the action of the uterine environment.

Birth Weight. In crosses between Aberdeen-Angus and Herefordshire cattle, the weights of hybrid calves are similar regardless of which of the two breeds the mother comes from—birth weight depends mainly on the genotype of the fetus. In contrast to this, crosses between the large Shire horses and Shetland ponies yield hybrids whose size is greatly influenced by the breed of the mother. In man, both the mother and the fetal genotype contribute to variability in birth weight. The correlation between the birth weights of identical twins is high, namely, 0.67, and this seems to suggest that it is the identical genotype of the two fetuses that causes them to be so similar in weight. However, since the correlation between weights of genetically unlike nonidentical twins is 0.59, not much lower than that of identicals, it is clear that a large part of the similarity in both types of twins is due to their simultaneous development in the same mother.

Support for this conclusion comes from the observation that infant weight is correlated more highly with height of mothers than of fathers. This difference may persist for some time, but at maturity the correlations between weight of offspring and stature of mothers and fathers has become the same, the genotype of the offspring having overcome the prenatal maternal influence.

The correlation between the birth weights of separately born sibs, 0.50, is lower than that of nonidentical twins in spite of the fact that the genotypes of nonidentical twins are no more similar than those of separate sibs. A comparison of the two correlations suggests that the uterine environment provided the growing fetus by a mother is variable from one pregnancy to another. In order to discover whether this maternal environment also has a constant genetic component, comparisons have been made between the birth weights of first cousins. There was a small, but significant, positive correlation, 0.13, when the mothers of cousins were sisters, but a nonsignificant correlation of only 0.02 when the cousins were offspring of brothers or of brothers and sisters. Thus, the genetic similarity of sisters expressed itself in similarity of prenatal influences on their children—influences that outweighed by far the effect of similarity of the genotypes of the cousins themselves, which is the same regardless which of the parents are sibs.

On the basis of these findings Penrose has attempted a quantitative partition of the causes of the variability of birth weights (Fig. 140). Four kinds

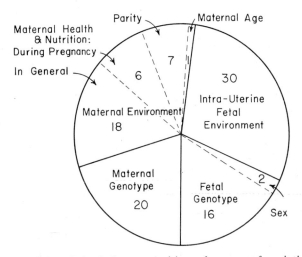

FIG. 140. Birthweight of single born: partition of causes of variation. Numbers indicate partition in per cent. (After Penrose, *Science Progress*, **169**, 1955; and *Proc. 9th Intern. Congr. of Genetics*, 1954.)

of influences can be distinguished: fetal genotype, maternal genotype, maternal environment, and an unanalyzed residue, "intra-uterine fetal environment." Specific items within these four groups are indicated in the figure.

Congenital Defects. It is not surprising that the frequency of congenital malformations is in part related to the physiological state of a mother during pregnancy. Infection of the mother with German measles (rubella) during the first three months of pregnancy may cause destruction or severe defects of the embryo. The rubella virus is capable of crossing the placental barrier between mother and child, and the damage to the embryo is the result of prenatal infection. Similarly, maternal infection with the rare protozoan parasite toxoplasma can cause serious congenital defects of the fetus, and the same has been suspected for Asian influenza. Irradiation of the pelvis of pregnant women with X-rays may impinge on the embryo and lead to malformation. Sugar diabetes in the mother seems to increase the chance for developmental abnormalities of her offspring. Excess of the amniotic fluid surrounding the embryo may also lead to defects, but it is not clear whether the excess is caused by the state of the mother or that of the embryo itself.

Age of the mother is correlated with the frequencies of certain kinds of congenitally abnormal children. In a study of congenital malformations that lead to early death, Murphy found a continuous rise in the frequency of malformed children, relative to normally developed sibs, as the age of mothers increased from thirty to forty-nine (Fig. 141). In the group of mothers from forty-five to forty-nine, the relative frequency of malformed offspring was more than three times as high as for mothers between fifteen and twenty-nine. Other investigators, who singled out specific abnormalities, found that congenital cardiac disease and some developmental abnormalities of the nervous system, e.g., anencephaly, hydrocephaly, and spina bifida, increase in frequency with age of the mother (Table 48).

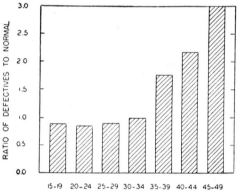

FIG. 141. Sublethal congenital defectives as related to age of mothers. Frequencies are expressed as the ratio of defectives (%) to normals (%) among 2,190 children of 570 mothers with at least one defective child. (Murphy, 1947.) The reality of the relative rise in defectives has been questioned recently.

Harelip, with or without cleft palate, is also slightly more common in children of older mothers. In mice the opposite trend for cleft palate has been observed.

Lenz has pointed out that apparent correlations between age of parents

TABLE 48. *Frequencies of 144 Congenital Abnormalities of the Nervous System in Relation to Age of Mothers.* (The frequencies are expressed relative to the frequency for the youngest age group which is arbitrarily designated as unity.) (Penrose, 1939.)

Maternal Age Group	Abnormalities
16–20	1
21–25	2.7
26–30	2.3
31–35	4.3
36–40	6.0
41–45	10.0
46–50	7.0

and frequency of defective children may disappear when the data are corrected for bias in ascertainment. In the future, a re-evaluation of the findings reported in the preceding paragraphs will be necessary.

The most striking correlation between age of mother and frequency of a defect exists for mongolian idiocy. It is now known that this correlation is not caused by a prenatal interaction but is due to the increased frequency with which chromosomally abnormal eggs are produced in relatively older women (see pp. 472–474).

Some abnormalities are more common in the children of younger mothers. This probably holds for hypospadia, in which the opening of the urethra is shifted from its normal position, and for pyloric stenosis, an obstruction of the opening of the stomach into the intestine.

Maternal Age and Correlated Properties. A correlation of frequency of congenital abnormality with age of mother does not necessarily indicate a causal connection between the two phenomena. Age of mother itself is highly correlated with other variables, such as weight of mother, age of father, occurrence of a first birth (primogeniture), and number of preceding births (birth rank, parity). It is possible, by means of statistical techniques, to unravel the various connections between these variables. Thus, if mothers are divided into groups of similar ages, the relation between the age of the fathers and the frequency of an abnormality in the offspring can be studied. No such studies have shown a significant correlation between the age of the father and the incidence of a specific abnormality, although it is known from census data of the State of New York that the age of the father, independent of that of the mother, is associated with the rate of stillbirths and neonatal mortality (Yerushalmy). The causes of these paternal age effects are obscure.

Similar studies, however, have indicated that parity, and not age alone, plays some role in the origin of the above-mentioned malformations of the nervous system and probably the main role in hypospadia and pyloric stenosis. The incidence of the latter defect per thousand live births in Birmingham,

England, at different birth ranks was found to be: first birth, 4.3; second, 2.8; third, 2.5; and fourth and over, 1.4. Birth rank also seems to be a factor in the frequency of stillbirths, many of which are probably caused by fetal malformations.

Cancer of the chorionic membrane is more frequent in first than later pregnancies, and leukemia in childhood, though not strictly congenital, also has its highest incidence among first-born. In many of these diseases or malformations it is apparent that maternal age itself, after separation from its correlated variables, is an important, and sometimes the only important, causal factor responsible for the statistical correlation between age of mother and frequency of the abnormality.

What specific physiological conditions change with the age of the mother or with other variables and are responsible for changes in the incidence of abnormalities is still to be discovered. One malformation whose incidence depends on maternal variables is an anatomical abnormality of the pregnant uterus. Instead of the embryo being implanted in the posterior part of the uterus, as is normal, the placenta may become attached near the orifice that opens into the vagina (Fig. 142). Such a placenta praevia often results in severe hemorrhage before childbirth. Penrose and Kalmus have shown that the frequency of the so-called central type of placenta praevia is correlated with maternal age and, apart from maternal age, also with parity. In this connection it may be mentioned that the frequency of "spontaneous" cleft lip in a certain strain of mice also depends on the embryo position in the uterus.

In some invertebrates, in rainbow trout, and in frogs, aging of eggs before they are fertilized results in defective development of embryos. Whether this is true in mammals, including man, is not known. Neither is information available on the effect of overripeness of sperm on development.

Independence of Traits from Maternal Physiology.   Many traits are *not* affected by the age of the mother or correlated variables. Feeble-mindedness is one of these. In Table 49, the numbers of feeble-minded children are given separately for the first and second halves of a group of affected sibships. No significant difference between birth order and frequency of the condition is shown.

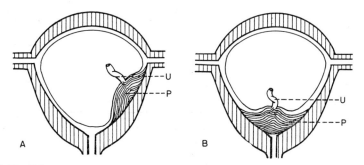

FIG. 142. Diagrammatic longitudinal section through uterus. A. Normally located placenta.   B. Placenta praevia. P = placenta; U = umbilical cord.

TABLE 49. *Feeble-Mindedness (excluding mongolism).* (M. Murphy, 1936.)

Half of Family	Affected*	Normal*
First half	44.5	135.5
Second half	55.5	124.5

* The fraction in the observed results arises from the division of cases occurring in the midposition of families containing an odd number of children.

It must be kept in mind, however, that the interrelations between maternal condition and penetrance or expression of traits are complex and that various maternal influences may partly cancel each other. Absence of an obvious correlation between the phenotypes of the offspring and known maternal variables cannot, therefore, prove absence of correlation between phenotypes of offspring and the physiological condition of the mother. The unexpected fact that, in mice, maternal influences are responsible for the number of lumbar vertebrae in the offspring suggests that prenatal influences of the uterine environment are, perhaps, of greater significance in the expression of traits, within their normal range of variability, than hitherto suspected.

On the other hand, one must also be careful in one's interpretation of correlations. Thus, it has been established that the intelligence of individuals, as expressed by performance in intelligence tests, is slightly, but significantly, correlated with month of conception: On the average, children conceived in winter score slightly higher than children conceived in summer. This was interpreted by some as signifying that the environmental influence of the seasons on the mother affected the developing fetus, but Roberts disproved this. When the scores of children conceived in winter are compared with those of their *sibs* who were conceived in summer the difference found in the general population disappears.

The lack of correlation between season of conception and intelligence score in children from the *same* parents seems to indicate that season of conception has no influence on intelligence score. Consequently, the presence of a correlation in comparisons of children from the general population probably signifies the existence of slight differences in the seasonal distribution of conceptions in different families. In families whose children have high scores, a higher proportion of conceptions occur in winter than in families whose children have low scores. Here is an opportunity for speculation: What biological or sociological factors might be responsible for this correlation?

The Causes of Prenatal Effects.   Most of the abnormalities discussed run in families. Although the incidence of more than one case of a given abnormality in a sibship is low, it is considerably higher than expected by chance, and the appearance of a trait or some symptoms of it in relatives other than sibs is also relatively high.

Increased incidence of congenital malformations within certain families is, by itself, no proof of genetic predisposition, since it is also possible that environmental circumstances prevalent in such families or acquired physiologic conditions of the mother may be responsible. In experimental animals such as rats, mice, guinea pigs, rabbits, and pigs, severe "insults" to the pregnant females may cause various kinds of defects in the embryos. Warkany first showed that a critical deficiency of vitamin A in pregnant female rats may lead to congenital abnormalities of the eyes, lungs, and other organs in their offspring. Subsequently, he and other investigators were able to produce specific skeletal defects, such as cleft palate, or specific defects in the central nervous system, such as spina bifida or hydrocephaly, by a variety of agents, including vitamin deficiencies, reduced atmospheric pressure with an attendant decrease in oxygen, and injections of hormones and of various chemical substances. Many of the defects produced by experimental interference with embryonic development are also known to be caused under normal conditions by abnormal genes. The artificially induced malformations are thus phenocopies.

In most of these animal experiments the treatments applied are so drastic that they will rarely or never be encountered by pregnant women. Nevertheless, it is possible that less intense deficiencies in vitamins or oxygen, or other disturbances that affect the maternal physiology, which may take place in times of famine or war or in other unfavorable social circumstances, may interfere with normal fetal development. It has even been found that when vitamin supplements were added to the diet of pregnant women from poor families, their children had intelligence quotients several points higher, on the average, than those in a control group whose mothers received no dietary supplement. But the interpretation of this correlation as a cause-effect sequence is not proven.

The opinion has been expressed that some congenital malformations can be produced by severe emotional disturbance of the mother, particularly during the earlier months of pregnancy. Stress, as well as physical agents, is likely to result in increased secretion of the hormone cortisone, and experiments with pregnant mice have shown that injection of heavy doses of this substance will produce cleft palate in the embryos. It is possible that stress plays a role in the origin of human malformations, but the necessary critical analyses are still to be made.

The genotypes of both mother and fetus may influence the degree to which external prenatal influences lead to the occurrence of abnormal phenotypes. This has been shown by the results of some animal experiments. Ingalls and his collaborators subjected five different strains of mice to reduced atmospheric pressure equivalent to that at an altitude of 29,000 feet—the height of Mount Everest. Among the malformations studied were those of the sternum (Fig. 143). From 0 to 29 per cent of unexposed controls of the five strains showed deviations from a standard type of sternum. Reduced atmospheric pressure for five hours on the ninth day of pregnancy caused from more than 20 to more than 70 per cent deviations from the norm. These

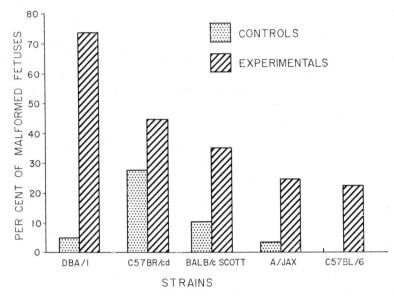

FIG. 143. Frequencies of minor malformations of the sternum in five genetically different strains of mice. The experiments consisted of exposure to low atmospheric pressure. (After Ingalls, Avis, Curley and Temin, *J. Hered.,* **44,** 1953.)

figures show that the five strains differed in the spontaneous incidence of deviations as well as in the frequency of induced variants. Moreover, strain DBA, which had the highest frequency of induced variants, had a lower frequency of spontaneous ones than did some of the other strains.

Deeper insight into the prenatal interaction of mother and child is provided by another series of experiments on mice, in which a heavy dose of cortisone was injected into female mice of three different genotypes, pregnant with young of a variety of genotypes (Table 50). The same hormone treatment caused 100 per cent of the embryos of strain A to develop with cleft palate but only 17 per cent of the embryos of strain B. When A mothers

TABLE 50. *Inheritance of Susceptibility to Induction of Cleft Palate in the Young of Pregnant Mice Treated with Cortisone.* (A = strain A/Jax., B = strain C57BL/6 Jax.) (After Fraser, Kalter, and others. See Fraser.)

Mother	Young	Treatment	Cleft Palate (%)
A	A	—	0
A	A	+	100
B	B	—	0
B	B	+	17
A	A × B	+	43
B	A × B	+	4

pregnant with A × B hybrid young were injected with cortisone, 43 per cent of the offspring had cleft palate while only 4 per cent of the same A × B young in B mothers were affected. The much greater frequency of the defect in A young from A mothers than in A × B young from A mothers shows the influence of the embryo's genotype; the greater frequency of the defect in A × B young from A mothers than in young of the same genotype from B mothers shows the influence of the mother's genotype.

Two final examples of prenatal interaction resulting in congenital malformations are not concerned with specific external treatment, but with the interaction of the genotypes of mother and embryos in producing abnormalities during an undisturbed pregnancy. A certain highly inbred strain of mice contains two types of individuals, one normal (*fu fu*) and the other heterozygous for an incompletely penetrant dominant gene, *Fu,* which causes abnormalities of the skeleton of the tail and other parts of the vertebral column. Embryos heterozygous for *Fu* carried by two different types of mothers have been studied, and the frequencies of fused vertebrae were determined as follows:

in *fu fu* mothers,   65 per cent
in *Fu fu* mothers,   34 per cent

Clearly, the genotypes of both mother and child are involved in the production of the defect. Without the *Fu* allele the offspring is normal, but the penetrance of the *Fu* allele when present depends on the genotype of the mother. If she carries *Fu* she produces fewer affected offspring than if she herself is genotypically normal. Results like these suggest that even external influences so slight as to escape notice may lead to malformed offspring if particularly sensitive genotypes are involved.

It seems peculiar that the abnormal *Fu fu* constitution of mothers tends to act beneficially rather than harmfully on the developmental processes of her young. A somewhat related interaction between mother and fetus has been found by Hollander and Gowen. It concerns the recessive allele *hl* (hair-loss) in the mouse. Nothing unusual happens in matings of homozygous recessive hair-loss mice inter se, nor in matings of homozygous *hl hl* males with normal females. But in matings of *hl hl* females with heterozygous normal males, the expected 1:1 segregation is changed to roughly 2 hair-loss : 1 normal by differential mortality. Deaths occur principally at birth and during the first two weeks of age, the non-hair-loss young showing variably inferior growth with fragility of bones. When *hl hl* females are mated with homozygous normal males, all the young are affected. The physiologic nature of the antagonism between hair-loss mothers and normal-hair offspring may be related to their calcium metabolism. Apparently this antagonism is not immunological in nature (in contrast to such antagonisms described in the following section). It is interesting that the normal-hair progeny and not the abnormal progeny are at a disadvantage.

In experimental work it is often easier to cause the appearance of abnormalities than to hinder their development. Undoubtedly, however, it will be

CH)

possible to work out methods by which animals with genotypes usually highly penetrant in leading to congenital malformations can be treated in order to suppress defective development. The successful application of such prenatal therapy to human mothers of children with possibly unfavorable genotypes will prevent a great deal of human suffering. In addition, general public-health measures—better nutrition, lowered incidence of certain diseases, and others—may help to reduce the frequency of congenital malformations due to prenatal influences of environmental agents on the manifestation of those ill-defined genotypes that have a tendency to produce defects.

Immunogenetic Prenatal Interactions

In general, the genetic causes of abnormal embryonic development reside in either the mother or child alone, but delicate prenatal interactions whose existence is difficult to prove may sometimes influence the expression of incompletely penetrant genotypes. In addition, however, an important group of rather well-understood prenatal interactions has been discovered that result from a genetically determined immunological incompatibility between mother and child and may lead to disease or death of the offspring.

Rh Incompatibility.   The best-known interaction of this kind, which was the first to be discovered, depends on a difference between the genotypes which determine the Rh blood groups. Soon after the discovery of the Rh factor, Levine recognized that it was involved in the occurrence of hemolytic disease of the newborn, or erythroblastosis fetalis, that consists of an anemia due to hemolysis (breakdown of the blood) in the child and consequently results in jaundice. One aspect of the disease, which has given it its name, is the presence of immature red blood cells, the erythroblasts, in the blood stream. Normally, these immature cells are found only in the bone marrow and other organs, not in the circulating blood. Frequently, fetal erythroblastosis leads to stillbirth or neonatal death, but a child who recovers is usually completely healthy thereafter.

The disease was known to have a familial occurrence, but in spite of various attempts to formulate a genetic interpretation, the hereditary mechanism remained unknown until the Rh antigen was found and its mode of inheritance determined. Levine then noticed that more than 90 per cent of erythroblastotic children were Rh positive—that is, had blood containing the antigen—and had Rh-negative mothers. He concluded that the blood cells of the Rh-positive newborn were hemolyzed by an antibody provided by the Rh-negative mother, and was able to show that such an antibody existed in the serum of Rh-negative mothers who were, or had been, pregnant with Rh-positive offspring. It was lacking in most Rh-negative women who had never been pregnant or had only nonaffected children: the few such women who had the antibody had received repeated blood transfusions, some of them many years earlier.

This led to the following explanation of the origin of erythroblastosis (Fig. 144). Normally, human blood does not contain specific antibodies against the Rh antigen, but the antibodies may be produced in Rh-negative persons by repeated transfusions with Rh-positive blood. This iso-immunization, the production of antibodies in the same species (here, man) from which the antigen comes, is comparable to the experimental production of antibodies in rabbits or other animals by injection of blood from different species. When an Rh-negative woman carries an Rh-positive fetus, the Rh antigen from the latter may penetrate the placenta, enter the blood of the mother, and cause the production of an antibody. This antibody does not harm the blood cells

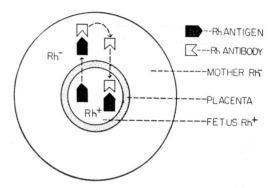

FIG. 144. Diagram of the course of events leading to erythroblastosis fetalis of an Rh-positive embryo in an Rh-negative mother.

of the Rh-negative mother, since they lack the antigen. When, however, the antibody finds its way through the placenta to the Rh-positive fetus, an immunological reaction between the antibody and the red blood cells of the fetus takes place, resulting in erythroblastosis fetalis.

In the inverse case—that of an Rh-positive mother carrying an Rh-negative child—iso-immunization does not occur. The antibody-forming mechanism of a child does not mature until about six months after birth, and the fetus is therefore unable to produce antibodies against the antigens in its mother's blood.

Because Rh-positive erythroblastotic children from Rh-negative mothers trace their R allele to their fathers, the fathers of affected children are Rh positive. The frequency of erythroblastosis fetalis among all pregnancies is determined by the frequency of the R allele in the population. The frequency of the R allele (p) and that of the r allele (q) can be determined by the use of the Hardy-Weinberg Law. Since Rh-negative individuals are $r\ r$, their frequency is q^2, and the allele frequency of r is equal to the square root of the frequency of Rh-negative individuals. In a white population, this frequency is close to 16 per cent (0.16), so that q = 0.4 and p = 0.6. From this, it follows that the frequency of homozygous $R\ R$ individuals is 36 per cent (p^2) and that of heterozygotes $R\ r$, is 48 per cent ($2 \cdot p \cdot q$).

Rh-positive pregnancies in Rh-negative women result from two kinds of marriages: $r\ r$ (females) $\times R\ R$ (males), and $r\ r$ (females) $\times R\ r$ (males). And the frequencies of these marriages are $p^2 \times q^2 = 5.76$ per cent, and $q^2 \times 2pq = 7.68$ per cent. In the first, all pregnancies result in production of an Rh-positive fetus, but only one-half of the children in the latter type of marriage are Rh positive. Thus, the frequency of all potentially unfavorable pregnancies in the population is $5.76 + 3.84 = 9.60$ per cent, or about one-tenth of all pregnancies.

The incidence of the disease is very much lower than the incidence of potentially unfavorable pregnancies. It is estimated to occur once in from 200 to 500 pregnancies in white populations: that is, only in from 1 out of 20 to 1 out of 50 of all potential cases. The reasons for this fortunately low occurrence will be discussed at the end of the present chapter.

If the disease has occurred during one pregnancy, it recurs, often more severely, in every succeeding pregnancy in which the genotype of the fetus is the unfavorable $R\ r$. This means that if the father is homozygous $R\ R$, all succeeding pregnancies lead to illness of the child. If, on the other hand, he is heterozygous $R\ r$, there is a $1:1$ chance that the child will be healthy.

The practical consequences of the immunological and genetic understanding of erythroblastosis are great. Immunologically, it is clear that Rh-negative females should not be given transfusions of Rh-positive blood before the end of their reproductive period, since they may build up antibodies which may react with an Rh-positive fetus in a subsequent pregnancy, and that newly born children with serious cases of erythroblastosis should be given transfusions primarily to replace the affected red blood cells. In extreme cases, in order not only to replace the affected cells but also to remove the antibodies derived from the mother, all of the child's blood should be replaced with blood from Rh-negative donors.

Genetically, determination of the Rh constitution of prospective parents permits a prediction regarding the possible occurrence of erythroblastosis in the offspring. (Some selected cases in which such genetic prediction is desirable are given in the problems at the end of this chapter.)

In many hospitals, it is routine procedure to test a pregnant woman for the presence or absence of the Rh antigen. If she is Rh positive, no special precautions are required. If she is Rh negative, the husband is tested. If he is also Rh negative there is no problem; but even if he is Rh positive, the chances that the child will be healthy are very high, since erythroblastosis, as we have seen, occurs in only a small fraction of Rh-positive pregnancies in Rh-negative mothers.

It was shown in an earlier chapter that many different R alleles exist in human populations (see pp. 195–197). Erythroblastosis fetalis may occur whenever the fetus carries an R allele which produces antigens not present in the mother. The terms Rh positive and Rh negative do not take into account the great diversity of antigenic constitutions. Although the majority of children with erythroblastosis are the result of presence of the antigen Rh_0 (D) in the child and its absence in the mother, the disease may also be produced by presence of any one of the other Rh antigens in the child—rh′ (C), rh″ (E), or even hr′ (c) and hr″ (e)—and its absence in the mother. Thus, a family has been reported in which an Rh-positive mother had an affected child. Examination showed the presence of antigens Rh_0, rh′, and rh″ in the child and of Rh$_0$ and rh′ in the mother. Accordingly, it was suspected that the rh″ antigen was responsible for the disease, and this hypothesis was proven correct by finding antibodies against rh″ in the mother's blood.

ABO Incompatibility.   Occasionally, erythroblastosis fetalis results from incompatibility between mother and child for blood-group antigens other than the Rh antigens. The disease has occurred in Kell combinations as well as in $L^{M,N,S,s}$ and some of the "private" family blood groups.

Of particular interest are the results of incompatibilities involving the ABO blood groups. Although rare, erythroblastosis fetalis has been observed in A and B children from O mothers, and in other combinations in which the child forms an A or B antigen that is not present in the mother herself. Such mothers normally carry anti-A or anti-B isoantibodies in their blood. These antibodies occur in two forms: one does not penetrate the placenta in appreciable amounts and therefore does not harm the fetus; the other easily passes the placental barriers and may lead to a mild form of hemolytic disease. Very rarely, the concentration of these antibodies becomes so high that enough diffuses into the child's blood to cause serious damage.

Much more important than the very uncommon erythroblastosis of the late fetus or newborn from ABO incompatibility is an embryologically earlier ABO interaction between mother and child. From an antigenic point of view, one can distinguish between "compatible" and "incompatible" marriages. The former are those in which the husband cannot transmit an I^A or I^B allele to his children which they could not also get from the wife; the latter are those in which the husband can transmit an I^A or I^B allele which is not present in the wife. Examples of compatible marriages are A ♀ × O ♂, A ♀ × A ♂, and AB ♀ × O or A or B or AB ♂; of incompatible marriages, O ♀ × A or B or AB ♂, A ♀ × B ♂, and B ♀ × AB ♂. In compatible marriages the mother's blood will contain only those anti-A or anti-B antibodies for which her children lack the corresponding antigens; in incompatible marriages children may be produced whose antigens can be attacked by the mother's antibodies. It has been observed that spontaneous abortion before the sixth month of pregnancy is significantly lower in compatible than in incompatible marriages. Thus, in Japan, 90 out of 763 pregnancies from A mothers and O father (compatible matings), or 11.8 per cent, terminated prematurely; whereas relatively many more, namely, 97 out of 568 pregnancies from O mothers and A fathers (incompatible matings), or 17.1 per cent, had a like outcome. That the higher rate of abortion was partly due to mother-child incompatibility may be deduced from the percentages of live-born O and A children in each of the two reciprocal matings (Table 51). The proportions of the two types of children from A mothers corresponded closely to expectation as derived from the calculated frequencies of homozygous $I^A I^A$ and heterozygous $I^A I^O$ fathers in the population. In contrast, the O mothers bore a significantly lower proportion of A children. Similar data signify that incompatibility for B antigens also leads to an appreciable number of abortions.

TABLE 51. *Number of O and A Children from Compatible and Incompatible O × A Matings.* (Matsunaga, *Am. J. Human Genet.,* **7**, 1955.)

Mother	Father	No. of O Children		No. of A Children	
		Obs.	Exp.	Obs.	Exp.
A	O	282	284.5	430	427.5
O	A	320	275.3	369	413.7

Further evidence which indicates that some early abortions may be due to ABO incompatibility comes from data on nonidentical twins. Such twins are more frequently in the same ABO groups—particularly in group O—than expected by chance. This unexpected degree of similarity could be brought about by selective survival if both twins were compatible with the mother and by death before birth of a twin who was incompatible. It is also conceivable that incompatibility between the twins rather than between one twin and the mother may result in the death of one of them.

Rh and ABO Incompatibilities.   ABO incompatibility between mother and child does not always have undesirable effects: on the contrary, the effects are generally beneficial. This surprising state of affairs arises from an interaction of Rh and ABO incompatibility. We have seen earlier that only a fraction of the potentially incompatible Rh combinations of mother and child results in erythroblastosis. One of the reasons for this low incidence is clearly connected with the fact that it takes at least one Rh-positive pregnancy of an Rh-negative mother to build up enough antibodies to lead to hemolytic disease in the next Rh-positive child. Additional reasons which have been suggested are possible differences between one woman and another or among embryos, in placental permeability to antigens, and differences in the ability of mothers to produce antibodies. The main reason for the low incidence of Rh-dependent erythroblastosis, however, is that ABO incompatibility between an Rh-negative mother and an Rh-positive child greatly diminishes the probability of Rh hemolytic disease. Levine noted this early in his studies, and others confirmed his findings. To take two extreme examples: Rh hemolytic disease occurs very rarely in the offspring of the ABO-incompatible mating of an O mother and an AB father; but in the ABO-compatible mating of an AB mother and an O father the second child may be affected. According to Levine, the explanation for this protection of Rh-incompatible fetuses by ABO incompatibility lies in the fate of the child's red blood cells if and when they reach the mother's blood stream. It is assumed that the passage of antigens from fetus to mother is due to regular passing of some whole red blood cells through minor breaks in the placental barrier. Rh-positive cells of the fetus that are ABO-incompatible with the mother will be destroyed by the normally present anti-A or anti-B antibodies of the mother before they are able to stimulate the production of anti-Rh antibodies in her blood. If, however, the Rh-positive blood cells that pass into the mother are ABO compatible, they will survive and stimulate the formation of anti-Rh antibodies. A statistical analysis based on considerations of allele frequencies has shown that this explanation accounts well for the detailed frequencies of Rh hemolytic disease in the various types of ABO marriage combinations.

The prenatal interactions discussed in this chapter were recognized by their bad effects. It may not be amiss to remind ourselves that the majority of pregnancies result in children with perfect health and that this happy result is due to the beneficial multiple interactions of the two partners involved in gestation, mother and child.

Problems

136. In a sample of 228 children affected with cleft palate or harelip, the incidence was 40 per cent in first-born, 27 per cent in second-born, 19 per cent in third-born, and 14 per cent in later-born. (a) What do these figures indicate concerning the relationship between birth order and defect? (b) What bearing on the preceding question has the information that, in a comparable sample of 15,000 children in the general population, the distributions according to birth order were 38.1, 32.6, 15.1, and 14.2 per cent, respectively?

In Problems 137–141, assume the existence of two alleles only, R and r.

137. A baby girl affected with erythroblastosis fetalis recovers and reaches adulthood. Her fiancé was the last child born healthy in a family in which several later children died from erythroblastosis. Discuss the prospects for healthy or affected children in the proposed marriage.

138. Of a couple's three children, the third was erythroblastotic at birth. The couple asks for advice regarding the prognosis of a future child. Questioning discloses that a younger sister of the husband died from erythroblastosis as a baby. Which advice is the sounder: (a) No more healthy children to be expected? (b) A chance of 50 per cent for healthy children?

139. In a certain population, 4 per cent of all people are Rh-negative. What is the frequency of marriages in which erythroblastosis may occur among the offspring?

140. All Chinese, but only about 91 per cent of Negroes, are Rh-positive. (a) What frequency of erythroblastosis fetalis is to be expected in each group separately if k, the fraction of actually affected among the potentially affected, is 0.05? (b) After intermarriage of equal numbers of Chinese and Negroes and many generations of random mating, what proportion of Rh-positive and Rh-negative individuals are to be expected? (c) What frequency of erythroblastosis is to be expected in the mixed population (k = 0.05)?

141. If statistics were available from the preceding century on the ratio of erythroblastotic (but not necessarily lethal) children to normal children in sibships in which this disease occurred, and regarding the ratio of albino to normal children in sibships in which albinism occurred, it would probably be found that the proportion of the erythroblastotic children has decreased in this century, while that of albinism has increased? Why would this be true?

References

Anderson, R. C., and Reed, S. C., 1954. The likelihood of recurrence of congenital malformations. *Lancet* (Minn.), **74:** 175–176.

Badtke, G., Degenhardt, K. H., and Lund, O. E., 1959. Tierexperimenteller Beitrag zur Ätiologie und Phänogenese kraniofacialer Dysplasien. *Zeitschr. F. Anat. u. Entwcklungsgesch.*, **121:** 71–102.

Böök, J. A., Fraccaro, M., Hagert, C. G., and Lindsten, J., 1958. Congenital malformations in children of mothers aged 42 and over. *Nature,* **181:** 1545–1546.

Cawley, R. H., McKeown, T., and Record, R. G., 1954. Parental stature and birth weight. *Am. J. Human Genet.*, **6:** 448–456.

Conference on Parental Age and Characteristics of the Offspring. 1954. *Ann. New York Ac. Sci.,* **57:** 451–614.

Fraser, F. C., 1955. Thoughts on the etiology of clefts of the palate and lip. *Acta Genet. Stat. Med.*, **5:** 358–369.

Grebe, H., 1954. Gene und Phänokopien in der Ätiologie menschlicher Missbildungen. *Acta Genet. Med. Gemel.,* **3:** 197–209.

Harell, R. F., Woodyard, E., and Gares, A. I., 1955. The effect of mothers' diets on the intelligence of offspring. Bureau of Publ. Teachers College, Columbia University, New York.

Hollander, W. F., and Gowen, J. W., 1959. A single-gene antagonism between mother and fetus in the mouse. *Proc. Soc. Exp. Biol. Med.,* **101:** 425–428.

Kalmus, H., 1947. The incidence of placenta praevia and antepartum haemorrhage according to maternal age and parity. *Ann. Eugen.,* **13:** 283–290.

Kalter, H., and Warkany, J., 1959. Experimental production of congenital malformations in mammals by metabolic procedure. *Physiol. Rev.,* **39:** 69–115.

Lenz, W., 1959. Der Einfluss des Alters der Eltern und der Geburtennummer auf angeborene pathologische Zustände beim Kind. *Acta Genet. Stat. Med.,* **9:** 169–201.

Levine, P., 1946. The present status of the Rh factor. Ward Burdick Lecture. *Am. J. Clin. Pathol.,* **16:** 597–620.

———, 1958. The influence of the ABO system on Rh hemolytic disease. *Hum. Biol.,* **30:** 14–28.

Levine, P., Burnham, L., Katzin, E. M., and Vogel, P., 1941. The role of isoimmunization in the pathogenesis of erythroblastosis fetalis. *Am. J. Obstetr. Gynecol.,* **42:** 925–937.

McKeown, T., MacMahon, B., and Record, R. G., 1951. The incidence of congenital pyloric stenosis related to birth rank and maternal age. *Ann. Eugen.,* **16:** 249–259.

Murakami, U., 1955. Experimental embryologic and pathologic study on malformation of the central nervous system. *Acta Pathologica Japonica,* **5** Suppl.: 495–513.

Murphy, D. P., 1947. *Congenital Malformations.* 2nd ed. 127 pp. Lippincott, Philadelphia.

———, 1956. The obstetrician and congenital malformations in brothers and sisters. *Eugen. Quart.,* **3:** 161–163.

Murphy, M., 1936. The birth order of mongol and other feeble-minded children. *Hum. Biol.,* **8:** 256–266.

Neel, J. V., 1958. A study of major congenital defects in Japanese infants. *Am. J. Human Genet.,* **10:** 398–445.

Penrose, L. S., 1939. Maternal age, order of birth and developmental abnormalities. *J. Mental Sci.,* **85:** 1141–1150.

————, 1946. Familial data on 144 cases of anencephaly, spina bifida and congenital hydrocephaly. *Ann. Eugen.,* **13:** 73–98.

Roberts, J. A. Fraser, 1944. Intelligence and season of conception. *Brit. Med. J.,* **1:** 320–322.

Russell, W. L., 1948. Maternal influence on number of lumbar vertebrae in mice raised from transplanted ovaries. *Genetics,* **33:** 627–628.

Warkany, J. (Ed.), 1957. Congenital malformations. Conference on Teratology, *Pediatrics* **19,2:** 719–792.

CHAPTER 18

POLYGENIC
INHERITANCE

Mendel's discovery of segregating alleles accounted immediately for the sharply defined segregation of phenotypes in single factor inheritance. The occurrence, in a population and in individual sibships, of albinos and pigmented persons or of brachydactylous and normal individuals, was readily explained by the existence of two different alleles. However, a large number of traits that are known to be inherited do not manifest themselves as sharply defined pairs of phenotypes. Normal body height, for instance, covers a wide range. Measurements of height in a population show a continuous gradation, and even sibs vary in size from their parents, as well as among themselves. Other examples of such "quantitative" characters are found among traits that can be classified according to a numerical scale: longevity, degree of resistance to diseases, age of onset of disease, score in mental tests, degree of hair pigmentation, amount of skin pigment in negro-white hybrids, basal metabolism, rate of heart beat, level of vascular tension, and dimension of any particular bodily structure, such as length of finger or weight of thyroid gland.

Undoubtedly, some of the variability of these characters is due to a response of the genotypes to differences in the external or internal environment. If, for instance, there were three genotypes for body height, A^1A^1, A^1A^2, and A^2A^2, which in identical environments determined the development of three phenotypes, short, medium, and tall, and if each of these genotypes, in different environmental conditions, expressed itself in different phenotypes, then a continuous series of body heights might well be produced. There is, indeed, evidence that the environment influences the expression of body height and many other quantitative characters, although it is not the only agent responsible for the wide array of intergrading phenotypes. Thus, studies of genetically identical twins show that, in general, environmental differences produce differences in body height and other traits that are smaller than differences normally found between genetically nonidentical twins.

Multiple Allelism. It may be suggested that the genetic component of the continuous variability of quantitative characters is multiple allelism at a single locus responsible for the variability. But although it may be true that part of the hereditary variability of quantitative traits in a population is due to the existence of genotypes A^1A^1, A^1A^2, A^1A^3, A^2A^3, etc., all of which determine a different degree of phenotypic expression, multiple allelism cannot explain the wide range of variation.

This may be shown by considering the variability of a trait within a single sibship. Two parents can supply, at a single locus, no more than four different alleles, as in the marriage $A^1A^2 \times A^3A^4$. Among the children of such parents, the maximum number of genotypes based on multiple alleles at one locus that may appear is thus four—namely, A^1A^3, A^1A^4, A^2A^3, and A^2A^4. Observations of such traits as height or hair color in large families show that, more than four different degrees of genetically determined phenotypes often occur.

Polygenic Inheritance. A satisfactory genetic interpretation of the inheritance of quantitatively graded characters was first suggested by Mendel. In addition to his famous experiments with peas, he reported on a cross between white and purple-red flowering beans. The hybrids had flowers with less intense coloration than the purple-red parent. In the second generation, Mendel obtained a whole series of different colors—from white through pale violet to purple-red—instead of the expected two types in the simple 3:1 ratio discovered in other experiments. His tentative explanation was that *more than one pair* of genes was involved in the observed variation of color. This hypothesis of *multifactor, or polygenic, inheritance* was later proven to be correct by Nilsson-Ehle in an analysis of a graded series of seed pigmentation in wheat crosses.

Differences in Pigmentation Between Negroes and Whites

We shall describe the theory of polygenic inheritance as it was first applied to a case of human genetics by Gertrude and Charles B. Davenport in 1910 and 1913. These investigators were interested in the inheritance of differences in skin color and, since the normal differences between members of the Caucasian race are relatively slight, they collected data on negro-white crosses, primarily in Bermuda and Jamaica where intermarriages between negroes and whites were relatively common and the number of illegitimate births, which would obscure the records, relatively low.

There was considerable variation in skin pigmentation both within white groups without negro ancestry and negro groups without white ancestry, and a very great variation among those of mixed ancestry. The Davenports devised an objective classification of the different degrees of pigmentation by

TABLE 52. *Classification of Skin Color According to Davenport.*

Black Area (%)	Color Class	Designation of Skin Color
0–11	0	White
12–25	1	Light mulatto
26–40	2	Mulatto
41–55	3	Dark mulatto
56–78	4	Negro

means of a "color top," which is a rotating circular disc on which different sectors bear different colors. By varying the size of these sectors and rotating the disc so rapidly that the eye blends the different colors into one, it was possible to match any skin pigmentation. Thus, a certain dark skin was matched by a top which had a black sector covering 75 per cent of its surface, the rest consisting of 13 per cent red, 2 per cent yellow, and 10 per cent white; a specific white skin was matched by 5 per cent black, 34 per cent red, 15 per cent yellow, and 46 per cent white.

In classifying the array of pigmentation found in the population investigated as expressed by the percentage of black on a color top, the investigators were able to distinguish five different classes of skin color (Table 52).

Genetic Interpretation. The first-generation hybrids, the typical mulattoes, showed considerable variability in pigmentation, with the majority falling into Class 2 (Table 53). The two individuals in Class 1 were almost dark enough and the five individuals in Class 3 almost light enough to be in Class 2. This variability was probably due to the minor genetic factors which cause the observed variations within the original races—for instance, the light skin of many Northern Europeans in contrast to the dark skin of many Mediterranean whites, or the yellow-brown of Africans from the Sudan in contrast to the black of those from Liberia.

A simple single locus interpretation of the skin color of the first generation would assign the genotype A^1A^1 to the white parents, A^2A^2 to the negroes, and A^1A^2 to the hybrids. If this were correct, marriages between hybrids $A^1A^2 \times A^1A^2$ should segregate into $1/4$ A^1A^1 (white), $1/2$ A^1A^2 (mu-

TABLE 53. *Pigmentation of White–Negro Hybrids.* (Davenport.)

Color Class	First-generation Hybrids	Offspring of Two First-generation Hybrids
0	—	3
1	2	10
2	22	13
3	5	5
4	—	1

latto), and $1/4$ A^2A^2 (negro). The actual distribution was different. Marriages between first-generation hybrids produce offspring who were distributed over the whole range of pigmentation (Table 53). In the small number of sibships available for study, a few children were as light as typical whites (Class 0), one as dark as a typical negro (Class 4), many were "light mulattoes" (Class 1), many "dark mulattoes" (Class 3), and the largest group typical mulattoes (Class 2). It is clear that a single locus interpretation does not explain the manifold color types.

A more satisfactory hypothesis is based on the assumption that skin color is controlled by two independent loci, each with one or the other of two alleles, A^1 and A^2 at one locus and B^1 and B^2 at the other. According to this hypothesis, whites are $A^1A^1B^1B^1$, and negroes $A^2A^2B^2B^2$. The darker pigmentation of negroes is considered to be due to *additive* action of the A^2 and B^2 alleles, and it is assumed that substitution of A^2 or B^2 for A^1 or B^1 leads to equal increases in pigmentation. The amount of pigment produced by A^2 in A^1A^2 heterozygotes is assumed to be intermediate between that in A^1A^1 and A^2A^2 homozygotes, and the same holds true for B^2.

First-generation mulattoes are $A^1A^2B^1B^2$. Their intermediate phenotype is the result of the presence of one of each of the A^2 and B^2 alleles which makes the individuals darker than whites, who have neither of these alleles, and lighter than negroes, who have two of each. When first-generation mulattoes produce gametes, independent assortment will lead to the formation of four different kinds—A^1B^1, A^2B^1, A^1B^2, and A^2B^2—containing either none, one, or two alleles for increased pigmentation. The children of two mulattoes will have from zero to four such alleles and thus fall into five different pigmentation classes:

		$A^1A^1B^2B^2$		
	$A^1A^1B^1B^2$	$A^1A^2B^1B^2$	$A^1A^2B^2B^2$	
$A^1A^1B^1B^1$	$A^1A^2B^1B^1$	$A^2A^2B^1B^1$	$A^2A^2B^1B^2$	$A^2A^2B^2B^2$
Class 0	Class 1	Class 2	Class 3	Class 4

The two-locus hypothesis thus accounts, qualitatively, for the appearance of all five classes in the offspring of two mulattoes. It implies, further, that typical mulattoes may have any one of three different genotypes, and both light and dark mulattoes either of two different genotypes. Consequently, marriages of light, typical, or dark mulattoes may produce various numbers and proportions of pigmentation types in the offspring. For example, a marriage of two typical mulattoes, both of whom are $A^2A^2B^1B^1$, will result in children who are all phenotypically and genotypically like their parents; a marriage between two typical mulattoes, one of whom is $A^2A^2B^1B^1$ and the other $A^1A^2B^1B^2$ with A^2B^1 gametes produced by one parent and A^1B^1, A^2B^1, A^1B^2, and A^2B^2 by the other, leads to three types of offspring—light mulatto ($A^1A^2B^1B^1$), typical mulatto ($A^2A^2B^1B^1$, $A^1A^2B^1B^2$), and dark mulatto ($A^2A^2B^1B^2$)—in the proportion $1:2:1$.

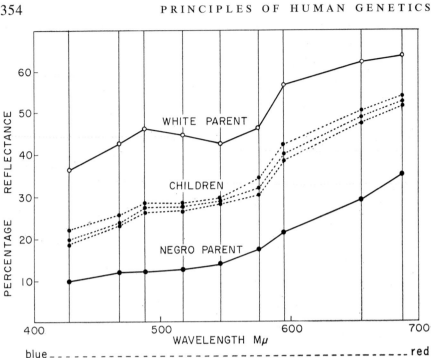

Fig. 145. The reflectance curves for lights of different wavelengths between 400 and 700 Ångstroms for a white ♀ × negro ♂ family. (After Harrison, *Eugen. Rev.*, **49**, 1957.)

Davenport concluded that his data on the proportions of pigmentation types of offspring from various types of parents showed that observation and expectation according to his theory agreed reasonably well. Later workers have pointed out discrepancies which require expansion of the simple two-locus theory to one involving a greater number of loci. For example, the original division of color types into five classes was artificial; actually, there is a continuous distribution. This is clear not only from the color-top studies but also from modern reflectance spectrophotometry, which measures the amount of melanin pigment in the skin by the amount of light reflected from it at different wave lengths (Fig. 145). Harrison and Owen, who have applied this method to the skin of a group of white Englishwomen, their West African Negro husbands, their hybrid children, and their as-yet-few grandchildren, found that the skin color of the Africans varied much more than that of the whites. Very likely, the genes that modify pigmentation have a better chance of phenotypic expression if a large amount of melanin is present than if only a little melanin occurs. The color of first-generation mulattoes varied considerably even in the same sibship. This is evidence for segregation of modifying genes—particularly, perhaps, those from the white parents. It may be added that, on the average, the pigmentation of the mulattoes was somewhat closer to that of the white than to that of the negro parents.

Even refined determinations of the relative amounts of melanin in the skin of different individuals and groups do not provide data from which the exact type of inheritance of skin color can be deduced. It is, however, possible to proceed in the opposite direction. One can formulate hypotheses on the number of gene pairs involved, on whether the different pairs have equal or unequal effects on pigmentation, on whether the phenotypes of the heterozygotes for each pair are intermediate between those of the homozygotes or whether they are closer to one or the other homozygous phenotype, and on whether the effects of the different genes on the amount of melanin formed are simply additive or more complicated. Expectations from any specific hypothesis can then be compared with observations.

One series of such comparisons makes use of a large sample of the American Negro population for which older pigmentation measurements based on the color top were available. The frequency distribution (Fig. 146) shows that the percentage of black in the color tops varied from less than 25 to more than 90, with the largest group comprising individuals with about 80 per cent black. It is known that the American Negro group is a

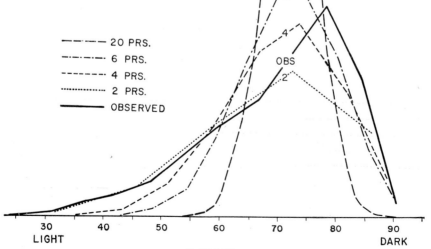

FIG. 146. Skin pigmentation, frequency of observed (by Herskovitz) and expected distributions, based on models for additively acting 2, 4, 6, and 20 loci. The percentage of black was obtained from color-top readings corrected to include the black contribution of the "red" sector of the color top. (After Stern, *Acta Genet. Stat. Med.,* **4,** 1953.)

── ─ ── 20 PRS.

─·─·─·· 6 PRS.

─ ─ ─ ─ 4 PRS.

············ 2 PRS.

──────── OBSERVED

30   40   50   60   70   80   90
LIGHT   DARK

% BLACK

hybrid population which has derived approximately 70 per cent of its genes from African and approximately 30 per cent from Caucasian ancestors. One may assume, in deliberate oversimplification, that random mating occurs and equilibrium has been reached. Under these circumstances Davenport's hypothesis of two pairs of genes with additive properties implies that this population contains A^2 and B^2 alleles, each with a frequency (p_N) of 0.7, and A^1 and B^1 alleles, each with a frequency (q_W) of 0.3. Therefore the frequency of individuals with all four color alleles from African ancestors would be $(0.7)^4 = 0.2401$, that of those with all four color alleles from Caucasian ancestors $(0.3)^4 = 0.0081$; and the frequencies of the individuals with 3, 2, or 1 allele from one side and the other 1, 2, or 3 from the other would be obtained from the appropriate terms of the binomial $(0.7 \, N + 0.3 \, W)^4$ (see Chap. 9). When the calculated frequencies of all five different types are plotted and the five points connected (Fig. 146), it is seen that there is good agreement in the lower range of color intensities between observation and the expectation derived from the two-locus model. At the higher intensities the two curves deviate considerably.

Better over-all agreement between fact and theoretical expectation is reached on the basis of hypotheses that assume that more than two gene pairs of equal and additive nature control color differences between African and Caucasian. The best agreements are obtained for four, five, and six pairs (Fig. 146). Models with still higher numbers of pairs again lead to expectations which deviate greatly from observation, as shown for 20 pairs.

With a model of five equal and additive pairs, the color genotypes of Caucasians and Africans would be $A^1A^1B^1B^1C^1C^1D^1D^1E^1E^1$ and $A^2A^2B^2B^2-C^2C^2D^2D^2E^2E^2$, respectively, and the American Negro population would be composed of $3^5 = 243$ different color genotypes, containing from zero to ten "dark" alleles and thus forming eleven pigmentation phenotypes. The relatively satisfactory, but by no means adequate, fit of the five-pair curve with that derived from color-top measurements should not be taken as conclusive support for a five-pair hypothesis, although the poor agreement of the models with very low or very high numbers of pairs seems to indicate that they should be rejected. This applies also to a three-pair theory, proposed by Gates, in which the effect of the pairs is unequal.

Pigmentation of Offspring from Segregants. According to the two-locus hypothesis, white-skinned segregants in later generations of a negro-white union are genetically $A^1A^1B^1B^1$, just like a Caucasian of unmixed ancestry. In fact, on any hypothesis not assuming dominance, white-skinned segregants should be of the same color genotype as their white forebears. Consequently, neither a marriage between a white segregant and a pure white or between two white segregants should give rise to darkly pigmented children. This expectation is fulfilled as far as our knowledge goes in spite of the popular belief that "black" children may be born to "white" parents one or both of whom had segregated out in the offspring of a past negro-white cross. The belief may, perhaps, be based on marriages between two light mulattoes who may be nearly white-skinned and yet produce children darker than themselves. In marriages of a "near-white" person of negro-white ancestry to a white, no child should be darker than the near-white parent, apart perhaps, from some effect of minor modifying alleles. But, since the genetic basis of skin-color differences is not established beyond doubt, it would be unscientific to deny the possibility that, in marriages of whites and near-whites, children somewhat darker than their near-white parent could be produced.

It is most improbable, however, that "black" or even very dark children can issue from such unions, and it can be stated with certainty that, up to the present, no well-established case of this nature has been reported. On the contrary, the few alleged instances which it has been possible to investigate either turned out to be based on hearsay and not on fact, or were, apparently, due to illegitimacy involving a darkly pigmented parent.

The genetic basis of other physical traits that differentiate the whites and negroes is independent from that of pigmentation, and it is possible that some genotypes which underlie negro phenotypes can be reconstituted among the offspring of two negro-white segregants in whom these traits do not appear. If this should occur together with pigmentation that is some-what increased but still within the normal range of variation, it may serve to make an observer aware of an individual's negro ancestry when skin color alone would not have done so. By themselves, traits other than color are seldom used in social discrimination, for custom has selected as an index the rather meaningless but easily noticed property, "amount of skin pigment."

Pigmentation after Random Mating. It is illuminating to consider what kind of a population would result from complete intermarriage of whites and negroes after genetic equilibrium had been established. If the frequency of the African alleles in the white group is close to zero and in the negro group 0.7, and if the negroes make up one-tenth of the whole population, then the frequency of African alleles in the population is $q_N = 0.07$ and that of the Caucasian alleles $p_W = 0.93$. If we assume the validity of the five-locus model, the frequencies at equilibrium of the eleven color types with from zero to ten African alleles are obtained from the binomial $(0.93 \text{ W} + 0.07 \text{ N})^{10}$. The calculations show that 48.4 per cent of the population will have only white genes, 36.4 per cent nine white genes, 12.3

TABLE 54. *Frequencies, in per cent, of the Eleven Types of Color Segregants Expected from a Model of Five Pairs of Equally Additive Loci in a Panmictic Population Consisting of $p_w = 0.93$ of Caucasian and $q_N = 0.07$ of African Alleles, at Equilibrium. (Stern, Acta Genet. et Stat. Med., 1953.)*

No. of African Alleles										
0	1	2	3	4	5	6	7	8	9	10
48.4	36.4	12.3	2.5	3×10^{-1}	3×10^{-2}	2×10^{-3}	8×10^{-5}	2×10^{-6}	4×10^{-7}	3×10^{-10}

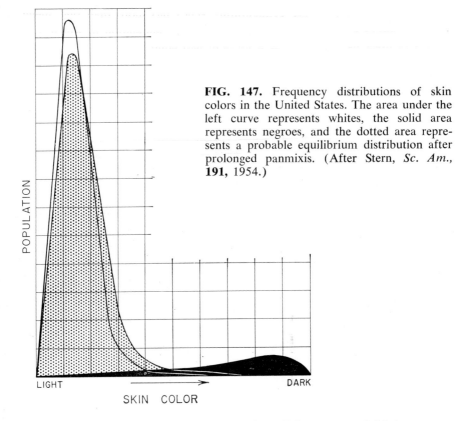

FIG. 147. Frequency distributions of skin colors in the United States. The area under the left curve represents whites, the solid area represents negroes, and the dotted area represents a probable equilibrium distribution after prolonged panmixis. (After Stern, *Sc. Am.*, **191,** 1954.)

per cent eight, and 2.5 per cent seven. These light types total 99.4 per cent, the remaining 0.6 per cent being composed of seven types with from four to ten genes derived from Africans (Table 54). A diagram (Fig. 147) of the approximate distribution of color types in the large white and the small negro segment of the present American population and the distribution that would exist at equilibrium after panmixis shows that the average skin color would be only slightly darker and that very few deeply pigmented individuals would appear in each generation.

There is no quantitative trait in man for which a truly well-founded *specific* hypothesis of polygenic inheritance has been proposed: that is, no hypothesis that adequately defines the number of factors involved, their individual effects in heterozygous and homozygous state, and their joint effects in combination with one another. In spite of this lack of specific information, the theory of polygenic inheritance of quantitative traits is supported by much detailed evidence from experimental organisms, as well as being a logical extension of simpler genetic concepts. Complex traits such as growth, as reflected in adult body height, or mental development, as measured in psychological tests, are the result of the collaboration of numerous physiological and psychological processes, each of which is under the control of one or several pairs of genic loci. If any of the collaborating genes has more than one allelic form, variations in the genetic composition of the population in which they are found must be expressed in a more-or-less continuous series of graded phenotypes.

Frequency Distribution in Polygenic Inheritance.   Not only do quantitative characters extend over a scale of measurable values, but many have a charac-

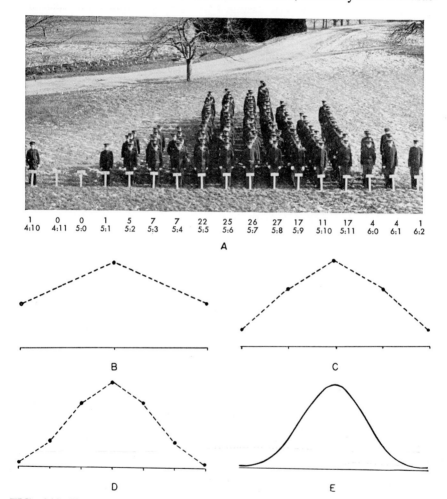

FIG. 148. Frequency distributions of phenotypes in polygenic inheritance.   A. Company of 175 soldiers arranged in groups according to height, from 4 feet 10 inches to 6 feet 2 inches. The lower row of numbers indicates the height of the groups, the upper row the number of men in the groups.   B. One pair of alleles: distribution over three phenotypes.   C. Two pairs of alleles: distribution over five phenotypes.   D. Three pairs of alleles: distribution over seven phenotypes. E. An infinite number of pairs of alleles: distribution over a continuous array of phenotypes. For details of underlying assumptions, see text. (A, Blakeslee, *J. Hered.*, **5**, 1914.)

teristic frequency distribution in which the largest group of individuals lies close to the mean measure of the range; and the greater the deviation from the mean, the smaller the groups become (Fig. 148, A). This distribution is represented graphically by the so-called normal curve. It will be shown, in the following pages, that although the polygenic theory can account for this distribution, the same distribution may also be produced by action of the environment, or by combinations of genetic and environmental agents.

In this discussion, it will be assumed that a trait is enhanced if the allele A^2 is substituted for the allele A^1, or if the alleles B^2, C^2, etc., are substituted for B^1, C^1, etc., at any given loci. It will be assumed, further, that the alleles are equal in effect, cumulative in action, and all of equal frequency in the population ($p_{A^1, B^1, C^1}, \ldots = q_{A^2, B^2, C^2}, \ldots = 0.5$). An individual may have none, one, two, or any possible higher number of "enhancing" alleles; each number results in a different phenotype as measured on a scale for the trait.

If only one locus is considered, an individual may have none, one, or two enhancing (E) and two, one, or none nonenhancing (e) alleles, respectively. The frequencies of the three combinations, derived from the binomial $(1/2\,E + 1/2\,e)^2$, are in the ratio 1:2:1 (Fig. 148, B).

If two loci are considered, the probabilities for zero, one, two, three, or four enhancing alleles are derived from $(1/2\,E + 1/2\,e)^4$, which gives the ratio 1:4:6:4:1 (Fig. 148, C). With three loci, the formula is $(1/2\,E + 1/2\,e)^6$ and seven classes are expected, in the ratio 1:6:15:20:15:6:1 (Fig. 148, D).

All these distributions have one common feature: the largest number of individuals is found in the mean class, with a symmetrical decrease in frequency toward plus or minus deviation from the mean. With each increase in the number of loci considered, the number of classes increases, and the phenotypic differences between them decrease, so that each succesive series consists of phenotypes that grade more and more closely into each other. The frequencies of the numerous classes follow a mathematical extension of the binomial ratios listed above to an extension which, for an infinite number of loci, would give a perfect "normal" distribution (Fig. 148, E).

Frequency Distributions in Environmental Variability.

If a trait were controlled by the same genotype in all individuals, all variations in a quantitative measure of the trait in a population would be caused by variations in the environment. If the environment varied in only two alternative ways— for example, in the presence or absence of a specific factor—two phenotypic classes would exist: an enhanced phenotype if the factor were present; a nonenhanced phenotype if it were not. If presence and absence of the factor during the development of an individual were of equal likelihood, the two phenotypic classes would be equally common. With two such factors, and assuming identical and cumulative enhancing action, three phenotypic classes would be found, according to whether neither, one or the other, or both factors were present, and the frequencies of these classes would follow the ratio 1:2:1. Thus, if one of the factors in a plant's environment were fertilizer and the other good sunlight, both of which could be either present or absent, then one-quarter of the plants would not have either favorable agent, one-half lack one or the other, and one-quarter would have both.

With four different factors, five phenotypic classes, produced by the impact of zero, one, two, three, or four enhancing actions, would exist in the ratio 1:4:6:4:1. The greater the number of environmental factors concerned in phenotypic variability, the more nearly would distribution approach "normal."

It is thus clear that the same frequency distribution of graded phenotypes may be produced by environmental factors as by genetic agents. In reality, quantitative traits such as growth or psychological-test scores depend on both genetic and environmental entities; and the existence of a normal frequency distribution of phenotypes is often the result of the variability of both influences.

Dominance in Polygenic Inheritance

If the effects of alleles at different loci are not equal and cumulative, skewed frequency distributions, instead of the symmetrical normal distribution, will usually result. The same is true if dominance is involved in the expression of alleles at one or more loci.

In agricultural genetics, much attention has been paid to the analysis of quantitative variation of characters, such as the length of ears of corn or the body weight of fowls, and special statistical methods have been worked out to derive information from first- and second-generation data and those from crosses of hybrids to the parental types. The complexity of the interaction of many loci, each with at least two alleles, and of environmental variability, raises difficulties even in controlled experimental organisms. It is not surprising that our insight into the interactions that affect man is still more limited. Only a few theoretical situations in which dominance in polygenic inheritance has some interesting consequences will be outlined here.

When two individuals marry or two populations interbreed, and each is homozygous and isogenic for a different genotype controlled by two loci, and there is also complete dominance at each locus, the constitutions of the contrasting individuals or groups are either *AABB* and *aabb,* or *AAbb* and *aaBB.* (We shall assume that each of the dominant genes, *A* and *B,* has an enhancing, additive action, so that *A,* present either homozygously or heterozygously, makes the measurement of the trait 10 units greater than in *aa,* and that *B* acts similarly in relation to *bb.* With an index of measurement of 100 for *aabb,* the index is then 110 for *AAbb* and *aaBB,* and 120 for *AABB.*)

The cross *AABB* × *aabb* yields *AaBb* offspring whose index, 120, is like that of the "higher" parent, and, in later generations, segregation will produce all three possible phenotypes: 100, 110, 120. The cross *AAbb* × *aaBB,* in which the parents have equal indexes, namely 110, produces *AaBb* children, whose index, 120, is greater than that of their parents! Again, in later generations, segregation leads to all three phenotypes: 100 (that is, less than either original ancestor), 110, and 120. To use a slightly different example, let both A and B again be dominant and additive, but of different action, so that A leads to enhancement by 10 units and B by 5 units. In this case, the parental phenotypes of the cross $AAbb \times aaBB$ have indexes of 110 and 105, respectively, and the offspring $AaBb$ an index of 115, again higher than either parent. This phenomenon—the stronger expression of a trait in certain polygenic heterozygotes than in their parental polygenic homozygotes—is at least partly the basis for "hybrid vigor." We shall return to it in the chapter on race mixture.

Polygenic Inheritance of Alternative Traits

Although polygenic inheritance was first discovered in continuously variable traits, it is not confined to them. There are stages in the development of many organs and structures where growth and differentiation may take one of several alternative paths. Either a limb bud forms the normal number of digits, too many, or too few; either the lateral parts of the embryonic face grow together and form a typical upper lip and palate, or the fusion is incomplete and results in harelip and cleft palate. For some traits, the choice of alternatives may be determined by the presence of a specific allele at a single locus; but for others, a polygenic system governs the developmental decision.

This was first demonstrated by Sewall Wright, who cross-bred two strains of guinea pigs, one of which was normal, with three toes on the hind feet, the other polydactylous, with four toes. First-generation hybrids were three-toed, and the second generation segregated into 3 three-toed individuals to 1 four-toed. This would seem to show simple single factor inheritance in which the allele for three toes was dominant over that for four toes. But this interpretation was not supported by further tests of the second-generation segregants. It became clear that approximately 4 pairs of additively acting genes differed in the two original strains, so that each strain had 8 alleles that controlled the number of toes. A minimum number of "four-toe" alleles —about 5, Wright deduced—was necessary to direct development of poly-dactyly (Fig. 149). The first-generation hybrids were nearly all three-toed, since they obtained only 4 "four-toe" alleles. In the second generation, segregation should lead to a series of nine types having from 0 to 8 "four-toe" alleles. Most with less than 5 of these alleles and some with 5 or more (variable penetrance could account for these) would be three-toed, but the great majority of those with 5, 6, 7, or 8 "four-toe" alleles would develop four toes.

Quasi-continuous Traits. The alternative appearance or nonappearance of a trait may be less sharp than assumed above. Thus, the fourth toe of a polydactylous guinea pig may be either a well-developed digit or a "poor"

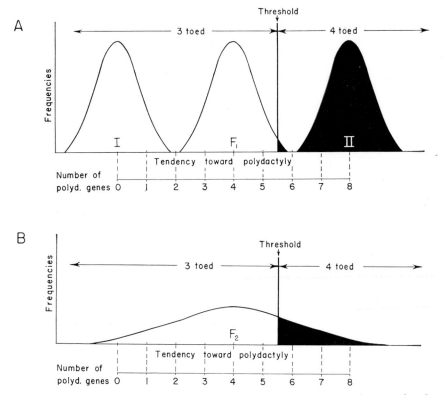

FIG. 149. Genetic and developmental aspects of polygenic inheritance of poly-dactyly in guinea pigs. A. Strain I possesses no allele for polydactyly, Strain II possesses eight alleles (four pairs). The F_1 individuals have four such alleles. Ani-mals with any one of the three genotypes vary in their tendency toward polydac-tylism (see curves), but only those with tendencies beyond the threshold form extra toes. It is assumed that a small fraction of F_1 animals would cross the thresh-old. B. The overlap of the nine segregated genotypes in the F_2 generation gives a continuous distribution of the tendency toward polydactylism. Approximately one-fourth cross the threshold and form extra toes. (After Wright, 1934.)

toe, the latter being characteristic of animals who have only the critical number of 5, or perhaps 4 or 6, "four-toe" alleles. Grüneberg has studied inheritance of variations in the size of the third molar tooth in mice. Vari-ability is continuous over a range from normal to small, and some mice have no third molars. A polygenic system determines both size and, at a certain threshold, presence or absence of the tooth.

In man, singing voice may be classed as a quasi-continuous trait. Although we are used to distinguishing a few voice types such as tenor, baritone, and bass in men, there is actually a continuous gradation from one type to another. Polygenic determination of singing voice is suggested not only by family and population data but also by the fact that type of singing voice depends on variable physiological and psychological properties and on ana-

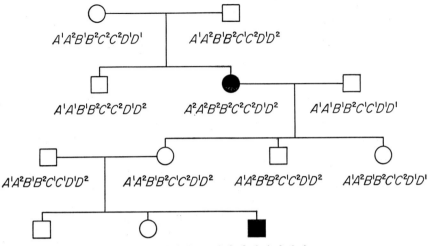

FIG. 150. Hypothetical pedigree showing the appearance of a rare defect caused by the presence of at least seven additive alleles. A^1, B^1, C^1, D^1 do not lead toward development of the abnormality, but A^2, B^2, C^2, D^2 do.

tomical details of the chest, breathing musculature, lungs, and trachea, of the cartilaginous and bony parts of the larynx, its muscles, cords, and mucous membranes, as well as on variations in lips, tongue, palate, throat, and nasal chamber. Each of these parts is under the influence of genetic variables which constitute a polygenic system affecting singing voice.

Polygenic Traits and Defects in Man. There is, as yet, no conclusive proof of polygenic determination of alternative development in man, but evidence from other organisms indicates that many human traits must be so determined. It could account for the appearance of many traits, particularly abnormalities, that seem to have a genetic basis but that do not occur in any regular sequence of generations or in clear-cut ratios. If, for example, a rare defect develops only when an individual has at least seven additive, potentially defect-causing alleles out of eight possible from four pairs, the parents of an affected child might each have four such alleles (Fig. 150). These parents would thus be normal in phenotype and might well have had normal parents themselves. The child with the rare abnormality will be likely to marry an individual with none or few of the defect-causing alleles, and thus produce offspring who, although they may carry several such genes, have less than seven, and are consequently normal. But if some of these offspring marry persons who are phenotypically normal but also carry several of the defect-causing genes, affected children may again appear in the pedigree. Among other traits that are probably polygenically determined are resistance to various infectious diseases or liability to organic weaknesses: although both may be continuously variable, it is likely that the decision be-

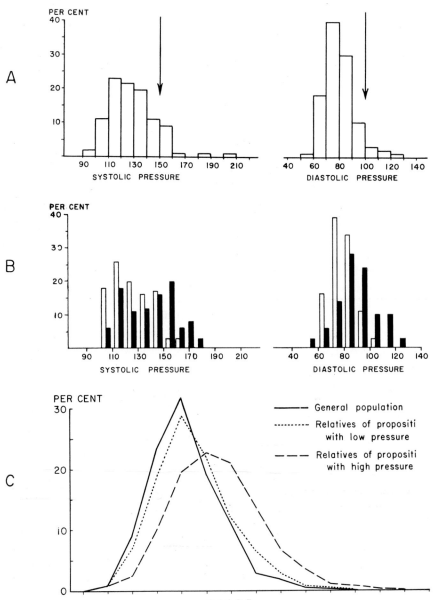

FIG. 151. Arterial blood pressures.   A. Sample of 227 women, 30–39 years old. The arrows point to the pressures often used to separate groups with normal and high blood pressure.   B. Forty-six female relatives of propositi with low pressures ("controls," light columns) as compared with 41 female relatives of propositi with high pressures ("hypertensives," dark columns); ages 30–39 years.   C. Frequency distributions of diastolic pressures for 867 persons from the general population, 371 relatives of "controls," and 1,062 relatives of hypertensives; males and females, 10–79 years old. Since different age groups as well as both sexes have different mean pressures, the curves are adjusted for age and sex. (After Hamilton, Pickering, Roberts, and Sowry, *Clinical Science,* **13,** 1954.)

tween the alternatives "healthy" and "ill" is controlled by the presence or absence of a critical number of specific alleles.

Some distinctions between normal and affected are rather artificial. This has been emphasized by Pickering in a study of high blood pressure. In many earlier studies, this condition was attributed to a single dominant gene that produced "essential hypertension" (high pressure without a specific known cause); normal blood pressure was produced by its recessive allele. In these older studies the propositi were patients with high pressure, and their relatives were classified according to the alternative phenotypes: affected and nonaffected. The validity of this classification was questioned by Pickering and his colleagues. Measurement of the arterial blood pressure of individuals in a given population shows a continuous distribution of both systolic and diastolic pressures—not a separate group with high pressures and another with low (Fig. 151, A). To divide a population into two groups, calling those with pressures below a certain figure "normal" and above "hypertensive," is a somewhat arbitrary procedure. By choosing an appropriate figure, it is possible to make almost any data fit a preconceived 1:1 ratio of normal to affected and, if there is some evidence of genetic control of blood pressure, to conclude that a dominant gene is involved. In reality, the blood pressures of close relatives of propositi (parents, sibs, and children) that are above the often-used dividing line 150/100 (systolic/diastolic pressure in mm mercury) range nearly as widely as the pressures of relatives of propositi that are below the line (Fig. 151, B). Although this excludes simple single locus interpretation, inheritance does seem to be involved, since the mean blood pressure of relatives of propositi with high pressures is significantly higher than that of relatives of propositi with low pressures (Fig. 151, C). This suggests polygenic inheritance.

There are all gradations of the control of traits, from those whose phenotype is altered by alternative alleles at a single locus to those which require allelic substitutions at many loci. The expression of a "major locus" may be dependent on minor modifying loci, or a number of loci with unequal or equal effectiveness may have to collaborate to produce a given phenotype. The control of penetrance and expressivity of a gene by the genetic background (pp. 308ff.) is only a special case of polygenic determination in general. It is therefore possible to revert to the interpretation of blood-pressure genetics in terms of a single pair of alleles, if one admits the existence of modifying loci and, in addition, of environmentally conditioned variability.

Useful as are the terms "major" and "minor" in describing the influence of different genes on specific traits, it must be remembered that the primary action of all genes is of a chemical nature, and that chemical compounds and reactions are not classified as major or minor. From this point of view, the concept of polygenic inheritance must be looked on as a statistical one which is an important tool in the analysis of variability, but which at a different level of analysis may be reinterpreted in terms of individual genic action. In the future, detailed studies of the biochemistry of polygenic traits should lead to the recognition of the individual, qualitatively different, single-locus-controlled reactions whose compound effect is now measured on a single quantitative scale. Thus, one locus among the many governing blood pressure may be found to control properties of the kidneys; another locus, those of the adrenal glands; a third, those of fat metabolism; and so on. Such a separation of polygenic assemblies into their individual components may well reveal a partial justification for the earlier assumption that a dominant allele is responsible for high blood pressure. More important, the recognition of separate components can form the basis for specific controls of abnormal phenotypes.

In this chapter, it has been shown that the concept of polygenic inheritance provides insight into the causes of variability of numerous human traits—variability that cannot be explained in terms of individual genic loci. In later chapters, particularly when dealing with heredity and environment, we shall find that there is evidence for genetic control of many traits for which it is not possible to give a specific genetic formula. Polygenic inheritance can explain both the heritability of these traits and the absence of knowledge regarding the action of the individual loci involved.

Problems

142. Assume the correctness of Davenport's 2 gene pair theory of skin color inheritance. What are the types and proportions of colors among the offspring of the following marriages:

(a) First generation mulatto × negro?   (c) Light mulatto × negro?
(b) White segregant × white?   (d) Light mulatto × dark mulatto?

(e) Assign all possible genotypes to the marriages whose partners have the following phenotypes: white × light mulatto; light mulatto × light mulatto; mulatto × mulatto. (f) What phenotypes, and in what proportions, are expected among the offspring of the marriages listed in Part e?

143. Assume the existence of five additive gene pairs responsible for the white-negro difference in pigmentation. A random-mating population originated from intermarriages of a white and a negro population whose sizes were in the proportion of 2:1. What proportion of people with skin color of whites and with that of negroes is to be expected?

144. In the preceding question, if the two groups had been in the ratio 99:1, what would the answers have been?

145. Assume that *aabbcc* leads to 150 cm height and that any "capital letter" allele will "add" 5 cm to the initial height. (a) List all genotypes of individuals of size 165 cm. (b) If only people of 165 cm height married, list the genotypes of all possible combinations of spouses. (For Parts c and d, assume that each marriage type, Part b, consisting of several nonrelated families, is restricted to a single community.) (c) Give the range of adult size among the children in each community. (d) What would be the shortest adult height possible among the grandchildren in each community? The tallest?

146. Assume that a defect is caused by the additive action of three pairs of loci. All individuals with three or more normal genes are not affected, one-half of those with two normal genes and all with only one or no normal gene are defective. (a) Each of two parents has the genotype $A^1A^2B^1B^2C^1C^2$, where $A^1B^1C^1$ are the normal genes. List the genotypes and frequencies of all possible children. What is the probability of their having a defective child? (b) If the normal and defect-causing alleles at each locus are equally common in a population, what is the frequency of the defect? (c) If the normal genes have a frequency $p = 0.9$, what is the frequency of the defect?

References

Barnes, I., 1929. The inheritance of pigmentation in the American Negro. *Hum. Biol.,* **1:** 321–381.

Blakeslee, A. F., 1914. Corn and men. *J. Hered.,* **5:** 511–518.

Brues, Alice M., 1946. A genetic analysis of human eye color. *Am. J. Phys. Anthrop.,* **4**n.s: 1–36.

Davenport, C. B., 1913. Heredity of skin color in negro-white crosses. *Carnegie Inst. Wash. Publ.,* **188:** 106 pp.

Davenport, G. C., and Davenport, C. B., 1910. Heredity of skin pigmentation in man. *Am. Naturalist,* **44:** 641–672.

Gates, R. R., 1953. Studies of interracial crossing. *Internat. Anthrop. and Linguist. Rev.,* **1:** 15–67.

Grüneberg, H., 1951. The genetics of a tooth defect in the mouse. *Proc. Roy. Soc., B.,* **138:** 437–451.

Hamilton, M., Pickering, G. W., Roberts, J. A. Fraser, and Sowry, G. S. C., 1954. The aetiology of essential hypertension. 4. The role of inheritance. *Clinical Sci.,* **13:** 273–304.

Harrison, G. A., 1957. The measurement and inheritance of skin color in man. *Eugen. Rev.,* **49:** 73–76.

Mather, K., 1949. *Biometrical Genetics.* 158 pp. Dover, New York.

Pearl, R., and Pearl, R. D., 1934. *The Ancestry of the Long-lived.* 168 pp. Johns Hopkins University Press, Baltimore.

Wright, S., 1934. The results of crosses between inbred strains of guinea pigs differing in number of digits. *Genetics,* **19:** 537–551.

―――, 1952. The genetics of quantitative variability. In Reeve, E. C. R., and Waddington, C. H. (Eds.). *Quantitative Inheritance.* pp. 5–41. H. M. Stationery Office, London.

CHAPTER 19

CONSANGUINITY

Marriages between relatives—"consanguineous marriages," as they are often called—are important genetically. Since closely related individuals have a higher chance of carrying the same alleles than less closely related individuals, the children from consanguineous marriages are more frequently homozygous for various alleles than are children from other marriages.

In some societies, consanguineous marriages have been encouraged. For example, the ancient Egyptians and the Incas favored marriages of brothers and sisters of the reigning dynasty—"royal blood" being considered worthy only to mix with other "royal blood" (Fig. 152). Although marriages between relatives are still preferred to marriages between unrelated persons in a few societies, customs or laws of most societies discourage or prohibit marriages between close relatives. This restriction is the result, perhaps, of observations on the progeny of consanguineous marriages.

In the United States, all states prohibit marriages between sibs and between parent and child. Most of the states also declare that marriages between a person and his parent's sib—that is, between niece and uncle, or nephew and

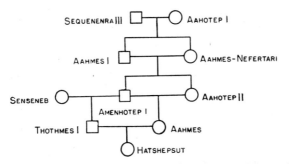

FIG. 152. Marriages between sibs and half-sibs in the Eighteenth Dynasty of Egypt, ca. 1580–1350 B.C. (After Roberts, 1940.)

aunt—are illegal, and marriages between first cousins are prohibited in more than one-third of the states. In some states, even more distant degrees of consanguinity—for instance, the unions of second cousins—are prohibited. In many other parts of the Western world, however, no objection is raised against consanguineous marriages, with the exception of those between sibs and between parent and child. The Catholic church does not permit first-cousin marriages without special dispensation.

It is not uncommon for custom or law also to prohibit marriages between certain classes of healthy individuals who are not related to each other by close common descent. Marriages which have at various times and places fallen under a ban, are those between a person and his step-parent or between a person and his deceased uncle's or aunt's spouse or his deceased wife's sister. Such prohibitions, based either on biological misconceptions or on non-biological grounds, are genetically meaningless. A slightly different example of biologically unjustified discrimination against certain unions was a Chinese regulation which prohibited marriages between first cousins who are the children of two brothers but not between children of a brother and sister or of two sisters. This differentiation was a consequence of the social custom which assigned a woman to the family of her husband and thus regarded children as "not belonging" to the biological family of the mother. On the other hand, the children of two brothers, considered to be of the same family, fell under the ban of consanguinity, although their genetic endowment is parallel to that of children of two sisters or of brother and sister.

It may be useful to define a few of the more common types of close consanguinity. First cousins are the offspring of sibs married to unrelated spouses. Double first cousins come from sibs married to unrelated sibs. Second cousins are the children of first cousins who married unrelated spouses. The terms "first cousins once removed" or "one and a half cousins" apply to the relation between an individual and the offspring of one of his first cousins. Other degrees of consanguinity, such as third cousins or second cousins once removed, specify more distant relationships which can be easily derived from the foregoing examples.

In the civil law, consanguineous relations are defined according to the number of "steps" within a pedigree which lie between two related individuals. First-degree consanguinity is that between parent and offspring; second degree is that between grandparent and grandchild or between sibs. Examples of other consanguineous relations are those between uncle or aunt and nephew and niece (third degree), between first cousins (fourth degree), and between second cousins (sixth degree). The canon law defines consanguineous relations by the number of steps from a common ancestor to only one of the related individuals, namely, the one more remote from him.

The Extent of Consanguinity. Consanguinity and genetic nonrelatedness cannot be sharply distinguished from each other. Undoubtedly, there are many people descended from common ancestors who are unaware of the fact that they are relatives. In most geographical regions, mankind does not reproduce within pedigrees completely isolated from one another but, rather, in a complex network of relationships which joins all, or most, strains together in a single reproductive unit. This is true even in many places where custom or society favors a separateness of population layers, of castes, or of different races inhabiting the same territory. In the course of generations, such barriers against intermarriages prove ineffective, particularly since legitimate and illegitimate unions lead equally to an interchange of genes between officially separate groups. Therefore, a careful tracing of the pedigrees of any group of apparently unrelated individuals of similar territorial origin will show many of them to possess common ancestors within the last few centuries. It follows that if two such "unrelated" people marry, they contract, in reality, a distant consanguineous marriage.

The magnitude of consanguineous unions can also be demonstrated in a different way. If no consanguinity occurred, then the number of ancestors of any one individual would be 2^n, where n represents the number of ancestral steps removed from the individual. The individual would have 2 parents, 4 grandparents, 8 great-grandparents, etc. Going back one thousand years and estimating three to four human generations per century, we find that an individual would have from 2^{30} to 2^{40}, or from approximately one thousand millions to one million millions ancestors. Although we have no reliable data on the number of men alive one thousand years ago, available estimates of the total human population three hundred years ago yield figures of between four hundred and five hundred millions. It may safely be assumed that the population of the world was larger in the seventeenth century than in the tenth century. Thus, a thousand years ago, the whole of humanity comprised only a fraction of the theoretical number of ancestors which every now-living individual should have had, provided no consanguineous marriages had occurred. It follows, obviously, that every individual possesses fewer ancestors than the maximum possible number, 2^n. Such "loss of ancestors" can be due only to consanguineous marriages in past generations. For example, the offspring of a marriage between two first cousins—that is, between the children of sibs—have not 8 but 6 great-grandparents, since 2 of these are common ancestors from both parental sides (Fig. 153).

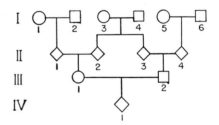

FIG. 153. A pedigree involving a marriage between first cousins.

From the long-range point of view of past evolution, the brotherhood of all mankind is not only a spiritual concept but a genetic reality.

Consanguinity and Homozygosity

What effect do consanguineous unions have in producing offspring homozygous for an allele a? Specifically, what is the frequency with which con-

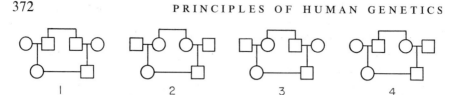

FIG. 154. The four types of first-cousin marriages according to the sex distributions of the parents of the cousins.

sanguineous unions lead to the appearance of homozygous recessive phenotypes? In answering this question, primary consideration will be given to marriages between first cousins. The quantitative treatment of this problem depends only on the mechanism of allelic transmission and thus applies equally well to recessive, intermediate, dominant, or codominant alleles. For the last three types of alleles, the problem is of minor interest. The presence of these alleles in the parents is phenotypically observable, and the consequences of close-relative marriages can be easily derived from the appearance of the parents. When the allele is recessive and thus the phenotypes AA and Aa are indistinguishable, it becomes of great importance to judge the result of consanguinity in terms of the production of aa children.

It is obvious that consanguinity has no genotypic influence on the sex-linked genes of males, since males are hemizygous for sex-linked loci, which they receive solely from their mothers. The popular impression that hemophilia in males of the royal families of Europe was due to "inbreeding" is therefore not valid. It would have existed in these men regardless of whom their mothers had married. For females, an evaluation of the effect of cousin marriages on sex-linked genes requires knowledge of the four possible kinds of cousin marriages as classified according to the sex of those parents of the cousins who are sibs: (1) these sibs may be brothers; (2) they may be sisters; (3) the female cousin's mother may be the sib of the male cousin's father; or (4) the female cousin's father may be the sib of the male cousin's mother (Fig. 154). The frequencies of the four kinds of cousin marriages in actual populations are often strikingly different, types (1) and (3) usually being rarer than (2) and (4).

Cousin Marriages of Heterozygotes. As a first approach, let us over-simplify the problem by assuming an allele a of very low frequency in the population. Let us assume, also, that a person is heterozygous for this allele (Aa) and ask: What is the probability of his or her first cousin being like-wise Aa?

Referring to the diagrammatic pedigree of Figure 153, we may consider III–1 to be the Aa individual and III–2 the cousin whose genotype is to be determined. Since we assume that the frequency of a is very low, we shall disregard the possibility of a entering the pedigree more than once. This reduces our question to the following: What is the probability that III–2 has inherited the a allele from the same ancestor as did III–1? Now, III–1 could have obtained *a* from either one of his parents—from II–1 with a probability of 1/2, or from II–2 with an equal probability. Of these, only II–2 is derived from the common line of descent of the two cousins and thus relevant to our question. If II–2 carries *a*, he must have inherited it from one of his parents, I–3 or I–4, who, in turn, had a 1/2 chance of transmitting *a* to II–3, the parent of cousin III–2. Since II–2 carries *a* with only 1/2 probability, there is only 1/2 probability of either I–3 or I–4 carrying it, and, thus, 1/4 probability of II–3 containing *a*. There is a final step from II–3 to the object of the inquiry, III–2. If II–3 carries *a*, III–2 has 1/2 chance of inheriting *a*; and since II–3 carries *a* with the probability 1/4, III–2 has 1/8 chance of carrying it. Thus, the chance of both cousins being carriers of *a*, when one of them is certain to be a carrier, is 1/8.

The significance of this remarkable fact is perhaps best understood if we compare the 1/8 chance for heterozygosity of the cousin of a heterozygote with the chance for heterozygosity of an unrelated individual. The chance of a heterozygous person marrying at random a spouse heterozygous for the same allele depends on the frequency q of this allele. If it is as rare as, for instance, 1 in 50, the chance of its being present in an individual chosen at random is 2pq, or close to 1/25; or, if the allele is as rare as 1 in 200, the chance of its being present in a random individual is only about 1/100. In both cases, however, the chance of the allele's presence in a first cousin is the same, namely, 1/8. This chance is about three times as great as the random expectation 1/25, and more than twelve times as great as 1/100.

The constancy of the figure 1/8 implies that the *relative* probability of an *Aa* person marrying a cousin who is likewise *Aa* increases with rarity of the allele *a*. That this is so is obvious without recourse to arithmetic: the rarer the allele *a*, the less chance of meeting it in a random partner, in contrast to the fixed chance, determined by the fixed-descent relation, of meeting it in a cousin.

The primary purpose of the question of heterozygosity of two spouses is in determining the expectation of homozygous affected children. This expectation is 1/4 for any one child from two carrier parents. Consequently, the probability of a child, IV–1, being affected is $1/4 \cdot 1/8 = 1/32$ if a heterozygote has married an unaffected first cousin, in contrast to $1/4 \cdot 2pq$ if he married at random a nonaffected person.

Cousin Marriages of Homozygotes.   If the propositus is himself affected, the probability of his first cousin being a carrier is not 1/8, but 1/4. This is so, since a homozygous individual, III–1, derives one of his *a* alleles from II–2 with certainty instead of with a probability of 1/2. Consequently, there is certainty of either I–3 or I–4 carrying *a*, 1/2 chance of II–3 inheriting it, and 1/4 chance of it being transmitted to III–2. This example may serve as a warning against accepting the fraction 1/8 as an invariable expression of the probable presence of a specific allele in a first cousin. Different genetic situations may lead to different values.

Homozygotes from Cousin Marriages. In the preceding treatment of the genetic implications of cousin marriages, we neglected the possibility that an allele a in two cousins may have come from more than one source, except when the propositus is homozygous aa. Following Lenz and Dahlberg, we shall now generalize our question. Instead of assuming that one of the cousins is heterozygous, we will make no specific assumption. Let us ask: What is the probability of aa offspring from marriages of first cousins? Again we refer to Figure 153. The child IV–1, the offspring of the cousin marriage, can be homozygous aa for two different reasons: (1) because of consanguinity, which can bring together two a alleles of common origin; and (2) because of the coming together of two a alleles of independent origin. These two different ways of acquiring an aa genotype will be treated separately.

1. If an a allele is carried by one of the two common ancestors of IV–1, for instance, his great-grandparent I–3, then the probability of it being transmitted to IV–1 overall three steps I–3 $\rightarrow$ II–2 $\rightarrow$ III–1 $\rightarrow$ IV–1 is $(1/2)^3$. Likewise, the probability of the a allele being transmitted over the alternate three steps I–3 $\rightarrow$ II–3 $\rightarrow$ III–2 $\rightarrow$ IV–1 is $(1/2)^3$. The probability of a having descended to IV–1 over both paths is $(1/2)^3 \cdot (1/2)^3 = 1/64$. This, then is the probability of IV–1 being homozygous aa as a result of two a alleles both descended from the same a allele in I–3. The probability value $1/64$ was obtained under the specific assumption that I–3 carried a on one chromosome. Actually, the probability of a, and not A, being carried is given by the allele frequency q, so that the probability of a being carried in I–3 at one locus is q and of it becoming homozygous in IV–1 is $1/64$ q. The same probability $1/64$ q of homozygosity for an a allele of common origin exists if the other chromosome of I–3 had carried an a allele or if either of the two chromosomes of the great-grandparent I–4 had carried it. Therefore, the total probability of homozygosity aa of IV–1 owing to consanguinity is $4 \cdot 1/64$ q $= 1/16$ q. We have thus derived an expression for homozygosity due to the meeting of a alleles of identical origin derived from either one or the other of the four loci in the two common great-grandparents.

2. If $1/16$ q is the probability of any one of the four possible a alleles "meeting itself" in IV–1, then $15/16$ q is the probability of it not doing so. In the latter case, a given a allele can meet either an A allele or an a allele of independent origin (either from another locus of the two common great-grandparents or from any one of the four other great-grandparents). The chance of meeting an a allele of independent origin is q, so that the probability of IV–1 being aa owing to the coming together of different a alleles is $15/16$ q$\cdot$q $= 15/16$ q^2.

Altogether, the probability of aa offspring from a first-cousin marriage is

$$\frac{1}{16}q + \frac{15}{16}q^2 = \frac{q}{16}(1 + 15q). \tag{1}$$

Once more, and in a general way, this formula indicates how much greater is the probability of aa offspring from cousin marriages (more than q/16) than from random marriages (q^2, which takes on a very low value if q is small). It also indicates that the probability of *aa* from the two kinds of marriages decreases at a different rate with decreasing q: for random marriages, the decrease is steep, being proportional to the square of q; for cousin marriages, the decrease is moderate, being proportional primarily only to q itself.

Cousin Marriages among the Parents of Homozygotes.   In a population, individuals of the genotype *aa* are derived from two kinds of marriages, consanguineous and unrelated. The preceding considerations enable us to answer this important question: What proportion of the *aa* individuals in a population comes from cousin marriages? Or, stated differently, how often do *aa* individuals have parents who are first cousins? The answer to this question will obviously depend on the gene frequency q and also on the frequency of cousin marriages in the population. In different populations, cousin marriages take place with frequencies varying between the two possible extremes of nonoccurrence and exclusive occurrence. Although specific data will be quoted later, it should be pointed out now that cousin marriages are expected even in random mating. If an individual may potentially marry any one of 1,000 individuals and if these should include 10 first cousins, then random mating would include cousin marriages with a probability of 10 out of 1,000, that is, 1 per cent. In many Western societies the frequency of cousin marriages is not greatly different from that expected in random mating. We shall first restrict our discussion to this simple expectation.

From equation (1) we found that the probability of *aa* children from cousin marriages is $q/16(1 + 15q)$. If cousin marriages occur in a fraction c of all marriages, then the frequency of *aa* children from cousin marriages is $c \cdot q/16(1 + 15q)$. The frequency of *aa* children from all marriages is q^2. Therefore, the proportion of *aa* children from cousin marriages to *aa* children from all marriages is

$$k = \frac{c \cdot \frac{q}{16}(1 + 15q)}{q^2},$$

which becomes

$$k = \frac{c(1 + 15q)}{16q} = \frac{c}{16q} + \frac{15}{16}c. \tag{2a}$$

This relation, which may be called Dahlberg's formula, tells us how often it can be expected that individuals homozygous for a recessive allele have parents who are first cousins. (Since the second term of the formula is usually small, as compared to the first term, it is sometimes disregarded.) From the complete formula, the factor k, expressed in per cent, has been calculated and listed in Table 55 for a number of different allele frequencies q of *a*, and a number of different possibilities for the frequencies c of cousin marriages in the population at large (for a discussion of the last two columns of the table, see p. 379). Studying the first row of the table, we see that with *a* being as

TABLE 55.   *Proportions,* k, *of Recessive Homozygotes* aa *Deriving from Cousin Marriages.* (q = allele frequencies; c = frequencies of cousin marriages in the population; F = coefficient of inbreeding.) (Partly from Dahlberg, 1947.)

Allele Frequency (q) of a	k *in Per Cent in Panmixis When:*			k *in Per Cent When* c = 1% *and,*	
	c = 0.1%	c = 0.5%	c = 1%	F = 0.0005	F = 0.015
0.001	6.34	31.72	63.44	61.52	32.74
0.01	0.72	3.59	7.19	7.16	6.57
0.1	0.16	0.78	1.56	1.56	1.55

rare as 1 in a 1,000 and c = 0.1 per cent, the proportion of first-cousin marriages among the parents of affected individuals is more than 6.3 per cent. In other words, the parents of *aa* individuals should be first cousins sixty-three times more often (6.3:0.1 = 63) than the parents of individuals taken at random. This striking fact is, of course, an expression of the genetic situation which makes an *aa* individual, in many cases, a signpost for a preceding cousin marriage. Certainly, it does not mean that a carrier of an *a* allele is more inclined to marry a cousin than is a noncarrier. To say it differently, the fact that a person is a carrier will more often remain unknown when he marries a nonrelative than when he marries a cousin.

Moving to the right in line 1 of Table 55, we see, even more dramatically, the same relation of increased frequency of cousin marriages among the parents of *aa* individuals as compared to that of cousin marriages in the general population. Thus, with a frequency of c of 1/2 per cent, more than 30 per cent of the parents of *aa* children should be first cousins. And at a frequency of 1 per cent, 63.4 per cent (or nearly two-thirds) of all *aa* children should have parents who are first cousins.

Following the columns of Table 55 downwards—that is, considering the consequences of increasing gene frequencies—we see that the proportion of cousin marriages among the parents of *aa* children decreases. This is to be expected. The more common the *a* allele, the more frequently will a carrier marry an unrelated carrier, and, therefore, the relatively more rarely will the spouse be a cousin.

The Coefficient of Inbreeding

Dahlberg's formula is based on the assumption that the frequency of cousin marriages in a given population is equal to that expected in a random-mating population. In many populations, however, there are deviations from panmixis. One of the important causes of these deviations is the fact that in some societies or in individual family groups marriages between relatives are preferred to marriages between unrelated persons. This inbreeding increases the frequencies of all degrees of consanguinity. As has been pointed out earlier, a careful tracing of the ancestors of spouses would show that many so-called unrelated unions are consanguineous, but measures of the degree of inbreeding in a population are usually derived from the frequencies of close marriages of relatives, such as uncle-niece and aunt-nephew, first cousins, second cousins, and other similar or intermediate degrees of consanguinity.

Both Wright and Bernstein have devised measures of the degree of inbreeding for individuals and populations. Their coefficients of inbreeding—F and α, respectively—are equivalent. We shall use the symbol F. It may be defined as the probability that an individual is not only homozygous at a given locus, but that the two alleles are "identical" in the sense that they were both derived from an allele present in a certain ancestor. This is obviously possible only if the parents of the individual had the ancestor in common.

When used in measuring inbreeding in populations, F indicates the frequency of homozygotes in a specific population as compared with that in a panmictic population. Being a measure of probability, F values vary between 0 and 1. Thus, F = 0 signifies absence of inbreeding, that is, panmixis; F = 1 signifies complete inbreeding. This value of F = 1 would be obtained in a population containing the alleles A^1 and A^2 if each of the alleles were derived from a single ancestral A^1 or A^2 and if A^1 gametes fused only with A^1 and if A^2 gametes fused only with A^2.

F can be calculated for any specific individual by tracing his lines of descent to the common ancestor of his parents. Consider as one of the theoretically simplest relations the offspring of a brother-sister union (Fig. 155, left). Let the alleles of a specific locus in the two grandparents be A^1, A^2, A^3, and A^4. What, then, is the probability F of the grandchild being either A^1A^1, A^2A^2, A^3A^3, or A^4A^4? In order for the grandchild to be A^1A^1, the grandparental allele A^1 must be transmitted a total of four steps, two on each par-

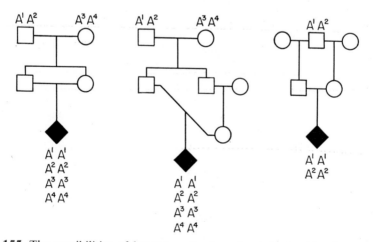

FIG. 155. The possibilities of homozygosity for a locus in the offspring of unions between brother and sister (left), uncle and niece (middle), and half-brother and half-sister (right).

ental side. Since the probability of transmission at each step is 1/2, the probability of transmission over all four steps is $(1/2)^4$. This same probability also applies, separately, to the other three cases, A^2A^2, A^3A^3, and A^4A^4. Therefore, the total probability F for the product of a brother-sister union is $4\cdot(1/2)^4 = 1/4$. For the offspring of uncle-niece or aunt-nephew marriages (Fig. 155, middle), there are five steps in the path along which a given ancestral allele can be traced: two steps through the uncle or aunt to the common ancestor and three through the niece or nephew. To each of the four alleles belongs a separate path, so that the coefficient of inbreeding becomes $F = 4\cdot(1/2)^5 = 1/8$. For offspring from first cousins, $F = 1/16$. For offspring from first cousins once removed, $F = 1/32$; and from second cousins, $F = 1/64$.

If the parents of an individual have not two but only one ancestor in common, then the number of possible paths is not four but two (Fig. 155, right). If we designate the number of steps from the inbred individual through each of his parents to the common ancestor as n_1 and n_2, respectively, his inbreeding coefficient can be written as

$$F = 2\cdot(\tfrac{1}{2})^{n_1+n_2} = (\tfrac{1}{2})^{n_1+n_2-1}.$$

Since the number of *ancestors*, N, on the path from the individual through one of his parents and back through the other is one less than the sum of the numbers of *steps* $n_1 + n_2$, we can write

$$F = (\tfrac{1}{2})^N.$$

This expression refers to a single common ancestor, who himself is not inbred (ancestral inbreeding coefficient $F_a = 0$). Should the ancestor be of consanguineous origin, his inbreeding coefficient F_a is larger than zero. Under these circumstances, the inbreeding coefficient, F, of his descendant is obviously larger than indicated above. Specifically, as Wright has shown, the general formula for the inbreeding coefficient of an individual in relation to a single common ancestor who is himself inbred is

$$F = (\tfrac{1}{2})^N(1 + F_a).$$

For an individual with more than one common ancestor, the total inbreeding coefficient is the sum of the F's as derived from each of the ancestors.

If, instead of single individuals, a population is considered, a mean coefficient of inbreeding can be calculated by averaging the value for not-inbred individuals (F = 0) with the values for groups of different degrees of relatedness. For example, if a population of 1,000 contained 909 individuals of random parentage, 1 individual from an uncle-niece marriage, 30 from first-cousin marriages and 60 from second-cousin marriages, it would have the following mean coefficient of inbreeding:

$$F = \frac{909 \times 0 + 1 \times \tfrac{1}{8} + 30 \times \tfrac{1}{16} + 60 \times \tfrac{1}{64}}{1,000} = 0.00294.$$

Mean coefficients of inbreeding have been determined for many populations. Those listed in Table 57 vary between 0.00044 and 0.01563.

Earlier (p. 375) we derived Dahlberg's formula for k, the frequency of cousin marriages among the parents of homozygotes. At that time a random-mating population (F = 0) was assumed. If there is inbreeding (F > 0), Dahlberg's formula must be refined. The new formula (no derivation will be given here) is

$$k = \frac{c(1 + 15q)}{16(1 - F)q + F},$$

or, since (1 − F) is approximately equal to 1,

$$k = \frac{c(1 + 15q)}{16q + F}. \tag{2b}$$

If F is small (e.g., 0.0005), k values are not very different from those obtained with Formula (2a) for random mating (Table 55, next to last column). If F is large (e.g., 0.015), k values are significantly smaller than those in panmixis, particularly for low allele frequencies of q (Table 55, last column).

Observed Consanguinity in Various Populations. The expectations for k, which have been derived above, will now be compared with some actual data. As a first step in this comparison, we must find the observed frequencies of

TABLE 56. *Percentage Frequencies of Various Types of Consanguineous Marriages. (After Woolf, Stephens, Mulaik, and Gilbert, Am. J. Human Genet., **8**, 1956; Neel, Kodani, Brewer, and Anderson; Freire-Maia, Am. J. Human Genet., **9**, 1957; Dahlberg, 1929; Bell.)*

Type of Marriage	Utah, Nevada (9 small communities)	Hiroshima (city)	Rio de Janeiro (city)	England and Wales	Prussia
N	625	3,283	1,172	49,315	—
Uncle-niece, aunt-nephew	—	—	0.09	0.006	0.03
First cousin	0.64	3.93	0.42	0.606	0.20
First cousin once removed	1.44	1.16	0.17	0.004	—
Second cousin	3.68	2.10	0.09	0.107	—
Second cousin once removed	2.08	0.55	—	—	—
Third cousin	1.12	0.18	—	—	—
Third cousin once removed	—	0.03	—	—	—
Total	9.92*	7.95	0.77	0.723	0.23

NOTE: A dash (—) signifies absence of data, not necessarily nonoccurrence of the type of marriage. The data cover different periods.

* Includes 0.96 per cent "Other Consanguinity."

cousin marriages in various populations. Sources for this information are official data from those few countries, such as France and some German states, whose census reports routinely include questions on consanguinity; the records of the Catholic church in various dioceses if made available for demographic purposes; the records of the Mormon church; and the reports of special investigations conducted in specific regions or villages in various countries, on hospital populations, and on other groups.

Table 56 lists not only first-cousin marriages but also other types of consanguinity in various populations. The total frequencies of consanguinity vary from less than 1 per cent to nearly 10 per cent. It is noteworthy that uncle-niece and aunt-nephew marriages are very rare, and that marriages between first cousins may be the most frequent consanguineous unions, as in Hiroshima, or be much less frequent than other, more distant degrees of inbreeding, as in the small communities in Utah. In the Utah populations, it may be assumed that marriages of close relatives were discouraged, but that the limited availability of unrelated marriageable partners led to unions between distant relatives. Further data, restricted to first-cousin marriages and to the inbreeding coefficient F, are given in Table 57. In the populations reported here, cousin marriages vary from a minimum of 0.05 per cent, from Baltimore, to 29.7 per cent from villages in the Fiji Islands. Both Tables 56 and

TABLE 57. *Percentage Frequencies of Cousin Marriages and Coefficients of Inbreeding* (F) *in Seventeen Populations.* (After Böök, *Am. J. Human Genet.,* **8,** 1956; Freire-Maia; Woolf, *et al., Am. J. Human Genet.,* 1956; Neel, *et al.;* and Valls, Spain, unpublished.)

Population	Period	No. of Marriages	First-cousin Marriages (%)	F
1. Austria, Vienna (urban)	1929–1930	31,823	0.53	0.0006
2. Brazil, Rio de Janeiro (urban)	1946–1956	1,172	0.42	0.00044
3. Brazil, Parnamirin (village)	1950–1951	179	19.55	0.01563
4. Fiji Islands (villages)	±1850–1895	448	29.7	—
5. India, Bombay (Caste of Parsees)	1950	512	12.9	0.0092
6. Japan, Nagasaki (urban)	1953	16,681	5.03	0.0039
7. Japan, Dainu (village)	1948–1949	323	7.12	—
8. Netherlands (national statistics)	1948–1953	351,085	0.13	—
9. Portugal (national statistics)	1952–1955	276,800	1.40	—
10. Spain, Salamanca (urban)	1920–1957	21,570	0.59	—
11. Spain, Las Hurdes (rural)	1951–1958	814	4.67	—
12. Sweden, Pajola (rural)	1890–1946	843	0.95	0.0008
13. Sweden, Muonionalusta (rural)	1890–1946	191	6.80	0.0058
14. Switzerland, Alpine community	±1885–1932	139	0.7	—
15. Switzerland, Alpine community	±1890–1932	52	11.5	—
16. United States, Baltimore (urban)	±1935–1950	8,000	0.05	—
17. United States, Mormons and relatives	1930–1950	30,061	0.06	—

57 show that only about 1 per cent, or much less, of all marriages in Western populations are between cousins. There are, however, outstanding exceptions: in a district in northern Sweden, 6.8 per cent; in an alpine community in Switzerland, 11.5 per cent; and in a Brazilian group, nearly 20 per cent of the marriages were between first cousins. These exceptional frequencies are not the expression of special systems of mating, in which cousin marriages are preferred. They are, rather, the consequence of the fact that these populations constitute unusually small isolates, owing either to geographical or sociological isolation, or to restricted mobility. This can be seen from the total number of marriages in the different isolates. If the group from which a mate must be selected is small, the proportion of first cousins in it is higher than in larger populations, and random mating will more often result in consanguinity.

Consanguinity in small isolates may be complex and manifold. For instance, the pedigree of a Navaho Indian, No. 17 in Figure 156, shows that his parents were simultaneously first cousins, first cousins once removed, and third cousins! Detailed genealogies of whole isolated villages in Switzerland and in Japan have been worked out by Hanhart and Yanase, respectively. The pedigrees often show a bewildering series of multiple, interrelated marriage lines. In Toksenoedao, in Japan, for example, the members of four sibships A, B, C, and D are related to one another as first cousins. In addition to marriages with unrelated or distantly related persons, the following consanguineous unions are recorded: (1) man from sibship A to cousin from B; (2) another man from A to cousin from C; (3) man from B, two marriages, both to cousins from D; (4) woman from B to cousin from D. Furthermore, the woman from C in marriage (2) was herself the offspring of a cousin marriage, as was her father.

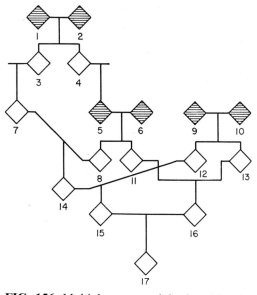

FIG. 156. Multiple consanguinity in a Navaho kindred. The parents of No. 17 have six ancestors in common. (After Spuhler and Kluckhohn, *Hum. Biol.*, **25**, 1953.)

Besides isolation, differing attitudes influence the frequency of consanguineous marriages. The high frequencies of such unions among the Fijis, the Indian Parsees, and the general population of Japan are expressions of certain social preferences. In contrast to attitudes which favor consanguinity are some state and religious regulations which disapprove of such unions. Personal fear of unhealthy offspring may also limit consanguineous marriages. The Swiss community, No. 14, had a lower frequency of cousin marriages (0.7 per cent) than did the Swedish community, No. 13 (6.8 per cent), although the sizes of the two isolated groups were similar. It seems that the Swiss group consciously reduced the frequency of cousin marriages below random expectation, while the Swedish group did not show signs of aversion to consanguinity.

These differing attitudes may possibly depend on the frequency of easily recognizable abnormalities caused by recessive genes. If such genes are present, it may be noticed that cousin marriages result in homozygous phenotypes; if such genes are absent, cousin marriages lack serious consequences. Furthermore, if such genes are rare, cousin marriages will bring them to light more often than nonrelated marriages; if the genes are common, offspring of cousin marriages will not stand out more conspicuously than offspring of nonrelated marriages.

An interesting point may be raised concerning the figure for cousin marriages listed for England and Wales in Table 56. It is seen that the frequency of 0.61 per cent, while low, is about three times that of the frequency in Prussia. Should this difference between British and German populations be regarded as a true one? It is impossible to answer this question with certainty. The German data come from unselected total populations, those from Britain from a hospital population. If an appreciable number of individuals who enter a hospital do so on account of being homozygous for a recessive condition, then it is to be expected that they are more often the offspring of cousin marriages than a similar-sized sample of individuals who have not gone to a hospital. This consideration would suggest that the over-all frequency of consanguinity in the British population, as a whole, is less than 0.61 per cent. On the other hand, there are factors which may work in the opposite direction. The population studied was from "general" hospitals; it included only a few patients with chronic diseases, since these patients seldom find their way into the wards of general hospitals. Many chronic diseases—for instance, many diseases of the nervous system—have a hereditary basis. If recessive genes are responsible for some of these, we might expect a high rate of consanguinity among the parents of patients with chronic diseases. The non-inclusion of these patients in the general-hospital population would have the effect of giving too low a frequency of consanguinity for the population as a whole. It is indeed difficult to avoid unsuspected bias in sampling, and to draw valid conclusions even from carefully collected data.

Observed Consanguinity among Parents of Homozygotes.   If we turn to specific records of consanguinity among the parents of persons affected with rare hereditary conditions, we find many observations incidental to descriptions of the traits. Many pedigrees show the parents of individuals affected with various conditions to be closely related. There is a simple means of iden-

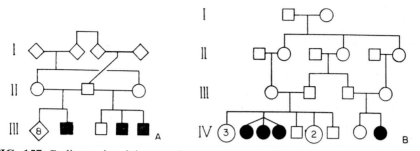

FIG. 157. Pedigrees involving cousin marriages. A. Recessive albinism. B. Hypotrichosis. (A, after Pearson, Nettleship, and Usher, pedigree No. 455; B, after Gates, *Human Genetics,* 1946, Macmillan.)

tifying consanguinity in the pedigrees in the published literature. Consanguinity means partly common descent of two spouses. Graphically, this results in the appearance of a "closed field" in the pedigree (see Figs. 156–159): the marriage line connecting the spouses usually providing the base of the field, the two vertical lines leading to their ancestors forming the sides, and the upper limit of the field the sibship line which joins the two lines of descent of the parents to the common ancestor. Sample pedigrees, selected for their unusual features, are reproduced in Figures 157–159. The first pedigree (Fig. 157, A) is of a man who married twice. His two wives were sisters and also his first cousins. Of the 9 offspring of one marriage, 1 was an albino; of the 3 offspring of the other marriage, 2 were albinos. The second pedigree (Fig. 157, B) also pictures two first-cousin marriages, involving four different individuals. Two brothers married cousins: one marriage resulted in 10 offspring—7 normal children and identical girl triplets who lost their hair at six months of age (hypotrichosis); the other marriage resulted in 1 normal and 1 affected child. A third pedigree (Fig. 158, A) includes a marriage of first

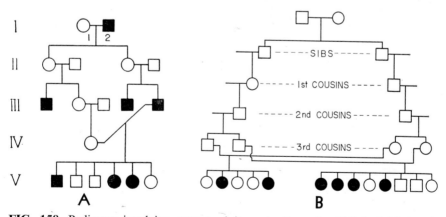

FIG. 158. Pedigrees involving consanguinity. A. Recessive X-linked ichthyosis vulgaris. B. Juvenile amaurotic idiocy in two sibships from third-cousin marriages. (A, after Gates, *Human Genetics,* 1946, Macmillan; B, after Sjögren.)

cousins once removed. The original ancestor I–2 was affected with a skin disease (ichthyosis vulgaris) which, in this family group, was transmitted in recessive X-linked manner. Consanguinity has nothing to do with the appearance of affected males, since they show the trait if it is transmitted by the mother, irrespective of the father's genotype. Females, however, can be affected only if they receive an abnormal allele from each parent. This happened to two of the daughters from the consanguineous marriage. One more pedigree (Fig. 158, B) shows the appearance of the rare juvenile amaurotic idiocy in the offspring of marriages of two brothers of one sibship to two sisters of another. Here, the parents are only distantly related, being third cousins. Nevertheless, it was presumably one of the two common ancestors who had transmitted, over three generations, a recessive allele to each of the four parents. The last two pedigrees show the appearance of rare homozygous recessives from incestuous unions. Fig. 159,A, shows an albino child from a brother-sister union; B represents the offspring of a man by his two unrelated wives and by one of his own daughters. The legitimate offspring consisted of 22 normal children, but among the 8 illegitimate children, 2 suffered from a hereditary neurological disorder.

Although these pedigrees illustrate the production of homozygous recessive individuals from heterozygous carrier parents who presumably obtained their rare recessive allele from the same common ancestor, they cannot serve as a basis for comparison with the quantitative expectations regarding consanguinity cited earlier. Pertinent data on a few specific conditions are available from collections of many pedigrees. Thus, for Friedreich's ataxia, a disease in which muscular coordination is impaired by degeneration of tissue in the central nervous system, among the families of twenty-two propositi, Hogben and Pollack found two in which the parents were first cousins and one in which they were second cousins. This is a rate of about 10 per cent consanguinity. More extensive material concerning another disease of the nervous system is known from Sjögren's studies in Sweden. Juvenile amaurotic idiocy is a condition which begins with failing sight and blindness in children of from four to seven years and leads to progressive loss of sensory, mental, and physical powers and death some ten or twelve years later. The incidence of

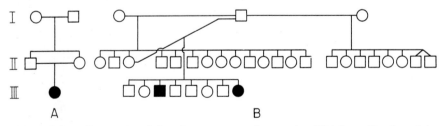

FIG. 159. Pedigrees involving incestuous unions.   A. Albinism. Brother-sister union.   B. Recessive neurological disorder (hereditary ataxia). Two affected individuals from a father-daughter union. (A, after Baur, Fischer, Lenz; B, original courtesy Drs. F. E. Stephens and F. H. Tyler, University of Utah.)

TABLE 58. *Percentage,* k, *of Affected Individuals from Cousin Marriages.* (Neel, *et al.*)

Trait	Whites	Japanese
Albinism	18–24	37–59
Tay-Sachs disease (see p. 116)	27–53	55–85
Ichthyosis congenita (skin disease)	30–40	67–93
Congenital total color blindness	11–21	39–51
Xeroderma pigmentosum (see p. 51)	20–26	37–43

first-cousin marriages among the parents of those affected is about 15 per cent. Alkaptonuria, the metabolic abnormality resulting in the presence of an oxidizable substance in the urine, shows 30–42 per cent ancestral consanguinity among pedigrees collected in different countries.

For phenylketonuria, frequencies of 5–15 per cent consanguinity among parents of affected individuals have been reported. Although the rates of consanguinity among parents of deaf-mutes in Ireland (3–6 per cent) and congenital blinds in the United States (4–5 per cent), as reported in older surveys, are lower, they still exceeded the average of consanguinity in these populations. Data on five other traits, given separately for Caucasian (predominantly European) and Japanese populations, are assembled in Table 58. The incidence k of first-cousin unions among the parents of affected offspring is very high, especially in Japan. This is to be expected since general consanguinity, c, is usually more common in Japan than in the Western world, and k is proportional to c (see formulas [2a] and [2b] and Table 55). A detailed comparison of the frequencies k in the two groups would also require a knowledge of the allele frequencies, q, for the five traits, since k (as we have seen) depends not only on c and F but also on q.

The high consanguinity rates among the parents of affected individuals were first recognized in the study of alkaptonuria by Garrod (1902), and the interpretation in terms of the then newly rediscovered Mendelian concepts was given by Bateson (1861–1926). Since that time an increased frequency of consanguineous marriages among parents of individuals affected with a given trait is regarded as important genetic evidence for a recessive basis of the trait.

Observed and Expected Consanguinity Frequencies.   Is the general agreement between observed and expected high rates of consanguinity also quantitative? In order to answer this question, we must have information on the gene frequency q of each condition and on c, the specific rate of consanguinity in the general population concerned. Such information is only partly available. Alkaptonuria seems to have an incidence of only 1 in 1,000,000 (q^2), making $q = 1/1,000$. Assuming c to be 0.5 per cent and entering these two values in formula (2a), we obtain $k = 0.32$, which is in rather close agreement with observation. For juvenile amaurotic idiocy, a similar treatment of the data leads to less satisfactory results. Dunn has shown that it is misleading to calculate the gene frequency q from the ratio of homozygotes to the whole Swedish population. The isolates in which the disease occurs represent perhaps 40 per cent of the population. In these isolates, q is higher than when "diluted" by the part of the population which is free from the allele. In the opposite direction, the rate of cousin marriages, c, in the isolates at the time when the affected children were born, was probably closer to 2 per cent than to the present over-all estimate for a Swedish population of about 0.45 per cent. Only when these corrections for true gene and consanguinity frequencies in the isolates are made, do observation and expectation lead to agreement. It must be admitted that the agreement is partly due to circular reasoning. The estimate of 40 per cent as the fraction of the isolates in relation to the whole population, while reasonable from the knowledge of the geographical distribution of the affected, has been specifically chosen to fit the expectation!

Another type of discrepancy seems to exist in regard to albinism. If $q^2 = 1/20,000$ and $q = 1/141$, then k according to formula (2a) takes on the values 4.9 and 9.7 per cent for the frequencies, c, of 0.5 and 1 per cent. Both values of k are much less than the observed incidences of at least 18 per cent. In order to obtain better agreement, if c were assumed to be as high as 2 per cent, k would become large enough, namely, 19.5 per cent, to be close to observation. Such a large value for k, however, would probably involve the assumption of isolates for albinism. Although such isolates may actually exist, their assumption would mean an increased estimate for q, and this, in turn, a decreased expectation for consanguinity. What is gained by a larger c might be lost by the larger q! A possible way out of this dilemma would be to assume more than one locus for recessive albinism. If, for instance, albinos originated in consequence of either one of two equally frequent homozygous genotypes a_1a_1 and a_2a_2, then the frequency of albinos, 1 in 20,000, must be divided into that of the a_1a_1 kind,

$$1 \text{ in } 40,000 = q^2_{a_1}$$

and, also, that of the a_2a_2 kind,

$$1 \text{ in } 40,000 = q^2_{a_2}.$$

The gene frequencies, q_{a_1} and q_{a_2}, then, are $1/200$. Using Dahlberg's formula, we find that k is 13.4 per cent for c of 1 per cent, and 26.9 per cent for c of 2 per cent. The observed value for k lies between these two expectations.

The only other evidence that albinism in man is produced by different recessive genotypes is very weak (p. 106). However, in a different mammal, the mouse, two different types of recessive albinism are well established. For another human trait, deaf-mutism, the fact that the frequency of consanguinity among the parents of affected persons is, as in albinism, higher than expectation suggested that more than a single recessive genotype was involved.

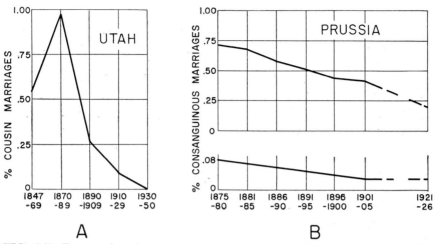

A   B

FIG. 160. Frequencies of consanguineous marriages in Utah and Prussia, during various periods.   A. Marriages between first cousins.   B. Marriages between first cousins (upper curve) and uncle and niece (lower curve). (A, after Woolf, Stephens, Mulaik, and Gilbert, *Am. J. Human Genet.,* **8,** 1956; B, after Dahlberg, 1929.)

And pedigree analyses bear out the multiplicity of recessive genotypes for deaf-mutism.

The Recent Decrease of Consanguinity.   An examination of the consanguinity rates in different periods for Utah, Prussia, and the French departments (administrative areas) reveals a general phenomenon (Figs. 160, 161).

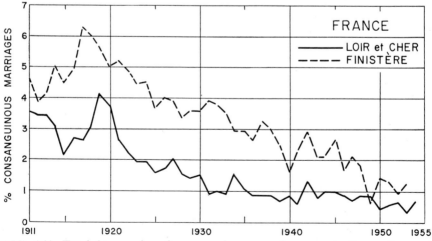

FIG. 161. Total frequencies of consanguinous marriages, up to those of second cousins, in two French departments, 1911–1954. Finistère, a more isolated district than Loir-et-Cher, had a higher frequency of consanguinity, but the downward trend led to very similar recent frequencies. (Sutter and Tabah, *Population,* **10,** 1955.)

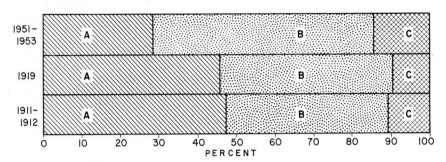

FIG. 162. Relative frequencies of different kinds of marriages in the Department Finistère of France according to the origin of the spouses. A. From the same community. B. From different communities of the same department. C. One spouse from a community in the Department Finistère, the other from another department. (Sutter, *Population,* **13,** 1958.)

Over the past hundred years, there has been a continuous decrease in the frequency of near-relative marriages. It is unlikely that this decrease has resulted from a conscious avoidance of such marriages. It is, rather, due to two different changes in population structure which have taken place in recent history. The first is the breakup of isolates. Modern transportation and the large-scale migration from country to country and, even more important, from farm to town have afforded a wider range of human contacts. Formerly, the choice of a mate was largely restricted to the members of a relatively sessile home community. Now, however, people from neighboring districts have an opportunity to meet, and, particularly in the larger cities, people from widely separated regions are brought together. Consequently, the proportion of marriages between people of the same community has decreased, while that between people of different communities has increased (Fig. 162). Since most rela-

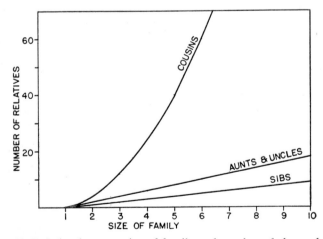

FIG. 163. Relation between size of family and number of close relatives.

tives used to live near one another, they formed a large fraction of an individual's acquaintances. With the extension of the sphere of acquaintances, the fraction of relatives among them decreases, quite aside from actual separation of relatives by migration. This comparative decrease of relatives among marriageable acquaintances naturally leads to a decrease in consanguinity.

The second cause of decreased consanguinity is due to an absolute decrease in the number of close relatives. This is simply a consequence of the modern trend toward smaller families. If b is the average number of children in a family, then an individual has on the average $(b - 1)$ sibs. To give some examples, if there are 7 children, each child has 6 sibs; if there are 4 children, each child has 3 sibs; and if there are 2 children, each has only 1 sib. Clearly, not only does the number of sibs become smaller with smaller family size, but the decrease in sibs is also greater than that of sibship size (Fig. 163). This is even more pronounced in more distant relationships. An individual whose parents come from sibships of size b will have $(b - 1)$ uncles or aunts on each parent's side, or a total of $2(b - 1)$. If each of these uncles or aunts has an average of b children, these children, his cousins, will number $2(b - 1)b$. And if one-half of these are of the sex opposite that of the propositus himself, he will have $b(b - 1)$ potentially marriageable first cousins. With this formula, if $b = 7$, the potential mates will number 42; if $b = 4$, the number decreases to 12; and if $b = 2$, it is only 2. In a stationary population —that is, one in which the number remains constant from generation to generation—b obviously is 2, the two children replacing their parents. Although the family size in many Western societies has increased since World War II, it can be expected that most populations will eventually become stationary and thus provide only small cousin groups. In the future, these two factors— the breakup of isolates and the small size of the modern family—may well reduce first-cousin consanguinity to 0.1 per cent, or even less.

The Size of Genetic Isolates.   Dahlberg (1893–1956) has shown how to estimate the average size of the isolate within which an individual marries. As we have seen, the frequency of consanguinity depends on the size of the isolate. Two specific relations, those concerning marriages between (1) first cousins and (2) uncle-niece and aunt-nephew, will be considered. The assumption will be made that consanguinity is as frequent as required by random mating.

1. If the number of individuals who make up the isolate is n, the number of persons of the sex opposite from that of any individual is $n/2$ (assuming equality in numbers of the sexes). The number of an individual's first cousins of opposite sex, as found earlier, is $b(b - 1)$, where b is the average number of children in a sibship. In panmixis, the probability of a first-cousin marriage is

$$c = \frac{b(b-1)}{n/2}.$$

Solving this equation for n, the size of the isolate, we obtain

$$n = \frac{2b(b-1)}{c}. \tag{3}$$

In the left half of Table 59, n is given for various values of c and for two values of b. Before discussing this table, we shall obtain similar information for the uncle-niece and aunt-nephew combinations of marriage.

2. We shall not present a derivation for Dahlberg's formula relating the frequency c′ of uncle-niece and aunt-nephew marriages to the size of the isolate. This relation is given by

$$c' = 2. \frac{2}{2+b} \cdot b \frac{(b-1)}{n},$$

which, solved for the size of the isolate, gives

$$n = \frac{4b(b-1)}{(2+b)c'}.$$

In the right half of Table 59, values of n are listed for various values of c′ and of b, as determined by this equation.

What does this table show us concerning the average size of the isolate within which an individual chooses his marriage partner? We can read off this size in the leftmost column, provided that information is available on the frequency of cousin marriages, c, or uncle-niece and aunt-nephew marriages, c′, as well as on b, the number of children per sibship. If c and c′ are truly random frequencies of consanguinity, the answer for n should be the same whether derived from the left or right half of the table. It will be a test of the assumption of random mating to see how closely the values of n agree if derived from the two types of near-relative marriages. Using an estimate of c = 0.4 per cent for cousin marriages and another of b = 2 for average size of sibship (values approximating those for western Europe), we find, from Table 59, left, that n = 1,000. Since only one-half of n represents indi-

TABLE 59. *Size of Isolate in Random Mating Related to Frequency of Cousin Marriages and of Uncle-Niece, or Aunt-Nephew Marriages. (Size of sibship, b = 2 and b = 3 children.) (After Dahlberg, 1929.)*

Size of Isolate (n)	Percentage of Cousin Marriages (c)		Percentage of Uncle-Niece, Aunt-Nephew Marriages (c′)	
	b = 2	b = 3	b = 2	b = 3
50	8	24	4	9.6
100	4	12	2	4.8
500	0.8	2.4	0.4	0.96
1,000	0.4	1.2	0.2	0.48
3,000	0.133	0.4	0.067	0.16
10,000	0.04	0.12	0.02	0.048

viduals of the sex opposite that of any member of the isolate, the size of the potentially marriageable isolate, n′, is 500. Using the European values for c′ of about 0.06 to 0.07 per cent for uncle-niece and aunt-nephew marriages, and again b = 2, we find, from Table 59, right, that n = approximately 3,000. This value signifies the size of the potentially marriageable isolate n′ as about 1,500. The two values for n′, 500 and 1,500, differ by a factor of 3. This is not too poor an agreement considering the simplifying assumptions made in the derivation of the formulas used to obtain these values.

The Consequences of Consanguinity

It is clear from a genetic discussion of consanguinity that inbreeding, by itself, is not responsible for the appearance of unfavorable phenotypes. Inbreeding tends to bring into the open recessive alleles present in heterozygous carriers, but, as has been aptly said, inbreeding is no more responsible for the presence of the alleles than a detective is responsible for the crimes which he lays bare. The genetic facts afford an understanding of the often contradictory effects of inbreeding, which sometimes result in undesirable phenotypes and, at other times, in normal or even better-than-average constitutions. Such different results are partly due to initial differences in the original mates, who may be carriers of unfavorable or favorable recessives. In part, the different results will be expected even from identical original genotypes, since the mating of two heterozygotes, $Aa \times Aa$, may of course give rise to different genotypes, AA, Aa, and aa. In small families, some sibships will be free of aa individuals, and others will contain them.

Unfavorable homozygous phenotypes are usually more obvious than favorable ones. Nevertheless, it is to be expected that recessive alleles exist which, in the homozygous state, endow their carriers with better-than-normal characteristics. To cite outstanding examples, the painter Toulouse-Lautrec and the writer John Ruskin were the products of cousin marriages. Yet it cannot be proven that the special accomplishments of these individuals were related to homozygous recessive genes nor, if this were the case, that these genes had become homozygous in consanguinity. (Toulouse-Lautrec's misshapen legs were probably the result of a dominant gene for osteogenesis imperfecta, and thus had nothing to do with the consanguinity of his parents.)

There is, however, one case known which, theoretically at least, indicates an advantage of consanguinity. We refer to the genetic basis of erythroblastosis fetalis and the mechanism of antigen-antibody incompatibility between Rh-negative mother and Rh-positive fetus. As seen earlier (pp. 342ff.), a potentially unfavorable situation is established when mother and child belong to the different genotypes, among others, rr and Rr. No unfavorable reactions result when mother and child are alike genetically. Since identical genotypes for a specific locus are more common in related marriage partners than in unrelated spouses, more children of consanguineous marriages than of other marriages should have the same Rh constitution as their mothers. Therefore, a lower frequency of erythroblastosis fetalis is to be expected among the offspring of close-relative unions than of other unions. The decrease in the incidence of the disease after cousin marriages has been calculated to be of the order of 13 per cent, but no observation is yet available to verify this predicted beneficial effect of consanguinity.

Occurrence of Several Unfavorable Traits in the Same Kindred.   Not infrequently, more than one unfavorable inherited trait occurs in family groups. The opinion is often expressed that these groups form a "degenerate strain." This view is not compatible with genetic knowledge. The hereditary make-up of individuals consists of particulate, independent units, the genes, while the concept of a "degenerate constitution" vaguely implies a homogeneous basis of heredity. How, then, can the simultaneous occurrence of more than one unfavorable phenotype, either in one individual or in different individuals of a family group, be explained? There are various possible explanations.

Abnormalities are not so rare that two or more cannot occur in one individual or group occasionally. To some extent, then, family strains containing more than one type of abnormality may only be selected cases. Furthermore, a family with one abnormality may have more chance of being scrutinized closely enough to lead to discovery of other abnormalities.

Another explanation is that one and the same gene may express itself in various ways, because of different types of expression in the heterozygous and the homozygous state, because of different genetic backgrounds, or because of different environmental conditions. In other cases, multiple symptoms may be common developmental effects of one and the same gene.

Finally, there exists a true genetic cause of positive correlation between the appearance of two or more rare homozygous recessive traits. This cause is consanguinity. If a person happens to be heterozygous for two different rare recessives, $AaBb$, the chance of his marrying an unrelated partner heterozygous for one or the other of these recessives will be low, and there will be virtually no chance of his marrying one heterozygous for both. Therefore, in a nonconsanguineous marriage, at most one trait, aa or bb, will appear among the children. However, should an $AaBb$ person marry a first cousin, the probability of the spouse being heterozygous for a is $1/8$, for b is $1/8$, and simultaneously for a and b is $1/64$. Since, in a consanguineous marriage of $AaBb \times AaBb$ parents, the expectation for aaB-, A-bb, and even $aabb$ children is rather high, sibships may be produced which contain some individuals affected with one recessive trait, others with another trait, and, occasionally, even an individual affected with both.

The Risk of Consanguineous Marriages

The advisability of cousin marriages is often questioned. If 20 per cent of albinos are the products of such unions, should two cousins to be married fear that they might have albino children? Obviously, this would be wrong reasoning. Although many albinos come from cousin marriages, most cousin marriages do not produce albino offspring. But if the specific fear of albinism is not justified, nor that of deaf-mutism, Friedreich's ataxia, or any one of many conditions caused by homozygous recessives, it is a different matter to wonder about the occurrence of any one unfavorable trait. What are the expectations and the facts?

Theoretical Risks.   Let us assume that an individual carries in heterozygous state one rare recessive gene of homozygously detrimental effect that causes premature death, a major congenital malformation, or some other serious defect. Since the probability of his cousin carrying the same gene is $1/8$, the probability of any one of their children being affected is $1/4 \cdot 1/8 = 1/32$, or 3.1 per cent (and consequently, of being nonaffected, 96.9 per cent). If the propositus carries a second different gene with detrimental effect, the probability of a child being affected on account of homozygosity for the second gene is likewise 3.1 per cent, and of being nonaffected, 96.9 per cent. Any one of the children of the cousins may be either free from both defects with a probability of $(0.969)^2$; affected by one or the other trait, $2 \cdot 0.969 \cdot 0.031$; or affected by both traits, $(0.031)^2$. If the propositus carries n different genes, the probability of a child not receiving any of them in homozygous state is $(0.969)^n$; or conversely, the probability of the child being affected by 1 or 2 or 3 or all n traits is $1 - (0.969)^n$. Thus, if $n = 2$, the risk is 6.1 per cent; if $n = 3$, it is 9 per cent; and if $n = 8$, it rises to 22.4 per cent.

These relations between the number of deleterious recessive genes heterozygously present in an individual and the frequency of affected children if he marries a cousin were first discussed by Russell. More refined treatments have been worked out by Slatis, Böök, Penrose, and by Morton, Crow and Muller.

Observed Risk.   How do these calculated predictions compare with observed results of cousin marriages? The main reports on this subject are an inquiry conducted in the United States more than a hundred years ago by Bemiss for the American Medical Association; another by Arner on older genealogical records in the United States; a smaller recent study by Slatis on Chicago families; a series of studies by Sutter and Tabah in France; another by Böök in Sweden; and analyses by Neel, Schull, and Morton of the births and deaths of children born recently in three Japanese cities. The results cited in these reports are not strictly comparable, partly because of the different methods of ascertainment used and partly because the rates of mortality vary considerably. Although this variability may have a genetic basis, it is certainly also caused by different public-health conditions in different times and places. The essential comparisons, however, are not of different populations but rather of the offspring of consanguineous and nonconsanguineous marriages within each population. Some of the data are assembled in Tables 60 and 61.

Nine relevant comparisons on mortality are listed in Table 60. In every

TABLE 60. *Mortalities among Offspring of Marriages between Unrelated Persons and between First Cousins.* (Bemiss, *Trans. Am. Med. Ass.,* **11,** 1858; Arner; Slatis, Reis and Hoene, *Am. J. Human Genet.,* **10,** 1958; Sutter and Tabah, *Population,* **7, 8,** 1952–53; Schull, *Am. J. Human Genet.,* **10,** 1958).

		Unrelated		First Cousins	
Deaths	Period	N	Mortality (%)	N	Mortality (%)
UNITED STATES					
Young children	Before 1858	837	16.0	2,778	22.9
Before age 20	18th–19th centuries	3,184	11.6	672	16.8
Children 0–10 years	1920–1956	167	2.4	209	8.1
FRANCE*					
Stillbirth, neonatal	1919–c. 1950	2,745	3.9	743	9.3
Infantile, juvenile, and later	1919–c. 1950	515	9.6	674	14.3
JAPAN*					
Stillbirth	1948–1954	63,145	1.5	2,798	1.6
Infants, to 1 month	1948–1954	63,145	1.8	2,798	2.8
Infants, during first 9 months	1948–1954	17,331	4.7	822	6.6
Between 1 and 8 years	1948–1954	544	1.5	326	4.6

* Deaths of children without visible major malformations.

one, the percentage of deaths is greater among the offspring of first cousins. Only for stillbirths in Japan is the difference negligible (1.5 for unrelated spouses versus 1.6 for cousin spouses). All other differences are significant and often striking. Thus, 22.9 per cent of the children from cousin spouses in the United States study (Bemiss report) died early versus 16.0 per cent

TABLE 61. *Frequencies of Diseases and of Physical and Mental Defects among Children of Unrelated and of First-Cousin Marriages.* (Sutter and Tabah, *Population,* **9,** 1954; Schull, *Am. J. Human Genet.,* **10,** 1958; Böök, *Ann. Eug.,* **21,** 1956; and, Slatis, Reis, and Hoene, *Am. J. Human Genet.,* **10,** 1958.)

	Unrelated		First Cousins	
Population	N	Aff. (%)	N	Aff. (%)
France*	833	3.5	144	12.8
Japan†	63,796	1.02	2,846	1.69
Sweden‡	165	4	218	16
United States§	163	9.82	192	16.15

* Morbihan and Loir-et-Cher. Children in completed families from marriages 1919–1925.
† Hiroshima, Kure, and Nagasaki. Children born 1948–1954.
‡ Three parishes, North Sweden. All cousin marriages registered 1947. The percentages of affected are estimates after various corrections applied to the data.
§ Chicago. Children born 1920–1956.

from unrelated parents; 9.3 per cent of the French children from cousins died at birth or during the first month versus 3.9 from unrelated parents; and 4.6 versus 1.5 per cent of children in the Japanese sample died between the ages of one and eight years.

The increased risk of consanguineous marriages for the offspring is also indicated by a correlation between the frequency of consanguinity and the frequency of perinatal death (stillbirths and death within one month) in the 90 French governmental departments. The coefficient of inbreeding varied from 0.0021 to 0.0236 and the mortality from 38 to 66 per 1,000 births, revealing a high and significant correlation, +0.72.

Data in Table 61 include frequencies for malformations, mental and physical defects, and tuberculosis in the French, Swedish, and United States groups; but only major congenital malformations for the Japanese group. Again the differences between children from unrelated parents and from first-cousin spouses are highly significant, indicating a greater risk for the offspring of consanguineous unions.

Other data on the French group show that the percentage of sibships with abnormal children is three times higher for cousin spouses than for unrelated parents, namely 28 versus 9.1 per cent. And among sibships with abnormal children, only 27 per cent from nonconsanguineous unions had more than one affected child versus 51 per cent from consanguineous ones.

Not all traits are so strikingly affected by consanguinity. Thus the birth weight and the weight at from eight to ten months of Japanese babies was only slightly lower among the offspring of cousins than of unrelated parents, and the height was essentially the same in the two groups (Table 62). By and large, however, the increase in mortality from before birth to adulthood, as well as the increase in malformations and other abnormalities, among offspring of consanguineous marriages strongly indicates the existence of detrimental recessive genes. These genes apparently include some which increase susceptibility to infectious diseases such as tuberculosis.

The conclusion that consanguinity leads to increased risks of illness and premature death is not based exclusively on data on offspring of first-cousin marriages, but also on results of closer and more distant degrees of consanguinity. Usually, the closer the degree of consanguinity, the greater the increase in detrimentally affected.

TABLE 62. *Weight and Height of Children from Unrelated and First-cousin Marriages.* (Morton, *Am. J. Human Genet.,* **10,** 1958.)

Japanese Infants (from Hiroshima, Kure, and Nagasaki, 1948–1954)	Unrelated		First Cousins	
	N	Meas.	N	Meas.
Mean weight of live births	70,088	3,074 g	2,928	3,046 g
Mean weight at 8–10 months	18,501	7,818 g	815	7,722 g
Mean height at 8–10 months	18,501	689.6 mm	815	687.3 mm

The Individual's Load of Detrimentals. As has been pointed out on page 393, for each recessive gene carried by an individual, 1/32 of his offspring from a first-cousin marriage will be homozygous. If, therefore, one wishes to know the number of detrimental recessive genes carried by the average individual, it is only necessary to determine the frequency of homozygous recessive genotypes from cousin marriages and to multiply it by 32. For example, deaths during the first eight years of life in the Japanese consanguineous group (Table 60) had a frequency of approximately 11.2 per cent, while those in the nonrelated group were approximately 6.2 per cent. Thus, consanguinity accounts for the difference of 5 per cent. If it is assumed that each death ascribable to consanguinity, is the result of the presence of a single homozygous gene pair—an assumption which will be redefined below—then the value $32 \times 0.05 = 1.6$ signifies that, on the average, the Japanese parents were heterozygous for 1.6 recessive genes causing childhood mortality. Bemiss' older United States data, with the much higher juvenile mortalities of 22.9 per cent for consanguineous and 16.0 for nonconsanguineous offspring, lead to a very similar figure. The difference in percentage is 6.9, or multiplied by 32, a mean of 2.2 recessives carried by the parent. The French, Swedish, and United States data for physical and mental defects (Table 61) place the number of genes involved in these traits in the range of from two to four.

Any detailed estimates must take into account various factors, such as nongenetic social differences between consanguineous and nonconsanguineous groups, the allele frequencies, the degree of inbreeding in the population, and the possible effect of the detrimental genes when present in the heterozygotes. Muller and others have made such estimates. For genes causing premature mortality (from stillbirth to early adult death), the estimates were first expressed in terms of recessive lethals, but later, in terms of "lethal equivalents." A lethal equivalent is either a single gene that is fully lethal in a homozygote, or a group of genes each of which, when homozygous, may cause death in a fraction of cases and which, if separately homozygous in different individuals, would on the average account for one death. The number of lethal equivalents carried by the average person seems to be between three and five. There must be additional lethal equivalents per person which cause early abortion and adult, but still premature, death. Another four to five nonlethal equivalents per person may be responsible for anatomical and other abnormalities. The total number of genes per person which are detrimental in homozygotes is likely to be much larger than the ±10 mentioned here. In Chapter 24, we shall discuss the nature of this load of detrimentals, and point out that it may be in part the result of constantly occurring spontaneous mutations and in part an expression of selection for heterozygotes which may be superior to homozygotes.

Counseling in Consanguineous Marriages. From the preceding data and discussion it is clear that the risk of detrimentally affected offspring is greater for related than for unrelated spouses. Even for related couples the chance of producing a normal child is considerably higher than that of producing an affected, but the latter, by no means negligible, possibility must be faced. A study of the families of prospective consanguineous parents affords relatively little helpful information. Most of the rare recessive detrimentals are carried unknown for many generations, and absence of homozygotes for such genes is hardly an indication of absence of the genes in a hetero-zygous carrier state. Conversely, although knowledge of a relative affected by a specific homozygous genotype may help in identifying one of the several detrimental genes presumably present in the prospective parents, it does not necessarily indicate a heavier-than-normal genetic load. If all marriages between close relatives were avoided, the effect would be a decrease in homozygous recessives in the following generation. Considering that, on the average, the frequency of consanguinity is low and the number of homo-zygotes resulting from such marriages small, the decrease in homozygotes, from the point of view of the population as a whole, would be of relatively small consequence. On the other hand, from the point of view of affected individuals and their relatives, any reduction in the number of abnormals is of great significance.

If one considers the fate not only of the first generation after elimination of close consanguinity but of future generations, then the problem takes on a new aspect. Changing the system of mating does not change the fre-quency of an allele but only its distribution over heterozygous and homo-zygous genotypes. A decrease in consanguinity, with its resulting decrease of homozygotes, will lead to an increase in heterozygotes. In the course of gene-rations, these heterozygotes will marry unrelated heterozygotes and produce homozygous affected offspring. In other words, the homozygotes prevented from appearing in the immediate future will appear in the more distant future. This is particularly so if the trait is so unfavorable as to exclude the af-fected individual from reproduction. In this case, consanguinity, which may lead to homozygous individuals, may result in the elimination of two recessive alleles per affected person. One generation undergoes a sacrifice and thus frees the later generations. On the other hand, if consanguinity is avoided, the two recessives will come together in some later generation and will then be eliminated. Thus, exclusion of consanguinity in one generation transfers the load of affected individuals to later generations. Which one of the two alternatives is preferable?

Problems

147. A man is homozygous for a very rare recessive gene a. What is the chance of a child being aa if the man marries his first cousin? (Assume that a enters into the pedigree from only one of the common grandparents.)

148. The frequency of a recessive gene is 1 in 90. What is the probability of affected offspring from the marriage of two cousins who are of normal phenotype?

149. A normal-appearing man is heterozygous for a very rare recessive gene which produces an anatomical defect. (a) Are defective offspring more probable if the man marries his first cousin or his niece? (b) And how much greater is this probability? (Assume that the gene enters the pedigree from only one source.)

150. In Table 55, columns 2–4, recalculate the values k for the frequencies of cousin marriages among the parents of the homozygotes by using only the first term of formula 2a (on p. 375). Note the degrees of errors introduced by using the simplified instead of the complete formula 2.

151. In a population, the frequency of homozygous recessives for the gene a is 1 in 6,400. (a) If the general frequency of cousin marriages in this population is 0.008, what is the expected per cent of cousin marriages among the parents of aa people? (b) If among the parents of 500 unrelated aa people 32 are first cousins, would you consider this proportion as significantly different from expectation?

152. How much greater than the frequency in the general population is the frequency of cousin marriages among the parents of homozygous affected persons if the general frequency of cousin marriages is c, and the frequency of homozygotes is f, for:

(i) c = 0.005; f = 0.0004.   (iii) c = 0.005; f = 0.000025.
(ii) c = 0.005; f = 0.000081.   (iv) c = 0.002; f = 0.000025.

153. If the general frequency of cousin marriages in a population is c, what will be the frequency of cousin marriages among the parents of color-blind men?

154. Double first cousins are people whose parents are two pairs of sibs. If a woman is heterozygous for a rare recessive a, what chance has her double first cousin to be heterozygous for a? (Assume that a enters the pedigree from only one source.)

155. Determine the coefficient of inbreeding F for the offspring of the marriage of: (a) double first cousins, and (b) half-brother and sister. Is there a genetic justification for laws which permit marriages of type (a) but prohibit those of type (b)?

156. A color-blind man has parents and grandparents who had normal vision. (a) If the man marries his first cousin, who is the daughter of his father's brother, compare the probability of color-blind offspring from this cousin marriage with that of noncousin marriages. (b) If the man marries the daughter of his mother's sister from a marriage to a normal-visioned man, what is the probability of color-blind offspring?

157. If cousin marriages occurred in panmictic frequencies, and if the number of children per sibship averaged b = 3, what would be the approximate sizes of the isolates, n, in the following populations referred to in Table 57 (p. 380):

(a) No. 3?   (b) No. 8?   (c) No. 16?

158. Assume that a population of one million consists of two generations, of which the parents' generation has an average of b children. If no deaths have occurred, how many individuals belong to the older and how many to the younger generation if b equals:

(a) 1?   (c) 3?   (e) 8?
(b) 2?   (d) 6?

159. The birthweight of children from consanguineous marriages was found to be similar to that from unrelated ones. What bearing have the data on birthweight, given on p. 334, on the interpretation of this fact?

References

Arner, G. B. L., 1908. Consanguineous marriages in the American population. *Columbia University Studies in History, Economics and Public Law,* **31:** no. 3.

Bell, J., 1940. A determination of the consanguinity rate in the general hospital population of England and Wales. *Ann. Eugen.,* **10:** 370–391.

Bernstein, F., 1930. Fortgesetzte Untersuchungen aus der Theorie der Blutgruppen. *Zeitschr. Abst. u. Vererbgsl.,* **56:** 200–273.

Böök, J. A., 1948. The frequency of cousin marriages in three North Swedish parishes. *Hereditas,* **34:** 252–255.

Dahlberg, G., 1929. Inbreeding in man. *Genetics,* **14:** 421–454.

——, 1947. *Mathematical Methods for Population Genetics.* 182 pp. S. Karger, Basle, Switzerland; Interscience Publishers, New York.

Dunn, L. C., 1947. The effect of isolates on the frequency of a rare human gene. *Proc. Nat. Acad. Sci.,* **33:** 359–363.

Freire-Maia, N., 1957. Inbreeding levels in different countries. *Eugen. Quart.,* **4:** 127–138.

Haldane, J. B. S., 1949. The association of characters as a result of inbreeding and linkage. *Ann. Eugen.,* **15:** 15–23.

Kishimoto, K., 1954. The effects of inbreeding in the distribution of mental disease and deficiency. *World Population Conf.,* **6:** 507–522.

Lenz, F., 1919. Die Bedeutung der statistisch ermittelten Belastung mit Blutsverwandschaft der Eltern. *Münch. Med. Wochenschr,* **66:** 2. 1340–1342.

Li, C. C., 1955. *Population Genetics.* 366 pp. University of Chicago Press, Chicago.

Morton, N. E., 1958. Empirical risks in consanguineous marriages: birth weight, gestation time, and measurements of infants. *Am. J. Human Genet.,* **10:** 344–349.

——, Crow, J. F., and Muller, H. J., 1956. An estimate of the mutational damage in man from data on consanguineous marriages. *Proc. Nat. Acad. Sci.,* **42:** 855–863.

Neel, J. V., Kodani, M., Brewer, R., and Anderson, R. C., 1949. The incidence of consanguineous matings in Japan. *Am. J. Human Genet.,* **1:** 156–178.

Penrose, L. S., 1956. A note on the prevalence of genes for deleterious recessive traits in man. *Ann. Human Genet.,* **21:** 222–223 (for a correction see Slatis, Reis, and Hoene, 1958, *Am. J. Human Genet.,* **10:** p. 461).

Schull, W. J., 1958. Empirical risks in consanguineous marriages: sex ratio, malformation, and viability. *Am. J. Human Genet.,* **10:** 294–343.

Sjögren, T., 1931. Die juvenile amaurotische Idiotie—klinische und erblichkeitsmedizinische Untersuchungen. *Hereditas,* **14:** 197–426.

Steinberg, A. G., 1959. Methodology in human genetics. *J. Med. Ed.,* **34:** 315–334 (also *Am. J. Human Genet.,* **11,** 2 Part 2: 315–334), see pp. 326–330.

Sutter, J., 1958. *Recherches sur les effets de la consanguinité chez l'homme.* 103 pp. M. Declume, Lons-le Saunier.

Woolf, C. M., Stephens, F. E., Mulaik, D. D., and Gilbert, R. E., 1956. An investigation of the frequency of consanguineous marriages among the Mormons and their relatives in the United States. *Am. J. Human Genet.,* **8:** 236–252.

Wright, S., 1922. Coefficients of inbreeding and relationship. *Am. Naturalist,* **56:** 330–338.

CHAPTER 20

SEX DETERMINATION

The discovery, early in this century, of the chromosome difference between females (XX) and males (XY) afforded a basic, and surprisingly simple, solution of the problem of sex determination. All mature eggs produced by a woman are alike in their possession of one X-chromosome (plus one set of autosomes), but there are two kinds of sperm produced by a man—those with an X-chromosome and those with a Y-chromosome (in both cases, plus one set of autosomes). Fertilization of any egg by an "X sperm" results in an XX zygote, which is destined to develop into a female, and fertilization by a "Y sperm" leads to an XY zygote destined to become a male.

Sex, in man and all other organisms with a similar chromosomal mechanism, is determined at the moment of fertilization and depends on whether an X sperm or a Y sperm unites with the egg. Before the moment of this union, the future of the egg is not fixed and either a female or a male may develop from it. The future role of any individual sperm cell, if it should fertilize an egg, depends on whether it contains and X- or a Y-chromosome. And since both types of sperm are produced simultaneously by every man, the sex of his future offspring is not decided until either one of his X or one of his Y sperm has joined with the egg.

The Male-determining Role of the Y-chromosome. Not until 1959 was it known that it is the presence of a Y-chromosome in a fertilized egg which causes it to develop into a male, and that it is the absence of the Y-chromosome which causes it to develop into a female. Although this would seem to have been obvious, the matter was not as clear-cut as it appears at first. Genetically, a male is distinguished from a female not only by his having a Y-chromosome, but also by his having only one X-chromosome instead of two. It was rightly wondered whether his sex is the result of the singleness of the X-chromosome rather than of the presence of the Y-chromosome.

400

Moreover, it had been established that the Y-chromosome of Drosophila does *not* contain sex determiners. This is shown by the fact that exceptional flies with one X- but no Y-chromosome (XO) are males, and flies with two X- and one or even two Y-chromosomes (XXY and XXYY) are females. (As discussed on pages 239–240, XO males arise from fertilization by X sperm of eggs which by rare nondisjunction at meiosis had both X-chromosomes pass into a polar nucleus, or by fertilization of normal X eggs by O sperm which by nondisjunction received neither an X- nor a Y-chromosome. XXY females arise from fertilization by Y sperm of eggs whose two X-chromosomes nondisjunctionally passed together into the egg nucleus, or from fertilization by nondisjunctional XY sperm of normal eggs. XXYY females appear among the granddaughters of XXY mothers.) Contrary to Drosophila, in the silkworm *Bombyx mori* chromosomally similar abnormal individuals made it clear that the Y-chromosome carries sex determiners. Does man's Y-chromosome resemble that of Drosophila or of Bombyx?

This question was answered in the same way as that concerning Drosophila and Bombyx. Humans were found who have 45 chromosomes (instead of 46) because they have only one X-chromosome and lack a Y-chromosome. Such XO persons are females! Other individuals were found who have 47 chromosomes because they have two X-chromosomes and a Y-chromosome. Such XXY persons are males! The Y-chromosome, then, determines maleness, normally in XY individuals, abnormally in XXY. And the absence of the Y-chromosome determines femaleness, normally in XX individuals, abnormally in XO. Thus, man's Y-chromosome, in sex determination, resembles that of the silkworm Bombyx and not that of the fly Drosophila. Man's Y-chromosome is not peculiar among mammals. At the same time the male-determining function of the Y-chromosome was discovered in man, proof of the same function was established for the Y-chromosome of the mouse. It needs to be added that the known exceptional human XO and XXY persons show certain abnormal traits. These will be discussed in more detail in the section on variations in sexual differentiation.

The Balance Theory of Sex Determination. Experiments with plants and animals, and particularly Goldschmidt's experiments on the gypsy moth *Lymantria,* have shown that the sex of an individual is not the result of either pure male or pure female tendencies. Rather, in the development of either sex, both male and female determiners are at work—stronger male than female ones in the origin of males, and the reverse in the origin of females. We may assume that the same "balance theory" of sex holds for man. Presumably, a human male has genes for maleness not only in the Y-chromosome but also in the X-chromosome, or the autosomes, or in both of these; and, in addition, genes for femaleness in the X-chromosome, or autosomes, or in both. He is a male because the male determiners "outweigh" the female ones. Conversely, although a human female presumably has genes for both maleness and femaleness, in the absence of the strong male-determining factor carried by the Y-chromosome, the female determiners out-weigh the male ones.

If the simplest situation is postulated, only one F locus for femaleness and one M locus for maleness could be assumed to exist in the complement of X-chromosome and autosomes and one additional M_Y locus in the Y-chromosome. If we assign an F and an M locus to an autosome, the female, with its two sets of autosomes, would have the genetic formula $FFMM$; and the male, with its two sets of autosomes and the Y-chromosome, the formula $FFMMM_Y$. This formulation would imply that in females femaleness FF is stronger than maleness MM, but that a reversal in the balance in favor of maleness occurs when FF is opposed by MMM_Y. It is likely that several types of F and M occur at different loci, rather than as one gene each at a single autosomal locus. The essential aspects of the balance theory of sex determination would remain unchanged.

The biochemical action of the different postulated F and M genes may differ from locus to locus. Some loci may control the quantity or the molecular make-up of substances which act as embryonic sex hormones, and thus direct development into male or female direction; other loci may control the developmental response of embryonic tissues to such hormones; and still other loci may determine the sexual development of cells and tissues autonomously. We shall return to these possibilities in the course of this chapter.

Balance Theory and Intersexuality. There are various ways in which the developmental effect of one or the other of the opposing sex genes may be weakened. These genes, like other types of genes, may occur in different allelic forms. If, for instance, a specific F' allele had a weak female influence, the balance between F and M, even in an individual without a Y-chromosome, might not be shifted enough in favor of femaleness to form a normal female, and an "intersex" would develop. The same result could be due to a special allele M' with stronger male tendencies than the usual M allele, so that a fertilized egg, in spite of having no Y-chromosome, might develop not into a female, but into an intersex. Conversely, a fertilized egg with one X- and one Y-chromosome might develop not into a male but into an inter-sex, if it possessed either an unusually strong F allele or an unusually weak M allele. The unusual alleles could be either dominant or recessive, and, if there are many F and M loci in all chromosomes, either sex linked or autosomal. These considerations suggest that intersexes may be either XX or XY in constitution and that the degree of intersexuality may vary with degree of allelic strength. Detailed studies of human anatomical sex deviants support these opinions (see pp. 415–418).

Parthenogenesis and Sex. In various animals which reproduce by fertiliza-tion of eggs by sperm, very rarely unfertilized eggs have been known to develop. This parthenogenetic development in mammals, with the possible exception of some special experiments with rabbits, has never been observed to lead to living young. If parthenogenesis occurred in man, could it be identified with certainty, and what would be the sex of a parthenogenetically produced child? The first part of the question has been answered by skin grafting. Since a parthenogenetic offspring would not possess any genes which are not also present in the mother, skin from the child grafted onto the mother should not produce the usual antigenic reaction between the host tissue and the genetically different graft—a reaction which leads to sloughing off of the latter (Fig. 216, p. 549). A number of presumed parthenogenetic children and their mothers have been tested by blood-group determinations, and for all but one there was evidence of blood-group genes contributed by a father. In the one case in which fertilization could not be proven on blood-grouping and certain other grounds, recourse was made to skin grafting. The graft did not survive, a fact which made it seem very likely that the child did have a father.

Since a parthenogenetic child could obtain only X-chromosomes and no Y-chromosome from its mother, its sex would most likely be female. It is obvious that, at present, biological discussions regarding human parthenogenesis are purely theoretical.

Normal Sex Differentiation

The mechanism of normal sex determination—by means of the XX–XY alternative—forms only the genetic basis for the developmental processes which transform a fertilized egg into either a female or a male.

Embryonic Sex Differentiation.   A zygote of either XX or XY constitution transforms itself, within six to seven weeks after fertilization, into an embryo which, morphologically, is neutral; that is, neither female nor male in its sexual morphology. The embryo possesses gonads which consist of two parts: an external layer of tissue, the cortex, characteristic of an ovary; and, also, an internal mass, the medulla, characteristic of a testis (Fig. 164). Furthermore, two pairs of ducts are present in the neutral embryo (Fig. 165)— the Mullerian and the Wolffian ducts—only one of which is found in a normal, sexually differentiated individual, the Mullerian ducts persisting in the female and the Wolffian in the male. Finally, the region which is destined to include the openings of the urinary and genital ducts, the urogenital sinus, and the embryonic parts which are to be transformed into the external genitalia are still in such a primitive state that either sexual form may develop from them.

Only after the neutral stage of development of sexual rudiments, does the genetic sex constitution of the embryo begin to exert a visible differential effect. In an embryo whose cells are XX, the cortical part of the gonad develops greatly, while the medullary part becomes inconspicuous; in other words, the neutral gonad is transformed into an ovary. In an embryo whose cells are XY, the reverse happens: the medullary part of the gonad enlarges

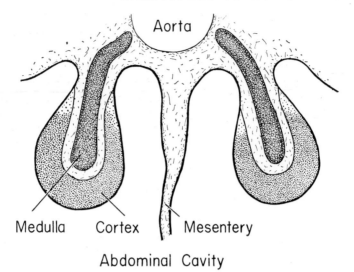

FIG. 164. Diagram representing the arrangement of cortex and medulla in the embryonic gonads as seen in a cross section of the embryo (After Witschi, *Recent Progr. Hormone Res.,* **6,** 1951.)

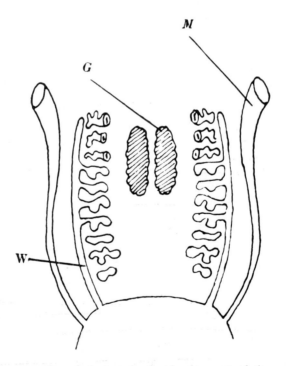

FIG. 165. Diagram of neutral stage in the development of the genital ducts in mammals. M = Mullerian duct; W = Wolffian duct; G = gonad. (Goldschmidt.)

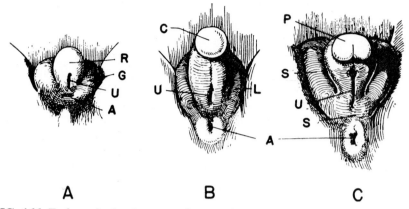

FIG. 166. Embryonic development of external genitalia in man.   A. Neutral stage.
B. Female differentiation.   C. Male differentiation. R = genital rudiment; C =
clitoris; P = penis; G = genital wall; L = labium majus; S = scrotal regions; U =
urogenital opening; A = anus. (Goldschmidt.)

and differentiates, while the cortical part disappears, except for remnants,
and the neutral gonad becomes a testis.

While these sexual differentiations are occurring in the gonads, other differentiating processes are taking place in the internal sexual ducts and the
embryonic rudiments of the external genitalia. In an XX embryo, the Mullerian ducts become the oviducts, uterus, and upper part of the vagina of a
female, while the Wolffian ducts degenerate, except for small remnants. In
contrast, in an XY embryo, the Wolffian ducts become the sperm ducts of
a male, while the Mullerian ducts disappear, except for small remnants. The
urogenital sinus and the external genital rudiments enter two divergent courses
of development (Fig. 166). In an XX embryo, the sinus forms the lining of
the lower part of the vagina; in an XY embryo, the urethra. In an XX
embryo, the external genital rudiments become the clitoris and the labia; in
an XY embryo, the penis and the scrotum.

Secondary Sex Differences.   In a newborn child, sexual differentiation is
not yet complete. Secondary differences between men and women—that is,
differences apart from internal and external genital ones—develop during
puberty. These are anatomical differences between the larynx of XX and
XY individuals, resulting in female or male voice; differences in general body
growth and relative growth of various parts of the body, resulting, for
instance, in the female or male morphology of the pelvic region and in the
development of the female breasts or the undeveloped mammary glands of
the male; differences in growth of hair; and many other differences.

Sex Hormones and Adult Differentiation.   The development of the secondary sex characters throws some light on the problem of how the XX and the

XY genotypes produce their effect. Experiments involving removal, replacement, and exchanges of gonads in experimental animals—particularly
rats, guinea pigs, and rabbits—and operations performed for various medical
or sociological reasons on men and women have shown that the differentiation
of secondary sex characters is brought about by hormones. Young males
and females from whom the gonads have been removed retain an immature,
infantile body form and develop no secondary sex differences. If an ovary
is again implanted into a castrated female, or a testis into a castrated male,
differentiation of the secondary characteristics takes place. Experiments such
as these show that the sex glands (ovaries in females and testes in males)
secrete hormones into the blood stream which cause the sexual differentiation
of various parts of the body. These hormonal relations are more complicated
than the preceding sentence indicates. Actually, the glands of each sex secrete
several types of both female and male hormones; and it is, primarily, a
matter of male hormones being in excess of female hormones, or vice versa,
which controls differentiation. This hormonal dualism in both sexes is a
counterpart of the genetic balance in sex determination.

The gonads are not the only organs which control the production of the
sex hormones. A complex functional interaction among the various glands
of internal secretion leads to a balanced stimulation and inhibition of
hormonal output in the mammalian body. Particularly important in this
interacting system are the gonads, the pituitary, and the adrenals. Some of
the secretions of the adrenal cortex itself act as sex hormones, some male
and others female.

By means of hormonal treatment certain secondary sexual characters can
be transformed from one type into another. Thus, if the testis of a male
guinea pig is removed and an ovary implanted, the rudimentary male mammary apparatus enlarges and milk secretion may occur. The same results
achieved with implantation can be obtained by injection of sex hormones
into castrated animals.

Even primary sexual characters, such as clitoris and penis, are influenced
by sex hormones. In males, a decrease in amount of male sex hormones
may lead to decreased size of the penis; in females, an excess of male hormones may cause the clitoris to enlarge. These experiments demonstrate that
the body does not develop female or male secondary characters because
its cells are either XX or XY, but that either type of body cells is able to
react developmentally in two directions. In a female hormonal "environment,"
both XX and XY cells may tend to build a female body; and in a male
hormonal "environment," the same XX and XY cells may tend to build a
male body. The formation of secondary sexual traits is, in our terminology
(see Chap. 3), not a fully autonomous process controlled by the genotype
of the cells which participate in it, but a process which is partly dependent
on the distant control of the gonads and other organs.

In the embryo the normal alternative sexual differentiation (of the internal
genital ducts and of the external genitalia) is likewise dependent on the

Progestational agents
als agents

type of gonad present. Presence of an embryonic testis is necessary for male-type development of ducts and external organs. The Wolffian ducts are made to persist and to differentiate, while the Mullerian ducts are inhibited and disappear. The neutral primordia of the external genitalia are stimulated toward development of male structures. It is remarkable that female-type development is not the result of the presence of an embryonic ovary, but rather of the absence of an embryonic testis. This has been shown experimentally in rabbits and mice, where removal or destruction of the embryonic gonad—regardless of whether it was destined to develop into a testis or an ovary—results in disappearance of the Wolffian ducts and in typical female differentiation of the Mullerian ducts, the urogenital sinus, and the external genital organs. It may be expected that the same course of development would be taken by human embryos whose embryonic gonads failed to develop, but decisive evidence is still lacking (see p. 412).

The nonautonomous alternative sexual development of various parts of the body applies to the germ cells themselves. An XX primordial germ cell typically develops into an egg, not because it has two X-chromosomes, but rather because it finds itself in the cortical part of a gonad; and an XY primordial germ cell develops into sperm cells, not in response to its own chromosomal constitution, but as directed by its medullary location in a gonad.

Somewhere, of course, in normal development, the genetic constitution is decisive. This decisive stage is apparently reached when the neutral gonad is laid down. If the somatic cells of the gonad are XX, then the germ cells located in the cortical layers proliferate more than do those in the medulla, while the opposite happens when the gonadal cells are XY. It seems that the sexual genotype exerts its influence directly at this stage only, delegating the further control of the suitable sexual development to various hormonal influences.

The concept of hormonal determination of sexual traits is by no means opposed to the theory of genetic sex determination. Hormones are the "tools" by means of which the genetic constitution of the embryo normally directs its sexual development. An understanding of the causal chain which begins with genes, continues with hormones, and ends with sexual differentiation leads one to expect, rather than to be astonished by, the fact that the genetic mechanism may be partly overridden experimentally. As we have seen, the mammary glands of a male guinea pig can be made to develop a female phenotype by introducing female sex hormones artificially. In women, tumors in an adrenal gland may cause it to secrete a large amount of a male sex hormone, resulting in excessive facial hair growth, deepening of voice, and other secondary male characters. Considering that the phenotypic expression of a genotype is not fixed but depends on the environment in which it becomes realized, we should be no more surprised by these facts than by the fact that starvation of a genetically tall child may cause development of a small adult.

Variations in Sexual Differentiation

In almost all embryos, the XX–XY mechanism of genetic sex determination results in the successful formation of individuals of the appropriate normal sex. Occasionally, however, variations in development occur which lead to abnormal sex differentiation. In extreme cases, zygotes of a given "chromosomal sex" may develop into persons of the opposite "bodily sex," or into individuals who possess, side by side, traits typical of both sexes. An understanding of the origin of such variations depends on an understanding of many aspects of sexual differentiation: genetic, developmental, hormonal. Although great progress has been made in these fields, much still remains undecided. One fact stands out already: The diversity of abnormal sex types in man cannot be arranged along a simple scale from normal males to normal females. Rather, there is evidence for a diversity of processes which may lead to the different variations in the development of sexual traits.

Certain inherited variations in sexual traits are not caused by abnormal processes of sex determination but represent the specific development of normal sexual attributes. These variations include racial differences, as well as normal differences between individuals of the same population, in size and configuration of external genitalia and breasts, and in type of beard. Some genetically caused abnormalities in the development of sex characters are likewise not part of sex determination as such. Presence of supernumerary mammary glands, in males and females, in some kindreds obviously has a genetic basis, analogous to the inheritance of extra fingers and toes (Fig. 167). The opposite result, absence of nipples and breasts in both sexes, has also been encountered (Fig. 168). Another abnormality of the mammary gland, gynecomasty, is more interesting, since it leads to female-type development of the organ in otherwise often typical males (Fig. 169). In some cases of gynecomasty, there is evidence for genetic causation. Perhaps the genotype of the mammary tissue of these males results in a changed response to the normal mixture of male and female sex hormones—a response which leads to well-developed breasts. This possibility is suggested by the

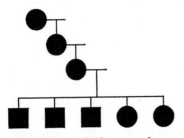

FIG. 167. Inheritance of supernumerary mammary glands (polymasty). (After Komai, 1934.)

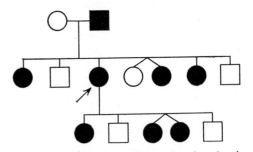

FIG. 168. Part of a pedigree showing dominant inheritance of absence of nipples and breasts. (After Fraser, in *Novant'Anni delle Leggi Mendeliane,* L. Gedda edit., 1955.)

existence in races of chickens of roosters that are hen-feathered. Experiments on these roosters have shown that the testicular hormones are perfectly normal, but that the feather primordia respond to them in atypical fashion.

Another abnormality of male development which occurs once in every few hundred births is hypospadia, the misplacement of the opening of the ureter from the end of the penis to a lower position. Since, in the female, the ureter typically does not enter the clitoris, hypospadia is an approach toward a female trait. Some types of hypospadia are indeed part of fundamentally intersexual development (as discussed on pp. 415–418), but the common forms are only localized developmental deviations. in some cases there is no evidence for a genetic basis, but in others recessive as well as, more rarely, dominant transmission is encountered (Fig. 170).

As an example of genetically conditioned sexual variations, extreme sexual precocity may be cited. Males in certain kindreds and females

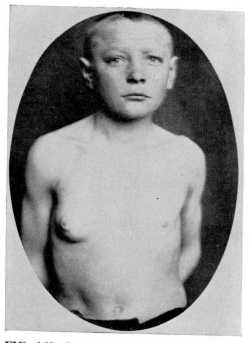

FIG. 169. Gynecomasty on the right side of a 14-year-old boy. For a discussion of the possible origin of this mosaic phenotype, see p. 420.

in other kindreds develop signs of sexual maturity, such as growth of axillary and pubic hair or development of the breasts, years before the normal ages of adolescence. Figure 171 shows part of a kindred in which altogether 27 males, in four generations, showed precocious maturity, in some as early as two years of age. Inheritance is clearly dominant, through both males and females, with no expression in any female and incomplete penetrance in the male. A short pedigree of sexual precocity in females, transmitted through an unaffected male, is shown in Figure 172. It is noteworthy that sexually precocious individuals in both kindreds married when they attained adulthood and that they had children.

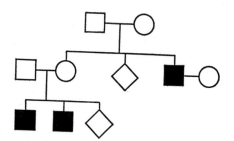

FIG. 170. Hypospadia. (Heuermann, 1767, after Kemp, in *Hdbch. Erbbiol. d. Mensch.*, **2**, 1940.)

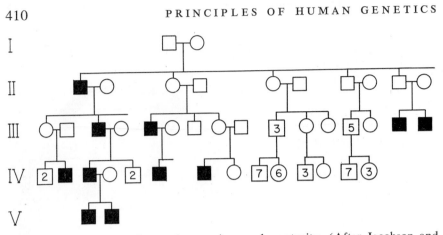

FIG. 171. Part of a pedigree of precocious male maturity. (After Jacobson and Macklin, *Pediatrics,* **9,** 1952.)

The "Chromosomal Sex." Hardly any information was available until 1949 on the chromosomal constitution of developmental sex deviants. This lack of knowledge was due to the difficulties of obtaining clearly analyzable mitotic or meiotic division stages.

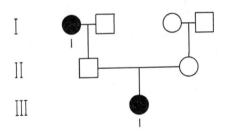

FIG. 172. Two cases of precocious female maturity. I–1 matured at 8 years, III–1 began to mature shortly after 6 years. (After Wilkins.)

A simple method for the determination of the "chromosomal sex" seemed to have become available in 1949, when Barr and his associates discovered that most nondividing nuclei in nerve cells of some cats possessed a special, small, stainable body which was absent in most nuclei of other cats, and when they showed that the cats in the first group were all females and those in the second all males. It was soon established that the *sex chromatin,* as the stainable body is called, occurs also in normal human females in cells from many tissues, including among others the epidermis, the oral mucosa, and the amniotic fluid of female fetuses (Fig. 173). It is absent or rare in cells of normal human males. The nature of the sex-chromatin body is not yet established. It seems to be related to special staining properties of the X-chromosome.

A variant of the sex chromatin occurs in the so-called neutrophil white blood cells. Here a "drumstick," consisting of a fine stainable thread and a round stainable head, protrudes from a nuclear lobe in a small percentage of female cells but is nearly absent in male cells (Fig. 174).

The discovery of the sex chromatin initiated a fruitful period, during which the cells of various types of developmental sex deviants were investigated. Individuals whose cells contained sex chromatin were usually interpreted

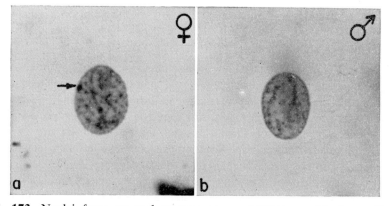

FIG. 173. Nuclei from an oral mucosa smear. 1800×. a. Nucleus with sex chromatin from a female.   b. Without sex chromatin from a male. (Grumbach and Barr, *Rec. Progr. Hormone Res.*, **14**, 1958. Acad. Press, New York.)

as "chromosomal females," and individuals whose cells contained no sex chromatin as "chromosomal males." Although these interpretations were valid for almost all sexually normal humans, they were only partly applicable to developmental sex deviants. This became known when C. E. Ford obtained and cultivated bone marrow cells from developmental sex deviants and analyzed the individual chromosomes in dividing cells with the use of modern methods (compare Chap. 2, p. 22). Sex-chromatin-positive individuals usually have two X-chromosomes and no Y-chromosome, and thus are truly chromosomal females; but the rare XXY individuals, who are chromosomal males, as judged by the possession of a Y-chromosome, are likewise chromatin positive. Conversely, sex-chromatin-negative individuals are usually XY, and thus chromosomal males; but the rare XO individuals, who are chromosomal females, as judged by the absence of a Y-chromosome, are likewise chromatin negative. It is now clear that decisive determinations of

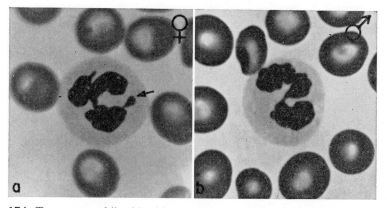

FIG. 174. Two neutrophil white blood cells.   a. With an accessory nuclear lobe ("drumstick").   b. Without the accessory lobe. (Grumbach and Barr.)

the chromosomal sex require detailed analysis of the numbers and kinds of chromosomes present.

Absence of Gonads (Gonadal Dysgenesis or Agenesis). Rare fundamental types of abnormal sexual development are found in certain persons who, according to their external and internal genital organs, appear to be females, but who, from surgical exploration, are found to have either no gonads or only rudimentary traces of them. Usually, these individuals are of small stature and retain an infantile development of the mammary glands and other parts (Turner's syndrome). Approximately 20 per cent of these individuals have sex-chromatin-positive nuclei, but most are sex-chromatin negative. The sex-chromatin-positive individuals are probably chromosomal XX females whose ovaries, for unknown reasons, did not develop. The sex-chromatin-negative individuals were at first interpreted as being chromosomal XY males whose testes, for unknown reasons, failed to develop. The female differentiation of their ducts and external genitalia would have been the result of the absence of an embryonic testis, or a condition similar to that obtained in the experiments on castration of young rabbits and mice (described on p. 407). This interpretation in terms of an XY chromosomal sex is correct for some such females. However, most individuals with true Turner's syndrome, whose chromosomes have now been studied in dividing cells, clearly possess 45 chromosomes, including one X-chromosome but no Y-chromosome. Therefore, they are chromosomal females, with not two but only one X-chromosome. It is probable that not all XO individuals are devoid of gonads. Perhaps some may be fertile females with or without Turner's syndrome. (The known XO mice are normal fertile females.)

Individuals of the chromosomal type XO probably originate in one of three ways: either from eggs which, in consequence of an accident in chromosomal distribution such as nondisjunction, did not receive a maternal chromosome and were fertilized by a normal X-chromosome-bearing sperm; or from normal X eggs fertilized by a sperm which, in consequence of abnormal chromosome distribution, did not receive either an X- or a Y-chromosome; or from fertilized XX or XY eggs in which one of the sex chromosomes was eliminated from a cell at an early cleavage stage with the descend-

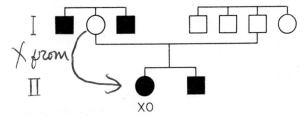

FIG. 175. Part of a pedigree containing a deuteranopic female affected with Turner's syndrome. (After W. Lenz.)

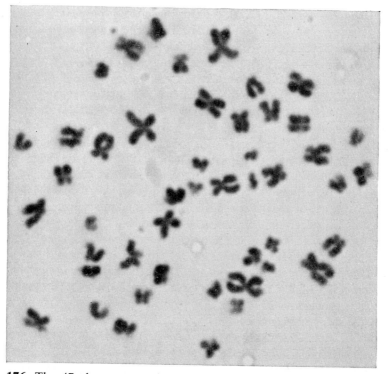

FIG. 176. The 47 chromosomes in a bone marrow cell of an XXY individual with Klinefelter's syndrome. (Original from Dr. C. E. Ford.)

ants of the resulting XO cell forming most or all of the embryo (see p. 419).

Independent proof of the single X constitution of females with Turner's syndrome has been provided by kindreds in which (sex-linked) red-green color blindness (deuteranopia) was present. In the kindred represented in Figure 175, II–1 was female-like, with the stigmata characteristic for gonadal dysgenesis. The sex-chromatin test was negative. The mother of the proposita had two color-blind brothers and was herself heterozygous for deuteranopia, as proven by a color-blind son. The father of the proposita had normal color vision and his daughter, the proposita, should therefore not be color blind—but she was. Presumably, this is due to her having only a single X-chromosome, derived from the mother. Apparently, her father's sperm carried neither an X- nor a Y-chromosome, or if it did carry either chromosome, it was lost early in the development of the zygote.

Underdevelopment of the Testes. In certain males with defective hormonal constitutions, the testes are abnormally small and usually do not contain mature sperm. These males are said to exhibit Klinefelter's syndrome. Approximately one-quarter of these men have sex-chromatin-negative nuclei, but the majority have chromatin-positive nuclei. Chromosomal study of one sex-chromatin-negative individual of the Klinefelter type showed him to be an XY male. Several affected sex-chromatin-positive individuals were found to be XXY males (Fig. 176). Underdevelopment of the testes may thus have at least two different causes, namely, either abnormal chromosomal constitution, XXY, or other factors acting in an XY male. Not enough normal males have been studied chromosomally to decide whether an occasional XXY individual is among them.

According to the cytological diagnosis, it had been expected in sex-chromatin-negative individuals with Klinefelter's syndrome, XY, that red-green color blindness would occur in the high frequency typical for males, but be rare in sex-chromatin-positive individuals, XXY. This expectation has been verified in individuals in the sex-chromatin-negative group. In the chromatin-positive group, color-blind Klinefelter individuals have been found whose fathers were normal, C, and whose mothers were heterozygous for color blindness, Cc. Presumably, the affected Klinefelter individuals had received two X-chromosomes from their mother and a Y-chromosome from their father, with both X-chromosomes carrying the allele c for color blindness. This production of homozygous nondisjunctional eggs from heterozygous females has long been known from Drosophila. It is the result of the presence of four X-chromosome strands at meiosis carrying C,C,c,c (see Fig. 118) and nondisjunctional assignment of two strands carrying c,c to the egg nucleus. The "creation" of homozygous XXY Klinefelter individuals from heterozygous mothers results in a higher frequency of color blindness among them than among XX females.

Individuals of XXY constitution presumably originate either by fertilization of an exceptional XX egg by a Y sperm or of a regular X egg by an exceptional XY sperm, or by nondisjunctional duplication of the X in an XY zygote. Persons of XXY constitution are thus "origin opposites" of those with XO constitution, since the latter—except for cases of chromosomal loss in early development—come from exceptional O eggs or O sperm. As irregular distribution of the sex chromosomes might lead either to XX or to O eggs and either to XY or to O sperm, it is not surprising that a sibship is known which contains both a Klinefelter-type individual and a Turner-type individual.

A Human XXX Female.   Exceptional eggs which, before being fertilized, contain two X-chromosomes should give rise to either XXY or XXX zygotes. Both types have been found in Drosophila. Since in this organism sex determination is independent of the Y-chromosome and depends, in the diploid, on the number of X-chromosomes—one X = male, two X = female—the constitution XXX genetically represents a greater degree of femaleness than does XX. Therefore the term "superfemale" has been applied to the XXX flies, although phenotypically they are "very tattered, very late hatching, hardly able to live and completely sterile" (Bridges). In view of their phenotype, the term "metafemale" (from the Greek *meta = beyond*) has recently been proposed as a substitute for superfemale.

In man the role of the X-chromosome in sex determination is not yet clear. Persons with Turner's syndrome who have one X- and no Y-chromosome are anatomically female-like. The female differentiation of their genital ducts and external genitalia may be regarded as the result of a female genotype or as the "neutral" consequence of the virtual absence of gonads. In either case one can only say that a single X-chromosome and two sets of autosomes, in the absence of a Y-chromosome, permit female-like development—the absence of gonads being a result of chromosomal unbalance, unknown as to its sex-determining or simply developmentally disturbing nature.

In the mouse, XO animals are fertile females indistinguishable from XX females. In this mammal at least, the X-chromosome seems to have no over-all male- or female-determining tendency. If an XXX mouse should be found, one might expect it to be a female, like XX and XO mice, and perhaps somewhat abnormal in various ways on account of the unbalance caused by too many X-chromosomal genes. In man, an XXX individual, having a total of 47 chromosomes, has been discovered. This person is a female but with underdeveloped primary and secondary sex characters—defects which may be the consequences of general genic imbalance and not necessarily of imbalance in regard to sex-determining genes, or they may be unrelated to the XXX constitution of this woman.

Intersexuality.   Occasionally, individuals are born who possess gonads of one sex but ducts and external genitalia typical of, or approaching, those of the other sex. Some of these individuals possess both ovarial and testicular tissues, either more or less mixed in "ovotestes" or in separate ovaries and testes. Frequently, the gonads on opposite sides of the body are not alike: one may be an ovary, the other an ovotestis; or one an ovotestis, and the other purely testicular. In some individuals, an ovary and a testis have been found on each side, possibly the result of separation of ovotestes into male and female parts.

In many of these intersexes, the sexual ducts are incompletely formed. The intersexes may have parts derived from both the Mullerian and the Wolffian ducts, or only male or female ducts may be present. Externally, they may be predominantly female or male in appearance, or may represent mixtures of the characters of the two sexes. In no case is a person provided with two complete and functioning sexual systems. In a few individuals, one system is developed well enough to function, but almost all intersexes are sterile.

People who possess characteristics of both sexes have always awakened curiosity. The Greeks imagined the existence of beings who were endowed with the full attributes of both men and women. Such beings were called *hermaphrodites,* after the god Hermes and the goddess Aphrodite. In modern times, the term hermaphroditism is frequently used in the medical literature, but it refers to the various imperfect phenotypes which have been labeled intersexual in this book.

For descriptive purposes it has been customary to distinguish "true" hermaphroditism, in which both ovarial and testicular tissues occur, from pseudohermaphroditism, in which only one type of gonad exists, together with internal or external traits of the other sex. One speaks of male pseudohermaphroditism when testes are present and of female pseudohermaphroditism when ovaries are present. Each of these types of hermaphroditism comprises a variety of phenotypes, and it is probable that various mechanisms are responsible for them. In the following discussion, only some of the main types will be described.

Pedigree studies show that human intersexuality may be caused by a specific genetic situation which overrides the typical XX–XY mechanism of sex determination. Often, however, only a single intersex appears in a kindred, and no hereditary transmission can be demonstrated. Nevertheless, even the appearance of sporadic intersexes may be determined by genetic causes: There may be rare recessive genes which become homozygous in an individual, or a combination of polygenes may reach the threshold of intersexual determination. Or, possibly, mutations, autosomal dominant or sex linked, may occasionally give rise to intersexuality, the mutant allele disappearing again from the genic population when the intersex dies without having left offspring. In addition, some intersexes may be phenocopies, caused by developmental accidents.

Most frequently, female pseudohermaphroditism is caused by an overdevelopment of the fetal adrenal cortex. Although the excess of male hormone released by the cortex results in masculinization, it never leads to a fully developed male. Normal oviducts and a normal uterus are present, but a small vagina may open into the urethra. The external genitalia, although not typically male, approach this type of sexual differentiation. These female pseudohermaphrodites are sex-chromatin positive. Excessive adrenal cortical secretion, which can also occur in later life, is sometimes caused by a tumor of the gland. Women in whom this happens undergo a change of voice, grow heavy facial hair, and develop other male traits. These symptoms of "virilism" disappear after successful treatment of the adrenal cortex.

Female pseudohermaphroditism from adrenal overactivity often appears in more than one member of the family, and side by side with boys in whom the adrenal effect causes sexual precocity. The trait is often genetically conditioned, but the exact mode of inheritance is not known.

Testicular Feminization. There is a type of inherited male pseudohermaphroditism in which genetic transmission is rather clear. These relatively common intersexes resemble, and regard themselves as, females. Internally, except for a small vagina, they lack female structures and possess testes and derivatives of the Wolffian ducts. These male pseudohermaphrodites (sometimes referred to as cases of testicular feminization) often marry male partners. Reproduction obviously cannot occur. Part of a pedigree from

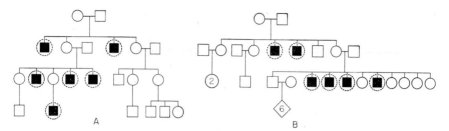

FIG. 177. Pedigrees of male pseudohermaphroditism (testicular feminization). Solid square inside interrupted circle = affected individual. (A, after Petterson and Bonnier; B, after Burgermeister, *J. génét. hum.*, **2**, 1953.)

Switzerland and a pedigree from Sweden are given in Figure 177. The pedigrees show that the intersexuality is transmitted by normal females and that, among the sibs of the 6 male pseudohermaphrodites in B, there were 8 normal sisters and 2 normal brothers. One of these had 6 normal children. From the combined data on fifteen families reported from various countries, it was found that the proportions of females to males to intersexes are 75:20:63. The numbers, and an inspection of the pedigrees, suggest strongly that carrier women are heterozygous for an abnormal allele which, in an XY individual, results in male pseudohermaphroditism. According to this assumption, some of the 75 normal females are free from the abnormal allele and some carry it. The 20 normal males are free from it, but the 63 intersexes have obtained it from their mothers. Among the children of carrier females, one might expect equality between the number of males and the number of intersexes. The proportion, 20:63, at first does not seem to agree with this expectation. The disagreement is, however, spurious, because it depends on the method of ascertainment (pp. 133ff.): Since the sibships were ascertained through the presence of the intersexes, and since the compilation included only those pedigrees in which at least 2 affected individuals were reported, all those sibships which contained only normal females and normal males from carrier mothers escaped notice. Had it been possible to include these sibships in the total, a 2 female:1 male:1 intersex ratio presumably would have resulted. Some investigators have failed to appreciate the fact that, under the method of ascertainment, a deficiency of males, as compared to intersexes, is an expected feature of the simple genetic interpretation. This has led to some ingenious, but unnecessary, genetic or developmental hypotheses.

It may be added that this type of inheritance—of an allele which is without effect in females but which causes pseudohermaphroditism in males—is compatible with either autosomal or sex-linked transmission. If the allele is called *Tr* and assumed to be in an autosome, then XX *Tr tr* = female, XY *Tr tr* = intersex. If *Tr* is in the X-chromosome, then $X^{Tr} X^{tr}$ = female, $X^{Tr} Y$ = intersex. It may be possible to determine the method of genetic transmission if the transmission of red-green color blindness, *c,* is followed in pedigrees with male pseudohermaphroditism. If Tr is autosomal, women who are heterozygous for both $Tr\,tr$ and Cc would show independent assortment of the two pairs of genes in their offspring since C is sex linked. They might show linkage if both loci are in the X-chromosome.

Sex-chromatin studies on more than forty male pseudohermaphrodites have exclusively yielded chromatin-negative nuclei, and chromosome analyses on some have shown the presence of 46 chromosomes, including an XY pair.

The genic action in male pseudohermaphroditism is suspected to be mediated by abnormal testicular hormones. This permits or directs the development of embryonic and adult tissues of the genital organs, the mammary glands, and other parts into a female, instead of a male, pathway. The Tr gene may also have a slight effect in otherwise normal carrier women, since some of them, like their intersexual offspring, lack axillary and pubic hair, and their sexual maturity seems to be delayed.

True Hermaphroditism. True hermaphroditism—the presence of both ovarian and testicular tissue, either in separate ovaries and testes or in ovotestes—is much rarer than pseudohermaphroditism. In intersexual animals and plants, the formation of both female and male parts in the same gonad is well known. Although the balance of M and F genes in normal individuals is clearly established, so that M outweighs F in males, and F outweighs M in females, in intersexes it is so close to an unstable equilibrium that minor accidental fluctuations within the same gonad may shift some cells into male and others into female differentiation. In human intersexes, the presence of both ovarian and testicular tissue, either within ovotestes or in separate ovaries and testes, may be the result of a constitution which permits a tipping of the scale of differentiation here toward one and there toward the other sex.

Hermaphrodites may have internal organs derived from either Wolffian or Mullerian ducts, or both. The variability from individual to individual is great. This variability can be better appreciated if it is realized that the masculinizing secretion of a fetal testis does not seem to exert its influences equally on all suitable parts of the body, but particularly on the tissues located close to the testis. If, in a fetus, much testicular tissue occurs on one side of the body and ovarian tissue mostly on the other side, then a vas deferens may form on the testicular side and an oviduct and uterus on the ovarian side.

The nuclei in most of the hermaphrodites studied have been found to be sex-chromatin positive, though in at least one case the dimensions of the sex chromatin seemed smaller than usual. The reasons for this are not understood. One hermaphrodite is reported to have had sex-chromatin-negative nuclei only.

Gynandromorphism

In insects, we are acquainted with a type of sexual abnormality which is different from intersexuality and is known as gynandromorphism (*gynē =*

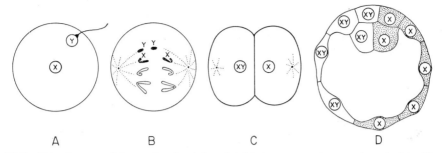

FIG. 178. One possible mode of origin of a human gynandromorph.   A. Fertilization of an egg by a Y sperm.   B. First cleavage division with abnormal distribution of the sister Y-chromosomes.   C. The resulting two-cell stage consisting of one XY (male) and one XO (female) cell.   D. Cross section through blastocyst with XY and XO cells.

woman; *anēr, andros* = man). Gynandromorphs are individuals who are composed, mosaic-like, of normal female and normal male parts. Their chromosomal constitution corresponds to their mosaic appearance. In a Drosophila gynandromorph, for instance, the female parts have two X-chromosomes in their cells, the male parts only one X-chromosome. (It should be remembered that in Drosophila, the female–male alternative is controlled by the 2X–1X alternative, the Y-chromosome not being sex determining.) The two different constitutions in cells which developed from a single egg are the result of some irregularity in the formation of the mature egg or in the distribution of the X-chromosomes in the divisions of the fertilized egg.

Instead of describing such an irregularity for an insect egg, in which it is well understood, let us consider an analogous hypothetical example in a human egg (Fig. 178). At the left of the figure (A), an egg is shown fertilized by a Y sperm. During the first, or a later, cleavage division (B), one of the daughter halves of the Y-chromosome happens to lag behind on the mitotic spindle and fails to become included in one of the daughter nuclei (C). Consequently, the derivatives, by further division of the two nuclei, will belong to two different types (D): XY and XO, the first of male and the second of female chromosomal sex. Later, when gonadal tissue is formed in the embryo, the XY cells might form testes and the XO cells ovaries, given that the latter genotype does not always result in gonadal dysgenesis. Gynandromorphs with testicular and ovarial tissue could also be produced by embryos which start as exceptional XXY zygotes, but lose, in part of their cells, the Y-chromosome, and thus consist of male XXY and female XX tissues.

Sex hormones, as found in mammals, are absent in most insects, whose sexual traits are determined autonomously according to the genetic constitution of the cells which form each part. This accounts for the sharply mosaic character of insect gynandromorphs. In man, a genetic setup for gynandromorphism could not lead to clear-cut sexual mosaics, since the mixture of sex hormones present in an individual with both ovary and testis would cause intersexual development of internal and external sex structures irrespective of their XY or XO or their XXY and XX constitution. The gonads themselves would probably not be typical either, but would presumably be influenced by the existence of both types of cells in the same body.

Are human hermaphrodites indeed gynandromorphic mosaics of male and female cells? Or are they uniform in their chromosomal constitution, and thus purely developmental intersexes? Sex-chromatin determinations of cells taken from different parts of the bodies of the few hermaphrodites studied have shown only one type of nucleus in each individual, either all positive or all negative. This suggests, but does not prove, the absence of gynandromorphism in these hermaphrodites. If, in an early stage of development of a human egg, one-half of the cells should remain chromosomally male and the other half female, it is not necessarily to be expected that a bilateral gynandromorph would result. The distribution of the two types of cells and their descendents to different parts of the developing embryo probably varies from embryo to embryo. Therefore, it is possible that, for example, large parts of the skin on both sides of the body are derived from, and consist of, cells of one chromosomal type, while internally one side may possess chromosomally female cells and the other side male cells. It will not be surprising if some hermaphrodites will be found to be true chromosomal sex mosaics, but many of them are probably chromosomally uniform intersexes.

Kemp has published photographs of a person whom he regards as a true gynandromorph. This individual has a female-type breast on the right and a male-type mammary gland on the left side. On part of the left side of the chin, a beard has grown. No detailed description of the genitalia or gonads is available. Sex-chromatin studies could not be made. Although the information is incomplete, this individual may well have been a true gynandromorph. If so, it would show that the cells of the mammary glands and of the hair follicles of the chin respond differentially to the same hormonal mixture as it circulates in the blood stream of this individual. The female cells of one mammary gland form a breast, the male cells of the other do not; and the female cells of part of the chin do not produce beard growth, the male cells do.

Perhaps cases like that of the one-sided gynecomastic boy shown in Figure 169 can also be explained by the absence of the Y-chromosome from a cell whose descendents formed tissues including those of his right breast.

There exists some additional evidence for chromosomal sex mosaicism. Among the very rare known cases in which twin embryos of different genotypes have exchanged blood-forming cells and later contain mixtures of red blood cells with different antigens, several pairs have been found in which the two twins are of different sex. Two of the male twins, 86 and 61 per cent, respectively, of whose blood cells came from their own tissues and

14 and 39 per cent from transferred tissues of their twin sisters, showed drumsticks—indicative of female chromosomal constitution—in some of their white blood cells. These twins were blood and sex mosaics.

Direct proof of mosaicism in chromosomal type has apparently been obtained for one of the individuals with Klinefelter's syndrome. The majority of bone marrow cells from this male had 47 chromosomes, including two X and one Y, but nearly one-third of the cells had 46 chromosomes and lacked the Y-chromosome. No specific hermaphroditic condition was apparent, and it is likely that the initial loss of a Y-chromosome from a cell had occurred late enough in development to have left as XXY most of the tissues involved in sexual differentiation.

Medical Treatment of Intersexuality. The details of intersexual development are complex, and this account has touched upon only a few of them. An understanding of the typical hormonal interrelations between gonads and secondary sex characters makes it easy to see that the removal of a gonad or the use of hormonal treatment may, in some cases, help in changing the phenotype of an intersex toward that of a normal person. If, for instance, an ovary and an ovotestis are present, removal of the latter may, through the action of the remaining ovary, result in female development. Only those parts of the body, such as the mammary glands, which may still have enough plasticity to respond to the ovarian hormones can be influenced by such a removal. Surgery may provide further means of restoring a normal phenotype.

The discussion of these abnormal conditions serves to illuminate the nature of sex determination in general. The margin of safety between the balance of female and male genetic tendencies is ample in most developing individuals. Only very rarely is the balance so abnormal that an imperfect sex results.

Genetic and Psychological Aspects of Sex. We have seen that in individuals with developmental sex deviations or in intersexes there may be disagreement between the chromosomal and the phenotypic sex. Psychologically, most of these persons regard themselves as belonging to that sex which they phenotypically represent, or approach. These psychological identifications are presumably the result of sociological influences, such as being "assigned" a sex by parents and the consequent rearing either as a boy or a girl. In general, the chromosomal sex as such seems to play no role, or at most only a subordinate one, in a person's sex identification.

It is not known whether some of the variations in the sex behavior of men and women have a genetic basis. In other mammals, a genetic basis for variations in sex behavior is known to exist. Thus, to identical treatment with male sex hormones, different strains of guinea pigs respond with different intensities of sex drive. In cattle, different strains of bulls kept under equal environmental conditions produce very different amounts of sperm, a property which may be related to sex behavior. In man, it is at present impossible to separate nongenetic from genetic factors and to assign them proportional responsibility for sex behavior. In male homosexuality, sex-chromatin studies have shown chromatin-negative-nuclei, suggesting that the chromosomal sex is male. In studies on twins, Kallmann has found that the genetically identical twin brother of a homosexual nearly always possesses the same tendency, but that a genetically nonidentical twin brother of a homosexual possesses the same tendency in less than one-half of the cases (see Chapter 27). Although such evidence is regarded by some as indicative of genetic factors, there is still the possibility of an explanation based primarily on environmental influences.

Problems

160. If it were possible to change the development of an XX-zygote so that a functional male resulted, what would be the sex of the offspring of such an individual?

161. If an XY-zygote could develop into a functional female, what would be the sex ratio among her offspring? (Note: A fertilized egg without an X-chromosome will probably die.)

162. It is possible—though not established (1960)—that human XXY and XO individuals may sometimes be fertile males and females, respectively. (a) If these individuals marry chromosomally normal spouses, what sex ratios would be expected among the offspring? (b) If a fertile XO individual who carries hemophilia were to marry a nonhemophilic spouse, what would be the genotypes and phenotypes of the offspring?

163. Assume that nondisjunction of the sex chromosomes occurs at the first meiotic division in 2 out of 1,000 oocytes and spermatocytes each. If the nondisjunctional gametes were to fuse with normal gametes, what would be the frequencies of XXY and XO individuals from nondisjunction in: (a) the mothers, and (b) the fathers?

164. For inherited testicular feminization, as represented in the pedigrees in Figure 177, it has been assumed that an X-linked allele Tr is responsible for the transformation of male zygotes into intersexes. What, according to this assumption, are the genotypes of all individuals in the pedigrees? If more than one genotype is possible, list alternatives.

165. The nucleus of a fertilized egg contains two X-chromosomes, one with the gene for normal color vision, the other with an allele for color blindness. Assume that the first X-chromosome is eliminated during an early cleavage division and that approximately the right half of the developing individual is formed from the descendants of the cell which had received only one X-chromosome. In this individual, what type of color vision would you expect in: (a) the left eye, and (b) the right eye? (c) What would be the sexual type of the individual?

166. Assume that a fertilized egg has two X-chromosomes, one with the gene for normal color vision, the other with an allele for color blindness.

(a) If an abnormality in the distribution of the chromosomes in an early cleavage mitosis resulted in one daughter nucleus receiving two X-chromosomes, each with the gene for normal, and the other daughter nucleus receiving two

X-chromosomes, each with the allele for color blindness, what might be the color vision of the two eyes?

(b) What would be the sex of this individual?

(c) If the germ cells formed in this individual happened to be descended from: (i) The cleavage cell with the two normal alleles, (ii) the cleavage cell with the two color-blind alleles, what types of sons could be produced?

References

Booth, P. B., Plaut, G., James, J. D., Ikin, E. W., Moores, P., Sanger, R., and Race, R. R., 1957. Blood chimerism in a pair of twins. *Brit. Med. J.,* **1**: 1456–1458.

Ford, C. E., Jones, K. W., Polani, P. E., deAlmeida, J. C., and Briggs, J. H., 1959. A sex-chromosome anomaly in a case of gonadal dysgenesis (Turner's syndrome). *Lancet,* **1**: 711–713.

Ford, C. E., Polani, P. E., Briggs, J. H., and Bishop, P. M. F., 1959. A presumptive human XXY/XX mosaic. *Nature,* **183**: 1030–1032.

Goldschmidt, R., 1931. *Die sexuellen Zwischenstufen.* 528 pp. Springer, Berlin.

Greenblatt, R. B., 1958. Clinical aspects of sexual abnormalities in man. *Recent Progr. Hormone Res.,* **14**: 335–397.

Grumbach, M. M., and Barr, M. L., 1958. Cytologic tests of chromosomal sex in relation to sexual anomalies in man. *Recent Progr. Hormone Res.,* **14**: 324–335.

Jacobs, P. A., and Strong, J. A., 1959. A case of human intersexuality having a possible XXY sex-determining mechanism. *Nature,* **183**: 302–303.

Jones, H. W., and Scott, W. W., 1958. *Hermaphroditism, Genital Anomalies, and Related Endocrine Disorders.* 456 pp. Williams & Wilkins, Baltimore.

Jost, A., 1953. Problems of fetal endocrinology: the gonadal and hypophyseal hormones. *Recent Progr. Hormone Res.,* **8**: 379–418.

Kallmann, F. J., 1952. Twin and sibship study of overt male homosexuality. *Am. J. Human Genet.,* **4**: 136–146.

Lenz, W., 1957. Rotgrün–Blindheit bei einem heterogametischen Scheinmädchen, zugleich ein Beitrag zur Genetik der heterogametischen Pseudofemininität. *Acta Genet. Med. Gemel.,* **6**: 231–246.

Petterson, G., and Bonnier, G., 1937. Inherited sex-mosaic in man. *Hereditas,* **23**: 49–69.

Smith, D. R., and Davidson, W. M. (Eds.), 1958. *Symposium on Nuclear Sex.* 188 pp. Wm. Heinemann, Ltd., London.

Sörensen, H. R., 1953. *Hypospadias, with Special Reference to Aetiology.* 94 pp. Munksgaard, Copenhagen.

Taillard, W., and Prader, A., 1957. Etude génétique du syndrome de féminisation testiculaire totale et partielle. *J. Génét. Hum.,* **6**: 13–32.

Welshons, W. J., and Russell, L. B., 1959. The Y-chromosome as the bearer of male determining factors in the mouse. *Proc. Nat. Acad. Sci.,* **45**: 560–566.

Wilkins, L., 1950. *The Diagnosis and Treatment of Endocrine Disorders in Childhood and Adolescence.* 384 pp. C. C. Thomas, Springfield, Ill.

Witschi, E., Nelson, W. O., and Segal, S. J., 1957. Genetic, developmental and hormonal aspects of gonadal dysgenesis and sex inversion in man. *J. Clin. Endocr. Metabol.,* **17**: 737–753.

Young, W. C., 1957. Genetic and psychologic determinants of sexual behavior patterns. In H. Hoagland (Ed.). *Hormones, Brain Function and Behavior,* pp. 75–98. Academic Press, New York.

CHAPTER 21

THE SEX RATIO

The XX–XY mechanism not only accounts for the occurrence of XX and XY individuals among the offspring of a couple, but also seems to be responsible for the production of approximately equal numbers of the two sexes. Two X- and two Y-containing spermatozoa develop from each germ cell which goes through meiosis. The expectation, therefore, would be that fertilization with equal numbers of X and Y sperm would take place, and the numbers of women and men would be equal.

Sex Ratios in Populations

Sex Ratio at Birth. Contrary to the expectation of equality, male and female babies are not born in a 1:1 ratio. Among United States whites, the ratio is approximately 106 boys to 100 girls ($p = 0.5146$, $q = 0.4854$). The data on which this and most other sex ratios are based are so large that the deviations from equality become statistically quite significant. In the literature, sex ratios are given either as the fractions of males (or females) in the total population or as number of males per 100 females.

Among the United States negroes, the sex ratio is less biased in favor of males than it is among whites, but there are still 102.6 males for every 100 females born. In other countries, the ratio is sometimes higher, sometimes lower, than in the United States. Greece and Korea, respectively, list values as high as 113.2 and 113.1 males, while the negro population of Cuba is reported to have as few as 101.1 males for 100 females.

Sex Ratios of Stillbirths. The sex ratio at birth, called the *secondary sex ratio,* does not necessarily equal the *primary sex ratio,* that is, the ratio at the time of fertilization. During the interval between conception and birth, a considerable number of fetuses die. If the prenatal mortality affected the two sexes differentially, then the secondary sex ratio would differ from the pri-

TABLE 63. *Sex Ratios of Stillborn Reported by the United States Bureau of the Census (1925–1934).* (After Ciocco, 1940.)

Month of Pregnancy	Sex Recognized (n)	Sex Unknown (%)	Sex Ratio (males per 100 females)
<2	82	89.9	228.0
2	563	72.2	431.1
3	2,388	36.8	361.0
4	6,401	10.5	201.2
5	12,541	2.6	139.6
6	17,857	1.0	122.7
7	23,109	0.6	112.4
8	28,903	0.4	124.7
9	68,932	0.2	134.6
10+	2,671	0.4	133.2

mary. The primary sex ratio, in man, is not accessible to direct study, since it would involve the determination of the sex-chromosomal constitution of large numbers of newly fertilized eggs. It is possible, however, to investigate the sex ratio among prenatal deaths. Could it be that the surplus of live-born males is the result of a surplus of female deaths before birth?

This hypothesis is not borne out by observable facts. All available data on the sex ratio of aborted embryos and stillborn children show a greater number of males than females. The degree of surplus of prenatal male deaths is a matter of uncertainty. Data on registered prenatal deaths reported for several European cities and by the United States Bureau of the Census agree in showing that there is not only a deviation from the 1:1 ratio among live-born children, but the younger the fetus the greater the rate of male mortality. As seen in Table 63, for the earliest months, the males among stillborn are from two to more than four times as numerous as the females. But it is also clear, from the third column of the table, that uncertainties as to the sex of very young embryos make these figures less reliable than the figures for older embryos. Sufficient data are not available for the first two months of development. The very youngest embryos do not yet show any anatomical or histological differences which indicate their sex, and even the older embryos which are less than two months old are very similar in both sexes.

The sex ratios of registered prenatal deaths do not agree with the sex ratio of specimens in the collection of the Department of Embryology of the Carnegie Institution of Washington. This collection consists of somewhat less than 6,000 embryos and fetuses contributed over a number of years by various physicians. The sex ratio of the whole sample is 107.9 males to 100 females, and in no month of prenatal life does the sex ratio deviate significantly from the average (Table 64; note that the greatest ratio deviation, in the third month, is based on only 120 embryos).

The findings on prenatal deaths from the census data and from the Carnegie

TABLE 64.   *Sex Ratios of Stillborn in the Collection of the Carnegie Institution.* (Tietze, *Human Biol.,* **20,** 1948.)

Month of Pregnancy	No. of Males	No. of Females	Sex Ratio (males per 100 females)
3	58	62	93.5
4	598	555	107.7
5	771	667	115.6
6	801	730	109.7
7	775	770	100.6
Total	3,003	2,784	107.9

collection may not really be in conflict. The very high surplus of registered aborted males in the first months of pregnancy may well be the result of misclassification of female fetuses as males, since midwives or physicians without specialized training in embryology may easily mistake the relatively large clitoris of the female embryo for the penis (Fig. 166). For accuracy of sex classification, the Carnegie tabulations, which have been obtained by experts, are more reliable. Errors in classification of older embryos, however, can not explain the differences between the two sets of data. Possibly, the Carnegie sample is a selected one and contains a larger proportion of stillbirths with malformations than is found in the general population. According to McKeown and Lowe's studies from Birmingham, England, malformed stillbirths are predominantly female, at least in the seventh and later

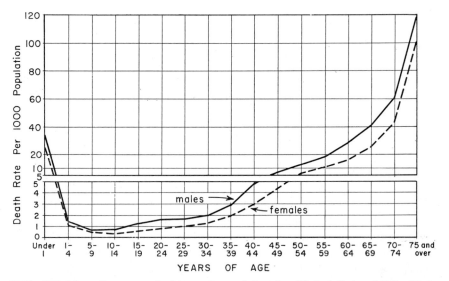

FIG. 179. Mortality rates of white males and females, United States, 1950. (Data from U.S. Dept. of Health, Educ. and Welfare, Natl. Off. Vit. Stat., *Special Rep. 37,* 1953.)

months of pregnancy. A higher proportion of malformed fetuses in the Carnegie data than in the census data would be reflected in the over-all number of female fetuses, that is, in a reduction of the high ratio of males. It should be added that more recent census data than those listed in Table 63 do not show the great disparity of the sexes among the early stillborn and thus are similar to the data from the Carnegie collection.

Postnatal Sex Mortality.   The higher mortality of males than of females is not a peculiarity of embryos, but is found throughout all age classes (Fig. 179). Proportionally, more males than females die during every age period.

The effect of the postnatal differential mortality is that the secondary sex ratio of live births gives way to tertiary ratios which are different for each age group. The surplus of males at birth is progressively diminished, until, during a certain age period, the sex ratio is equal. Still later, however, more females than males are alive, since more males than females die during every age period. At what age the tertiary sex ratio reaches equality and then again deviates from it in favor of a high proportion of females depends on the specific mortality figures. Because of medical knowledge and care, and other factors, mortality figures have changed considerably over recent decades. Assuming mortality rates as they existed for the different age classes in 1950, a United States white population which started out with its typical secondary sex ratio would reach equality in numbers of females and males around the age of fifty years. As in many other countries, there is a surplus of males during the marrying ages.

Causes of Differential Sex Mortality.   Why the male, at every stage, is less resistant to death than the female is not understood. A study of the causes of death shows that there are a few diseases, such as whooping cough and, for anatomical reasons, gonococcal infections, which are fatal more often for females than for males; but, for most other diseases, the reverse is true. For some causes of death, the greater biological weakness of the male sex is, at least partly, understandable. Thus, the higher rate of mortality at birth of males may be connected with their somewhat larger size, which may make the process of being born more hazardous for them. In most cases, however, no obvious reason can be given for the higher mortality of the males.

It has been suggested that the greater constitutional weakness of males may be due to their having only one X-chromosome. If X-chromosomes carry recessive alleles for lower viability, sublethality, or even lethality, then many hemizygous male zygotes would be subjected to the influence of these alleles, while most female zygotes would be heterozygous and not be affected. No exhaustive statistical analysis has yet been made of the number of X-chromosomes which would have to be carriers of unfavorable alleles and of the number of loci which would have to be involved in order to account for the observed mortality differences between the two sexes.

Unfavorable X-chromosomal alleles will be eliminated rapidly from a population by their exposure to selection in the hemizygous males. To counteract this disappearance of alleles which the theory assumes to be present at unchanged frequencies from generation to generation, new mutations from normal alleles to unfavorable ones would have to occur constantly in a large number of X-chromosomes. These assumptions are not incompatible with our knowledge of mutation rates and with estimates of the total number of loci in a human X-chromosome which may give rise to unfavorable alleles, but the reasonableness of the assumptions does not prove their correctness.

Primary Sex Ratio.   The ratio of females and males throughout life may be represented by two contour lines superimposed upon each other (Fig. 180). At birth, the proportional widths of the male and female diagrams indicate the secondary sex ratio. With increasing age, the absolute width of both diagrams decreases— though at different rates—as a result of death till, at the age of 100, few individuals of either sex are left. For prenatal stages, the higher proportion of male stillbirths, as reported in census data, signifies that the ratio of males to females is still higher than at birth. Therefore, somewhat arbitrarily, the two contour lines have been drawn as being more separate before birth than after.

The diagrams suggest a specific primary sex ratio which, as pointed out, is not directly accessible to observation. If death during the first two months of embryonic life did not differentiate between the two sexes, then the primary sex ratio would be the same as that in embryos two months of age. Should the same type of differential mortality which discriminates against males at all later ages also be effective during the first two months, then the primary sex ratio would be still higher than that of the two-month-old survivors. Only if the greater weakness of males were replaced by a greater weakness of females in the earliest period, would the primary ratio be closer to equality

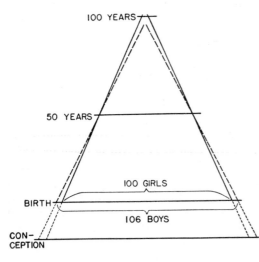

FIG. 180. Changing sex ratios from conception to 100 years of age. Mortality reduces the numbers of males at a higher rate than the numbers of females. The prenatal sex ratios are hypothetical.

than the ratio at two months of prenatal life. Such reversal of the relative mortality of the two sexes is unlikely.

In summary, we find, to our surprise that most probably the primary sex ratio differs greatly from the theoretically expected equality. By taking into account the secondary sex ratio, the differential mortality of stillbirths, and other data—rather unsatisfactory in reliability—on the fraction of all pregnancies which do not come to term, the primary sex ratio has been estimated at 125 to 135 male to each 100 female conceptions. Some estimates have gone as high as 170 males to 100 female conceptions, while an estimate based on the prenatal sex ratio of the Carnegie specimens and recent census data would yield a primary sex ratio as low as about 107 males to 100 females. Whatever the correct value, there seems little doubt that more eggs are fertilized with Y sperm than with X sperm. Undoubtedly, sex-chromatin studies will soon provide information on the sex ratio of very early embryos. Even then, however, only inferences can be drawn concerning the primary sex ratio itself.

The Deviation of the Primary Sex Ratio from Equality. Why the primary sex ratio is different—if it really is—from 1:1 remains a subject for speculation. It is generally assumed, without true evidence, that immature and mature X and Y sperm have equal survival rates in the testes and sperm ducts, and therefore that, after mating, they are present in equal numbers in the female genital tract. Here three different possibilities may influence their fate: (1) the environment of the female ducts may be less favorable to the survival of X sperm than of Y sperm; (2) Y sperm may be intrinsically more capable of reaching the egg than X sperm; and (3) the egg may react more readily to the approach of a Y sperm than of an X sperm, so that fusion of egg and sperm would be due to preferential or selective fertilization.

There is, at present, no evidence in support of any of these possibilities. The most frequently discussed one, that of greater ability of the Y sperm to reach the egg, has usually been expressed in terms of speed of sperm locomotion. It is reasoned that Y sperm may be lighter than X sperm because of the smaller size of a Y-chromosome, as compared to an X-chromosome. The travel of spermatozoa upward in the uterus and oviducts is sometimes pictured as a race in which the lighter Y sperm are speedier than the heavier X sperm. This comparison, however, is at best of limited value. The upward motion of spermatozoa is not primarily due to their own irregular motility, but to muscular contraction and to ciliary action within the longitudinal grooves of the female ducts. In order to account for a greater ability, by means of differential motility, of Y sperm than of X sperm to reach the egg, one would have to assume that the contractions and the currents and countercurrents produced by the cilia either aid or hinder one kind of sperm to some degree. (In the rat, approximately twenty million spermatozoa are present in the uterus after mating, but only five to ten spermatozoa are recovered from the part of the oviduct nearest the ovary. In the rabbit, also, very few spermatozoa are found in the corresponding segment of the oviduct. It is likely that a similarly small fraction of inseminated spermatozoa may reach the upper part of the human oviduct.)

However obscure the reasons are for the probable surplus of males at the time of conception, we have perhaps been inclined too strongly to think that all spermatozoa are equal before they enter an egg. Should we really be unwilling to admit that a sperm with an X-chromosome and no Y-chromosome may be physiologically different from one without an X but with a Y?

It has sometimes been suggested that the deviation of the secondary sex ratio from equality may be due to a small percentage of the chromosomally female zygotes developing into actual males. However, we have no evidence for the occurrence of true sex reversals. And if the rare XXY and XO sex types resulting from nondisjunctional gametes affect the sex ratio at all, they would account for no more than a small fraction of the difference between the secondary sex ratio and a hypothetical 1:1 ratio.

Variations of the Secondary Sex Ratio. Some data have already been quoted which show that the secondary sex ratio is different in different countries and within the same country in different racial groups. There are other normally slight but significant variations in the sex ratio, and their exploration has been a fascinating pastime of numerous students. For many years and for different countries it used to be true that the sex ratio of males to females was higher among legitimate than among illegitimate babies, but more recently the differential has apparently disappeared. Similarly, the often reported higher ratio of males to females for rural, as compared to urban, populations has now apparently changed to near equality. Sometimes the upper socioeconomic groups had a higher ratio of males to females than the lower groups, as shown by older data from England and Wales; the number of males per 100 females were: upper and middle classes 106.1, skilled workers 105.7, unskilled workers 103.4. Another curious difference was found by M. Bernstein, who classified the occupations of men listed in *Who's Who in America* according to the number of women in those same occupations. The sex-ratio of the children of men from occupations which have a low proportion of women was 120 males: 100 females; that of men from occupations with a high proportion of women was only 85:100. Still more striking differences were found when the occupations of both parents were taken into account. Perhaps these variations are related to findings by Martinez, on differences in the sex ratios among the children of men and women who were classified according to the bodily proportions (somatotypes, see p. 603).

During times of war, or shortly afterwards, the ratio of males has been found to be higher than during times of peace, not only in the warring countries but also in neutrals. This was first determined for European countries, but also holds for the United States. The change in the sex ratio was not related to a change in birth order or in age of parents, but possibly to early-fertile, as compared to late-fertile, marriages. From the German *Wer ist's* (*Who's Who*) it was found that: marriages concluded between 1900 and

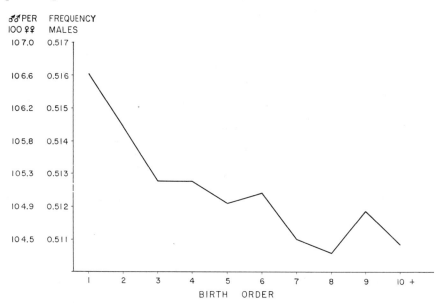

FIG. 181. The secondary sex ratio of live born according to birth order. White population, United States, 1947–1952. (Novitski and Sandler, *Ann. Human Genet.*, **21**, 1956.)

1918 in which the first child was born within 18 months gave a 124:100 sex ratio of first born; but those in which the first child was born later gave a ratio of 99:100. In wartime, when many husbands are away from home except for short periods, the early-fertile couples may contribute an increased proportion of male children to the population. Whether or not this is the real explanation for the higher ratio of male babies at times of war, it is at least more rational than the popular belief that Nature compensates for war losses by a higher male ratio, which in any case can not benefit the generation in which the losses occurred.

A well-established variation of the sex ratio is correlated with order of birth. In nearly all populations, the ratio of males is highest for the first births and decreases with successive births (Fig. 181). Such a correlation may have various components. It may be directly related to birth order itself; or to ages of parents, which obviously increase with increasing birth order; or to more complex interrelations. Analysis has shown that the age of the mother has no influence on the sex ratio; but, curiously enough, the age of the father does, to a very slight degree. The latter variable, however, does not act alone since, for constant age of the father, the sex ratio is still related to birth order.

It is impossible, at present, to draw final conclusions from these facts. In some cases, a correlation has been observed between high sex ratio and low prenatal mortality. In several European countries, for instance, there are more stillbirths in unmarried, as compared to married, mothers. Since more males than females are stillborn, it has been reasoned that the stillbirths among illegitimate conceptions eliminate a higher number of males among them, and thus account for the reduced sex ratio at normal birth. In other studies, no persistent correlations could be demonstrated between variations in the secondary sex ratio and the rate of stillbirths.

Altogether, the variability of secondary sex ratios may be due both to different frequencies in prenatal mortality and to differences in the primary sex ratio. Such hypothetical variations in the latter can be thought of as both genetically and environmentally conditioned. If the inequality of the primary sex ratio is due to differential survival of X and Y sperm or to selective fertilization, then genetic factors, either in the sperm itself or in the female, may affect the relative survival of X or Y sperm or the response to selective forces in fertilization. It is equally possible that environmental factors, nutritional or metabolic, for example, may exert an influence on the frequency of survival of X versus Y sperm or their relative ability to fertilize. However, no such environmental factors, if they exist, are known; and it is important to realize, in any case, that most of the observed variations in the sex ratio of different population groups are small.

Sex Ratios in Sibships

Unisexual Sibships.   Everyone is acquainted with families in which the children are all the same sex. It is an understandable reaction to suspect that a peculiar mechanism is determining the production of only one sex. A consideration of the statistical nature of sex determination should make us cautious about accepting such a conclusion too readily. If the probability of a male birth is p and of a female birth is $q(= 1 - p)$, then the probability in a family of n children that all are boys is p^n, or that all are girls is q^n. If we assume p or q to be 1/2, which is, for the present purpose, a sufficiently close approximation to the secondary sex ratio, the probability of an all-boy sibship, as well as of an all-girl sibship, is $(1/2)^n$. If n, the number of sibs, is as large as 10, this probability becomes 1/1,024. This means that, in sibships of 10, chance alone will give rise, on the average, to 1 sibship in 1,024 of all boys and another of all girls, or to 1 unisexual sibship, either male or female, in 512 sibships.

Similar considerations apply to sibships in which both sexes are represented, but in which there is a preponderance of one sex, such as 8 boys to 2 girls or 3 boys to 7 girls.

The assumption that a specific unisexual or very uneven-sexed sibship is the result of an unusual mechanism of sex determination is thus unnecessary, since the normal mechanism yields a certain number of such sibships purely by chance. This statement, however, does not exclude the possibility that, superimposed on chance, may be agents causing unisexual or very uneven-sexed sibships. In *some* families, there may be special mechanisms acting to cause such sibships. A test of this hypothesis can be made in two ways: by studying the relative frequencies of the various types of sibships among all sibships of population samples, and by study of individual pedigrees.

Statistical Studies.   An analysis of sibships in populations is statistical in nature. Basically, it rests on the question: Do the observed frequencies of the various types of sibships agree with those expected from chance alone? If there is agreement between observed and expected frequencies, then there is no need for assuming special mechanisms effecting unisexual or uneven-sexed sibships. If, however, there should be disagreement, then a search has to be made for the responsible mechanisms or agents.

A statistical inquiry can be applied to families with different numbers of children. If p and q again represent the probabilities for male or female births as determined by the observed secondary sex ratio, then the inquiry consists of comparing the observed fraction of 2-children sibships with 2 boys, 1 boy and 1 girl, and 2 girls with the expected fractions p^2, 2 pq, and q^2; or of comparing the observed fraction of 3 children sibships with 3 boys, 2 boys and 1 girl, 1 boy and 2 girls, and 3 girls with the expected fractions p^3, 3 p^2q, 3 pq^2, and q^3. In general, the observed fractions of n-child sibships of all possible sex distributions can be compared with expectations according to the binomial $(p + q)^n$, as discussed in Chapter 9, Genetic Ratios.

Before reporting on the results of several relevant studies, a factor which might produce a bias in the observed data must be mentioned. In populations in which birth control is practiced, parents may limit the size of their families not simply after a certain number of children are born, but after some desired sex distribution has been attained. Some parents may desire to have a daughter and may terminate the procreation of children after the birth of a girl; others may wish to have a son and terminate procreation after the birth of a boy. Still other parents may want children of both sexes and may limit their families after at least one of each sex is born.

An inquiry by Dahlberg, in a Swedish population, has shown that most parents like to have both sexes represented among their offspring. The great majority of expectant parents who already had children all or most of whom were of the same sex stated that they wanted their unborn child to be of the opposite sex. The hypothesis that parents to whom children of both sexes were born have a tendency to terminate procreation has been tested in several populations by Gini and others. They investigated whether the last-born child made the sex ratio of the sibships more equal or more unequal. The results indicate some family planning as to sex, mainly for representation of both sexes, but the degree of this planning was low.

It may be thought that the sex ratio in a population might depend on family planning, but a simple consideration shows that this is not true, provided all families are basically alike in their sex-determining mechanism. If, for instance, all parents desired the birth of a son and terminated their families after a boy is born, the first child would be a boy or a girl in the proportion p:q. If only the parents whose first child is a girl have a second child, this second child again will be a boy or a girl in the proportion p:q. In the same way, each next child, in families which have had only daughters, will be a male or a female in the proportion p:q, so that the sum of the sex ratios of all children in the population remains p:q, regardless of family planning.

The example shows, however, that family planning may lead to a distribution of types of sibships which deviates from chance. If all parents terminated their families after the birth of a boy, and if all parents who have had no boy succeeded in having another child, then all one-child sibships would consist of a boy, all two-children sibships of a girl and a boy, all three-children sibships of two girls and a boy, and so on. If, to use another example, all parents limited their families to the minimum number which gave them at least one child of each sex, then all two-children sibships would be either boy–girl or girl–boy, all three-children sibships boy–boy–girl and girl–girl–boy, and so on. Actually, these schemes of family planning according to sex of children are artificial extremes.

The bias in the distribution of different types of sibships that is introduced by parents who terminate their families after the birth of a child of a specific sex can be reduced by disregarding the last (n-th) child of each sibship and considering the distribution of the sibships with (n − 1) children.

Observed and Expected Distributions. In an Ohio community, Rife and Snyder collected data on the sex distribution in 1,269 families with from one to five children and compared their observations with chance expectations. They showed that the small deviations between observed and expected distributions were statistically insignificant and that, therefore, chance alone could account for the occurrence of preponderantly, or exclusively, unisexual

TABLE 65.   *Frequencies of Various Sex Ratios in Sibships of Twelve.* (Saxony 1876–1885.) (After Geissler.)

Ratio per Sibship ♂	♀	Number Observed	Expected Sex Distribution Probability	Frequency*	Observed Frequency*	Sign of (Obs. − Exp.)
12	0	7	p^{12}	346	655	+
11	1	60	$12p^{11}q$	3,916	5,613	+
10	2	298	$66p^{10}q^2$	20,303	27,877	+
9	3	799	$220p^9 q^3$	63,793	74,743	+
8	4	1,398	$495p^8 q^4$	135,299	130,776	−
7	5	2,033	$792p^7 q^5$	204,058	190,178	−
6	6	2,360	$924p^6 q^6$	224,408	220,767	−
5	7	1,821	$792p^5 q^7$	181,313	170,346	−
4	8	1,198	$495p^4 q^8$	106,819	112,067	+
3	9	521	$220p^3 q^9$	44,751	48,737	+
2	10	160	$66p^2 q^{10}$	12,655	14,967	+
1	11	29	$12p q^{11}$	2,169	2,713	+
0	12	6	q^{12}	170	561	+

* Per million sibships.

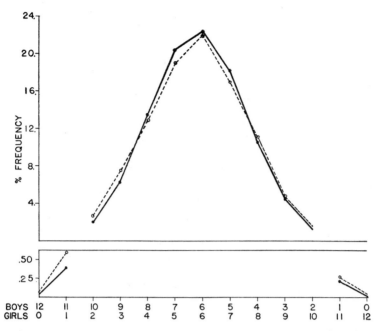

FIG. 182. Per cent frequencies of various sex ratios in sibships of twelve. Solid line = expected frequencies; broken line = observed frequencies. Note that two different scales were used for the percentage of frequencies. (Data from Geissler.)

sibships. A similar conclusion, by Edwards and Fraccaro, was based on a study of the sex distribution in sibships from 5,477 Swedish ministers of religion during the period 1585–1920. Studies by Geissler on a very much larger census (nearly five million births in Saxony, 1876–1885) do not fully bear out the conclusion that chance alone can account for the frequency of unisexual sibships. It is in the nature of statistical phenomena that chance deviations from expectation become smaller the larger the sample. With a small sample, a given deviation between observation and expectation may be within the range of lack of statistical significance, but the same proportional deviation in a large sample may become highly significant. This is probably the main reason for the results of the studies in Ohio and Sweden differing from those of the study in Saxony. Another possible reason will be mentioned on pp. 437–438.

Let us follow Geissler's treatment of one representative set of his data, that of families with 12 births (Table 65). The expected frequencies have been calculated from the secondary sex ratio in the Saxonian population, which was 106.087 males: 100 females (p = 0.5147676 and q = 0.4852324). That there is, on the whole, very good agreement between the observed and expected frequencies is seen in the table and, particularly, in the plotted data (Fig. 182). In at least the overwhelming majority of families the sex ratios agree with those expected by chance. The deviations between observed and expected frequencies of the different sex distribution are in both directions. For nine types of sibships, the observed frequency is larger than expected, and for three types smaller than expected.

Yet, a closer scrutiny reveals systematic deviations between the chance expectations and the observations. Not only is the observed frequency of unisexual sibships more than twice as high as expected, but the observed frequencies of seven types of sibships with preponderances of one or the other sex are also higher than expected by chance. Conversely, the frequencies of the remaining four types of sibships—those with equal or nearly equal sex distribution—are lower than expected. The differences between observation and expectation are not always statistically significant particularly for the relatively rare types of sibships with preponderantly or exclusively one sex. However, as shown in Table 182, the trend of the differences—positive and increasing in magnitude in the two tail ends of the distribution and negative in the middle—is beyond doubt.

A correction must be applied to Geissler's material, because the census data in Saxony did not separate single births from twin (or higher-multiple) births. Multiple-birth children who are derived from a single egg are all of the same sex. Such children represent one single event of sex determination and should, therefore, be counted as a single-birth event. Actually, each child was entered separately, so that the data are slightly biased in favor of too many children of the same sex. It has been shown that corrections for single-egg twin births reduce considerably the excess of sibships with high preponderances of one or the other sex, but the remaining excesses are still significant.

It may be noted that the data in Figure 182 or in Table 65 show a considerable asymmetry in the number of those sibships which one might presume to be equally numerous. For example, for 346 families with 12 boys, only 170 with 12 girls are expected; for 3,916 with 11 boys and 1 girl, only 2,169 with 11 girls and 1 boy; and so on. This asymmetry is of course due to the higher ratio of males at birth. Although the probabilities for male and female births differ only slightly (being approximately $p = 0.515$ and $q = 0.485$), raising them to a power of 11 or 12 gives strikingly different values for the comparable types of sibships.

In general, Geissler's analysis of sibships with numbers of children other than 12 has led to the same conclusion: in the great majority of sibships, a specific sex distribution—whether equal or close to equality, or equal or close to unisexuality—may be regarded as the result of chance. There remains, however, a fraction of sibships whose sex distribution cannot be explained on the basis of chance alone. What kind of explanation will fit all the facts?

For his analysis, Geissler had assumed, and had clearly said so, that the probabilities p and q for male and female births are the same for all parental pairs. As we have seen, this assumption left some of the sex distributions unexplained. If, however, it is assumed, with Gini, that p and q vary in the

TABLE 66.   *Frequencies of Sex Distributions in Sibships of Four in Four Populations.*

Population		Frequencies of Sibships with Sex Ratios				
Type	p	0:4	1:3	2:2	3:1	4:0
A	0.5	0.0625	0.2500	0.3750	0.2500	0.0625
B	0.4	0.0256	0.1536	0.3456	0.3456	0.1296
C	0.6	0.1296	0.3456	0.3456	0.1536	0.0256
(B + C)	$\overline{0.5}$	0.0776	0.2496	0.3456	0.2496	0.0776
obs. (B + C) − exp. A		+	−	−	−	+

population, then a better fit of observed to expected frequencies can be obtained. This will be shown by a simplified example, using 4-children sibships. Assume first a population A with a constant sex ratio of p = q = 0.5. Then $(0.5 \, \delta + 0.5 \, \female)^4$ yields the expectations for the different sex distribution (Table 66, first line). Now assume a population B with p = 0.6 and q = 0.4, and another one C with p = 0.4 and q = 0.6. For B the expectations for the different sex distributions are derived from $(0.6 \, \delta + 0.4 \, \female)^4$ and for C from $(0.4 \, \delta + 0.6 \, \female)^4$, as given in lines 2 and 3 of Table 66. If a population consisted of two subpopulations of the types B and C, and of equal sizes, the mean probabilities p and q would be 0.5, as are the constant probabilities in A. The mean expectations for the frequencies of the different sex distributions would not be like those in A, but rather be the averages of the frequencies for B and C (line 4, Table 66). If we compare these average frequencies with those in line 1, we find too many all-male and all-female sibships and too few of the others (line 5).

The assumption that the probabilities for male and female births vary in a population is, as discussed earlier, in agreement with observations on the sex ratio in different socioeconomic groups, different occupations, and other subpopulations. In order to see whether the Saxonion data fit the expectations according to variable probabilities for the sex ratio, Edwards has assumed that these probabilities vary in a specific manner from family to family over a considerable range. On this assumption, calculations then show good agreement between observed and expected frequencies of sibships of only or preponderantly one sex, and no longer a surplus of observed over expected frequencies.

Following Geissler, several authors in England, France, the United States, and Finland have reported unisexual sibships in excess of those expected from constant probabilities for male and female births. The data have not been analyzed in all detail, but it would seem likely that the excess is mainly the consequence of variable probabilities for the sex ratio, and is not to any considerable extent due to the existence of parents who can produce children of one sex only. Those populations in which surveys did not encounter an excess of solely or preponderantly unisexual sibships (see p. 435) were perhaps

unusually homogenous ones in which there was little variation in the probabilities for producing one or the other sex.

A direct way of demonstrating differences in the probabilities for the sexes
in different families of a population is to compare the sex ratio of second
children of sibships in which the first child was a boy with those in which
the first child was a girl. In his study, Geissler noted a higher frequency of
males after a first male than after a first female. More recently, and for a
smaller sample in a United States study, M. Bernstein found a probability for
males after a male of $p = 0.5387$, but after a female of only $p = 0.4988$, the
difference being highly significant. Renkonen, in Finland, similarly determined
$p = 0.5132$ and $p = 0.4955$, respectively. Thus there is a slight but real trend
in families for the sex of the second child to be the same as the first, and the
same is true for the third as related to the second, and perhaps also for the
fourth as related to the third child. This, however, is not yet the whole story.
Gini has pointed out that, in Geissler's data, there is not only a surplus (compared to the simple binomial expectation) of preponderantly or exclusively
male or female sibships, but usually also a slight surplus of sibships with
equal members of both sexes. (The comparisons in Table 65 on sibships of
12 do no. show this excess of 6 male and 6 female sibships, but it appears
when comparisons are made with the expectation according to variable probabilities within the population.) According to Gini, this suggests a variation
in the probabilities of producing a male or female not only between different
families but also *within* single families. Older parents would tend to produce
children of the sex opposite that of the children produced during their younger
years.

In spite of the effort which has been expended in the analysis of population
data on the sex ratio, doubts remain concerning some of the basic results.
Geissler's material, for instance, seems to show internal inconsistencies, which
suggest errors in the reporting of numbers and sexes of births. This, of course,
could invalidate certain conclusions drawn from his material. Independently
of the reliability of census data, we have seen that biasing factors, such as
various types of family planning, may lead to deviations from the binomial
expectations. Although such planning has been widely practiced only in more
recent times, it was not unknown earlier.

Genetic Factors in the Variability of the Sex Ratio

A finding that different families vary in the probabilities of having males or
females could be explained by either genetic or nongenetic differences, or
combinations of such differences. Light can be thrown on this question when
sibships from related parents are combined. This was done by Slater for the
families of about 1,000 patients in a hospital for psychopaths. The frequency
of sibships with a preponderance of either males or females exceeded simple
binomial expectation. If families were taken in a larger sense to include
nephews and nieces as well as the sibs, the excess of predominantly male or
female families was even more noticeable. This indicates common proba-

bilities for specific sex ratios for related parental pairs. Still more significant is the fact that the sibs of preponderantly male families produced more males than females (490:429), and the sibs of preponderantly female families produced more females than males (408:466). The difference between the two ratios is highly significant and suggests, but does not prove, that inherited properties are involved. An older compilation by Nichols points in the same direction. He collected genealogical data, mostly for the period 1640–1800, on the sex ratio among New England families. There were 40 groups of sibships, all sibships in a group descended in the male line from a common ancestor, with the sibships selected so as to contain 6 or more children. The sex ratios in the different groups, based on from 63 to 428 children, varied between 177 and 72 males to 100 females. Although in most of the groups the sex ratio did not differ significantly from the mean, there were a few in which the great preponderance of either males or females was probably statistically significant. It seems that the tendency to rather extreme sex ratios was shared by a number of related sibships in successive generations.

The nature of the variation in the probabilities of producing males or females is obscure. Different families may have either different primary sex ratios or different prenatal survival rates. A high number of abortions and early stillbirths could shift the secondary sex ratio, provided the mortality acted differentially on the two sexes, more against the males in some families than in others. It is perhaps likely that more than one mechanism is involved in the variations of the probabilities to produce a given sex.

One source of the variability of the sex ratio at birth is suggested by tabulations according to the ABO blood groups. As shown by Sanghvi and others, in white populations the male ratio among O children is significantly higher than among A children, both in general and from specific types of mothers; and the same is true for the male ratio from AB mothers as compared to the rest. If these findings can be accepted as conclusive, it would seem likely that the immunologic mother-fetal interactions in the ABO groups serve to modify the secondary sex ratio.

Sex-ratio studies on mice by Weir provide experimental evidence for significant genetic variability of the probability of male and female births. Of two different strains, one has a high male ratio, $p_H = 0.556$, and one has a low male ratio, $p_L = 0.437$. Reciprocal matings between the two strains have shown that it is the male which is responsible for the sex ratio of the litter. Artificial inseminations, with sperm removed from the seminal duct of one strain and suspended in sperm-free seminal fluid of the other strain, gave the sex ratio of the strain from which the sperm was obtained. It is likely that the two different sex ratios at birth are due to differences in the primary sex ratio, but the possibility of differential mortality of the sexes in very early stages of development has not yet been excluded.

Pedigrees with Unusual Sex Ratios. A few pedigrees with many births show such a great deviation from the expected sex ratio that the always de-

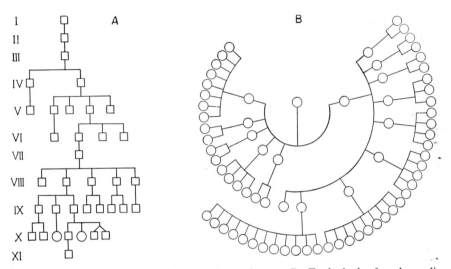

FIG. 183. A. Nearly exclusively male pedigree. B. Exclusively female pedigree. (A, after Harris, *Ann. Eugen.,* **13,** 1946; B, after Lienhart and Vermelin, *C. R. Soc. Biol. Paris,* **140,** 1946.)

sirable caution against selection for oddity seems to be unnecessary. Two such pedigrees are reproduced in Figure 183. The first pedigree (A), from England, shows thirty-five births over ten generations and dates back to the early seventeenth century. Thirty-three of the births were male and only two female. One of the latter died early and nothing specific is known about her; the other female had masculine traits and may have been an intersex. It is somewhat disturbing that the only two females recorded appear in the next-to-the-last generation, since it raises some doubt regarding the reliability of earlier entries in the family Bible on which the pedigree was based. Probably these doubts are not really justified and the pedigree may be accepted as bona fide. In this pedigree, the production of male progeny is clearly transmitted through the males from generation to generation, irrespective of the diversity of their wives. It may be assumed that the functional sperm produced by these men consists almost exclusively of Y sperm. Since all these men derived their Y-chromosome from a common ancestor, this specific chromosome may, itself, be the cause of the near nonexistence or nonfunctioning of the X sperm.

The second pedigree, Figure 183, B shows, still more strikingly, a case of sex tendency opposite to that in A. It represents a French kindred which has been rather ungallantly referred to as "a monstrous regiment of women" because of the seventy-two births, in three generations, exclusively female. This pedigree, if reliable, points to an inherited property of the females to permit fertilization of their eggs by X sperm only or to cause embryonic death of XY zygotes. In order to have this property transmitted by the original female parent to all fourteen of her daughters and granddaughters whose offspring has been recorded, a cytoplasmic inheritance or some complex chromosomal mechanism would have to be assumed.

Mechanisms Underlying Unisexual Offspring. Whatever the reason for these two remarkable human pedigrees may be, there are similar examples in other organisms, and, in some cases, the mechanism is known. In several species of Drosophila, in natural populations males have been found which produce nearly all daughters. The males carry a gene called "sex ratio" which acts on spermatogenesis. Instead of the first meiotic division segregating the X- and Y-chromosomes, the X-chromosome divides in both meiotic divisions and the Y-chromosome usually degenerates. In this manner, practically all sperm formed are X sperm, accounting for a shift in the sex ratio of the offspring to all, or nearly all, females.

In contrast to the "sex ratio" gene, which acts through the male parent, another mechanism, which acts through the female parent, for the production of almost exclusively female offspring has been found, again in Drosophila. Certain females carry in their cytoplasm a virus-like agent which enters into all eggs. Its presence is fully compatible with the development of XX zygotes, but it kills, at an early embryonic stage, XY zygotes. Perhaps the women in the all-female pedigree (Fig. 183, B) likewise harbor a virus which kills, discriminately, their potential sons. A genetic disposition for "male sex ratio," similar to that shown in the human pedigree in Figure 183, A, has also been found in Drosophila; affected males produce mostly sons.

Control of Sex Determination

Someday, the determination of sex in man will be subject to willful control. Theoretically, this might be accomplished by overriding the XX or XY zygote constitution by means of hormones so as to leave the desired sex unchanged but transform the undesired one into its opposite. This approach is not likely to be successful. The intricate processes of early development in an embryo a few weeks of age may well prove to be beyond practical reach for such sex reversal. The selection of X or Y sperm for fertilization seems to be much more promising. If physicists have been able to separate isotopes of atoms, biologists should find it possible to separate two classes of bodies whose sizes and differences are immense in comparison to those of the atoms.

Several methods of sperm separation have been tried, and more will be tried in the future. These methods are of two general types. In one type, the attempt is made to control the environment provided for sperm in the female body so as to favor fertilization by one or the other of the two sex-determining kinds of sperm.

In the other type, which has been used with experimental animals, sperm is treated outside of the body. There, separation of X from Y sperm is attempted, and the separated portions are then used for artificial insemination. One method uses centrifugation of sperm (of bulls) in an attempt to separate X and Y bearing portions. Another method involves passing an electric current through a sperm suspension, which causes some sperm (of rabbits) to migrate to one pole and others to migrate to the other pole. Lindahl, with centrifugation, and Shreder and Gordon, with electrophoresis, have obtained suggestive results. It hardly seems audacious to predict a full solution of the problem in the not-so-distant future.

Very likely, willful sex determination will first be accomplished in animal husbandry, where artificial insemination is widely practiced. Man's control of the sex of children will be one more step in his efforts to control nature and himself, which has constituted so much of the history of civilization. Such control will raise new social and personal problems, but it should not prove too difficult to cope with them.

Problems

167. The sex ratio of fetuses stillborn during the fourth month of pregnancy was found to be 107.7, and that of fetuses stillborn during the fifth month 115.6. Using the data given in Table 64, determine whether the difference is statistically significant.

168. In the United States (1925–1929) the sex ratios at birth, according to order of birth, were as follows: first birth 106.32; second 105.99; third 105.90; and fourth 105.33. What would be the sex ratios in a population in which there were only sibships with from 1 to 4 children, and these were in the percentages: (a) 25, 40, 25, 10; or (b) 10, 25, 40, 25?

169. The chance of a newborn child being a boy is (approximately) 0.52. What proportions of sibships of four children do you expect to be: (a) Only boys? (b) Only girls? (c) Two of each sex?

170. During a certain period, 14 boys and 27 girls were born to the wives of workers in a radar factory. During approximately the same time, the wives of draftsmen in the offices had 22 boys and 19 girls. (a) Is the difference between the sex ratios of the two groups significant? (b) Approximately, what is the probability of the first ratio being a chance deviation from the expected U. S. sex ratio of 106 boys to 100 girls?

171. Assume that, in a number of families, a special system of sex determination results in a preponderance of boys, while, in an equal number of families, another system of sex determination results in an equal preponderance of girls. If parents were to terminate their families after the birth of a boy, which sex would be preponderant in the pooled data?

References

Allan, T. M., 1959. ABO blood groups and sex ratio at birth. *Brit. Med. J.,* **1:** 553–554.

Bernstein, M. E., 1952. Studies in the human sex ratio. 2. The proportion of unisexual sibships. *Hum. Biol.,* **24:** 35–43.

———, 1958. Studies in the human sex

ratio. 5. A genetic explanation of the wartime increase in the secondary sex ratio. *Am. J. Human Genet.*, **10:** 68–70.

Ciocco, A., 1938. Variation in the sex ratio at birth in the United States. *Hum. Biol.*, **10:** 36–64.

————, 1940. Sex differences in morbidity and mortality. *Quart. Rev. Biol.*, **15:** 59–73, 192–210.

Colombo, B., 1957. On the sex ratio in man. *Cold Spring Harbor Symp. Quant. Biol.*, **22:** 193–202.

Crew, F. A. E., The sex-ratio. *Am. Naturalist*, **71:** 529–559, 1937, and *British Assoc. Report 1937.*

Dahlberg, G., 1948. Do parents want boys or girls? *Acta Genet. et Stat. Med.*, **1:** 163–167.

————, 1951. The primary sex ratio and its ratio at birth. *Acta Genet. et Stat. Med.*, **2:** 245–251.

Edwards, A. W. F., 1958. An analysis of Geissler's data on human sex ratio. *Ann. Human Genet.*, **23:** 6–15.

————, and Fraccaro, M., 1958. Sex distribution in F_1 of 5477 Swedish ministers of religion 1585–1920. *Hereditas*, **44:** 447–450.

Geissler, A., 1889. Beiträge zur Frage des Geschlechtsverhältnisses der Geborenen. *Zeitschr. K. Sächs. Statist. Bureaus*, **35:** 1–24.

Gini, C., 1951. Combinations and sequences of sexes in human families and mammal litters. *Acta Genet. et Stat. Med.*, **2:** 220–244.

Gittelsohn, A. M., 1960. Statistical problems related to the numerical distribution of the sexes at birth in man. (Ph.D. thesis, University of California, Berkeley.)

Gordon, M. J., 1957. Control of sex ratio in rabbits by electrophoresis of spermatozoa. *Proc. Nat. Acad. Sci.*, **43:** 913–918.

Harvey, E. N., 1946. Can the sex of mammalian offspring be controlled? *J. Hered.*, **37:** 71–73.

Hewitt, D., Webb, J. W., and Stewart, A. M., 1955. A note on the occurrence of single-sex sibships. *Ann. Human Genet.*, **20:** 155–158.

Lawrence, P. S., 1941. The sex ratio, fertility, and ancestral longevity, *Quart. Rev. Biol.*, **16:** 35–79.

Lindahl, P. E., 1958. Separation of bull spermatozoa carrying X and Y chromosomes by counter streaming centrifugation. *Nature*, **181:** 784.

Martinez, M., 1956. *Constitucion Humana y Determinacion del Sexo.* 171 pp. Editorial Litografia Colombia, Bogota.

McKeown, T., and Lowe, C. R., 1951. Sex ratio of stillbirths related to cause and duration of gestation. *Hum. Biol.*, **23:** 41–60.

Nichols, J. B., 1905. The sex composition of human families. *Am. Anthrop.*, **7:** 24–36.

Novitski, E., and Kimball, A. W., 1958. Birth order, parental ages, and sex of offspring. *Am. J. Human Genet.*, **10:** 268–275.

Rife, D. C., and Snyder, L. H., 1937. The distribution of sex ratios within families in an Ohio city. *Hum. Biol.*, **9:** 99–103.

Shreder, W., 1934. Die physikalisch-chemische Analyse der Spermienphysiologie. V. Mitteilung. Über die künstliche Geschlechtsregulierung bei Säugetieren. *Biol. Zhur.*, **3:** 465–476.

Slater, E., 1944. A demographic study of a psychopathic population. *Ann. Eugen.*, **12:** 121–137.

Strandskov, H. H., and Bisaccia, H., 1949. The sex ratio of human stillbirths at each month of uterogestation and at conception, *Am. J. Phys. Anthrop.*, n. s., **7:** 131–143.

Turpin, R., and Schützenberger, M. P., 1949. Sur la détermination du sexe chez l'homme. *Semaine des Hôpitaux Paris,* **25:** 2544–2545.

Weir, J. A., 1958. Sex ratio related to sperm source in mice. *J. Hered.,* **49:** 223–227.

CHAPTER 22

OCCURRENCE
OF MUTATIONS

The appearance of a trait, subsequently inherited, among one or more members of a family in whose ancestry the trait was unknown, suggests to the naïve observer the origin of genetic newness. The geneticist, however, realizes that such a conclusion is not always justified. If a character is based on either an autosomal or a sex-linked allele that is dominant and fully penetrant, then, indeed, the first appearance of the character signifies the origin of the allele in the immediately preceding generation. If, however, the character is due to a dominant but incompletely penetrant allele, then lack of penetrance in early generations, and not absence of the allele, may account for the unexpected phenotypic expression of the character in a later generation. Or, if an autosomal recessive allele is responsible for a character, then, of course, carriers may, unknown to themselves, transmit the allele heterozygously for numerous generations, and the homozygous occurrence of the allele, with its resulting specific phenotype, may be far removed from the origin of the allele itself. Finally, should the allele be X-linked and recessive, it may be carried in heterozygous females for several generations without becoming known, revealing itself by its characteristic phenotype only if transmitted to a male.

The Detection of Gametic Mutations

A new allele always arises from one already in existence, and the process that either transforms the allele itself or causes it to produce a new allele is called *gene mutation*.

Mutations may occur either in somatic or in germ cells. A mutation that occurs in a germ cell can be discovered when this cell or its descendants become gametes, thus transmitting the mutant gene to the next generation. We

445

shall first discuss such gametic mutations, and later take up somatic mutations.

In experimental organisms, various breeding procedures have been worked out in order to reveal gametic changes from one allele to another, either dominant or recessive to the first, and called dominant or recessive mutations. In relation to dominant mutations the original allele is, of course, recessive, and in relation to recessive mutations it is dominant. The detection of mutations of recessive to dominant alleles is simple, since it is only necessary to interbreed homozygous recessives and to watch for the occurrence of dominant mutant phenotypes among the offspring. Mutations of dominant autosomal alleles to recessive ones can be ascertained only after special breeding procedures involving self-fertilization in hermaphroditic animals or plants, or sequences of brother-sister matings in bisexual organisms. In man, brother-sister matings are so rare that mutations to recessive autosomal alleles cannot be ascertained directly; only mutations to dominant alleles—whether autosomal or sex linked—and to sex-linked recessives can be recognized.

It is useful to distinguish between the terms mutation and mutant. Mutation refers to the process of change, mutant to its result. A mutant allele is one that has either been produced by an immediately preceding mutation or has been derived from the original mutant by replication. We shall discuss various causes of mutations later.

Dominant Mutations.   An example of a dominant autosomal mutation is presented in a pedigree from England, in which a pathological, severe blistering of the feet occurred for the first time in 1 out of 6 children of unaffected parents (Fig. 184). The condition reappeared in three successive generations in a manner which agrees with full penetrance of a dominant gene. The only reasonable basis for exception to the statement that the first appearance of the character was the result of a mutation of an allele from normal to abnormal is the assumption that the sire of II–5 was not the legal father but an un-

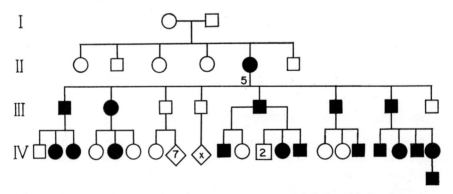

FIG. 184. Dominant mutation. Pedigree of severe blistering of the feet. (x = several individuals, exact number unknown.) (After Haldane and Poole, *J. Hered.*, **33**, 1942.)

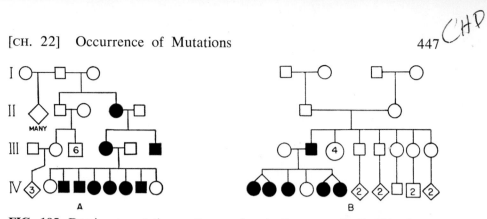

FIG. 185. Dominant mutation pedigrees of: A. Cataract. B. Combination of brachyphalangy and hypophalangy. (A, after Danforth, *Am. J. Ophthalmol.*, **31,** 1914; B, after Liebenam, *Zeitschr. Konstitl.*, **22,** 1938.)

known, affected man. The circumstances surrounding this case make illegitimacy so unlikely that the first appearance of blistering in the pedigree may be regarded as the result of a true mutation.

Two other pedigrees showing the first occurrence of autosomal dominant alleles—one for cataract and one for brachyphalangy—are given in Figure 185. In each case, the ancestors of the first affected individual were normal, and the generation or generations derived from him give evidence of dominant transmission. In still another example of this nature, referred to in an earlier chapter, a son with chondrodystrophic dwarfism appeared among the offspring of normal parents and the trait was transmitted to all succeeding generations (Fig. 186).

Among the numerous known cases of the unexpected appearance of a trait in a child whose ancestors were free from it, an appreciable number may be regarded as dominant mutations, even if proof of inheritance in later generations is lacking. In many, no proof is available simply because the affected individual has not yet reached maturity or has not become a parent. Even if he has produced children, their normality may be due not to lack of heritability of the trait, but, rather, to chance deviation from the 1:1 ratio expected from a heterozygous parent. Attribution of such an appearance of a trait to a dominant mutation is more justifiable if the trait has been shown to be dominant and fully penetrant in other pedigrees than if it has not.

CHD

Mutations do not necessarily lead to genes whose effects are abnormal. In experimental organisms, genes with deleterious effects have been known to mutate back to alleles with either fully normal or at least less harmful action. No such *reverse mutations* have yet been observed in man, but their occurrence could be demonstrated only under exceptional circumstances. There is some evidence for mutation from one normal to another normal human allele: perhaps the best comes from the study of somatic cells and involves the *I* alleles of the ABO blood groups (see pp. 465–466).

Sex-linked Mutations. Mutation from an X-linked normal to an abnormal recessive allele has been suggested by several pedigrees, particularly some of

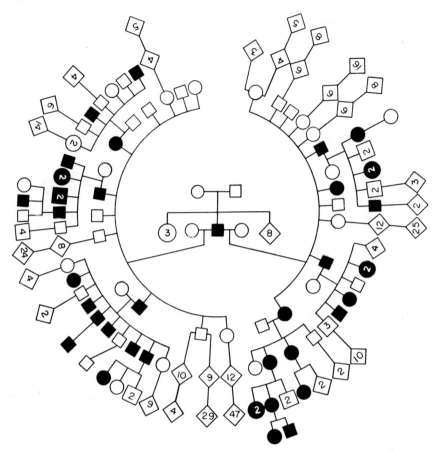

FIG. 186. Dominant mutation. Abbreviated pedigree of chondrodystrophic dwarfism, from Utah. (After Stephens, *J. Hered.,* **34,** 1943.)

hemophilia. For an example, we shall examine one such family (Fig. 187). After four generations of only nonhemophilic persons, a sibship with 6 hemophilic sons, plus 1 normal son and 1 normal daughter, appeared. Considering the hereditary nature of hemophilia, and that it is usually X-linked, it must be assumed that the mother of this sibship, IV–6, was heterozygous for the recessive allele *h.* She could have either inherited this allele from a parent who carried it, or her *Hh* genotype could have been the result of a mutation in one of the two gametes which gave rise to her. If there was regular inheritance, her father, III–7, was not involved, since he was not a bleeder. But her mother, III–6, from whom she must therefore (still assuming normal inheritance) have received the allele, does not betray heterozygosity for *h,* since none of her five sons was affected. While this does not rule out the possibility that III–6 was *Hh,* there is also no evidence, from her own ancestry, of the presence of the *h* allele. Her normal father, II–3, was certainly *H,* and if her mother, II–2, was a carrier, why did none of her five brothers receive the *h* allele? It is thus very likely that the mother, IV–6, of the affected children owed her heterozygosity to a mutation, even though the analysis cannot eliminate with certainty the possibility of regular transmission of an *h* allele through several generations of the pedigree, with chance having led to the production of only normal sons from *Hh* mothers, except in the last generation.

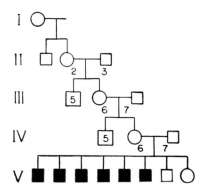

A similar analysis makes it seem extremely likely that the hemophilia occurring in the royal families of Europe during the nineteenth and twentieth centuries owed its origin to a mutation (Fig. 188). All affected individuals trace their ancestry to Queen Victoria of England, who, undoubtedly, was heterozygous *Hh*. Her father was normal, and nothing suggests that her mother was a carrier. Consequently, Queen Victoria seems to have received a new mutant allele *h* from one of her parents.

FIG. 187. Sex-linked mutation. Pedigree of hemophilia. (After Boggs, *Am. J. Med. Sci.,* **188,** 1934.)

Determination of Mutation Frequency—Direct Method

Not only is there evidence of the independent occurrence of the same mutation in different individuals, but the frequency of specific mutations has been estimated. Two different methods have been devised for deriving such estimates. The first, the direct method, is primarily applicable to dominant mutations. It is based simply on a census of the frequency of children with well-

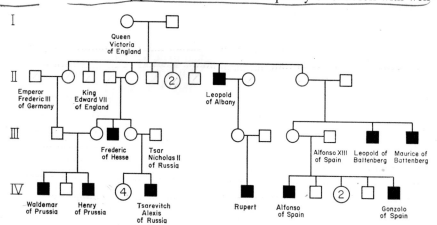

FIG. 188. Sex-linked mutation. Pedigree of hemophilia in the royal families of Europe. All of Queen Victoria's children are entered. Later generations comprise many more individuals than are indicated here.

known dominant traits who are born to parents without these traits. Underlying assumptions are: (a) that there is always full penetrance, (b) that the trait is never produced by recessive alleles, (c) that the trait is never produced by nongenetic agents, and (d) that dominant alleles at only one locus produce the trait.

In most cases the validity of these assumptions has not been verified, and full proof of their correctness may be difficult to obtain. Assumptions (a), (b), and (c) should be supported by evidence from numerous pedigrees in which affected individuals have produced offspring. The ratio of affected to nonaffected among their pooled children should be compatible with that expected, 1:1, and the frequency of individual sibships without affected individuals should not be greater than expected in small families as an extreme chance deviation from the 1:1 ratio. Assumption (a), that there is always full penetrance, and (b), that the trait is never produced by recessive alleles, would be invalidated if it were found that the trait skipped some generations. Assumption (c), that the trait is never produced by nongenetic agents, or, in other words, that it does not appear as a phenocopy (see p. 46), would be shown to be false if incomplete penetrance and recessive determination could be excluded but if significant numbers of affected persons had neither affected parents nor children. Assumption (d), that dominant alleles at only one locus produce the trait, can seldom be tested in man, though in the future linkage studies might provide the necessary data.

If any one of the four assumptions does not hold, an overestimate of the mutation rate in terms of change at a single locus would be obtained. Thus, the estimate will be high if the appearance of an affected offspring from nonaffected parents is considered to be due to a dominant mutation, although it actually results from expression of an already present incompletely penetrant gene, of homozygosity for a recessive gene, or of a phenocopy. Or, if dominant mutation at more than one locus is responsible for a trait, the mutation rate estimated for one locus will be too high, because it is really a composite of two or more rates. If, for instance, an abnormal dominant trait is caused by mutation in 1 out of 50,000 gametes, then the mutation rate is 1 in 50,000, provided a single locus, P, is concerned. But if two equally mutable loci, P and Q, can give rise to dominant alleles P' and Q', either of which would produce the abnormal trait, then the mutation rate per locus is obviously only 1 in 100,000. Since, in man, it is seldom possible to prove that the same locus is involved in the appearance of a specific trait in different kindreds, the figures to be given below for mutation rates of human genes may be too high, although some mutation rates may be underestimated. If, for example, certain mutations result in recognizable phenotypes in some individuals, but embryonic death without recognizable genetic cause in others, only the recognized occurrences will be available for an estimate of the mutation rate.

Chondrodystrophic Dwarfism.   A direct determination of the rate of mutation has been made in the case of chondrodystrophic dwarfism. The data were furnished by records on 94,075 children born in Lying-in Hospital in Copenhagen. Ten of these children were chondrodystrophic dwarfs, 2 of them from an affected parent. This leaves 8 mutant dwarfs, or 1 in nearly 12,000 births. Since pedigree studies in Denmark show simple dominant inheritance of the condition, the occurrence of 1 new case in 12,000 births has been regarded as evidence of mutation.

The rate of mutation is best expressed in terms of the number of alleles involved, not births. Since each individual has two alleles at the assumed single locus for chondrodystrophy, each birth represents a sample of two alleles, so that 1 mutant birth in 12,000 signifies one mutant allele in 24,000, or a rate of about $4 \cdot 10^{-5}$.

Later studies in Germany modify this conclusion. Chondrodystrophy occurs in several phenotypically different forms, which do not appear together in the same kindreds. Although most of these are inherited as dominants they are presumably due to different genes; recessive inheritance is also involved occasionally; and the occurrence of phenocopies cannot be excluded. The mutation rates for the different genes must, then, be lower than the earlier estimate, which was based on the assumption that a single gene controlled the abnormality.

Retinoblastoma.   Another direct determination of a dominant mutation rate has been made for the allele causing the disease retinoblastoma, which consists in the development of tumors of the retina: these appear early in childhood and result in death unless the eye or eyes are removed by surgery. In Michigan, from 1936 to 1945, there were 49 isolated cases of the disease among 1,054,985 children born to normal parents. From these numbers, Neel and Falls derived a rate of $2.3 \cdot 10^{-5}$ for mutation of a normal to an abnormal dominant allele—an estimate similar to, though higher than, one made by Sorsby from British data. More recently, Vogel has shown that approximately three-quarters of all individuals with retinoblastoma who have normal parents do not transmit the disease to any of their children, so that in these affected individuals the trait seems to be either a phenocopy or an expression of a somatic mutation (pp. 465ff.). In any case the frequency of mutation from normal to alleles for retinoblastoma in the gametes must be lower than formerly believed, since only about one-quarter of new occurrences are caused by such mutation. On the other hand, not all mutations are expressed phenotypically, since the penetrance of the abnormal allele is probably below 80 per cent: former unawareness of this tended to lower the estimate of the mutation rate. Taking these facts, as well as some others, into account, the gametic mutation rate of the gene for retinoblastoma is estimated to be about 0.4 per 100,000 gametes.

Determination of Mutation Frequency—Indirect Method

Before the direct method of estimating the rate of mutation of a human gene had been applied, an indirect method had been devised by Danforth and later, independently, by Haldane and by Gunther and Penrose. It is based on principles derived from population genetics. Most abnormal human traits, the reasoning goes, decrease the likelihood that the individual possessing them will have an average number of children. Some traits cause early mortality of affected individuals, eliminating them before they reach maturity; other traits reduce the prospects of marriage; still others cause the number of children produced to fall below the average for the rest of the population. Consequently, alleles causing abnormalities are not transmitted to as many individuals as are normal alleles, and this should lead to a decrease in the frequencies of abnormal alleles from one generation to the next. If, for instance, a dominant abnormal allele leads to death of its carriers at an early age, so that, on the average, they have only half as many children as the normal population, then the frequency of the abnormal allele would decrease by 50 per cent in each generation, and in the course of a few centuries the allele should have practically disappeared. With a reproductive rate that is half the normal, as assumed above, in ten generations—about 300 years—there would have been a reduction to $(1/2)^{10}$, or less than 0.1 per cent of the original relative frequency. Even with a reproductive rate as relatively high as $9/10$, ten generations would lead to a decline to $(9/10)^{10}$, or less than 4 per cent of the original relative frequency. Applied to such traits as chondrodystrophy or the dominant trait epiloia, this reasoning would suggest that the present low frequency of these conditions represents only the leftovers of frequencies that were hundreds of times higher a few centuries ago!

This is an absurd deduction, since we know from historical records that the relative frequencies of various inherited abnormalities could not have been strikingly higher in former times. But, since this is true, why are they not lower now?

Equilibrium for Dominant Mutations. An answer is provided by the hypothesis that recurrent mutations from normal to abnormal must have constantly replenished the steadily diminishing store of abnormal alleles of low reproductive fitness. If it is true that the frequencies of such alleles have not changed much in the course of many generations, an equilibrium must have existed between loss and gain; that is, the rate of mutation must have balanced the rate of loss.

This relation can be stated in terms of an equation. Let N be the total number of individuals in one generation, x the frequency of the abnormality among them, and f the reproductive fitness of the abnormal gene, that is, the frequency, relative to that of its normal allele, with which it is transmitted to the next generation. Finally, let u be the frequency per gamete of the mutation from normal to abnormal. Then, for a rare autosomal dominant, the following holds true: The number of mutant births depends on the total number of normal alleles and the frequency, u, with which they can mutate. There are xN affected parents who have xN abnormal and xN normal alleles, and

$(N - xN)$ normal parents who have $2(N - xN)$ normal alleles. The sum of the normal alleles is, therefore,

$$xN + 2N - 2xN = 2N - xN = N(2 - x),$$

and the number of mutations giving rise to mutant births,

$$\text{new cases} = uN(2 - x). \quad \textit{frequency of abnormality}$$

Since x, the frequency of the abnormality, is usually very small (e.g., 1/10,000 to 1/100,000), we can neglect x, and, thus, simplifying the last expression, obtain,

$$\textit{mutation rate}$$
$$\text{new cases} = 2uN, \quad \textit{# of persons in generation}$$

which is a good approximation if one makes the reasonable assumptions that the mutant gene is rare and its mutation rate low.

We must now obtain an expression for the number of "lost" cases. The number of abnormal individuals eliminated from the population is equal to the number of abnormalities present, xN, times the fraction lost because of reduced reproductive fitness. If the latter is f, then the lost fraction is $(1 - f)$. Thus,

$$\text{eliminated cases} = (1 - f)xN.$$

Postulating an equilibrium between new and eliminated cases means that

$$2uN = (1 - f)xN,$$

which, solved for the mutation rate, u, yields

$$u = \tfrac{1}{2}(1 - f)x. \tag{1}$$

Here, then, is a means of estimating the frequency of mutations on the basis of two observable data, the reproductive fitness and the frequency of the abnormality.

Chondrodystrophic Dwarfism.   We may apply this indirect method for estimating mutation frequency to the chondrodystrophic dwarfs of Denmark. The total number of chondrodystrophics known was 108, living and dead. These 108 dwarfs produced 27 children, of whom one-half would be expected to be dwarfs. (In reality, the ratio was 10 chondrodystrophics to 17 normals, which is not a statistically significant deviation from equality.) Therefore, of the 108 abnormal alleles present in the parents, only $1/2 \cdot 27 = 13.5$ were transmitted to their offspring. The proportion of abnormal alleles still in existence after one generation is thus, 13.5:108, or 0.125. In order to judge the relative reproductive fitness of the dwarfs, they were compared with their 457 normal sibs. These had a total of 582 children, which meant that the $2 \cdot 457 = 914$ normal alleles from normal sibs had decreased in the ratio 582:914, or 0.6368. Consequently, the relative fitness of the allele for chondrodystrophy is

$$f = \frac{0.125}{0.6368} = 0.1963.$$

In other words, relative to the normal alleles only 19.6 per cent of the abnormal alleles present in one generation were transmitted to the next—80.4 per cent, $(1 - f)$, were eliminated.

The best estimate of the frequency of the abnormality comes from the Lying-in Hospital data that have been cited. There were 10 dwarfs in 94,075 births, which yields

$$x = \frac{10}{94,075}.$$

Substituting in formula (1) the values found for $(1 - f)$ and x, we find

$$u = \frac{1}{2}(1 - 0.1963)\frac{10}{94,075} = 0.0000427.$$

This estimate of the mutation rate derived by the indirect method—namely, 4.27 in 100,000 gametes (4.27×10^{-5}) or 1 in about 23,400—agrees well with the estimate obtained by the direct method, 1 in 24,000 (p. 451). However, not too much weight should be given to this agreement. If, as mentioned above, not all chondrodystrophic phenotypes are genetically equivalent, applications of the direct and indirect methods may each involve the

TABLE 67. *Estimates Made by Various Authors of Mutation Rates of Certain Human Genes from Normal to Affected.* (After Neel, *Proc. Natl. Ac. Sci.,* **43**, 1957, and others.)

Trait	Mutant Gene per 100,000 Gametes
AUTOSOMAL DOMINANTS	
Huntington's chorea	<0.1
Retinoblastoma (tumors of retina)	0.4
Waardenburg's syndrome (developmental and pigmentary anomalies of eyes, deafness, etc.)	0.4
Aniridia (absence of iris)	0.5
Microphthalmus (abnormally small eyes) without mental defect	0.5
Marfan's syndrome (see p. 43, arachnodactyly)	0.5
Muscular dystrophy (dominant muscular wasting)	0.8
Epiloia (type of brain tumors)	0.8–1.2
Multiple polyposis of the large intestine	1–3
Pelger's nuclear anomaly (shape of nuclei of white blood cells)	2.7
Chondrodystrophy (dwarfness)	1–14
Neurofibromatosis (tumors of nervous tissue)	10
X-LINKED RECESSIVES	
Hemophilia, combined	2–3.2
Duchenne-type muscular dystrophy	4–9

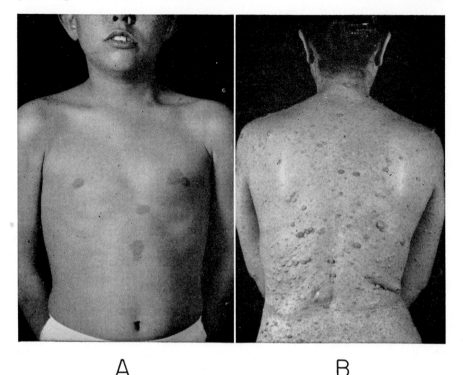

A   B

FIG. 189. Multiple neurofibromatosis.   A. Pigmented skin areas on a child.   B. Tumors of varying size on a woman. (Originals from Dr. V. McKusick.)

same biases. Some investigators have given reasons for believing that the mutation rate for chondrodystrophy may actually be only one-fifth of that calculated here from Danish data; others have found evidence for rates two or even three times as high in Sweden and Japan.

Rates of Other Dominant Mutations.   Application of the indirect method, and more rarely the direct method, has yielded information on the rate of mutation from normal to dominant abnormal of more than ten different genes. These mutation rates are all rather similar, varying only from less than 0.1 to 10 per 100,000 gametes (Table 67). The latter, the highest known rate in man, applies to neurofibromatosis (von Recklinghausen's disease), a syndrome characterized by spots of abnormal pigmentation (*"café au lait"*) of the skin and by numerous tumors that develop in association with the central or pheripheral nervous systems (Fig. 189). The disease occurs in approximately 1 out of every 3,000 births. The relative reproductive fitness of affected individuals has been calculated with particular attention to sources of error in the determination of the relative fertility of affected and normal sibs. For males, f = 0.41, for females, 0.75, these low values being in part due to a marriage rate lower than normal and in part to a smaller mean number of children per marriage. Both the direct and the indirect method suggest a mutation rate of approximately 1 per 10,000 gametes.

The lowest mutation rate listed in Table 67 is that for Huntington's chorea. As serious as this disease is, its relatively late onset is compatible with high reproductive fitness. Indeed, for a group of choreic families and a selected large kindred in Minnesota, S. C. Reed and Palm reported that the number of children from parents who bore the abnormal *Ht* gene was considerably higher than the number of offspring from the parents' normal (*htht*) sibs. A different result was obtained in studies of Japanese choreics reported by Kishimoto: their fitness was greatly below that of normals. T. E. Reed and Neel concluded that the relative fertility of *Htht* individuals in an unselected large group of families in Michigan, compared to that of Michigan's general population, was about 0.8 or higher. For this population the calculated mutation rate to genes for Huntington's chorea seems to be less than 1 in 1,000,000.

It is known from plants and animals that different genes, even in the same species, may vary widely in their mutability. This seems also to be true for man. Although most known human mutation rates are relatively similar, it may well be that other genes have much lower rates of mutation than those listed. In support of this supposition, it may be pointed out that there is a tendency, in studies of mutation rates, toward selection of genes which mutate relatively frequently. This refers particularly to the use of the indirect method, which works best when the fitness, f, is low and thus yields a mutation rate, u, that is high. On the other hand, it is also important to realize that most estimates of the rate of mutation are based on mutant alleles with easily recognizable effects. How much higher the rate would be if mutant alleles with very slight phenotypic effects could be included is not known, but it would probably be at least several times that usually recorded.

Equilibrium for Recessive Mutations.   It should be easy to adjust formula (1) to determine mutation rates for recessive abnormal alleles. Since equilibrium exists when the number of mutations equals the number of eliminated alleles and since, in a recessive trait, *two* alleles are lost with each individual eliminated, the mutation rate, u, for recessive mutations must be twice that of dominant ones: that is,

$$u = (1 - f)x. \qquad (2)$$

It is, however, not advisable at present to use this formula to estimate recessive mutation rates. First, the formula assumes that only the reproductive fitness of homozygotes is affected, but it is now known that many recessive alleles which reduce fitness in homozygotes produce an effect even in heterozygotes—an effect that may increase the fitness of some heterozygotes (heterosis; see p. 464), but decrease that of others. Because heterozygotes for rare recessive alleles are so much more common than homozygotes, even a slight effect on the fitness of heterozygotes would completely invalidate an estimate based solely on the fitness of homozygotes. Second, and even more important, present populations are not in equilibrium. The breakup of isolates in recent times is leading to a decrease in homozygotes and an increase in heterozygotes. Consequently, the number of unfit homozygotes that can be eliminated is decreasing. Unless this is counteracted by increased unfitness of heterozygotes, the unchanged rate of mutation must increase the number of abnormal recessive alleles. Haldane has estimated that this increase of allele frequency may continue for several thousand years, until a stabilized breeding system in mankind results again in a constant frequency of homozygous recessives.

Equilibrium for Sex-linked Mutations.   An adaptation of formula (2) can be used for actual estimates of sex-linked recessive mutation rates. Rare sex-linked recessive alleles will result mainly in elimination of males, and only of a negligible number of females. Since males have one-third of the X-chromosomes of a population, one-third of the sex-linked abnormal alleles are exposed by reproductive unfitness. In an equilibrium between mutation and elimination, the relation is

$$u = \tfrac{1}{3}(1 - f)x',\tag{3}$$

where x′ is the frequency of the abnormality among males. This formula has been applied to two X-linked conditions for which extensive data are available. One of these is the Duchenne type of muscular dystrophy. Since affected individuals hardly ever reproduce, $f = 0$, and the mutation rate becomes simply equal to one-third of the frequency of affected males, namely, 4 to 9 per 100,000 gametes, as calculated from different population samples from Utah and Northern Ireland (Table 67). The second X-linked trait for which the mutation rate has been estimated is hemophilia. We now know that there are several X-linked types of this disease; but no separate estimates have yet been made. Assuming the reproductive fitness of bleeder males to be $f = 0.39$, a combined mutation rate of between 2 and 3 per 100,000 from normal to any one of the alleles causing the more severe types of hemophilia has been calculated for both Danish and Swiss populations (Table 67). Some doubts have been raised about this value, since in a later study the heterozygous carrier women in a large Swiss kindred with hemophilia were found to have a larger number of children than did homozygous normal women. The reproductive fitness of the carriers was estimated to be 1.15, sufficiently above normal to counteract the low fitness of hemophilic males, estimated as being relatively high, namely, 0.64. If the apparent increased fitness of heterozygotes should be real and be confirmed, estimates of the mutation rate toward hemophilia will have to be lowered greatly.

The Equilibrium Level.   Readers not used to considering equilibria of the type discussed, which are not static but are maintained by a balance between in-

TABLE 68. *Frequencies of an Abnormal Dominant A Allele in Various Generations.* (Mutation rate 1 in 100,000. Size of the population 1,000,000. Reproductive fitness of A: 0.4.)

Generation	Normal Alleles a	Abnormal Alleles A		
		Left Over from Former Generations	Newly Mutated	Total
0	2,000,000	—	—	—
1	2,000,000*	—	20	20
2	2,000,000*	8	20	28
3	2,000,000*	$8 + 3.2$	20	31.2
4	2,000,000*	$8 + 3.2 + 1.28$	20	32.48
.	.	.	.	.
.	.	.	.	.
∞	2,000,000*	$8 + 3.2 + 1.28 + 0.512 + \cdots$	20	33.33

* More accurately, the number of normal alleles would be 2,000,000 minus the total number of abnormal alleles. This small correction is omitted as well as the small error which is introduced by this omission in the expectation for new mutants.

flow and outgo, may ask the question: Why do mutation and elimination balance each other? Is this balance just a fortunate chance? To answer this question, let us consider a specific example. Assume a population of 1,000,000 per generation, a rate of mutation to a dominant allele of 1 in 100,000 and a reproductive fitness of 0.4, and that there are no abnormal alleles yet present (Table 68). In the next generation, however, 20 such alleles have appeared. One generation later, these alleles have reproduced only 8, but 20

TABLE 69. *Frequencies of Abnormal Dominant A Allele in Various Generations.* (Mutation rate 1 in 10,000. Size of the Population 1,000,000. Reproductive fitness of A: 0.4.)

Generation	Normal Alleles a	Abnormal Alleles A		
		Left Over from Former Generations	Newly Mutated	Total
0	2,000,000	—	—	—
1	2,000,000*	—	200	200
2	2,000,000*	80	200	280
3	2,000,000*	$80 + 32$	200	312
4	2,000,000*	$80 + 32 + 12.8$	200	324.8
.	.	.	.	.
.	.	.	.	.
∞	2,000,000*	$80 + 32 + 12.8 + 5.12 + \cdots$	200	333.3

* More accurately, the number of normal alleles would be 2,000,000 minus the total number of abnormal alleles. This small correction is omitted as well as the small error which is introduced by this omission in the expectation for new mutants.

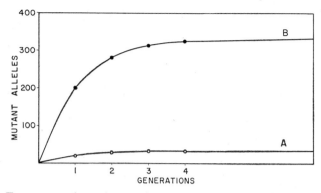

FIG. 190. Frequency of an abnormal dominant *A* allele in the course of genera-tions after onset of mutations from *a* to *A*. (Size of population: 1,000,000. Re-productive fitness of *A:* 0.4.)   A. Mutation rate 1 in 100,000.   B. 1 in 10,000.

new ones have been added, making a total of 28. In the third generation, the 8 alleles of the first generation have dwindled to 3.2, the 20 alleles of the second to 8, and 20 new alleles have been added by mutation, so that the total is now 31.2. In the fourth generation, the total of abnormal alleles has gone up to 32.48, and it can be seen that an equilibrium is approached in which the total number of mutant alleles is 33.33 (Fig. 190, A). Now let us assume that the rate of mutation is ten times as great, making it 1 in 10,000. The course of events is shown in Table 69 and Figure 190, B. In

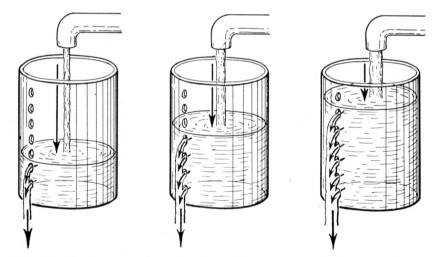

FIG. 191. The three vessels, each with a different content level, are analogous to three populations, each with a different number of mutant alleles. The level in each vessel remains constant—a result of the balance between input through the pipes above and outgo through the overflow holes. Similarly, the number of mu-tant alleles in each of the three populations remains constant—a result of the balance between "input" of new mutant alleles and "outgo" due to low repro-ductive fitness.

spite of the great increase, an equilibrium is reached, though at a higher frequency of the abnormal allele: the increased inflow of new alleles is balanced by increased outgo. Diagrammatically, this state of affairs is illustrated by Figure 191, in which varied rates of inflow into a tank are balanced by arrangements for overflow at different levels.

Keeping the mutation rate constant but varying the rate of loss of abnormal genes also influences the frequency of the allele. If reproductive fitness is zero—that is, if bearers of the allele have no offspring at all—the frequency of the allele at any time will be equal to its rate of production by immediately preceding mutations. The higher the degree of relative fitness produced by the allele, the higher will its frequency rise. Should the reproductive fitness of persons carrying the mutant allele become equal to that of those carrying its normal partner, then recurrent mutation would lead to a continuous increase in the frequency of the mutant. The result of such a process will be discussed in the final chapter of this book. Obviously, the alleles involved cannot be labeled "abnormal," since full fitness contradicts such a term.

Frequency of Mutation in Relation to Age and Sex.   Mutation rates derived by the indirect method of estimation are average rates and cannot indicate possible differences of rates in male or female gametes, or differences between different groups of individuals in a population. That such differences may exist is known both from extensive plant and animal studies and from human evidence. It is true, for instance, that rates of sex-linked lethal mutations are higher in Drosophila sperm than in eggs, that young Drosophila males produce sperm with a higher number of mutant alleles than older ones, and that stored Drosophila sperm, as well as stored plant pollen, accumulate mutant alleles.

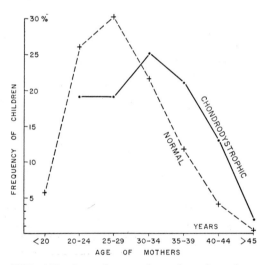

FIG. 192. Age of normal mothers in unions with normal fathers and percentage frequency of the mothers at the birth of normal and chondrodystrophic children. (Mørch.)

In man, a connection exists between frequency of chondrodystrophic mutations and age of mothers (Fig. 192), older mothers having a significantly higher relative rate of mutant births: this correlation is independent of the number of preceding births. It is possible, however, that it is the increased age of the father rather than that of the mother which is responsible. Older women usually have, of course, older husbands, but it is noteworthy that the fathers of mutant chondrodystrophics are disproportionally older than the mothers. This suggests that the older a man grows, the more likely it becomes that his sperm will contain chondrodystrophic mutant alleles.

Mutations at X-linked loci provide a particularly suitable material for the study of the relative rates of mutation in the two sexes. If the rates of mutation at an X-linked locus were alike in eggs and sperm, then there would be twice as many new mutant heterozygous women as new hemizygous men, since, after fertilization, half of the mutant eggs would develop into males and the other half into females and, in addition, all of the mutant sperm, being X-chromosomal, would produce females. Were mutations restricted to eggs, then equal numbers of affected males and carrier females of mutant origin would be expected; and were mutations exclusive to sperm, then only carrier females would mark the origin of a mutant allele. Comparing these different expectations with numerous published data on hemophilia, Haldane came to the conclusion that the mutation rate for this condition is much higher in male than in female gametes—possibly ten times as high. It is not certain, however, that this conclusion is final, since the data available to Haldane may have been biased by the methods used in collecting them. Data on the mutation rate for X-linked muscular dystrophy have also been critically examined in order to obtain information on the relative rates in the two sexes. They are compatible with either equal rates of mutation or with a somewhat higher rate in males.

It is not known whether similar differences between the mutation rates in the two sexes exist for any other human genes; neither is it known whether age and rate of mutation are always positively correlated, as in chondrodystrophy. It may well be that different genes mutate at different rates, and under different conditions, though there may be general circumstances which lead to similar relations for all of them. The possibility that the occurrence of mutations increases in proportion to the time that genes are exposed to the risk of spontaneous mutational changes will be discussed in the next chapter. If there is such a time relation, the age of a parent would be an important item in determining the occurrence of abnormal traits caused by new mutations. In any individual case, whether parents are relatively young or old may make a negligible difference in the expectation of such abnormal offspring; in terms of the "public health" of a population as a whole, the difference may be considerable. And, at least in hemophilia, the age of the father may be much more important than that of the mother, although, in this case, the harmful results of a mutation in a sperm cell will not become obvious until the birth of a grandson from a mutant carrier daughter.

We shall soon discuss one more trait, mongolism, in which hereditary newness based not on a genic but on a chromosomal change of a special kind is related to age of a parent, in this case, of the mother (see pp. 469ff.).

The Total Mutation Rate per Gamete. The estimated frequencies of rates of mutation of given normal alleles into clearly detrimental alleles range from one in ten thousand to one in hundreds of thousands (Table 67). Since each gamete carries many mutable genes, it is important to estimate the frequency with which gametes carry one or more mutated genes at one or another of their many loci. It would be easy to determine this frequency if we knew (a) the mean frequency of mutation per locus and (b) the total number of mutable loci. Simple multiplication of the two quantities would give the frequency of mutant gametes (though uncorrected for the rare event of two or more different mutations being found together in the same gamete).

We have seen that it is difficult to make a satisfactory estimate of the mean rate of detrimental mutations per locus, since the accuracy of the "known" rates is uncertain, and, even if they should be correct, their average may not reflect the true average of all known and unknown individual rates. Somewhat arbitrarily, this average rate is often assumed to be about 1 or 2 per 100,000 or, to select a single intermediate number, 1.5 per 100,000. It may well be higher if mutations with rather slight detrimental effects are included, or considerably lower if there should be many genic loci with low mutation rates. Estimates lying between 4 per 100,000 and 1 per 1,000,000 or even outside these limits may be well defended!

The total number of genic loci in man is likewise a matter of uncertainty. By analogy with not too reliable estimates in Drosophila, it has been assumed to be about 10,000 (see p. 29). It is possible to estimate the number of loci on the basis of mutation rates. If one knows the mean rate of mutations per locus, $\bar{u}$, and the total rate for all loci, U, the quotient $U/\bar{u}$ gives the total number of loci. In Drosophila this method has given a number close to 10,000.

If we now use 10,000 as the number of loci in man and multiply it by an estimated rate of 1.5/100,000 mutations per locus, we find that 1.5/10, or 15 per cent, of all gametes carry a new detrimental mutation. If, alternatively, we multiply 10,000 by either of the two extreme estimates listed above—namely, 4/100,000 or 1/1,000,000—we obtain 40 per cent and 1 per cent for the frequency of mutation in the gametes. Since each individual is the product of two gametes, these estimates indicate that a minimum of 2 per cent and a maximum of 80 per cent of all humans contain a newly mutated gene that is more or less detrimental. Sometimes the intermediate estimate of 30 per cent is used.

There is another method of estimating the number of newly mutant genes per individual. It is not based on direct determination of mutation frequencies, but makes use of the presumed number of lethal-equivalent mutant genes, old and new, carried by the average person. From studies of results of consanguineous marriages, this number has been estimated as approximately 4 (see p. 396). Assumption of an equilibrium between mutational input and selective outgo of mutants suggests that 2 per cent of the 4 lethal equivalents are of new mutational origin. In other words, $0.02 \cdot 4$, or 8 per cent, of all individuals carry one newly mutated lethal equivalent. This figure of 8 per cent is lower than the intermediate estimate of 30 per cent above quoted, partly because of the different assumptions which underlie the two methods of estimate, and also because the estimate of 30 per cent involves extrapolation from data on the frequency of lethals in Drosophila that includes those causing embryonic death, while the estimate of 8 per cent involves human deaths between birth and maturity only.

Whatever the actual value is, the estimates of percentages of zygotes with new mutants become particularly meaningful when they are considered in terms of the numbers of individuals in entire countries or in the world. Even the lowest estimate listed above—namely, 2 per cent—signifies that more than 3.5 million of the 180 million living Americans carry a detrimental gene that was not carried by their parents; in China, 13 million; and in all mankind, no less than 50 million carry such genes. We must assume that spontaneous mutations have taken place and poured new genes into the gene pool continuously ever since life existed on the earth. Individually, most of these mutations cause little harm, and some may even be beneficial, but the harmful mutants, accumulated over the generations and in the aggregate, either in heterozygotes or homozygotes or in polygenic combinations decrease the fitness of the population.

The Dominance of Detrimental Genes

One might expect that in order to evaluate the harm done by detrimental genes it would be necessary to know how many of them are dominant and how many recessive. Each single dominant would exert an effect, so that the total effect of dominants in a population would be proportional to their frequency. Recessives would have an effect only in homozygous combination, and the population would suffer in proportion to the square of their frequency. However, detailed studies of Drosophila as well as of other species have shown that, in reality, mutant lethals that seem to be recessive are not strictly recessive, but, on the average, reduce the fitness of heterozygotes sufficiently to cause the death of about 4 or 5 per cent, and may therefore be regarded as dominant lethals with very low penetrance. In any population, heterozygotes for rare alleles are much more common than are homozygotes. Consequently, the reduced fitness of heterozygotes with seemingly recessive lethals will lead to many more eliminations of lethal genes than will the invariable death of the rare homozygotes. If, on the basis of some evidence from Drosophila, one assumes that not only lethals but also other, less detrimental alleles have an incompletely penetrant dominant action in heterozygotes, then the same conclusion applies to them—namely, that the major part of their effect on a population is exerted in heterozygotes.

The Accumulation of Mutant Genes in a Population.   A dominant mutant that invariably leads to death of its carrier before the age of reproduction or which causes sterility, can occur in a population only at the frequency with which it is produced by mutation. By definition, it is eliminated within one generation, as soon as it has been produced. A similar mutant that is penetrant in only half of the persons carrying it has a probability of being eliminated in the first generation of 1/2 and correspondingly a remaining probability of being present in the second generation of 1/2. Those that survive the first generation have a probability of 1/2 of being eliminated in the second generation, and so on. On the average, such a gene with its selective disadvantage s, of 1/2 will persist for two generations. A dominant mutant which imposes on its carriers a selective disadvantage of 1/10 will, on the average, persist for ten generations. The general expression for the number of generations of persistence of a gene is 1/s.

Mutant genes that persist for several generations will accumulate in a population, the accumulation varying with the degree of selective disadvantage imposed by the mutant: The population will contain not only the newly mutated genes but also the leftovers from former generations that have not yet been eliminated (Tables 68 and 69; Fig. 190). The frequency of genes that persist for ten generations will be 10 times their mutation rate and that of genes which persist for 100 generations will be 100 times the mutation rate. It has been estimated (with considerable uncertainty) that about 50 times as many detrimental mutants are present in a population as would be produced by new mutations. This estimate takes into account both the genes lost by elimination of heterozygotes and the relatively small losses from elimination of homozygotes. The estimated frequencies of the homozygotes were not simply based on the Hardy-Weinberg Law but were adjusted for the existence of inbreeding in human populations.

Heterotic Mutants.   The foregoing estimates of the persistence and accumulation of mutant genes depend on the estimates of their penetrance in heterozygotes. The estimate of from 4 to 5 per cent for the dominant effect of lethals was an average derived from experiments with Drosophila that showed not only higher and lower penetrance of lethality in heterozygotes but also some cases of better-than-normal viability. Some of the mutant genes that were lethal when homozygous increased the chances of survival when present heterozygously! It is not known yet, either in Drosophila or in man, how common such heterotic mutants are (see Chap. 28). It is obvious that the accumulation of heterotic alleles has a trend different from that of those with detrimental effects in heterozygotes. A heterotic mutant allele will increase in frequency from generation to generation—an increase which is checked only by the selective disadvantage the mutant imposes on homozygotes. A detailed treatment of opposing forces will be deferred until Chapter 28, Selection and Genetic Polymorphism, but the discussion of the effect of mutations on human population in Chapter 23 will take account of the significance of heterotic mutants.

The Detection of Somatic Mutations

We have treated the process of mutation as if it occurred in the gametes only, but there is experimental evidence indicating that genes are susceptible to mutation in many or perhaps all cells. If one allele in a cell of a very early embryo mutated from A to A', further divisions of the unmutated AA cells and the mutated AA' cell would build up an individual whose tissues would consist partly of AA cells and partly of AA' cells. If A' were a dominant of autonomous phenotypic expression in body cells, the mosaic nature of such an individual might be observed directly. In various mammals, the rare appearance of mosaic coats when uniform ones were expected has thus been attributed to early somatic mutation. This interpretation cannot be tested rigorously when all AA' cells are part of somatic tissues, since proof of presence of a mutation consists of its transmission to later generations of individuals, which is obviously impossible if it exists only in somatic cells. However, in some of the mosaic individuals, proof of somatic mutation was obtainable, since cells descended from the original mutant AA' cell formed part of the germ cell tissue of the gonads. Some of the offspring of these mosaics inherited the mutant allele A', which was not present in the ancestors of the mosaic parents. Some mosaic human abnormalities have been suspected of being due to mutation during early embryonic development, but there is no definite proof of this. The later in development mutation occurs, the smaller should be the segment of tissue derived from the mutant cell. Thus, some of the fairly common mosaic eye colors—a brown segment in an otherwise blue iris, for instance—are perhaps due to late somatic mutation. Similarly, retinoblastoma in individuals whose parents and offspring do not have it may be caused by somatic mutation.

In the developing individual, mutation may also occur in an embryonic germ cell, which, on division, will produce a "cluster" of gametes of common descent which carry the mutant allele. Such an event may have occurred in a kindred in which a normal couple had 6 normal children and 4 with aniridia (absence of the iris). For three generations this trait was transmitted to 19 descendants in dominant fashion with complete or very high penetrance. It may be concluded either that one of the parents of the first 4 affected individuals carried the gene without penetrance or that four mutant germ cells were derived from a germinal mutation.

The red blood cells are particularly suitable material for the study of somatic mutations. These cells are formed all through life from stem cells located in the blood-forming tissues. A stem cell regularly divides into two daughter cells: one that remains a stem cell, and another that produces red blood cells. Should mutations occur in the stem cells, they may be presumed to persist indefinitely in the stem line and their accumulated number to increase with the age of the individual. A mosaic of nonmutant and mutant stem cells should be formed. This hypothesis can be tested by a study of such genetically determined traits as the antigens of the red blood cells. And it has indeed been found that the blood of $I^A I^B$ individuals regularly contains a small fraction of cells which do not possess the A antigen, and that $I^A I^O$ individuals also have some cells without it. This can be explained by the assumption that the I^A allele mutated to I^O. Other findings support this interpretation, but further studies are needed.

Genetic changes in somatic cells can be brought about by various mechanisms of which gene mutation is only one. Thus, if a cell is heterozygous for a pair of alleles, A and A', loss of the chromosome carrying A' will leave a cell hemizygous for A. Even loss of a chromosome without a "marker" gene is equivalent to a genetic change, as will be shown later in this chapter. Still another process leading to genetic changes is crossing over between homologous chromosomes in somatic cells. Its occurrence has been demonstrated in Drosophila and in molds, but no critical studies are available for man. Crossing over occurs in somatic cells, as well as in germ cells, between two of the strands at the four-strand stage (Fig. 193). In a heterozygous AA' cell it can lead to the mitotic distribution of AA into one daughter cell and of $A'A'$ into another. If A' is a dominant, then tissue with the recessive phenotype AA will develop from the AA somatic segregate. If all these genotypes, AA, AA', and $A'A'$, are phenotypically distinguishable, then an AA–$A'A'$ "twin spot" will originate on the AA' background.

Individuals mosaic for cells of different genotypes do not originate solely by changes in the genetic constitution of cells during development. In animals, some mosaics have arisen from eggs that had two or even more fertilizable nuclei, each of which fused with a separate sperm nucleus. In man, as well as in cattle and sheep, a few individuals possess not only blood-forming cells whose genotype is that of the rest of the body but also blood-forming cells

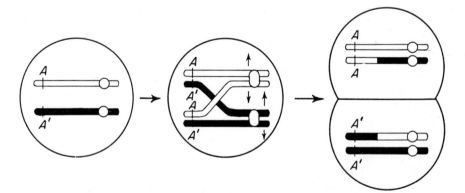

FIG. 193. Somatic crossing over in a cell of the genotype AA' and its possible consequences, the formation of AA and $A'A'$ cells.

of a different genotype that were derived from a nonidentical twin during embryonic life. Some of these individuals are not only "blood chimeras" (named after the mythical monster that had a lion's head, a goat's body, and a serpent's tail) but also sex chimeras. Their bodies are clearly those of one sex but the sex chromatin of their blood cells suggests that both male and female chromosomal constitutions are present (see p. 420).

Cancer and Somatic Mutation.   It has been suggested that cancer, in man and other organisms, may be the result of somatic mutation that leads to unorganized, deleterious proliferation of cells which have previously behaved normally. Such a hypothesis can neither be proved nor disproved at present: it is not the only hypothesis that would explain the permanent change in cells that become cancerous. The process of differentiation of genetically identical cells during normal development has always posed a problem. It is probable that typical mutational changes in genic composition do not account for embryonic differentiation, and as long as the nature of differentiation is obscure, the characterization of cancer as a somatic mutation must remain tentative. Should, however, such a designation turn out to be correct, it would lead to a specific interpretation of the heritable aspects of cancer. Inheritance of cancer would then be known to consist in an inherited tendency to mutate somatically. There is, as we have said, no evidence for this chain of reasoning, but each single link is based on reasonable or even well-established principles. Thus, inherited tendencies toward somatic mutation, though not to cancerous cells, have been shown to exist in animals and plants.

Some types of cancer, in organisms other than man, are caused by viruses, and the hypothesis that all cancers are virus diseases has been advanced. Should this prove to be correct, then the genetic tendencies to cancer which are known to exist (pp. 566ff.) would be based on genes that control the susceptibility of cells to respond to viruses by cancerous growth.

Chromosomal Changes

Gene mutation, which we have defined as a change from one allelic form to another, is only one of the changes that lead to new inherited properties. There are two others, namely, changes in the quantity of the chromosomal material and changes in its arrangement. The cellular and developmental functioning of an organism depends not only on the presence of the necessary alleles, but also on their harmonious interaction with each other. Like the musical effect of an orchestra, which depends both on the presence of different instruments and on the number of each, genic effects are not the same if different quantities of alleles are involved.

Normally, every somatic cell contains a pair of each type of autosome, each pair of autosomes has numerous pairs of homologous loci, and at each of these loci is one of a pair of alleles; harmonious genic action depends on this twofold presence of each locus. Occasionally, however, abnormalities in the division or the distribution of the chromosomes or of chromosomal sections may result in some loci existing in triplicate or singly instead of as a pair. In an early chapter, abnormal distribution of whole chromosomes that was due to nondisjunction or abnormal multipolar mitoses, was discussed (p. 19). It was shown that a cell which receives three instead of two of a particular chromosome will, by normal mitosis, give rise to more cells with three similar chromosomes, and that a cell with only one chromosome of a kind will transmit this property to its daughter cells. Should these cells be human gametes, zygotes with 47 or 45 chromosomes, respectively, would be formed.

Experience with such abnormal chromosomal types in many plants and animals has shown that development does not proceed normally. Such imbalance in the genic content of the zygotes—two alleles of most loci but three, or one, of the loci of a certain chromosome—may result in early death of the zygote. Or full development may occur, but the individual will not be normal—just as the sound of an orchestra would be different if the number of, say, the brass instruments were increased or decreased by one-half. Whether or not the abnormal chromosomal condition was known, the appearance of a new, abnormal phenotype would be noticed and the trait would be found to be inherited as a dominant. This is true because individuals with 47 chromosomes will form equal numbers of two kinds of gametes, one with 23 and one with 24 chromosomes. The former lead to normal phenotypes, the latter to the abnormal ones. Similarly, the new phenotype caused by the presence of 45 instead of 46 chromosomes will reappear in half the offspring of a 45-chromosome individual. The first appearance of these different types of individuals thus marks the origin of a new, dominantly inherited trait. To denote this first appearance of hereditary newness as mutation is justifiable, since without counting chromosomes, it is not possible to distinguish it from that caused by the mutation of genes.

As there are 22 pairs of autosomes in man, 22 kinds of zygotes with 47 chromosomes and 22 kinds with 45 chromosomes are possible, depending on which of the 22 autosomes are present in triplicate (*trisomic*) or singly (*monosomic*). If all 44 kinds could develop into viable offspring they would exhibit 44 different phenotypes, since the genic imbalance would involve different genes in the different chromosomes. Each phenotype would be transmitted in dominant fashion. It is possible that the developmental imbalance produced by the addition or subtraction of an autosome often leads to embryonic death, particularly if one of the larger autosomes is involved. We know, however, of one trisomic phenotype that is viable but abnormal (mongolism), and it may be expected that other viable phenotypes produced by trisomic or monosomic genotypes will be found.

Apart from zygotes which are monosomic or trisomic for a single chromosome, numerous combinations of monosomics for different chromosomes, trisomics for different chromosomes, and monosomics and trisomics for different chromosomes are possible. They may be further causes of embryonic death or of abnormalities of surviving infants. The modern methods of studying human chromosomes are opening up a period of new insights into the causes of faulty development.

Mongolism

One of the most remarkable and distressingly abnormal syndromes in man is that called mongolism, or mongolian idiocy. Affected individuals are characterized by physical abnormalities of the face, eyelids, tongue, and other parts of the body and are greatly retarded both physically and mentally. The term mongolism has been applied to this condition because the affected individuals often show a fold of the eyelid similar to that typical of members of the Mongoloid race. But, contrary to an earlier suggestion, there is no relation between the appearance of the abnormality and presence of Mongoloid genes derived from matings between Europeans and Mongolians during the historical invasions of Europe.

Unfortunately, mongolism is a relatively common congenital malformation, having an over-all incidence of about 0.15 in all births in Caucasoid populations. (Early death of many affected children results in a much lower frequency of living mongols.) The condition is also found in races other than the Caucasoid, though probably less frequently.

The appearance of mongolism in the newborn is closely related to the age of the mother. Several per cent of the children of women who become pregnant late in their reproductive years are affected, but only a very small fraction of 1 per cent of the children of young mothers. In relative terms, the incidence of the trait rises more than a hundredfold with increasing age of the mother (Table 70). From a different angle, the dependence of mongolian idiocy on age of mother is shown in Table 71. In sibships in which the trait was present, there were five times as many affected children among the second half of births as among the first half. Finally, the age effect is apparent from statistics on more than 1,700 affected children, nearly 40 per cent of whom were born to mothers aged forty or older, in

TABLE 70. *Relative Frequencies of 545 Cases of Mongolism in Relation to Age of Mothers.* (After Penrose, Ann. New York Ac. Sc., **57**, 1954).

Maternal Age Group	Incidence Relative to Youngest Group
15–19	1
20–24	1.3
25–29	1.3
30–34	3.7
35–39	11.0
40–44	41.3
45–	104.0

TABLE 71. *Mongolism* (see also Table 49). (M. Murphy, *Hum. Biol.,* **8,** 1936.)

Half of Family	Affected	Normal
First half	18	222
Second half	90	150

contrast to normal children in control populations, of whom only between 3.5 and 5 per cent were born to mothers over forty.

It is generally true that older women have older husbands, and it might therefore be thought that mongolian births were caused by either a direct or indirect influence of either the mother or the father. Penrose has shown, however, that the frequency of mongolism rises with the age of the mothers even if the age of the fathers is constant, and does not rise with the age of the fathers if the age of the mothers does not vary. In addition, it has been found that the age of the mother, not the number of preceding pregnancies, determines its frequency.

For many years it was usually assumed that mongolism is produced by an unfavorable interaction between mother and fetus. It seemed that some kind of unknown physiological changes in the mother that were correlated with her age led to retarded development of affected embryos, perhaps as early as the second or third month of pregnancy. It was clear, however, that the cause of the damage was not alone inherent in the mother but must also reside in the egg. This was deduced from studies of twins with mongolism. In all cases in which it is certain that the twins are identical, both are affected, whereas in the great majority of affected nonidentical twins only one is a mongol and the other is normal. This important finding showed that it is not the physiological condition of the mother alone, but its interaction with a specific condition of the embryo, that causes mongolism. Since identical

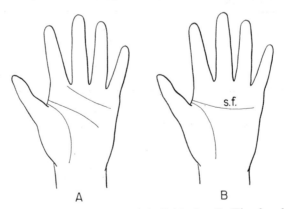

FIG. 194. A. The hand of a normal individual. B. The hand of a mongol individual (s. f. = simian fold). (After Schiller, *Ztschr. menschl. Vererbgsl.,* **25,** 1941.)

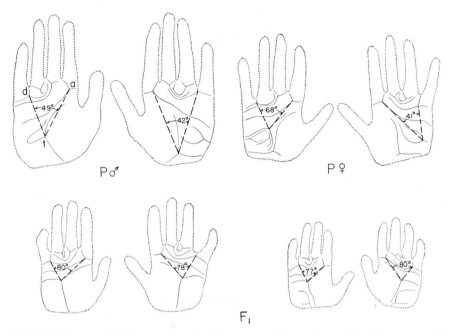

FIG. 195. The main lines on hands of two normal parents and their two mongol children. The numbers signify the degree of the maximal atd angle: a, t, and d being three points defined by the meeting of three lines each on the bases of the first and fourth finger and on the palm. (After Penrose, *Ann. Eugen.*, **19**, 1954.)

twins have identical genotypes, the most obvious explanation of both being affected with mongolism is that a specific genotype of the embryo is involved in the defect—an explanation for which there seemed to be some independent evidence. Thus the frequency of affected sibs following the birth of a mongol is somewhat greater than in the general population, and, more significantly, there is a slightly increased frequency of mongols among the offspring of relatives of both mothers and fathers of mongols. Further hints come from the few relatively lightly affected mongol women who have had a child: some of these children were normal, but others were mongols or mentally defective. The strongest indication of specific genic participation seemed to lie in the findings that certain physical traits present in most mongols occur with increased frequency among their normal parents and sibs. One of these is the simian, or four-finger, fold, a crease which passes across the whole palm of the hand (Fig. 194). Another is the relative position of several points on the palm as measured by the size of a certain angle between them (Figs. 195 and 196). An angle of greater than 57° is found in over 80 per cent of all mongols but in only 7 to 9 per cent of the general population. In mothers and sibs of mongols, the frequency of this abnormal configuration is from 14 to 16 per cent. The frequency in fathers is only slightly higher than normal.

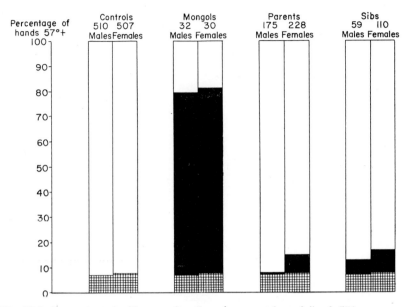

FIG. 196. Percentage incidence of a "maximum atd angle" of 57° or more in persons 15 years of age or older in the general population, in mongols, and in the parents and sibs of mongols. (Penrose, *Ann. Eugen.*, **19,** 1954.)

All of this made it seem that one or more specific genotypes might make an embryo susceptible to a damaging influence of the intra-uterine environment of an older mother and that most other genotypes would be immune to such damage.

This point of view must be abandoned. In France, Lejeune, Turpin, and Gautier, and, soon after, other investigators in England, the United States, and Sweden studied the chromosomes from tissue cultures of fibroblasts and bone marrow cells of a number of mongols and found that one of the small chromosomes is present in triplicate instead of in duplicate. The mongols thus have 47 chromosomes (Fig. 197). It must therefore be assumed that it is the imbalance of their genic content—the presence of three sets of genes in the triplicated chromosome—that is the cause of the specific maldevelopment of the embryos. Presumably the unusual trisomic chromosome constitution of a mongol is the result of the fusion of a normal haploid gamete with an abnormal one that carries two homologues of one small chromosome, although it is haploid for all others. It is possible that either parent may occasionally form such nondisjunctional gametes, but the relation between mongolism and age of the mother indicates that the majority of mongols are derived from nondisjunctional eggs. Contrary to the earlier opinion, mongolism is not caused by an unfavorable mother-fetus interaction but by abnormal chromosome behavior in the ovaries of the mothers or in the eggs produced by them.

The chromosomal uniqueness of the eggs that produce mongols explains the facts concerning identical and nonidentical twins discussed above. If a zygote which, as the result of nondisjunction, possesses 47 chromosomes gives rise to identical twins, both will have the abnormal chromosome number and both will be mongols; if two separate zygotes lead to nonidentical twins, only very rarely will the exceptional process of nondisjunction have occurred in the formation of both eggs, and usually only one will be a mongol. The chromosomal uniqueness of mongols explains also the fact that normal and mongol children have appeared in approximately equal proportion among the rare offspring of mongol women. Mongolism, once present, should behave as if produced by a dominant gene, since a mongol will form gametes of which 50 per cent have the normal number of chromosomes and 50 per cent have an extra chromosome.

Our knowledge of other organisms indicates that a tendency toward nondisjunction of a chromosome may be inherited—a phenomenon which could account for the slight increase in mongols among the relatives of affected individuals. But it is not yet clear why the normal relatives of affected indi-

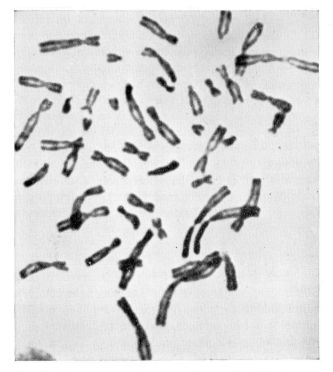

FIG. 197. The 47 chromosomes of a mongolian male child. Among the normal diploid chromosome content of a male cell, there are *five* small chromosomes with approximately terminal kinetochores—the Y-chromosome and two pairs of autosomes. The cells of mongolian males contain *six* small chromosomes—the Y-chromosome, one pair of autosomes and one trisomic autosomal assembly. (Lejeune, Turpin, and Gautier, *Ann. de Génét.*, **1**, 1959.)

viduals more often than unrelated ones have a simian fold or an enlarged palmar angle. It might be argued that these traits are indicators of the presence of the genotype which leads to a tendency toward nondisjunction. Why, however, should that genotype have a tendency also to produce the phenotypes of the hands which are stigmata of mongolism? Could it be that the presence of the extra chromosome does not always lead to mongolism and that some of the normal mothers and sibs of mongols are trisomics themselves, and that the manifestation of the trisomic genotype varies from complete nonexpression through rare phenotypes for hands to full expression of mongolism? And why do the fathers of mongols have a large palmar angle less frequently than the mothers and sibs? Answers to these questions will undoubtedly be forthcoming from the intense studies of human cytogenetics which are now pursued in many laboratories.

Breakage of Chromosomes

Changes in the quantity of genic material also occur when a section of a chromosome, rather than a whole chromosome, becomes doubled or is lost from a cell. Such changes may be caused by breaks in the chromosomes, which may occur spontaneously or may be induced under experimental conditions. If a chromosome breaks, the two fragments may either reunite later or remain permanently separate. If they unite, no lasting effect on the genetic property of the chromosome is produced, but permanent separation leads to important genetic consequences. In the overwhelming majority of chromosomes, only one specific region—the kinetochore—controls chromosome movement on the mitotic or meiotic spindle. And since only one of the two fragments will possess the kinetochore, while the other will be without it, this latter fragment or its daughter products will not be distributed by the spindle to the daughter cells in the normal way, but will be lost to the nuclei and degenerate in the cytoplasm (Fig. 198). The loss of the genes located in the fragment will upset normal development and a new phenotype may appear, as it may when a whole chromosome is lost.

The fate of the chromosome fragment that retains the kinetochore varies. After some types of breakages, or in some tissues, this fragment behaves like a typical whole chromosome, and its daughter products are distributed normally in later divisions (Fig. 198, A). Under other circumstances, the fragment reduplicates to form two fragments with broken ends, and these ends unite, forming a long compound chromosome with two kinetochores (Fig. 198, B). Such chromosomes are not stable, since the two kinetochores go to opposite spindle poles, with the result that the chromosome stretches and finally breaks at some point. Each newly created fragment is incorporated in a different daughter nucleus. As may be seen from Figure 198, B, one of the fragments may contain a certain doubled section that the other lacks completely. At the next division of the nuclei, the same cycle is repeated, namely, fusion of the broken ends of the sister chromosomes, formation of a "bridge" between the poles of each spindle, and a new break at some point on the stretched chromosome bridge. Repetition of the "breakage-fusion-bridge-breakage" cycle leads to more new genotypes for the cells involved, genotypes that are new not because they carry new alleles, but because of the quantity of alleles present—they may lack some alleles and possess others in multiple quantity.

The breakage-fusion-bridge cycle was discovered in 1938 by Barbara McClintock in highly technical studies of the genetics and cytology of maize. As we shall see in the next chapter, knowledge of this phenomenon is probably of importance in the understanding of the effect of irradiation on man—a typical example of the unforeseeable results of scientific endeavor.

Chromosomes may break at more than one place, or more than one chromosome may break in the same nucleus. If two breaks occur in the same chromosome, three fragments will be produced—two end pieces and

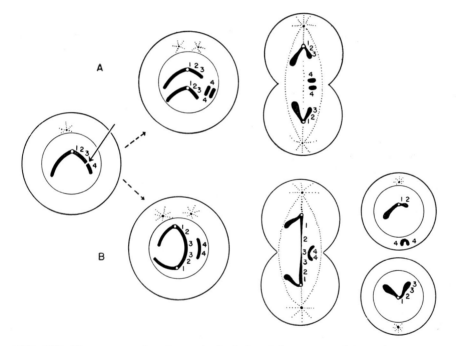

FIG. 198. Chromosome breakage. A single break has occurred in a chromosome between loci 3 and 4.   A and B: Alternative fates of the broken chromosome. A. The two parts of the broken chromosome reduplicate. The fragments with the kinetochore are distributed to opposite poles of the mitotic spindle. The fragments without the kinetochore remain in the equatorial region and will be eliminated in the cytoplasm.   B. The two parts of the broken chromosome reduplicate and the broken ends of sister parts unite, thus forming a chromosome with two kinetochores and another chromosome without a kinetochore. During mitosis, the two kinetochores move to opposite poles and the chromosome section between them breaks. The two daughter cells receive different, unbalanced chromosome constitutions. The fragment without a kinetochore is eliminated in the cytoplasm.

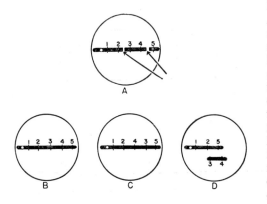

FIG. 199. Chromosome breakage. A. Two breaks have occurred in a chromosome, between loci 2 and 3, and 4 and 5. B, C, D. Different consequences of the double break. B. Reunion of the fragments in the original order: 1–2–3–4–5. C. Reunion of the fragments with the middle fragment inverted: 1–2–4–3–5. D. Union of the two outside fragments: 1–2–5; the inner fragment, 3–4, which has no kinetochore, will be lost in a subsequent division.

a middle piece (Fig. 199). These may reunite in the original way without further consequences, or they may reunite with the middle piece inverted. This new *inversion* chromosome has lost no genetic material and behaves normally in later mitotic divisions: its meiotic fate will be discussed below. As a third alternative, the broken ends of the end pieces may unite, leaving the middle segment by itself. This segment, lacking a kinetochore, is lost (sometimes after having formed a ring chromosome, by fusion of its two broken ends); but the other reunited chromosome, in spite of lacking a middle section, behaves normally in future divisions. A new transmissible genotype, lacking the alleles located in the middle section, is thus created.

If breaks occur in two separate chromosomes, still more genetic newness may result (Fig. 200, A). If two homologous chromosomes break at different places, reunion of the four fragments may lead to formation of a chromosome with two kinetochores and a fragment without one (Fig. 200, B). Such recombination of broken chromosomes may result in a breakage-fusion-bridge cycle similar to the one discussed above. Or reunion of the fragments may result in an exchange of nonidentical parts and the creation of two new stable chromosomes, one without a middle section, the other with this section duplicated (Fig. 200, C). A cell that contains both chromosomes

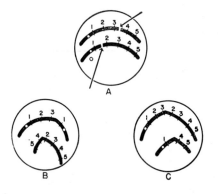

FIG. 200. Chromosome breakage. A. Two breaks have occurred, at different places in two homologous chromosomes. B, C. Different consequences of the double break: B. Union of the two fragments with kinetochores, and of the two fragments without kinetochores. C. Union of each fragment with a kinetochore with one without a kinetochore, resulting in one chromosome with a duplication and another with a deficiency.

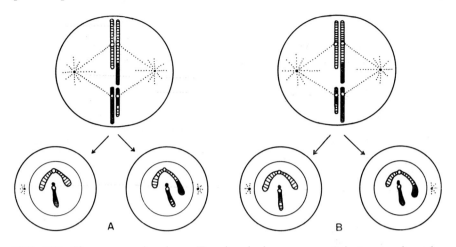

FIG. 201. Chromosome breakage. Two breaks have occurred, in two nonhomologous chromosomes. Union of fragments has resulted in an exchange of end pieces (translocations).   A, B. Meiosis in a "translocation heterozygote." Two different meiotic arrangements of the two chromosomes involved in the translocations and of their nontranslocated homologues: A. The meiotic distribution results in the formation of balanced gametes.   B. The meiotic distribution results in the formation of unbalanced gametes that lack one chromosomal section and duplicate another.

retains the normal number of all alleles, but when the two chromosomes segregate into different gametes, during meiosis, these gametes will possess either a *deficiency* or a *duplication* and will produce zygotes with new phenotypes.

Breaks in two nonhomologous chromosomes may result in reciprocal *translocations*—an exchange of end pieces between the chromosomes (Fig. 201). Again, a cell containing both chromosomes retains the normal number of alleles. In meiosis, however, either the two translocation chromosomes go together to the opposite pole from the two normal homologues, or one translocation chromosome and one normal chromosome go to one pole and the other translocation chromosome and the other normal chromosome go to the other pole. In the first case, two gametes with full genic complement are formed; in the second case, both gametes have one duplicated section, different in the two gametes, and also lack a section.

With more than two breaks, the variety of possible recombinations increases, but no recombinations are essentially different from those already discussed. Basically, the behavior of broken chromosomes is controlled by two things: (1) usually a broken chromosome has a tendency to unite with another broken chromosome, either a sister strand or part of a different chromosome, which may be either homologous or nonhomologous; and (2) a chromosome must have one, and not more than one, kinetochore if it and its daughter chromosomes are to be distributed normally in mitosis or meiosis.

Position Effect.   Not all genetic newness produced by chromosome aberrations is due to changes in allelic quantity. There is evidence, in a few organisms, that rearrangement of genic position may lead to new inherited phenotypes. Many genes exert a different effect—either dominant or recessive—when placed in new chromosomal neighborhoods. Genes near a break find a new neighborhood whenever the broken fragment unites with another in such a way as to form a new type of chromosome. A new phenotype produced by a new position of a gene is transmitted in the same way as one produced by a mutated allele that had arisen at the locus, since the rearranged chromosome reproduces itself permanently in its rearranged form. In man such *position effects* have not yet been discovered, but they have been found in another mammal, the mouse.

Gene Mutation and Chromosome Change.   The existence of deficiencies, duplications, inversions, and translocations is well established in many animals and plants. Yet even in the most favorable material, there is a point at which recognition of these chromosomal aberrations becomes difficult or impossible. This point is reached when the chromosome section involved is so small as to be undetectable, but since all degrees of ease of detection have been encountered—from those involving nearly a whole chromosome to very short though still recognizable sections—there is no reason why we should doubt the existence of aberrations below the limits of optical observation. Even very small aberrations could exert a special phenotypic effect by changing the position of a gene or affecting the genic balance of a cell. It is possible that many "mutant" phenotypes ascribed to a typical mutation from one allele to another are produced by chromosomal aberrations too small to be seen. From another standpoint, mutations may often consist of very small chromosomal changes that affect the quantity or position of genes rather than of "real" allelic mutations. Thus, the distinction between genic mutations and chromosomal aberrations must often remain theoretical. In actuality, the line of demarcation lies between (1) gene mutation and those minute chromosomal changes that are stable and do not result in unbalanced cells and (2) those chromosomal changes which lead to unbalanced cells.

In mammals, including man, extensive rearrangements of chromosomes, among them translocations and duplications, occur in certain somatic tissues and particularly in tumors. The causation of mongolism by an extra chromosome and of abnormal sex types by exceptional presence or absence of a Y-chromosome is evidence for the production of genetic newness by chromosome changes transmitted by gametes. Other, rarer types of congenital abnormalities in man occur as a result of translocations, deficiencies, and duplications in the gametes. Undoubtedly, chromosomal aberrations in both somatic cells and gametes are important factors in genetic changes induced by external agents. This will be taken up in the following chapter.

Problems

172. In two families, there have been only normal people for many generations. In one family, a brachydactylous boy is born, who later marries and has four children, three normal and one brachydactylous. This brachydactylous offspring marries and has three children, all normal. In the other family, an albino child is born, who later marries and has four children, all normal. What are the most likely explanations for the appearance and disappearance of the traits in each of these two pedigrees? (Assume only legitimacy.)

173. A child with blue scleras and brittleness of bones is born to normal parents. Does the child represent a new mutation?

174. (a) Assume that the mutation rate of the normal allele x to the dominant allele X responsible for an abnormal trait is 1 in 50,000, and that the reproductive fitness of affected individuals is 0.2. In a population of 100,000,000 per generation which is initially free from X, how many affected persons will be present after 1 generation? After 2, 3, 4, 5 generations? At equilibrium? (b) What would the answer be if the allele X caused death in childhood?

175. Assume that the rate of mutation of the normal gene for sex-linked color vision to an allele for red-green color deficiency is 1 in 50,000 and that the frequency x' of color-blind men is 0.08. Assuming that the formula for the equilibrium situation is applicable, determine the reproductive fitness of color-blind men.

176. Assume that the mutation rate of the normal allele to that for hemophilia is ten times higher in male than in female gametes. What would be the ratio of new carrier females to new affected males?

177. If the reproductive fitness of heterozygous carriers of a recessive trait is somewhat less than 1, would this call for upward, or downward, or no revision of an estimate of the mutation rate which was originally based on the frequency and fitness of homozygotes only?

178. (a) What is the chromosome number of a boy who has both the Klinefelter syndrome and mongolism? (b) If he could be fertile, what types of offspring would be expected? (c) If he formed sperm with XX, Y, X, and XY in the ratio 1:1:2:2, what would be the proportion of the various types of offspring?

179. In different social groups, the age of people entering marriage varies considerably. What effect might this difference have on the incidence of mongolism in these different groups?

180. In a fetus with a genotype for blue eyes, a somatic mutation occurs in a cell, changing its genotype to one leading to brown eyes. If descendants of this cell form part of the iris of the left eye, what will be the appearance of the child after birth?

181. Tissue heterozygous for a histocompatibility locus, H^1H^2, does not usually persist if transplanted to H^1H^1 or H^2H^2 hosts. What would be the results of transplantation if occasionally some cells of the graft become genetically H^2H^2?

References

Andreassen, Mogens, 1943. Haemofili i Danmark. *Opera Ex Domo Biologiae Hereditariae Humanae Universitatis Hafniensis,* **6:** 168 pp.

Atwood, K. C., 1958. The presence of A_2 erythrocytes in A_1 blood. *Proc. Nat. Acad. Sci.,* **44:** 1054–1057.

Cheeseman, E. A., Kilpatrick, S. J., Stevenson, A. C., and Smith, C. A. B., 1958. The sex ratio of mutation rates of sex-linked recessive genes in man with particular reference to Duchenne type of muscular dystrophy. *Ann. Human Genet.,* **22:** 235–243.

Cotterman, C. W., 1958. Erythrocyte antigen mosaicism. *J. Cell. Comp. Physiol.,* **52,** suppl. 1: 69–96.

Crowe, F. W., Schull, W. J., and Neel, J. V., 1956. *A Clinical, Pathological, and Genetic Study of Multiple Neurofibromatosis.* 181 pp. C. C. Thomas, Springfield, Ill.

Danforth, C. H., 1923. The frequency of mutation and the incidence of hereditary traits in man. *Eugenics, Genetics and the Family,* **1:** 120–128.

Ford, C. E., Jones, K. W., Miller, O. J., Mittwoch, U., Penrose, L. S., Ridler, M., and Shapiro, A., 1959. The chromosomes in a patient showing both mongolism and the Klinefelter syndrome. *Lancet,* **I** (of 1959): 709–710.

Gunther, M., and Penrose, L. S., 1935. The genetics of epiloia. *J. Genet.,* **31:** 413–430.

Haldane, J. B. S., 1935. The rate of spontaneous mutation of a human gene. *J. Genet.,* **31:** 317–326.

———, 1937. The effect of variation on fitness. *Am. Naturalist,* **71:** 337–349.

———, 1947. The mutation rate of the gene for haemophilia and its segregation ratios in males and females. *Ann. Eugen.,* **13:** 262–271.

———, 1949. The rate of mutation of human genes. Proc. 8th Intern. Congr. Genet. *Hereditas,* Suppl. vol.: 267–273.

Hanhart, E., 1940. Die Entstehung und Ausbreitung von Mutationen beim Menschen. In Hdbch. Erbbiol. des Menschen, **1:** 288–370.

Jacobs, P., Baikie, A. G., Court-Brown, W. M., and Strong, J. A., 1959. The somatic chromosomes in mongolism. *Lancet,* **I** (of 1959): 710.

Kishimoto, K., Nakamura, M., and Sotokawa, Y., 1957. On population genetics of Huntington's chorea in Japan. *Ann. Rep. Research Inst. Environm. Med., Nagoya Univ.,* **1958:** 84–90.

Lejeune, J., Turpin, R., and Gautier, M., 1959. Le mongolisme, premier exemple d'aberration autosomique humaine. *Ann. Génét. Hum.,* **1:** 41–49.

Lieberman, I., and Ove, P., 1959. Estimation of mutation rates with mammalian cells in culture. *Proc. Nat. Acad. Sci.,* **45:** 872–877.

Mørch, E. T., 1941. Chondrodystrophic dwarfs in Denmark." *Opera ex Domo Biologiae Hereditariae Humanae Universitatis Hafniensis,* **3:** 200 pp. (see also Popham, R. E., 1953. *Am. J. Human Genet.,* **5:** 73–75).

Neel, J. V., and Falls, H. F., 1952. The rate of mutation of the gene responsible for retinoblastoma in man. *Science,* **114:** 419–422.

Øster, J., 1953. Mongolism. *Copenhagen Univ. Opera ex Domo Biol. Hered. Hum.,* **32:** 1–206.

Penrose, L. S., 1954. Observations on the aetiology of mongolism. *Lancet,* **267:** 505–509.

————, 1955. Parental age and mutation. *Lancet,* **269:** 312–313.

Puck, T. T., 1959. Quantitative studies on mammalian cells in vitro. *Rev. Mod. Physics,* **31:** 433–448.

Reed, S. C., and Palm, J. D., 1951. Social fitness versus reproductive fitness. *Science,* **113:** 294–296.

Reed, T. E., and Falls, H. F., 1955. A pedigree of aniridia with a discussion of germinal mosaicism in man. *Am. J. Human Genet.,* **7:** 28–38.

Reed, T. E., and Neel, J. V., 1959. Huntington's chorea in Michigan. 2. Selection and mutation. *Am. J. Human Genet.,* **11:** 107–136.

Robinson, R., 1957. Mosaicism in mammals. *Genetica,* **29:** 120–145.

Smith, S. M., and Sorsby, A., 1958. Retinoblastoma: some genetic aspects. *Ann. Human Genet.,* **23:** 50–58.

Steinberg, A. G., 1959. Methodology in human genetics. *J. Med. Ed.,* **34:** 315–334 (also *Am. J. Human Genet.,* **11,** 2 Part 2: 315–334), see pp. 330–333.

Swanson, C. P., 1957. *Cytology and Cytogenetics.* Chapters 10 and 12, pp. 349–399 and 419–447. Prentice-Hall, Englewood Cliffs.

Vogel, F., 1954. Über Genetik und Mutationsrate des Retinoblastems (Glioma retinae). *Zeitschr. Menschl. Vererbgs. u Konstit.,* **32:** 308–336.

CHAPTER 23

PRODUCTION OF
MUTATIONS

Although we do not yet know the detailed structure of any gene, it appears that every gene has one or another of the many possible molecular configurations of deoxyribose nucleic acid. Gene reproduction, which occurs constantly in the course of cellular reproduction during the development and throughout the life of an individual and with the passage of generations, is a process at the molecular level. The mother gene selects from its immediate cellular surroundings those molecular building materials which, organized correctly, form, or lead to the formation of, a daughter gene. In gene mutation either the original structure of the mother gene, that of the daughter gene, or that of both, is altered, and this alteration results in the continuation and reproduction of a new molecular pattern.

Mutant Gene and Mutant Trait. The mutant character which is the external sign of a mutant gene is the result of complex interactions of developmental processes. Although these processes are controlled by genes or their products, they take place largely in the cytoplasm of cells. They may result in movements of groups of cells, as in the folding of cell layers in development, and they include the action of secretions of glands located in one part of the body on the phenotype of another part and the many means by which differentiation and organization of an individual are brought about and maintained.

The "level" of formation of a character and the "level" of the reproduction of any one of the numerous genes which are somehow initially concerned with the development of the character are obviously different. These levels can be at least partly defined by calling them *developmental level* and *genic level*.

In a way, the relation between genes and the characters they control is like that between an assembly line and the automobiles created on it. Changes at any point on the assembly line result in changes in the automobile, but changes in an automobile made by individual adjustment—when it "develops" in the factory, or is repaired—will not affect the assembly line.

Acquired Characters and Genic Stability.   If this concept of distant unidirectional relation between the molecular gene and the differentiated character is correct, then it cannot be expected that changes in bodily characters caused by the influence of environmental agents will result in gene mutations. Such somatic changes occur constantly. Skin pigmentation increases or decreases with the amount of irradiation received; muscles become more powerful with exercise; learning consists in the acquisition of new skills or new intellectual or emotional attributes. Although these changes occur as a result of reactions in which gene-dependent products play important roles, they take place far from the genic level.

The remoteness of the developmental from the genic level raises a point worth stressing anew: the collaboration of numerous genes in the production of a trait. Many different processes, controlled by alleles at many different loci, are involved in the formation of a muscle of normal size and activity. A mutation at any of these loci may result in a weakened, abnormal muscle. There is neither a specific gene for normal muscle nor one for abnormal muscle. Rather, a large number of genes control reactions that, at early embryonic stages, are not yet part of muscular physiology or structure and whose products are but intermediaries in the interwoven processes that finally lead to the formation of a muscle.

The deduction from genetic principles that acquired characters—that is, individual adjustments or individual qualities of form or function which arise in response to specific environmental conditions—do not result in genic changes or mutations has been substantiated by numerous experimental studies. Historically, there was not a one-sided attempt to prove this, but rather a scientific campaign conducted by two opposing groups of investigators. One group, starting from pre-Mendelian concepts, tried to show that acquired characters could be inherited; the other tried to disprove alleged cases of such inheritance. Objective weighing of the findings has gradually led to a clear decision: there is no evidence, in spite of very extensive attempts to find it, that modification of complex traits causes genic changes that are, in turn, responsible for the inheritance of these modifications.

Mutagenic Agents.   Evidence that acquired characters are not heritable does not mean that mutations may not be produced by external agents. Such agents have, indeed, been discovered in experiments on various animals and plants. The best-known mutagens are penetrating ionizing radiations such as X-rays, gamma rays from radium and other radioactive atoms, and neutrons from nuclear reactors. Many chemicals—mustard gas and various nitrogen- or sulfur-mustard compounds, formaldehyde, and others—are also mutagenic.

These agents produce mutations only in cells on which they act directly: presumably, only if they act directly on the nuclei. Thus, if X-rays are applied to any part of the body, but with the gonads out of their range, no mutations are induced in the gametes, but, if they are applied to the gonads or to the gametes themselves, "artificial transmutations" of genes and chromosomal aberrations result. Similarly, ultraviolet radiation does not cause gametic mutation in most organisms because it cannot penetrate deeply enough to reach the germ cells. But if the gametes are directly exposed to ultraviolet light, mutations are produced. Mutagenic chemical compounds, also, can cause mutation only in cells that they penetrate. Obviously, the fact that chemical solutions have mutagenic effects on the cells of plant seeds soaked in them, or on microorganisms directly exposed to them, does not necessarily signify that they have mutagenic effects on man: chemicals that enter a human body may decompose before they can reach the interior of cells. Nevertheless, it is by no means impossible that various chemical substances may cause mutation in man.

In general, the agents which can cause mutation are not specific for particular loci or groups of loci. Thus, ionizing radiation seems to act so effectively that any gene which is in its path will mutate. The known chemical mutagens have some degree of specificity, and it seems possible that mutagens that affect only specific genes may be found in the future. Such mutagens would be powerful new tools that would enable us to explore genic nature much further than we have, or even to eliminate harmful genes by changing them or to create desirable new alleles.

In any one cell, only one or few genes and only one allele of any pair can be made to mutate by irradiation or chemicals. This low yield of mutations per cell is apparently determined by the small amount of irradiation or of the chemical that can be employed without killing the cell; below the lethal level, the mutagenic agent is still relatively "dilute." In general, the nonspecificity of mutagenic agents for mutations at different loci holds also for chromosome breakages: induced breakages are widely scattered among the different chromosomes and the different regions of chromosomes. Some mutagens, however, increase the frequency of breaks in the so-called heterochromatic regions. These are chromosome segments that at some stages of the nuclear cycle stain differently from the rest of the chromosome.

Origin of Spontaneous Mutations

We are now ready to deal with a question that must have been present in the reader's mind for some time. Why do genes mutate "spontaneously"? Two different kinds of processes are conceivable. The first would consist of "errors" in the replication of genes. In spite of the great accuracy with which a gene duplicates itself during each cycle of chromosomal replication, we might assume that the copying process is occasionally inaccurate and thus produces a molecular structure different from that of the original gene. A second kind of mutational process might be caused by influences impinging on the genes when they are not replicating, that is, in "resting" cells. There is insufficient evidence for or against copying errors as causes of mutation, but we know of three classes of agents that can cause mutation of genes not in replication in various experimental organisms: naturally occurring high-energy radiation, mutagenic chemicals, and randomly occurring energy fluctuation. These agents may also be responsible for errors in the replication of genes.

When, in 1927, H. J. Muller discovered the mutagenic effect of X-rays, it was wondered whether the naturally occurring radiation from rare but ever-present radioactive atoms in the soil, air, food, within the body, and from cosmic rays could account for natural, so-called spontaneous muta-bility. Calculations soon showed that, for the fruit fly Drosophila at least, it could not. Although the rate of spontaneous mutation is low, naturally occurring radiation would have to be more than a thousand times as great as it actually is to produce the observed rate of mutation. Consequently, other agents must account for the great majority of spontaneous mutations in Drosophila. At present, we know of the two additional classes of such agents mentioned above: chemicals and random energy fluctuation.

We have noted that some experimentally applied chemicals can induce mu-tations, and there is evidence that radiation exerts its effect on the genes indirectly by producing highly reactive chemicals inside cells. It is, therefore, reasonable to suppose that some chemical substances derived from the envi-ronment—in food, water, and air—as well as some internal products of normal cellular metabolism, occasionally cause spontaneous mutations.

In contrast to chemical agents as mutagens, energy fluctuations represent physical agents. If genes are molecular configurations, then the laws which govern the stability of molecules should apply to them. From these laws it is known that, given enough energy, bonds between atoms will break and permit the formation of new molecular structures. The high stability of genes seems to signify that a considerable amount of energy is required to effect changes in their molecular structure, but it may be expected that natural fluctuations in energy can be large enough to cause genic changes. These natural fluctuations may be of external origin—for example, tempera-ture oscillations in the immediate environment of a gene—or they may occur inside the gene itself, perhaps as a chance concentration of the interatomic energy which is normally distributed over the whole gene molecule on some specific atomic bond.

Are the spontaneous mutations of human genes caused by the same agents which affect the genes of Drosophila? One might be inclined to say they are, but a quantitative examination suggests that at least the relative importance of these agents may differ considerably in fly and in man. The frequency of spontaneous mutation in Drosophila is far too large to be accounted for by the amount of natural radiation which a gene receives during the life of the fly carrying it. The newly mutant genes found in a mature fly's gametes represent the genetic changes that have accumulated during the brief period from its origin as a fertilized egg to its maturity. The life span of a human is much longer than that of a fruit fly. Whether the frequency of mutations is proportional to the length of time genes are exposed to natural radiation, or whether it is proportional to the number of gene duplications (which occur with each cell division), there is a much greater chance that a gene will mutate during the life span of a human than during that of a Drosophila. Consequently, a much higher proportion of spontaneous mutations in man may be due to natural (or "background") radiation. The exact proportion depends not only on the relative amounts of natural radiation received by man and Drosophila but also on the relative sensitivity of the genes to radiation. Such simple factors as the oxygen tension within cells and various more complex factors are known to affect the frequency of mutations produced by radiation. We have no knowledge of the radiation sensitivity of human genes. If it is similar to that of the genes of the only mammal for which the results of experiments are available—the mouse—then it is higher than that of the fruit fly. Although it is not impossible that nearly all spontaneous human mutations are due to natural radiation, most geneticists think that only a small proportion of spontaneous human mutation is so caused.

One basis for this opinion is the unlikelihood that the metabolic activity of human cells is so different from that of Drosophila cells that it does not occasionally produce chemical mutagens within the cells. Another is that the gonads of a small fly are exposed to external β radiation and perhaps even to some α radiation while those of man are largely shielded from these weakly penetrating particles by overlying tissue. This means that the relative amount of natural radiation received by human germ cells is less than that received by those of flies in the same period of time.

A further reason for attributing only a small part of the total spontaneous mutation rate of human genes to natural radiation comes from experiments on mice. Extensive tests by Russell, in Oak Ridge, show that the amount of radiation accumulated during the relatively long life of a mouse cannot account for more than a fraction of 1 per cent of the spontaneous rate of mutation of seven selected genes.

Considering that human beings are exposed to radiation for a much longer time than are mice and assuming that a given amount of radiation causes human genes to mutate as frequently as those of mice, it would seem that the percentage of spontaneous human mutations caused by natural radiation is higher than the percentage for mice. A simple estimate of this percentage can be derived from (1) the rather well-established amount of natural radiation received by human gonads in thirty years and (2) the less well-established dose of artificial irradiation required to double the spontaneous-mutation rate.

All people do not receive the same amount of radiation. It increases with the altitude above sea level since exposure to cosmic rays is greater at high

TABLE 72.   *Average doses of Natural Radiation Received by the Gonads during Thirty Years.* (The doses are given in rad units which correspond closely to r units, see p. 490.)

Source	Rad
EXTERNAL	
Cosmic rays	0.84
Terrestrial radiation	1.41
Atmospheric radiation	0.06
INTERNAL	
Natural radioactive atoms (K^{40}, C^{14}, etc.)	0.69
Total	3.00

altitudes. It depends on whether the rock or soil is rich (e.g., many granites) or poor (e.g., sedimentary rocks) in radioactive atoms of the uranium or thorium series. It is influenced by the type of houses in which people live, since those built of rock containing much radioactive material will expose the inhabitants to higher doses than will houses built of wood or other less radioactive material.

A measure of the genetically relevant dose is the total amount of natural radiation received by an individual during the period from conception until the time when one-half of his children have been produced—a period whose average length in Western populations is about thirty years. In the United States and many other countries this average background dose is approximately 3r (Table 72). In a relatively small area in Kerala, southwestern India, the presence of highly radioactive monazite sands along the coast increases the exposure tenfold.

A "reasonable" estimate of the dose of chronic radiation that induces as many mutants as occur spontaneously, i.e., doubles the rate of spontaneous mutation, is 200r (see p. 499). Since 3r, the average background dose, is 1.5 per cent of 200r, it would follow that no more than about 1.5 per cent of spontaneous human mutations are caused by natural radiation. The great majority must be assumed to be the result of chemical mutagens and randomly occurring energy fluctuations.

We have referred to the possibility that a spontaneous mutation may be the result of either an error in the replication of a gene or of a change in a nonreplicating gene. Some of the evidence of the occurrence of the latter kind of mutation comes from studies of Drosophila sperm. A Drosophila female may store the sperm of its mate for many weeks before utilizing it for the fertilization of her eggs. During this period the spermatozoa remain inactive and presumably no gene replication takes place. Nevertheless, the sperm accumulates considerable numbers of mutations during storage—or accumulates agents which cause the production of mutant genes after the sperm has entered an egg and its genes multiply.

In man, the question of whether mutation occurs when a gene is replicating or when it is not has been approached by comparing the rate of mutation, as related to age, in males and females. The production of mature sperm is preceded all through adult life by a large number of divisions of primordial germ cells, the spermatogonia, but that of mature eggs is believed to be restricted to the growth of nondividing cells, the oocytes, laid down in the ovary during the development of the female fetus. If mutations occur only or mostly during gene replication, then their frequency in sperm, but not in eggs, should increase with age. One way of testing this possibility consists in determining the mean ages of fathers and mothers of children with newly mutated genes. If increasing age of the father causes more mutations than increasing age of the mother, then the difference between the two ages should be larger in parents of children with new mutations than in a control group of parents without newly mutant children. Penrose and Vogel have assembled the rather limited data that are available. No significant increase in the difference between parental ages was found in retinoblastoma and in a number of other mutant traits, but indication of an increase was noted in hemophilia and of a definite increase in chondrodystrophy. These findings are thus compatible with the idea that errors in genic replication may be a cause of spontaneous mutation. It is, however, at least as likely that the great physiological differences between spermatogonia and oocytes are in some unknown way responsible for the different rates of mutation of some of their genes.

It might be thought that a simple comparison of the rate of mutation in men and women, independent of their age, would answer the question of the significance of replication for mutation. Other things being equal, one would expect a higher rate of mutation in sperm than in eggs if replication is an important factor. This indeed has been reported for hemophilia, but some doubts exist concerning the reality of the difference. Even if it is real, more than one interpretation is possible. The phrase "other things being equal" cannot be applied with any certitude to testicular and ovarian cells. They differ not only in the number of cell divisions which precede maturity but also in their differentiation which undoubtedly is accompanied by differing metabolic events. At present, the various kinds of differences occurring in the development of eggs and sperm cannot be separated from one another. The difficulties in analysis are emphasized by Muller's finding that the frequency of mutation in the sperm of very young Drosophila males is higher than in that of older ones!

Artificial Induction of Mutations

Ever since the discovery of the mutagenic action of radiation in Drosophila, the question of artificially increased rates of mutation in man has been debated. It is still unknown whether chemicals that are present in man's surroundings have any noteworthy mutagenic effects. Though it has been shown that many chemical compounds cause mutations in bacteria, these same compounds, even if present in the blood stream, may never pass through the cellular and nuclear membranes—or if they do, the amounts may be too small to have a similar effect in human germ cells. Only laborious experiments with mammals such as mice can show whether or not we may expect human mutations to be caused by chemical compounds naturally present in food; substances such as caffeine, nicotine, or alcohol; hydrocarbons from automobile exhausts; insecticides and fungicides absorbed by vegetables and fruit; or drugs taken as medicine; or drugs contained in meat from animals routinely raised on drug-supplemented feed. It may well be that such substances are now responsible for a significant proportion of seemingly spontaneous mutations and that the mutation rate in man has increased as a result of their presence.

Evidence for chemical mutagenesis in man may be the recent increase in the occurrence of cancer of the lung. If the origin of these tumors is causally related to chemicals in the smoke from cigarettes, and if the tumors are consequences of somatic mutation in the epithelial cells of the lungs, then chemical mutagenesis is active at an ominous rate.

A possible source of part of the spontaneous mutation in man may rest on some time-honored customs of human societies which affect the temperature of the gonads. Although the location of the ovaries within the abdomen makes them largely immune to artificial interference with their temperature, the testes are exposed to variations in the external temperature which are only incompletely countered by regulatory response of the scrotum and the blood supply. Measurements of the gonad temperatures of clothed and unclothed men have shown those of the former to be more than 3°C higher, and temperatures must rise even more when men bathe in very hot water or take steam baths, as they do in various cultures. There is evidence from Drosophila that temperature of the testes as well as of mature sperm leads to an increase of mutations. The same may be expected in man.

We can only make guesses about the artificial induction of mutations in man by chemicals and by high gonad temperature. We are on much more secure ground when we consider the effects of ionizing radiations. Although direct observations of the effects of radiation on man are very limited, the results of experiments with numerous and diverse microorganisms and higher animals and plants imply that, beyond doubt, radiation produces mutations in man. Radiation, in the form of X-rays or γ-rays and to some degree in the form of α- and β-rays and neutrons, is being employed extensively in public health projects, in medical practice, and in industrial laboratories. Furthermore, the increasing use of atomic power for peaceful as well as military purposes forces an intensified consideration of the genetic effects of radiation.

Numerous individuals have contributed to such a consideration by experiments, theoretical analysis, and general discussion. The essential conclusions were summarized in 1956 by two representative committees, one of the National Academy of Sciences–National Research Council of the United States and the other of the British Medical Research Council. A third report was published in 1957 by an international panel working under the sponsorship of the World Health Organization, and a fourth report, by an international scientific committee, appeared under the auspices of the United Nations in 1958.

The great gaps that are still left in our knowledge can be filled only slowly. The rather close agreement of the experts on the expected effects of radiation on human germ plasm is partly based on their common knowledge of facts. Partly, however, the agreement is based on informed guesses—guesses which future work may either uphold, or prove to have been wrong.

Radiation Genetics

In order to discuss the significance of radiation as a cause of induced mutations, some general results of radiation genetics will first be presented, neglecting the minor differences within and between X-rays, γ-rays, and neutrons.

The amount of radiation received by irradiated tissues (called "dose") is measured in terms of one of several units. The "r," after Röntgen, defines the dose of X- or γ-rays by the amount of ionization produced. In tissue, 1r causes about two ionizations in a cubic micron (μ^3) or, stated differently, about 1.6×10^{12} ion pairs per cubic centimeter. Although this is a large num-

TABLE 73.   *Doses of Radiation Received by the Gonads during X-ray Examination of Various Parts of the Body.* (Selected from: Osborn in *The Hazards to Man of Nuclear and Allied Radiation,* 1956; Report of the Intern. Comm. on Radiolog. Protection, *Physics in Medicine and Biology,* **2,** 1957.)

Parts Examined	Dose in Thousands of r (= mr) Received by the Gonads		
	Male	Female	Fetal
Head	0.8; 0.6–1.0	0.2; 0.2–1.5	0.2
Teeth	4.7; 8	0.8; 2	0.8
Chest, large film	0.4; 1.2	0.1; 0.3	0.1
Chest, mass miniature	0.2; 1	0.1; 3	0.1
Abdomen	69; 200	200; 500	580
Pyelogram (kidney, ureter)	486; 2,000	1,290; 1,200	3,210
Skeleton of pelvis	1,100; 2,000	210; 1,000	800
Skeleton of pelv.-fluoroscopy	6,000	3,000	—
Spine, thoracic	22	15	15
Spine, lumbar	129	713	713
Obstetric examination (in pregnancy)	—	1,280; 260–2,500	2,680; 400–4,000

NOTE: The first dose listed refers to the report from one hospital in Britain, the second dose to reports from the United States. If only one dose is listed, it refers to the report from Britain, except for the data on fluoroscopy of the skeleton of the pelvis, which are from the United States. The British data combine estimates for photographic records and fluoroscopic examination, the United States data refer to photographic records unless otherwise stated.

ber, it is very small indeed when compared with the number of atoms in 1 cc of tissue, which is of the order of 10^{23} or 100,000,000,000 times as large.

The "rad" is a unit of absorbed dose, equivalent to 100 ergs per gram: this amount of energy is slightly larger than that absorbed after irradiation of 1r. The "rep" is another unit of absorbed dose, and has been used mainly in dealing with ionizing radiations other than X- and γ-rays. It is very similar to the rad, being equivalent to 93 ergs per gram.

Irradiation may involve either a whole individual or only some parts. However, genetic damage to future generations is produced only when the gonads or gametes or, in very young embryos, the cells destined to produce gametes are irradiated directly. Irradiation of various parts of the body with X-rays for diagnostic medical purposes may lead to some degree of exposure of the gonads. Such exposure can often be reduced by using highly sensitive photographic plates and by protective shielding of all areas not of immediate interest. In general, in such irradiation the ovaries, which are protected by the overlaying pelvic tissues, receive a lower dose than do the testes. Table 73 gives some data on estimated gonad exposures in X-ray photography. Most of these data were obtained in a hospital where particular care was taken to reduce gonad doses to the minimum. In other hospitals or in the offices of individual physicians the doses may be higher. Exposure to X-rays for direct observation on a fluoroscopic screen always requires much greater doses.

In discussing the mutagenic effects of radiation, it is important to distinguish between the induction of gene mutations and of chromosomal aberrations. Although, as pointed out at the end of the preceding chapter, the distinction between these two types of hereditary changes is not always sharp, it can be applied in many instances. In the following pages the term "mutation" denotes changes within a limited region of a chromosome—either a change within a locus or at most a change of minute dimension involving adjacent loci.

Dose and Intensity of Radiation and Frequencies of Mutation and Chromosome Breakage.   It has been established for a variety of experimental organisms that the number of mutations induced by radiation is proportional to the dose. This proportionality has been proven to hold over a wide range of dosages. Figure 202 shows that, for Drosophila, the relation is essentially linear over the range 25–12,500r (insects, unlike mammals, can survive after exposure to many thousands of röntgens). It would be desirable to extend the data toward dosages lower than 25r, for instance, to 10r, 5r, and still lower. Since, however, the expected differences are small between the rate of mutations in not-artificially irradiated control organisms and that in organisms exposed to low artificial doses, it is difficult to obtain significant results even with large experiments. Only in bacteria has it been possible to apply a dose of no more than 8r and to find that the number of induced mutations was that expected from the linear relationship found at higher doses.

It should be added that for exposure of the spermatogonia of the mouse

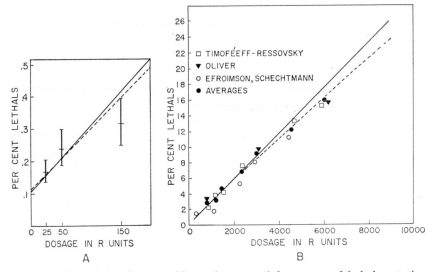

FIG. 202. The relation between X-ray dosage and frequency of lethal mutations induced in the X-chromosome of the sperm of *Drosophila melanogaster.* A. The relation for low dosages. The solid and broken lines represent the type of linear relationship obtained if certain data from other experiments with higher dosages are included. The data points for control (=0r), 25r, 50r, and 150r doses are shown as small horizontal marks. The ends of the vertical lines passing through these marks indicate the range within which the observations may vary statistically in a nonsignificant degree. B. The relation for high dosages according to the experiments of several investigators. The broken line represents the expected curve if some necessary corrections are applied to the straight, solid line. (A, Spencer and Stern, *Genetics, 33,* 1948; B, after Timoféeff-Ressovsky, Zimmer, and Delbrück, *Nachr. Ges. Wiss. Göttingen,* N. F. **1,** 1935.)

the relatively few data on induced mutations at doses of 0, 300, and 600r fit the linear relation, but that a dose of 1,000r produces fewer mutations than expected. It is possible that different spermatogonial cells have different resistance to the lethal effects of X-rays, as well as different sensitivities to their mutagenic effects. If 1,000r should preferentially kill those spermatogonial cells in which high numbers of mutations were also produced, then the relatively low number of recovered mutations at 1,000r may represent a sample selected for surviving cells which are relatively resistant to mutagenesis.

In most of the experiments on which the proportionality rule is based, irradiation was applied for a short period of seconds or minutes. Such exposures are termed "acute." Irradiation of Drosophila sperm has shown that it makes no difference to the yield of induced mutations whether a given dose of radiation is applied in a single acute exposure, is fractionated into two or more exposures separated by days or weeks, or is slowly and continuously, that is "chronically," given over a long period. Mutations in Drosophila were obtained at the same rate per röntgen whether the sperm was irradiated chronically with less than one five-hundredth (1/500) of 1r per minute or acutely within a few minutes at an intensity some 200,000 times higher. It is noteworthy that the low-intensity irradiation resulted, on the average, in a single track of ionization transversing a sperm head no more frequently than once in 30 hours.

In contrast to the finding of equivalence in mutagenic effects of acute and chronic irradiation of Drosophila sperm, Russell found (in 1958) that a dose applied chronically, at low intensity, to mouse spermatogonia yields significantly less mutations than the same dose applied acutely, at high intensity. Chronic exposure at a rate of 90r per week produced only one-fourth the number of mutations produced by acute exposure at the 10,000 times higher rate of 80–90r per minute. A similar situation, also in the mouse, seems to prevail for chronic versus acute irradiation of immature female gametes (oocytes). It is not yet understood why acute and chronic exposures cause different rates of mutations. It has long been known that the physiological and developmental state of a cell is a factor in the mutagenic efficiency of radiation, and that treatment of irradiated cells with physical or chemical agents can change the number of mutants recovered. Perhaps high and low intensities of radiation act on the spermatogonia differentially. Perhaps some mutations initiated by ionization can be repaired if little further radiation occurs for some time after chronic, low-intensity exposure; whereas less repair is possible if much further radiation occurs in acute, high-intensity exposure.

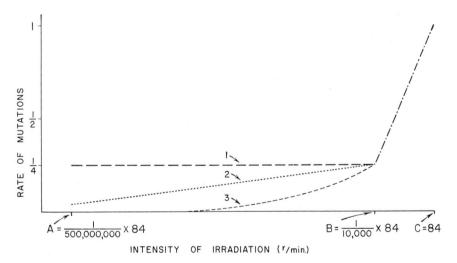

FIG. 203. Three of many possible relations between intensity of radiation for a given dose and rate of mutation. A, B, and C: Three intensities of irradiation, entered on an arbitrary scale. Line (1) represents the assumption that the rate of mutations is independent of the intensity of irradiation below the rate B. Line (2) assumes continuous intensity dependence. Line (3) assumes the existence of a threshold of effect, i.e., production of no mutations at doses appreciably lower than B.

Such concepts as "repair" are being tested in experiments with various types of cells.

If data from mice afford our best clue to the situation in man, then the discovery of mutagenic differences of chronic versus acute radiation in mouse spermatogonia is of greatest importance. Much of human exposure consists in an accumulation of small doses, but until Russell's discovery all considerations of human hazards were based on the assumption that the acute-exposure data were equally applicable to chronic irradiation. From now on, it will be necessary to consider the effects of acute and chronic irradiation separately. Unfortunately, it will require years of new work to establish the relation between intensity of irradiation and frequency of mutation over a wide range.

Will a further reduction in the intensity of radiation below 90r per week lead to a further decrease in the number of mutations for a given dose? Or will the same number of mutations be recovered at all degrees of low-intensity exposures (Fig. 203)? If the answer to the former question is yes, then probably very few mutations would be induced by natural background irradiation, whose intensity of about 0.000,000,2r per minute is more than 50,000 times less than that of 90r per week, which is equal to 0.01r per minute. If, on the other hand, the same number of mutations is produced at the rate of

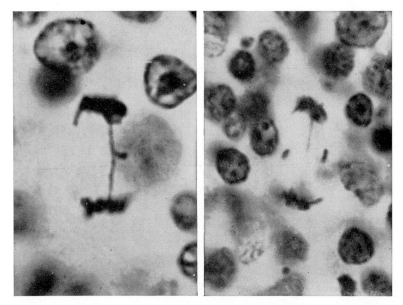

FIG. 204. Chromosome breakage, after irradiation with X-rays, of the white-blood-cell-forming lymph tissue of the rat. *Left:* Chromosome bridge and a fragment to right of bridge. 2110×. (The fragment and bridge are separate from each other and lie in different planes, but the camera makes them appear close together.) *Right:* Chromosome bridge and two fragments, to left and to right of bridge. 1744×. (Original photomicrographs from B. Thomas Stepka.)

background exposure as at the low experimental rate of 0.01r per minute, this would signify that the mutagenic effect of all degrees of low-intensity exposures is appreciable. As long as the trend of the relation between intensity of radiation at low levels and mutagenic action is unknown, it seems wise to assume the worst, namely, that the rate of mutation remains constant —even if one may hope that this will be found not to be true.

Chromosome breakage caused by different doses of irradiation has been investigated in the white-blood-cell-forming lymph tissue of the rat (Fig. 204); in embryonic nerve cells of grasshoppers, which can be studied in tissue cultures; and in plant cells. Recently, human cells in tissue culture have been irradiated, and a simple proportionality between frequency of breaks and dose of radiation has been found. Figure 205 shows, for cells of grass-hoppers, that, as in the case

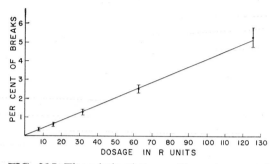

FIG. 205. The relation between X-ray dosage and frequency of induced chromosomal breaks in cells of a grasshopper. (Carlson, *Proc. Nat. Acad. Sci.*, **27**, 1941.)

of gene mutations, even a dose as low as 8.3r applied for about 2 seconds causes chromosome breakage, and that at 125r applied for 38 seconds 5.35 per cent of all chromosomes were broken. How great this effect of irradiation is becomes particularly clear if the percentages of chromosomes broken are translated into terms of *cells* damaged. Since each cell has many chromosomes, its chance of being affected is much higher than that of a single chromosome. Accordingly, it was found at 8.3r that 8 per cent of the cells had broken chromosomes, and at 125r that as many as 70 per cent had broken chromosomes.

Studies by Puck of human cells in culture suggest that acute exposure of 20r may be sufficient to induce at least one visible chromosome break in each cell.

Target Theory and Its Modification.   The genetic effects of radiation have been interpreted by the *target theory*, which assumed that a genic mutation or chromosomal break is caused within a specific volume, the "target," by a single ionization, a single "hit," which provides the necessary energy for molecular transformation. A low dose of irradiation produces a low number of ionizations; thus, there is a low probability of "hitting" the target. A high dose of irradiation produces a high number of ionizations; thus, there is a higher probability of a hit. This single-hit target theory accounted for the fact that duration of irradiation and fractionation of dosage seemed to be of no importance in the frequency of mutations as long as the total dose (the total number of ionizations) is kept constant.

The target theory yields an important point concerning the frequency of mutations expected from very low doses of radiation. If the theory is correct, then even a minute dose would be expected to induce a proportional number of mutations. Thus, there should be no threshold of radiation below which mutations will not be produced.

The experimental results of high-intensity irradiation of various cells and of high- and low-intensity irradiation of mature Drosophila sperm agree with this expectation. In these experiments the absence of a lower radiation threshold in the production of mutations contrasts with the biological effects of a great many other agents (such as chemicals, which at certain doses are physiologically harmful or lethal to man, but which can be administered in large amounts, with no ill effects, as long as they are given in small doses at properly spaced times). Radiation, likewise, has a threshold effect in respect to nongenetic bodily consequences. An X-ray dose of 900r, given for a few minutes, will cause second-degree burns, but the same dose given in ten fractions over a month will cause no irritation. The difference between (1) the threshold phenomena and (2) the time-independent proportionality effect seems to lie in the fact that the former are concerned with reversible physiological processes which permit continuous repair of small damage, or with situations which permit a damaged cell to be replaced by one not harmed; whereas the latter is irreversible, i.e., it involves a mutant change. The permanence of increased frequencies of mutations has been tested in mice. The offspring produced by an animal a long time after an acute irradiation is just as likely to contain a gene mutation as the offspring produced only a relatively short time after the exposure.

The original target theory has been considerably modified. It was found that different types of cells have different sensitivities to mutagenic action of radiation, that for a given dose the yield of induced mutations increases with increasing amounts of oxygen present during irradiation, and that various chemical compounds can influence the mutagenic effect of radiation. The different mutagenic effects of high- versus low-intensity irradiation in mouse spermatogonia are also evidence against a direct target theory.

It has therefore been deduced that radiation initiates the production, in the cell, of highly reactive chemical agents which in turn may attack and change the genetic material. The interpretation implies that the reactive agents usually have a short life span. If the original theory is represented by a target which had to be hit directly, in the newer theories the genic or chromosomal target can be thought of as being surrounded by material which, when hit, produces a shower of molecular particles, any one of which itself may hit the target. It is the type and effectiveness of these particles which can be changed by chemical agents, such as oxygen.

Estimates of Mutagenic Effects of Radiation.   As stated earlier, it is necessary to consider the effects of acute and chronic radiation exposure separately. Obviously, there exists a continuous range of radiation intensities, so it must be specified what intensities are to be called acute and what are to be called chronic. In practice, a distinct separation is possible. Medical exposures are acute and usually involve intensities of at least several röntgens up to occasionally thousands per minute. Acute exposures in atomic-reactor accidents may be of very high intensities, and even higher intensities may result from the immediate radiation of atomic explosions. In contrast to such acute, high-intensity exposures are well-controlled chronic exposures occurring in certain occupational groups and those resulting from natural background radiation, from radioactive contamination by atomic waste, and by fall-out. In general, exposures to these sources of radiation are of very low intensity, consisting of minute fractions of 1r per minute. Situations could arise in which radioactive contamination becomes so severe that it approaches or grades into high-intensity exposure. This has happened in the vicinity of nuclear test sites, and undoubtedly would occur in atomic warfare.

Acute Exposures.   For many years the only quantitative information on the frequency of induced mutations was based on Drosophila experiments. They indicated that a high-intensity dose of 1r applied to spermatogonia causes mutation of about 1.5 out of 100,000,000 genes ($=1.5 \times 10^{-8}$) from a normal allele to one which either produces an easily discernible different phenotype or acts as a recessive lethal. It was often wondered whether this figure could justifiably be used for human genes. This became more doubtful after it was found that the corresponding frequency for the mouse is approximately 15 times higher. In the mouse, 1r of acute exposure produces about 25 easily discernible mutants in 100,000,000 genes. Without direct evidence, it seems reasonable to use for human consideration the figure obtained for the mouse (2.5×10^{-7}), a mammal, rather than that obtained for the fly (1.5×10^{-8}).

The rate of induced mutations in mice has been derived from studies on large numbers of animals. However, it was only feasible to study seven separate genes, and these differ significantly in their rates of mutation. It is not known whether the average mutation rate of these seven genes, 2.5×10^{-7} per röntgen, is really representative of the average for the totality of genes in the mouse. The same uncertainty exists for Drosophila, whose average rate of mutations per röntgen, 1.5×10^{-8}, is also based on a few selected loci.

Both the fly and the mouse data are based on mutations induced in spermatogonia. For the mouse, the available information suggests that the rate per röntgen of induced mutations in the oocytes is similar to that in the spermatogonia. For post-spermatogonial stages, including mature sperm, the rates per röntgen are twice as high. In man, the post-spermatogonial period of the germ cells is only a few weeks. This is a very short time in comparison to the period as immature sex cells—a length of time which comprises most of the life of an individual. Therefore, for many purposes, it is realistic to use the spermatogonial rates of mutation. One should remember, however, that the offspring produced from a sperm which, in the mature state, had been exposed to irradiation has a greater likelihood of carrying induced mutations than does the offspring from a sperm which, at the time of exposure, was still in a spermatogonial stage.

If it is assumed that a human gamete possesses 10,000 mutable genic loci whose mean rate of induced individually recognizable mutations per röntgen is 2.5×10^{-7}, then 2.5 per 1,000 of all gametes ($10,000 \times 2.5 \times 10^{-7}$) would carry a mutation induced by irradiation with 1r. Twice as many zygotes (or 5 per 1,000) would have such an induced mutation—assuming for the moment that the sensitivities of male and female germ cells are alike. An irradiation with 10r would raise these figures proportionally to 2.5 per cent of all gametes and to 5 per cent of all zygotes carrying an induced mutation.

In the following sections and in the next chapter we shall continue to make use of the estimate that an irradiation dose of 10r given at high intensity to both parents of each of 100 children causes 5 of the children to carry an induced mutation, visibly or invisibly. It cannot be emphasized too strongly that at the present state of knowledge this estimate is very unreliable. We shall return once more to the uncertainties which surround the calculations made (see pp. 526–527).

Chronic Exposures.   The mouse data suggest that the effect of low-intensity exposure of immature human spermatogonia and egg cells is less than the effect of high-intensity exposure. It was pointed out above that we lack knowledge of the shape of the curve which relates intensity to mutation frequency. A conservative estimate will assume that the reduction of mutagenic action from high- to low-intensity exposure is never more than in the ratio 1:4, according to the horizontal line (1) in Figure 203. This estimate gives a frequency of mutations per röntgen of low-intensity exposures that is higher than the frequencies to be expected from a ratio of 1 to more than 4, according to lines (2) and (3). On this basis, a low-intensity dose of 1r would produce $1/4 \times 2.5 \times 10^{-7} = 0.625 \times 10^{-7}$ mutations per locus. If it is assumed that there are 10,000 loci and that both parents of each of 1,000 children are exposed, 1r would lead to 1.25 new mutations; and 10r given to both parents of each of 100 children would also cause 1.25 mutations.

"Doubling Doses."   An estimate of the rate of mutations induced by a given dose enables estimation of the absolute number of mutations for a given population and a given exposure. In addition, it has often seemed useful to express the mutagenic effect of artificial agents in relation to that of spontaneous mutation. Such a relative value is the *doubling dose*—that amount of irradiation which causes the appearance of a number of mutations twice that occurring spontaneously. As long as the frequency of induced mutations seemed independent of the intensity of irradiation, one could speak of "the" doubling dose. We must now distinguish between an acute and a chronic doubling dose. Assuming that chronic irradiation is only one-fourth as mutagenic as is acute, we may say that the chronic doubling dose is four times larger than is the acute. The lower the effectiveness of chronic irradiation, the higher the chronic doubling dose.

The concept of a doubling dose has had its critics. Not only is there no particular merit in selecting a factor of 2 relative to the spontaneous rate, instead of a factor of $1/10$, 5, or 10, but the concept implies that the proportions of various kinds of mutations induced by radiation are the same as the proportions of mutations occurring spontaneously. There is evidence, from studies on the mouse, that this is not so, and that spontaneous mutants are more frequently lethal as homozygotes than are induced ones. Notwithstanding these limitations of the concept, estimates of doubling doses will now be reported.

Acute Doubling Dose.   The acute doubling dose has been determined experimentally for Drosophila and for mice. It is very similar for these two different animals: approximately 30–80r, with perhaps 50r as a reasonable average. The estimate given earlier for the spontaneous mutation rate per gene in man (1.5×10^{-5}), combined with the assumption that the induced rate per röntgen as derived from data on acutely exposed male mice (2.5×10^{-7}) is applicable to man, yields a value of 60r for the human acute doubling dose ($[1.5 \times 10^{-5}]/[2.5 \times 10^{-7}] = 60$). Granting the uncertainties involved, the slightly lower value of 50r is often quoted. This value will also be used in some of the following pages.

What are the actual lower and upper possible limits of the acute doubling dose? It is easy to state the lowest possible value for man. If *all* spontaneous mutations were due to the chronic natural background radiation, which over thirty years is close to 3r, the chronic doubling dose would be the same— close to 3r. If it is assumed that the mutagenic efficiency of chronic irradiation is one-fourth that of acute irradiation, the minimum acute doubling dose would be 0.75r. It is likely, however, that many spontaneous mutations are due to causes other than natural radiation (p. 487). Moreover, if all spontaneous mutations were the result of such background radiation, then the frequency of spontaneous mutations of all genes should be linearly increasing with age of parents. There is no evidence of such a simple relation. Finally, the limited results of studies of the offspring of irradiated humans, which will be discussed in the next chapter, make it unlikely that the doubling dose is lower than 15r.

It is more difficult to estimate an upper limit for the acute doubling dose. If it were as high as 150r, then only $1/2$ per cent of spontaneous mutations (0.75×150) would be the result of background radiation. Under the assumption made here, the often-chosen value of 50r for the acute doubling dose implies that 1.5 per cent of spontaneous mutations are radiation induced.

Chronic Doubling Dose.   Whatever will be the value of the acute doubling dose, the chronic one is four times larger. As stated above, the minimum estimate for the chronic doubling dose is identical to the amount of the natural, chronically acting radiation, that is, 3r. If the acute doubling dose is taken as 50r, then 200r of low-intensity chronic exposure will be required to equal it.

Dose and Intensity of Radiation and Frequencies of Chromosomal Aberrations. It was indicated earlier in this chapter that there is proportionality between the frequency of chromosome breakage and dose of radiation, and independence from the duration or fractionation of a given radiation. It must now be pointed out that this does *not* imply that the frequency of all types of induced chromosome aberrations follows the proportionality rule. If only one break is induced in one chromosome of a cell, then, obviously, only chromosome fragmentation can be observed. Translocations and inversions cannot be induced, since they require the occurrence of at least two breaks. Since with low dosages the probability of breakage is low, the probability of two breaks—which is the square of the probability of a single break—becomes negligible. An increase in the dose results in a proportional increase of single breaks but in an exponential increase of multiple breaks. For instance, a dose which produces single breaks in 1 per cent of irradiated cells will produce two breaks in approximately 1 out of 10,000 cells. Doubling the dose doubles the total number of breaks (2 per cent) but quadruples the number of cells with two breaks ([2 per cent]^2 = 4 in 10,000). In agreement with theory, the frequency of translocations or other aberrations resulting from two breaks shows a dependence on dose which is exponential instead of linear; that is, a curve for the frequency of translocations remains close to the zero level for low doses, and for higher doses it rises at an accelerating rate (Fig. 206).

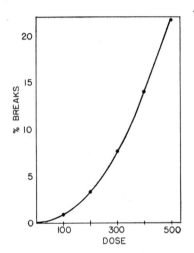

FIG. 206. The relation between X-ray dosage and frequencies of induced two-break chromosome aberrations in the plant, Tradescantia. (After Sax, *Genetics,* **25,** 1940.)

The dependence of translocations and other aberrations on the occurrence of two or more breaks implies that fractionation of a dose, or irradiation over a prolonged period, does not necessarily yield as many of these chromosomal aberrations as short, concentrated radiation. If two breaks are produced more or less simultaneously in a cell, exchange of broken ends may lead to a translocation. However, if two breaks are produced one after the other, a translocation can result only if the chromosome fragment resulting from the first break is still available for union when the second break takes place. From studies of chromosome breaks induced in mature sperm of Drosophila, it has been concluded that broken ends may retain their ability to fuse until fertilization. Other studies on breaks induced in immature germ cells or somatic cells, particularly of plants, show that broken ends soon become unavailable for translocations or similar aberrations. The ends either reunite in the original arrangement, or their duplicated sister strands unite, or they lose the ability to fuse.

These facts are of significance in judging the effect, on human chromosomes, of irradiation concentrated into a short time versus exposure over a long period. While it would perhaps not make a great difference in the frequency of single-hit chromosomal aberrations whether an individual, or individuals, in a population receive 50r within a fraction of a second from an atomic accident or over a period of months from radioactive contamination, the frequency of induced translocations and other multiple-hit events might be considerable in the first instance and negligible in the second.

Problems

182. A deficiency is induced in the chromosome of a sperm cell. An individual who receives this chromosome is abnormal. What types of offspring, and in what proportion, may the affected individual produce?

183. Assume that all parents of ten million children had been exposed to a dose of 25 r of acute irradiation. Assume further that (i) the frequency of induced mutation from A to a (albinism) is 2×10^{-7} per r, and that (ii) the frequency of the a allele in the panmictic population is $q = 0.00707$. (a) How many albinos would have been born if the parents had not been irradiated? (b) How many albinos will there actually be among the offspring of the exposed population?

184. Construct a table showing the minimum and maximum percentages of individually recognizable mutations induced by: (a) acute exposure to 20 r, and (b) chronic exposure to 40 r. Assume that the mutability of human genes irradiated acutely by 1 r is as low as 10^{-9} or as high as 10^{-6}, and that the number of mutable loci is as low as 5,000 or as high as 20,000.

References

Claus, W. D. (Ed.), 1958. *Radiation Biology and Medicine. Part 3. Mutational Effects of Radiation.* Chapters 6–9, pp. 145–228, by H. J. Muller; C. P. Swanson and T. Merz; W. L. Russell, L. B. Russell, and E. F. Oakberg; and C. Stern, respectively. Addison-Wesley, Reading, Mass.

Crow, J. F., 1956. The estimation of spontaneous and radiation-induced mutation rates in man. *Eugen. Quart.,* **3:** 201–208.

Medical Research Council, 1956. *The Hazards to Man of Nuclear and Allied Radiations.* 128 pp. H. M. Stationery Office, London.

Muller, H. J., 1927. Artificial transmutation of the gene. *Science,* **66:** 84–87.

———, 1954. The nature of the genetic effects produced by radiation. In A. Hollaender (Ed.). *Radiation Biology,* **1:** 351–473. McGraw-Hill, New York.

———, 1954. The manner of production of mutations by radiation. In A. Hollaender (Ed.). *Radiation Biology,* **1:** 475–626. McGraw-Hill, New York.

National Academy of Sciences–National Research Council, 1956. *The biological effects of atomic radiation.* Summary reports: 2–32.

Penrose, L. S., 1955. Parental age and mutation. *Lancet,* **269:** 312–313.

Russell, W. L., 1954. Genetic effects of radiation in mammals. In A. Hollaender (Ed.). *Radiation Biology,* **1:** 825–859. McGraw-Hill, New York.

————, Russell, L. B., and Kelly, E. M., 1958. Radiation dose rate and mutation frequency. *Science,* **128:** 1546–1550.

Spiers, F. W., 1956. Genetical effects of radiations from products of nuclear explosions. *Nature,* **177:** 226–227.

United Nations General Assembly, 1958. *Report of the United Nations Scientific Committee on the Effects of Atomic Radiation.* 228 pp. Official Records: Thirteenth session, Suppl. No. 17, New York.

Uphoff, D. E., and Stern, C., 1949. The genetic effects of low intensity irradiation. *Science,* **109:** 609–610.

Vogel, F., 1956. Über die Prüfung von Modellvorstellungen zur spontanen Mutabilität an menschlichem Material. *Zeitschr. Menschl. Vererb. u. Konstitsl.,* **33:** 470–491.

World Health Organization, 1957. *Effects of Radiation on Human Heredity.* 168 pp. Study group on the effects of radiation on human heredity, Geneva.

CHAPTER 24

THE GENETIC HAZARDS
OF RADIATION

Most spontaneously occurring mutations with clearly noticeable effects must be classified as abnormalities, either of form or of function. This has been demonstrated in extensive animal and plant studies and applies also to the human mutations listed in Table 67 (p. 454). In Drosophila the largest group of induced mutations is made up of lethals (this is true also of spontaneous mutations); another large group of "visible" mutations shows a considerably lower-than-normal viability; and only a very small group of visible mutations are as fit as or fitter than the normal. These findings are to be expected, since evolutionary selection in any species is likely to accumulate a majority of genes which work together harmoniously and most substitutions of mutant alleles for these genes result in less-than-perfect functioning of the developmental and metabolic machinery.

On the basis of the actual findings on fitness of mutants and evolutionary considerations, it is generally assumed that almost all human mutations are unfavorable. Nevertheless, this may be an exaggerated view. The mutants which are easily recognizable are, by definition, relatively striking in phenotypic effect and thus liable to be abnormal. Mutant alleles which produce effects similar to the norm usually escape notice. It is unknown how frequent are mutations to such normal iso-alleles. They may form a considerable fraction of all mutations. They may not be disadvantageous to their bearers, and in some cases they may be advantageous. R. A. Fisher has described the probable average deleteriousness of a mutant by saying that when its effect is extremely minute, it has "an almost equal chance of effecting improvement or the reverse; while for greater change the chance of improvement diminishes progressively, becoming zero, or at least negligible, for changes of a sufficiently pronounced character."

Selective advantage or disadvantage is not an attribute of an individual gene. The phenotype on which selective properties are based is the result of interaction of numerous genes. Some genes may load their bearers with a selective disadvantage, whatever their genetic background; but many genes may form unfavorable combinations within some genotypes, neutral ones within others, and even favorable ones within still others. Thus, a gene favoring growth within a polygenic system determining height may appear unfavorable when the background tends toward excessive height, neutral when the background tends toward intermediate height, and advantageous when the background tends toward suboptimal height. The very fact of the existence of numerous normal iso-alleles at many loci makes the human population continuously segregating. In the sequence of generations a given gene finds itself in ever-new background genotypes. Its fitness, therefore, is not rigidly fixed.

A special class of genes comprises those which are advantageous in heterozygous combination with another allele but less fit in homozygotes. For such alleles, fitness is obviously a property which depends on the allelic partner. In such cases, as well as in others, it is useful to distinguish between fitness of the individual and fitness of the population. The latter takes account of different individual fitnesses and the frequencies of the different genotypes. High fitness of a population is sometimes attained in spite of low fitness of certain, necessarily segregating genotypes.

When we consider the genetic effects of radiation, we may be justified at present in assuming that mutations in general are deleterious to the individual and to the population. Certainly this is true for very many mutations, but in the future we may have to ascertain more accurately the proportion of mutations which are unfavorable to those which are favorable.

Evolution and Induced Mutations. The evolution of species proceeds on the basis of mutations. Without such genetic variants among prehuman forms, man would not have evolved. The argument has therefore been voiced that artificial increases in mutation rates may be desirable, since they may serve to speed up further evolutionary changes. This argument neglects the fact that the gene pool of human populations is already extremely diversified and that increases in the frequencies of mutant alleles are not likely to add new types of such alleles. Furthermore, it neglects the fact that evolution, the establishment of genetically new organic systems, is a very different process from mutation, the provision of mutant alleles (see Chapter 33).

Since so many mutants are disadvantageous to their bearers, it is likely that each species builds up a genetic control system which reduces the frequency of mutations as much as is compatible with providing adaptive and evolutionary flexibility. If this is true, then an artificial increase of the human mutation rate is undesirable even from an evolutionary viewpoint. Although mutations have been induced which are useful to man (for instance, mutations in the mold penicillium have resulted in the production of a higher-than-normal amount of penicillin), they are very greatly outweighed by those which are unfavorable. If we wish to produce favorable mutations in man, we must pay a human cost in terms of numerous unfavorable mutations. If someday we should succeed in inducing specific, desirable mutations, only then could we look with satisfaction at the artificial induction of human mutations.

It was shown in the previous chapter that an acute radiation exposure to 50r or a chronic exposure to 200r may result in a doubling of the natural human mutation rate. How do these doses compare with the actual hazard? Let us consider the three principal sources of artificial radiation to which man is subjected: medical, occupational, and military.

Medical Exposure

As a result of diagnosis and treatment, the total amount of accumulated irradiation received during a lifetime in any part of a patient's body is usually below 50r. Not many individuals ever receive as much as 100r, although occasionally much larger doses have been administered.

From the point of view of later generations, only irradiation which hits the gonads is of importance. It is obvious that even exposure of the gonads is of no consequence after an individual has ceased to have children. The average dose to the gonads administered per person varies according to different medical practices in different countries. In the United States, it is estimated to be 3r per 30-year period. Somewhat lower doses are administered in several European countries. Thus, acute medical (primarily diagnostic) exposures approximate accumulated chronic natural background radiation.

Occupational Exposure

Exposure to radiation is an occupational hazard to certain groups of individuals: radiologists and other physicians; X-ray technicians; investigators using radioactive isotopes; and workers in uranium mines, atomic-energy plants, and certain factories.

When it became known that radiation can cause harm to individuals, such as burns and anemia, occupational protective measures were introduced to limit the amount of radiation reaching the body. This protection is primarily in the form of lead or concrete shields, which absorb most of the radiation. On the basis of experience, 0.1r per day was generally set as an upper permissible dose, that is, a dose to which the whole body of an individual can be exposed for a long time without showing any ill effects. Since 1956, various international and national organizations have lowered the upper permissible dose to 0.3r in any single week. In addition, a further limiting formula has been proposed, according to which artificial exposure should not begin before the age of eighteen and the accumulated exposure after that age should be limited to a total equal to 5r per year.

It is somewhat doubtful whether even this permissible dose may not gradually lead to physiological damage. Some recent evidence on the shortening of the life span of individuals (of several mammalian species) exposed daily to very low amounts of irradiation may lead to a revised definition of the permissible dose.

Genetically, mutations will be induced even by a very low permissible dose. With a chronic doubling rate of 200r, the gametes of a worker who has accumulated radiation at a yearly rate of 5r for 20 years would possess 50 per cent more mutations than those occurring spontaneously.

Military Exposure

Nuclear explosions result in the nearly instantaneous production of immense amounts of highly penetrating radiation and cause contamination by radioactive fall-out of large areas. Within the area reached by direct ionizing radiation, great amounts of radioactivity are induced. The dose of irradiation received by an individual depends on his distance from the center of the explosion. Most individuals who are near enough to receive a total body irradiation of about 450r or more do not survive. Consequently, the highest rate of induced mutations that may be transmitted by a survivor corresponds to less than 450r, that is, to about nine times the natural gene mutation rate.

Radioactive fall-out following a nuclear explosion can cover with high concentration hundreds or thousands of square miles, or, in lower concentration, the whole globe. The tests of atomic weapons by the United States, Russia, and England have resulted in the production of large amounts of radioactive fission products, much of which are present in the upper layers of the atmosphere. These products slowly fall to earth. In 1958, the total amount of very low-intensity radiation, due to fall-out, which had impinged on an average individual was estimated to be of the order of 0.1r. Even if no further tests are conducted, this dose will gradually increase, perhaps to as much as an accumulated 0.3–0.5r.

It is possible that the amount of radiation, exclusive of that from military sources, to which man is exposed will increase. The use of radiation for medical purposes will spread to many countries, and peaceful applications of atomic energy will create new sources of radiation, including those from radioactive waste products. Several proposals have been made to keep the mean exposure of individuals in large populations to, at most, 10r per 30 years, a figure that sometimes includes background radiation and sometimes is in addition to it. This amount of radiation, as we shall see, has far-reaching consequences, particularly if the exposure occurs at a high level of intensity. We are still considerably below such exposures. In the future it may well be decided that a reduction of this so-called permissible population dose is imperative.

The Phenotypic Consequences of New Mutations and Chromosomal Aberrations

Radiation-induced mutations may occur in two basically different anatomical regions: in body cells, and germ cells. Somatic mutations are not transmitted to later generations, but may cause changes in the irradiated individual. Gametic mutations may be transmitted to the offspring, but will not affect the irradiated individual. Therefore, since irradiation of an individual may produce mutations both in his somatic cells and in his germ cells, some effects may be produced in his body, and others, of quite a different kind, may be transmitted to his offspring.

Mutations in Somatic Cells. Somatic mutation effects depend on whether the mutation has been induced in a cell which does not divide any more or in a cell destined to divide in the future. In nondividing cells, as long as the dose is within a few hundred röntgen it is unlikely that there will be any noticeable mutation damage from either gene mutation or chromosome breakage. Broken chromosomes would remain within the nucleus; so no change in allelic quantities would be produced. Position effects, as well as induced gene mutations, might constitute in the most extreme case dominant lethals or, in the male, hemizygous sex-linked lethals which kill the cell. The death of single nondividing cells would go unnoticed, and even numerous nondividing cells in which radiation may have induced various dominant or hemizygous sex-linked lethals could probably be dispensed with.

In a somatic cell which will continue to divide, a gene mutation will be transmitted to all descendants of the originally affected cell (unless the mutation kills the original cell). If a recessive mutant is induced, leading from an original AA genotype to Aa, no phenotypic effect will be observable, but those mutant cells which obtain a dominant or hemizygous sex-linked allele will be phenotypically abnormal. If the descendants of the original mutant cell remain together, as they would in most tissues, a sector of mutant cells will be formed. If the daughter cells become dispersed, as blood cells do, a fraction of the total number of circulating cells will have the mutant genotype.

Since the majority of mutant alleles are recessives, will most somatic mutations remain permanently unnoticed, since they will result in heterozygous Aa genotypes? There are several possibilities of an Aa being converted into an aa cell. One is the occurrence, at some later time, of mutation in an Aa cell, which transforms A into a. Another is a chance abnormality in mitosis, which may give rise not to two daughter cells each with an A and an a chromosome, but to one daughter cell with both A's and the other with both a's. A third possibility is somatic crossing over (Fig. 193, p. 466), and subsequent segregation of two AA chromosome sections from two aa sections. Also, loss of the A-carrying chromosome will lead to a monosomic a cell.

Irradiation of part or all of the body may well produce mutations in an appreciable number of the many billions of cells which constitute an individual. If these mutations are recessive, they will remain unknown until perhaps years later, when homozygosity for aa may be attained in one of the somatic descendants of an Aa cell. Propagation of the homozygous recessive cell may then result in visible effects. It has been suggested that the proven fact of increased incidence of various types of cancer many years after exposure to irradiation may be explained by these processes.

Induction of chromosomal aberrations in cells destined to divide may have various consequences. Chromosomal fragments without a kinetochore will be lost during mitosis, resulting in cells deficient for chromosome sections. These cells, in many cases, will probably either die or function abnormally. If a breakage-fusion-bridge cycle is induced, the resulting cells again will be either abnormal or lethal. If only some of the body cells suffer chromosome breakage, the effect on the individual may be small, since it may be assumed that, in many cases, death of abnormal cells is compensated for by increased reproduction of those cells which did not undergo changes. Abnormally functioning cells, too, may not usually be seriously detrimental to the individual but, rather, will be so handicapped in their cellular survival that they will be replaced by normal cells. If the whole body is exposed to doses which produce on the average one or more breaks per cell, the consequences to the individual may be lethal.

Little is known about the quantitative aspects of radiation-induced changes in body cells. The sensitivity of different kinds of cells to radiation damage varies greatly. In the mouse, during certain early spermatogonial stages, the cells are so sensitive to X-rays that 50 per cent of them are killed by doses of 20–24r, and killing effects are observable with doses as low as 5r. For a variety of human cells kept in tissue cultures, the dose which kills 50 per cent of the cells (LD 50, the dose lethal to 50 per cent) has been found to lie in the range 50–150r. In contrast, brain cells within the intact individual are much more resistant to killing effects of radiation: most of them survive doses of thousands of röntgens.

Undoubtedly there are various reasons for the different sensitivities of different cells. Among them are variations in biochemical make-up. Another is the occurrence or nonoccurrence of cell divisions. Chromosome breakage will have cell-lethal effects primarily after mitoses have led to abnormal genotypes of daughter cells. Without mitoses, nondividing cells will usually not suffer noticeably from containing broken chromosomes. It has been suggested by Puck that chromosome breakage in dividing cells may be the main cause of death from irradiation in man.

Very likely, the induction rates of gene mutations are different for different types of body cells and for germ cells. Even if the rates were the same for all types, the effects on the exposed individual and on his offspring would be different. A low rate of mutation in germ cells implies a low expectation that the gametes involved in the creation of a few children will contain a new genetic property. A low rate of mutation in body cells implies a very high expectation that at least one if not many body cells will have a new property. It is therefore possible that irradiation of parts of the body, or of the whole body, even with low doses, may be hazardous.

It is known that heavy doses may have serious effects. Acute whole-body doses of 400r and higher are often fatal, and lower doses, above 100r, cause radiation sickness. These radiation effects occur within hours or days after exposure. Other effects are greatly delayed, often for years or decades. The

most significant of these are shortening of the life span, as studied primarily
in various laboratory animals, and the occurrence of various types of cancer,
and particularly leukemia, a fatal disease of the blood-forming organs. It
is not yet clear what the mathematical relation is between amount and intensity of exposure and frequency of induced malignant growth. There are
various data on leukemia among American and other radiologists exposed
in their occupations, among a special group of British patients who had been
heavily irradiated for medical reasons, and among Japanese citizens exposed to the atomic bombs. However, they are not sufficient to indicate
whether a linear relation holds between dose and effect or whether there is
a threshold of radiation below which leukemia is not induced. Genetically,
there is no fixed expectation concerning this fateful problem. Not only is there
no certainty that genic changes in somatic cells are prerequisites for cancerous
growth but, even if this were true, the relation between induced mutation and
onset of cancer cannot be predicted. Whether or not a potential cancer cell
will become active may depend on reactions between normal cells and the
new cell—reactions such as the occurrence or nonoccurrence of immunological destruction of the new cell. Such reactions may themselves depend on a
variety of events unrelated to the radiation received. Or, if it is assumed that
a potential cancer cell must be homozygous for a recessive mutant gene a,
then, if irradiation of AA cells produce an Aa heterozygote, it will require
further events such as aberrant chromosome behavior or somatic crossing
over in the descendants of the Aa cell to segregate an aa cell. Since the
frequency of somatic crossing over, if it exists in man, is likely to be variable
from person to person and from tissue to tissue, it is impossible to predict
the frequency of the origin of aa cells.

In general, the expression of a mutated genotype by a body cell poses
problems that are different from those of expression by a germ cell. A mutant germ cell involved in the formation of a new individual will result in
the presence of the mutant genotype in all of his cells, while a mutant body
cell and its descendants will be surrounded by a nonmutant body. The two
types of body cells may interact with each other; or the more vigorous type
will replace the less vigorous either to the benefit or the detriment of the
whole; or they may persist together without influencing each other.

Mutations in Germ Cells. Radiation-induced genetic changes in germ
cells may become phenotypically apparent in later generations in a way which
depends on whether they are autosomal dominant, sex linked, or autosomal
recessive, or on the type of chromosomal aberrations.

Gene Mutations.   Dominant autosomal gene mutations if fully penetrant,
will become phenotypically obvious among the children of irradiated individuals. If the mutants cause serious abnormalities, the reproductive fitness of
individuals carrying them will be low, and these alleles will die out within a
few generations. Sex-linked alleles will appear in an easily predictable manner in the first, or an early, generation, according to whether they are domi-

nant or recessive and to the sex of the irradiated parent. If affected individuals are relatively unfit to reproduce, the sex-linked recessive, too, will soon disappear from the population. Recessive autosomal mutants will become visible in the first generation only if two like gametes meet, either if one of the parents happens to be a carrier for the mutant allele, or if gametes with identical mutants produced in irradiated parents meet. The probability that the latter event will occur is negligible. In general, recessive mutant alleles will meet, in fertilization, normal dominants, and will therefore be transmitted unseen to later generations. Sooner or later, depending upon the breeding structure of the population (that is, depending on the amount of inbreeding and of isolate formation or isolate breakdown, and upon similar factors) two recessives will meet and will produce a homozygous individual. Then, low reproductive fitness will, in most instances, reduce the probability of transmission of the recessives.

Chromosomal Aberrations. Chromosomal aberrations may be induced in immature and in mature germ cells. Since the fate of these changes is different for each of the two stages, they will be taken up separately.

We shall begin with premeiotic germ cells. In the human male, the testes contain numerous "stem cells" which proliferate mitotically. After their divisions, some of the descendant cells retain the characteristic of stem cells, while the others enter the developmental path toward meiosis. In regard to what happens in the female, the opinion of investigators is divided. Very likely, none of the immature germ cells present in the ovaries at birth undergoes further mitosis, but is ready for meiosis. However, some workers believe that multiplication of the primordial female germ cells by mitosis may occur as in the male.

Chromosome breaks induced in a stem cell behave in the same manner as breaks in the chromosomes of body cells. After division, the daughter cells will sometimes have retained all genetic material—although newly arranged—while at other times elimination of fragments, or losses and changes due to a fusion-bridge-breakage cycle, will result in unbalanced conditions. Daughter cells with genetic material complete will be capable of entering meiotic processes, but those which suffer important quantitative changes may not undergo further development. If both daughter cells become genetically unbalanced as the result of chromosome breakage, and if this imbalance results in cell death, then both the cell originally destined for meiosis and the stem cell are eliminated. Thus, the divisions of irradiated stem cells serve to purge the gonad of some of the induced genetic changes.

What will happen to those stem cells which continue their premeiotic career or those immature germ cells, in males and females, which have been irradiated and have suffered chromosome breakage after the last mitosis and during the premeiotic or meiotic stages? It is not necessary to analyze, in detail, the diverse possibilities of distribution and elimination of the chromosomes and their fragments, since a general outline of these events was presented at the end of Chapter 23. Knowledge derived from experimental organisms indicates that, at least in many cases, both immature egg and sperm cells will probably transform into gametes capable of fertilization, irrespective of whether or not they contain a full and normal set of genetic material. There are two explanations for this phenomenon. Either the developmental processes which transform immature meiotic germ cells into mature gametes are set in motion early under the influence of the intact, unreduced gene content and may proceed successfully, even if an incomplete or abnormal genic complement is produced during meiosis; or the existence of cytoplasmic bridges between adjoining immature germ cells (which has recently been proven by means of the electron microscope) may permit a sharing of the genotypes so that genic deficiencies in one nucleus may be made harmless by the presence of the genes in a neighboring nucleus. Consequently, mature egg and sperm nuclei may be formed which lack a section of a chromosome, carry a section in duplicate, or have combinations of such abnormalities. Still other mature gametes may have a complete set of genes, some of which, however, are carried in chromosome fragments without a kinetochore. Fertilization involving the affected gamete results in an abnormal zygote. If the affected gamete is genetically unbalanced, the zygotic nucleus will be also; if the affected gamete is complete, but includes a fragment without kinetochore, then the first mitosis in the fertilized egg will cause loss of the fragment and thus lead to genetic imbalance in the daughter nuclei. Breakage-fusion-bridge cycles may also be set up by chromosomes with broken ends.

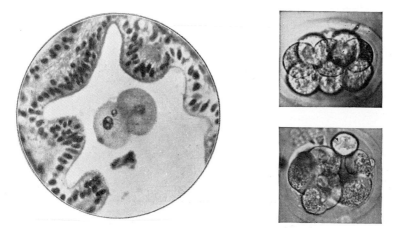

FIG. 207. Abnormal development of eggs fertilized by unbalanced sperm. *Left:* Cross section through a mouse egg after its first cleavage inside the oviduct. In consequence of chromosome breakage, part of the irradiated sperm nucleus was not included in the cleavage nuclei. The egg is destined for early death. *Right:* Degenerative development of an early embryonic stage in the rat. *Above:* Normal development of a normal egg. *Below:* Degenerative development of an egg fertilized by a sperm produced by a translocation heterozygote (compare Fig. 201). (*Left,* after P. Hertwig, *Zeitschr. Abstgs. u. Vererbgsl.,* **70,** 1935; right, after Bouricius, *Genetics,* **33,** 1948.)

It is known from studies on mice and rats that many, if not all, zygotes with chromosomal imbalance develop abnormally (Fig. 207). Depending on the extent of the imbalance and on the individual effect of the genes concerned, development may cease at an early cleavage stage or at an embryonic stage, either before implantation in the uterine wall or after. One may say that the gamete which leads to ultimate death of the zygote carries an induced dominant lethal. In man, very early cessation of development and subsequent disappearance of the embryo may cause the mother little trouble or go completely unnoticed. Death of an embryo after implantation may result in abortion or in stillbirth. Some types of genetically unbalanced embryos may develop into viable, but more or less abnormal, live births.

Certain types of individuals derived from gametes with chromosomal aberrations may be normal but will produce some abnormal offspring. They are "translocation heterozygotes," having received, from one parent, normal chromosomes, and, from the other, both of the chromosomes which had undergone a reciprocal exchange. The possession of both of these chromosomes insures the existence of all chromosomal sections and thus permits normal development of these individuals. However, during meiosis in their gonads, segregation results in two types of gametes: balanced and unbalanced. If the two reciprocally translocated chromosomes go jointly to one pole and the corresponding nontranslocated chromosomes go to the other, the gametes receive full genic complements (Fig. 201, A, p. 477). But if segregation takes place differently, unbalanced gametes are formed which are deficient for one translocated section and duplicate for the other (Fig. 201, B). Fertilization involving these unbalanced gametes will result in unbalanced zygotes, which usually leads to death of the embryo. Since the numbers of balanced and unbalanced gametes formed in translocation heterozygotes are frequently approximately equal, about one-half of the zygotes develop normally and the other half do not develop to term. Therefore, individuals heterozygous for a translocation are called *semisteriles*. It can easily be seen that they transmit the property of semisterility to one-half of their normal-appearing children.

TABLE 74. *Semisterility in the Rat Caused by Translocation.* (After Bouricius, *Genetics*, **33**, 1948.)

| Mating | Embryos (mean no.) | | | Degeneration (%) |
	Implanted in Uterine Wall*	Degenerating after Implantation	Normal	
Semisterile ♂ × Normal ♀	8.7	5.0	3.7	57.5
Normal ♂ × Normal ♀	9.5	0.6	8.9	6.5

* The lower number of implanted embryos in the semisterile as compared to the control matings is caused by degeneration of some unbalanced embryonic stages before implantation.

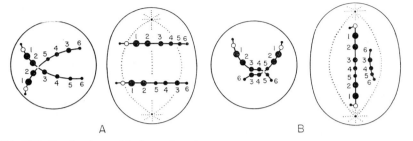

FIG. 208. Production of balanced and unbalanced gametes during meiosis in inversion heterozygotes. The sequence of loci in one chromosome is 1–2–3–4–5–6, in the homologous chromosome 1–2–5–4–3–6.   A. Crossing over outside the inverted section results in balanced chromosomes.   B. Following pairing of the two chromosomes in the regions 3–4–5, crossing over within the inverted section results in a chromosome bridge and a fragment. For the sake of simplicity, only two of the four strands of the chromosome pair are represented in this figure.

Data on semisterility caused by translocation in the rat are presented in Table 74.

Partial sterility due to formation of unbalanced, as well as balanced, gametes may also be caused by an inversion within a chromosome. As shown in Figure 208, A, two homologous chromosomes, one of which contains an inversion, will segregate normally in meiosis, as long as no crossing over occurs within the inverted section. Thus, each gamete resulting from this type of meiosis will have a whole chromosome of the pair considered. On the other hand, as shown in Figure 208, B, a crossover within the inverted section results in one chromosome with two kinetochores and a fragment without a kinetochore. The resulting gametes will be unbalanced and thus, after fertilization, will cause incomplete development of the embryo.

In summarizing the genetic effects to be expected from chromosomal aberrations produced in the germ cells of man, it may be said that: (1) Many aberrations initiated in stem cells will be eliminated before meiosis occurs. (2) Many aberrations induced in germ cells which are ready for, or in the process of, meiosis, or which are mature gametes, will lead to gametes which are able to participate in fertilization but which lead to early or late death of the developing zygote. (3) Reciprocal translocations and inversions present in gametes of irradiated individuals may permit normal development of the offspring, but a fraction—as high as 50 per cent—of the gametes produced by these translocation or inversion heterozygotes will cause death of zygotes among their potential children.

The first statement in this summary may contain at least part of the explanation for the fact that, in mice, the frequency of abnormally developing zygotes derived from sperm irradiated when mature is much higher than from sperm which come from irradiated stem cells (Table 75). It is to be expected, similarly, in man, that genetic effects of irradiation will be found more frequently among individuals who are conceived within a few weeks after irradia-

TABLE 75. *Early Mortality of Live-born Offspring from Irradiated Males of Mice.* (After Paula Hertwig, *Biol. Ztrbl.,* **58,** 1938.)

Offspring from Males Irradiated Within	Death (%) After Birth Within		
	1–7 Days	7–25 Days	22–75 Days
Two weeks before mating	13	12	18
Two or more months before mating	10	9	3
Not irradiated (control)	8	5	5

tion of the mature sperm stored in the male ducts of the father than among individuals who are the products of the sperm produced later from the irradiated paternal stem cells.

We have seen earlier that the frequency of single chromosome breaks is proportional to the dose of irradiation, but that the frequency of chromosomal aberrations occurring in consequence of two or more breaks is disproportionately very low at low doses, and particularly if the exposure has occurred over a long time. Since only low doses are usually administered to humans within a short period, any but single chromosome breaks must be rare. Double and multiple breaks are to be expected from severe acute exposures in atomic accidents or atomic warfare, or after (the now-rare) heavy medical irradiation of poorly functioning ovaries to induce ovulation or of well-functioning testes to produce temporary sterility. The total frequency of phenotypically expressed chromosomal aberrations is probably small, since many are eliminated in immature gametes and, by early death, in embryos which receive an unbalanced genotype. If 50r should be the acute doubling dose for gene mutations, then this dosage presumably adds to the phenotypic effect of mutations only a lesser amount due to chromosomal aberrations, and exposure to less than 50r will cause still fewer transmissible chromosomal aberrations.

The Frequency of Affected Offspring from Irradiated Parents

Everyone who expects to become a parent, even though he and his spouse are healthy and of healthy ancestry, must be conscious that it is not in his power to assure the well-being of the children to be born. Besides nongenetic developmental mishaps, the birth of abnormal offspring may be brought about by hidden dominants of low penetrance, recessives carried by both parents, polygenic combinations transgressing a threshold, or new mutations. It has been estimated that from 4 to 6 per cent of all children either possess or will develop tangible defects, sometimes slight, sometimes severe, of a skeletal, neuromuscular, sensory, physiological, or other nature. In from 1 to 2 per cent of all births, the defects are clearly discernible at birth. If one regards half of all defects, or from 2 to 3, per cent, as being genetically caused, this is probably an underestimate. If the germ cells of parents have been exposed to artificial radiation, how many additional defective children will be born as a result of mutations induced in these germ cells? This question may be asked from the "private" point of view of individual parents who want to know how much increased is the probability of their producing a defective child, or from the "public" point of view of the population who wants to know the additional number of defectives to be expected.

As bases of very provisional answers to these questions, we use the following, earlier-derived estimates: (1) number of mutable genic loci = 40,000; (2) number of induced mutations per locus per röntgen $= 2.5 \times 10^{-7}$ for acute and 0.625×10^{-7} for chronic exposures. An additional requirement for answering these questions is an estimate of the proportion of dominant to recessive mutations in man. This is a ratio whose value is not known. There are rather few dominant, defect-causing genes with complete penetrance, and probably more recessive, defect-causing genes with simple inheritance. Between these extremes, however, lies the whole range of conditionally dominant mutants with incomplete and often very low penetrance, and all those recessive mutants which in heterozygotes produce phenotypic traits detectable in some way even if the heterozygous carriers are normal. If one includes all these genes in the estimate, then one may be inclined, following Levit, to believe that dominant, defect-causing human genes are in the majority.

This, however, does not imply that the majority of induced mutants will find noticeable expression in the offspring of irradiated parents. It would be necessary to know the mean penetrance of the dominant mutants in order

TABLE 76.   *Proportions of Induced Mutations Which Become Apparent in the First Generation After Their Induction.* (A series of different assumptions are made concerning the proportion of dominant to recessive mutants and their mean penetrance. The allele frequency in the population of those acting as recessives is assumed to be q = .01.)

(a) Proportion Dominant Mutants (%)	(b) Mean Penetrance (%)	(c) Dominants Expressed (%)	(d) Proportion Recessive Mutants* (%)	(e) Homozygous Recessives (q = .01)	(f) Total Expressed (c) + (e) (%)
5	40	2	95	.95	2.95
10	20	2	95	.95	2.95
10	10	1	95	.95	1.95
50	10	5	90	.9	5.9
50	4	2	90	.9	2.9
100	4	4	90	.9	4.9
100	2	2	90	.9	2.9

NOTE: The sum of the dominant and recessives in most rows exceeds 100 per cent since one and the same mutant may produce a dominant effect in the heterozygote and a different, recessive effect in the homozygote.

* Penetrance 100%.

to predict the frequency of their phenotypic expression. Although we lack definite knowledge of both the proportion of dominant mutants and their mean penetrance, we may list a number of possibilities (see the first two columns of Table 76). Obviously, the more genes one counts as dominants, the lower one will have to assume their mean to be. The entries for the proportion of dominants in the first column, therefore, rise in an arbitrarily chosen range from 5 per cent to 100 per cent; whereas the entries for the mean penetrance in the second column fall from 40 per cent to 2 per cent. In any given case, the percentage of expressed dominant mutants (see the third column) is the product of the percentages in the first two columns. It is noteworthy that the values for expressed dominants are all rather similar, ranging from 1 per cent to 5 per cent.

The values for the expressed dominant mutants must be supplemented by those for expressed recessives. The new values will depend on the proportion of recessive mutants among all mutants, the mean penetrance of the recessive homozygotes, and the probability that a gamete with a given induced recessive will form a zygote with another gamete which carries the same recessive. It is assumed, in the fourth column of Table 76, that between 90 and 95 per cent of all induced mutants can act as recessives. This assumption implies that some or many dominant genes, particularly those with low penetrance as dominants, will usually be expressed, and in a more striking manner, if present in a homozygous state. The penetrance of the genes in homozygotes is assumed to be complete. This obviously gives a maximum value for the proportion expressed. The last value needed is that for the probability of two recessives meeting in fertilization, for which event two different possibilities exist: The first is the possibility of two independently induced allelic mutants, one from an egg and one from a sperm, meeting each other. The frequency of such an occurrence is negligibly low. Even if each parent had been exposed to a doubling dose, the probability of a specific mutant arising in one parent would be 3 in 100,000, and the probability of such a mutant encountering a like one from the other parent also only 3 in 100,000. In contrast to this very low probability is that of the second type of homozygosis involving an induced recessive mutation. It consists in the meeting of the induced mutant with one like it which is already present in the population in consequence of repeated spontaneous mutation. Allele frequencies for such genes vary considerably, and only a very few are directly known. It is probably a high estimate if the mean value is regarded as 1 in 100 ($q = 0.01$).

From the three values just discussed—the proportion of mutants with recessive expression (fourth column, Table 76), complete penetrance, and an allele frequency in the population of $q = 0.01$—the proportions of recessives expressed in the first generation of exposed parents are given by the products of the values in the fourth column and 0.01. These products are entered in the fifth column. Finally, in the sixth column are entered the sums of the third and fifth columns, which indicate the total proportion of induced mutants that may express themselves in the first generation. Depending on the assumptions made for each of the seven horizontal rows, the total proportion of expressed mutants is expected to lie between 1.95 per cent and 5.9 per cent. Since several of the underlying assumptions tend to lead to rather high expectations for expression of expected damage, the figure of 4 per cent chosen for the following discussions is probably an overestimate. We are now ready to consider quantitatively the expectations of mutational damage to the offspring of individual parental pairs and of populations.

Mutational Damage to the Offspring of Individual Parents.   Since the frequency of induced and expressed mutants depends on the exposure received, we shall assume a specific dose, 10r, given to both parents of a pair or to all prospective parents of a population. For lower or higher doses, the expectations for expressed mutants are proportionally lower or higher. We have estimated earlier that an acute dose of 10r will induce a mutation in approximately 2.5 out of 100 gametes (postulating that the same figure is valid for eggs and sperm). Since perhaps 4 per cent of all induced mutants are expressed in the offspring of a single exposed parent, the probability of affected offspring from both exposed parents is $2 \cdot 0.025 \cdot 0.04 = 0.002$, or 2 in 1,000. This is a low probability, particularly in comparison with the general probability of affected children from nonexposed parents, which was earlier estimated as lying between 4 per cent and 6 per cent (p. 514). These last percentages are from twenty to thirty times larger than that for additional affected children. An individual parental pair, acutely exposed to 10r beyond background radiation has thus a probability of from 95.8 to 93.8 per cent of having a normal child, as compared to the probability of from 96 to 94 per cent from unexposed parents. In view of such a slight increase, it would seem unnecessary for any individual parental pair to worry about the effect of low-dose exposure. Even with 50r—a considerably higher acute exposure than that assumed in the foregoing discussion—the calculated induced frequency of affected children would only be 0.01, which is one-fourth or one-sixth of the spontaneous rates 0.04 and 0.06. Unless prospective parents are exposed to acute doses much larger than 50r, the probability of their having normal children remains very great. If the parents have been exposed chronically at low intensities, all figures given for high-intensity radiation can be reduced to at least one-fourth of those for acute exposure. Thus, the risk of producing abnormal offspring in consequence of such exposure is correspondingly lower.

What are the prospects for the grandchildren and later descendants of irradiated parents? In general, they are not much different from those of the first generation. Genes with dominant effects of low penetrance have unchanged chances of expressing themselves in future generations, and the same is true for recessives becoming homozygous. A child in whom a dominant effect became expressed is, of course, more likely than a nonaffected child to cause the same effect to appear among his offspring, and, correspondingly, a nonaffected child has better-than-average prospects of having nonaffected descendants. This is true simply because an individual who is phenotypically affected on account of his genotype is known to carry the gene in question; whereas a nonaffected individual may either carry the gene without its being penetrant or, much more frequently, be free from it.

There are two exceptions to the statements concerning the appearance of mutant phenotypes in the second and later generations of exposed parents. One exception refers to sex-linked recessive mutants from exposed fathers. Such mutations will first appear among their grandsons and not among their immediate offspring. The second exception refers to consanguinity. If, to take the most significant case, marriages occur between first cousins, one of whose grandparents had been heterozygous for a mutant gene induced in one of his own parents, then the likelihood of both cousins carrying the same mutant gene becomes relatively high. Their children, who are five generations removed from the exposed ancestor, thus have an increased chance of becoming homozygous for the induced mutant. However, the increased chance would only slightly enlarge the already greater-than-normal chance of the children from cousin marriages being affected because of spontaneously mutated genes accumulated in the population. The same, to a still lesser degree, would apply in later generations to more distant degrees of consanguinity.

Mutational Damage to Populations.   We turn now to the public concern regarding the incidence of phenotypically recognizable induced mutant genotypes in irradiated populations. Again we shall consider separately the effects on the first generation and those on later generations. Let us assume that all prospective parents of a population will be exposed to a mean dose of 10r, at high intensity, within the 30 years which on the average precede reproduction. Then the number of affected children will be equal to the probability of such children from individual parental pairs (estimated as 0.002, p. 517) multiplied by the number of births in the population. For example, from 1,000,000 births the number of affected offspring from induced mutations would be 2,000. In the United States there are at present more than 4,000,000 births annually; so as many as, or more than, 8,000 affected children would be expected each year. For the population of the world (which will soon reach 3,000,000,000), the total number of affected children among the next generation of 3,000,000,000 individuals from parents exposed to 10r of high-intensity radiation would be 6,000,000. For low-intensity exposure this number would be reduced to 1,500,000.

These numbers would be superimposed upon those numbers of affected children whose defects occur independently of the added radiation. Since from 4 to 6 per cent of such children would be produced, their numbers among 1,000,000 births would be from 40,000 to 60,000, and among the world's total population from 120,000,000 to 180,000,000.

In later generations the frequencies of affected children from parents ex-

posed to radiation would depend on a number of circumstances. Among these
we may distinguish between the outcome if only the original parental generation, but none of their descendants, had been exposed, and the outcome
if a dose of 10r impinges on each successive generation. The outcome of a
third type of exposure, in which successive generations are exposed to doses
either lower or higher than 10r, can be derived easily from the results of the
following discussions.

If exposure is restricted to the parental generation, then the incidence of
affected children will decrease in successive generations. The reason for this
decrease is implicit, in that affected individuals are, on the whole, less fit
than nonaffected ones and therefore reproduce at a rate which is lower than
that of nonaffected individuals. If, in a not-exposed population, there is at
least an approach to a balance between spontaneous input of mutations and
selective outgo, and if this balance has been temporarily changed by an additional input of induced mutations, selection will tend to reduce the total
number of mutants and restore the natural equilibrium. In detail, the selective

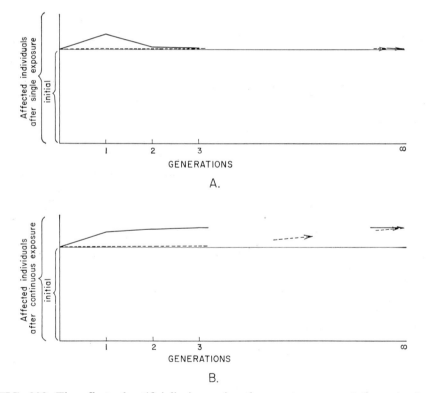

FIG. 209. The effect of artificially increasing the spontaneous mutation rates by
20 per cent for a dominant and a recessive gene. Solid lines = chondrodystrophic
dwarfism; broken lines = phenylketonuria.   A. Increased rate of mutation effective for one generation.   B. Permanently. (Modified from Medical Research
Council, *The Hazards to Man of Nuclear and Allied Radiations.*)

processes involved will be different for different genes, will depend on whether the genes act as dominants or recessives, and will depend on the selective disadvantage they confer on their bearers. A dominant gene with complete or at least high penetrance and with serious deleterious effects, such as chondrodystrophic dwarfism, is present in a low frequency in a not-exposed population. With 10r of high-intensity exposure, its incidence among the first generation might rise by 20 per cent (Fig. 209, A). Owing to the low fitness of its bearers, the total frequency of such a gene in the second generation will be no more than 4 per cent above that in a not-exposed group; in the third generation the total frequency will be about 1/2 per cent above that in a not-exposed group; and soon the population will have freed itself from nearly all induced mutants. For a dominant gene with lower penetrance and less serious effects, the lowering of its incidence will proceed in a similar but slower manner. Induced strictly recessive genes in homozygotes will raise the frequency of affected individuals only slightly above the spontaneous rate in the first generation. Thereafter, the number of affected homozygous individuals will gradually decrease, as was true of dominants. However, the course of events will be exceedingly slow, even with homozygous lethal mutants. This is so because in each generation only a very small percentage of induced mutants will appear in homozygotes, the great majority being sheltered in heterozygotes. In reality, as we have seen, it is likely that many so-called recessive genes have slightly deleterious effects, even in heterozygotes. Their elimination will tend to follow the course of events characteristic of dominant genes with low penetrance, rather than that of complete recessives. Even so, it may require thirty or more generations until most induced, nearly recessive genes are eliminated. Since the duration of a human generation is about 25 years, this means a very slow decrease over hundreds or even thousands of years.

It may not be superfluous to state specifically that recessive homozygotes, which are rare in the first generation, do not become frequent in F_2. An F_1 plant of the genotype Aa which can be self-fertilized will, of course, produce 25 per cent recessive aa homozygotes. A first-generation heterozygous human Aa will usually marry an AA individual and have second-generation AA and Aa children only. These, in turn, will not intermarry but will mate with AA individuals from the general population. Thus, again, no affected aa will be produced. Only if two cousins of this third generation marry is there 1 chance in 16 of both being Aa and, in this case, of one-quarter affected offspring. If all marriages in a population were of the first-cousin type, then there would be a noticeable increase of affected homozygotes four generations after exposure. However, since in most populations cousin marriages are a small fraction of all marriages, such an increase in the population at large would probably remain insignificant. Lower degrees of inbreeding in later generations would have effects even less noticeable.

In a population that is subjected to irradiation in successive generations, mutations will accumulate until a new, higher equilibrium is reached between mutational input and selective outgo. The rise in affected individuals in the first generation will, in the following generations, continue (Fig. 209, B). Its ultimate level will be proportional to the dose. From that point, with 10r of high-intensity radiation impinging in each generation, and on the basis of the various assumptions made throughout this discussion of induced mutations, there will be produced in each generation 20 per cent more genetically defective individuals than there were before the beginning of exposures. With dominant genes, the rise to the new level will take only a few generations if the penetrance is high, more if it is low. For fully recessive genes, the rise will be very gradual for a long time; finally, the new level, 20 per cent above the old, will be attained.

The reverse trend of events will follow if irradiation should be discontinued. Then, the population will return to its pre-exposed status, speedily for seriously deleterious dominant genes with high penetrance, slowly for less-deleterious or lower-penetrance genes, and particularly slowly for complete recessives.

The preceding discussions have dealt with mutant genes whose effects are deleterious to various degrees. There are other mutant genes whose fitness cannot be classified so simply. Two important classes of these genes will now be considered.

Mutations in Polygenic Systems

Graded characters such as height or intelligence performance depend on the collaboration of many genes, each of which contributes individually small effects. The different alleles at each locus differ only slightly in action, and represent iso-alleles. What effect will irradiation have on these genes? Experiments with animals have shown that irradiation can increase the variability of certain polygenic traits, both in a plus and in a minus direction. Mutations are produced from one iso-allele to another, so the range of variation of the trait is widened. It has been shown in experimental organisms that even after considerable exposure the increase in variability is small, as compared to the variability naturally present in populations occurring in nature. It may be assumed that graded traits in human populations, too, would change only slightly and very slowly after exposure. A number of different situations concerning the type of change expected can be envisaged. Among these, following Mather, two may be singled out.

The first situation is that in which radiation increases the degree of variation symmetrically on both sides of the average. It may be illustrated by a theoretical analysis of one of many possible examples, the distribution of intelligence performance. Let us assume that one-half of the observed variability of the trait in a population depends on hereditary factors (the other half depending on environmental factors) and that the genetic variability of the population is permanently doubled by continuous irradiation. Such a population may, before exposure, consist of 95.4 per cent of normal individuals within the I.Q. range of 70–130, 2.3 per cent of subnormal individuals with I.Q. below 70, and 2.3 per cent of persons with I.Q. above 130. After exposure, and in the distant future (when equilibrum has been attained again) only 89.8 per cent would be within the normal I.Q. range and the subnormals as well as the supernormals would have more than doubled, both being present in a frequency of 5.1 per cent.

The second situation, again using an example of intelligence performance, is that in which radiation increases phenotypic variability asymmetrically. Such an effect may be expected if natural selection has, in the past, favored genotypes that result in phenotypes at one side of the average. One might be inclined to think that high intelligence performance has had selective advantages. Therefore irradiation will tend to increase the frequency of alleles which lead to a lower level of performance. As a result, the induced greater variation of the phenotype will lead to a lowering of the mean intelligence, accompanied by a relatively high increase of the subnormal extreme of the population and a low increase of the above-normal extreme.

It is not simple to attach value judgments to the types of change just illustrated. If the variability is increased symmetrically, there will be the regrettable phenomenon of an increase in persons with subnormal intelligence accompanied by a presumably fortunate increase in highly endowed people. Who can say whether these two opposing increases will balance each other in value (for the individuals, for their relatives, for society) or, if they do not balance, which one will be more significant? Even if the variability is increased asymmetrically, it would be a matter of uncertainty how to weigh the large rise of the poorly gifted against the smaller one of the highly gifted. In any case, it is clear that the induction of mutations involved in polygenic, graded traits does not simply fall into the category of mutational damage.

Mutations in Heterotic Situations

Examples are known, particularly for other organisms, but also for man, in which heterozygous individuals A^1A^2 are superior in reproductive fitness to either homozygotes A^1A^1 or A^2A^2. In a population which contains both alleles A^1 and A^2, an equilibrium is attained when the heterozygotes are the most frequent class. (For a more detailed treatment, see Chapter 28, pages 618–622.) Obviously, the terms advantageous and disadvantageous can be applied to either allele, depending on whether one considers heterozygotes or homozygotes. If one considers a series of multiple alleles, it may well be that a whole array of fitness exists, with certain heterozygotes being inferior to other heterozygotes and superior to certain homozygotes, and the homozygotes themselves being of varying fitness.

It is likely that any given human population possesses only some of the many possible alleles, of a given series. The consequences of induced mutations in such populations will depend on the types of alleles already present. If a population with heterosis for A^1A^2 contains mostly A^1 and few A^2 alleles, gametes with new induced A^1 mutants will usually meet A^1 gametes.

This will lead to relatively unfit A^1A^1 zygotes. Only rarely will the induced A^1 mutant meet A^2, thus leading to a more fit A^1A^2 heterozygote. If, instead of an induced A^1 mutant, an A^x allele is produced by irradiation, it is conceivable that both A^1A^x and A^2A^x will be superior to A^1A^1 and A^2A^2, and perhaps even to A^1A^2. Here, then, advantageous effects will occur exclusively in the beginning. But A^xA^x homozygotes will segregate out in later generations, and, if they are of low fitness, such genotypes will be termed disadvantageous. With heterosis, the sweeping statement that mutations are harmful obviously must be qualified.

The Fitness of Populations and the Load of Mutations

Haldane and Muller have, in different though related ways, considered the impact of mutations on populations. They based their views on a treatment of mutations whose effects lower the reproductive fitness of an individual in both heterozygotes and homozygotes, or at least do not increase fitness in heterozygotes. Induced mutant alleles with unfavorable effects in heterozygotes will usually be eliminated from the population before they can become homozygous. Each allele of this type will therefore sooner or later cause one genetic extinction, owing to early or later prenatal death of a zygote that carries the gene, or to pre-reproductive death of an individual, or to relatively lowered or complete infertility of a perhaps otherwise little-or-not-at-all affected person. Completely recessive genes will be responsible for one-half extinction each, since two of them are required to produce their effect. In humans, the load of mutations encompasses more than the number of genetic extinctions might imply. Genes which lower the reproductive fitness of an individual by 10 per cent will, on the average, persist for 10 generations. Some of these genes may remain completely unexpressed before they become extinct, but others may cause suffering in each generation before they are eliminated.

This view of the fitness of a population implies that, ideally, the most-fit genotypes would consist of individuals who are homozygous, at all loci, for long-established normal alleles. Less-than-perfect fitness, which is an attribute of all existing populations, is a consequence of new, spontaneous, harmful mutations that are constantly injected into a population only to be eliminated by selection. The fitness of a population therefore is reduced in proportion to the rate of mutation.

No such proportionality exists for heterotic genes. The heterozygotes are the fittest type. In heterotic populations their mating in each generation leads to segregation of homozygotes whose reduced fitness may result in genetic extinction. In contrast to a hypothetical population consisting of nonsegregating heterozygotes exclusively, a heterotic population carries a "segregational load," which lowers its fitness. Induction of mutations to alleles already present will add a mutational load to the segregational one; this mutational load may be far smaller than the segregational. Whatever its relative part the fitness of a heterotic population is not proportional to the rate of mutation.

It is now known that in human populations there are genes of each of the two main types: genes with invariably harmful effects, and genes with harmful effects in homozygotes but beneficial effects in heterozygotes. Admittedly, this distinction draws a sharper dividing line between the two types than is fully justified, since the attributes "generally harmful" or "heterotic" may apply to certain genes in certain genic backgrounds, but may be changed in other backgrounds, and may also vary according to varied environments. Whatever the importance in details is, it is useful to consider separately the significance for harmful and for heterotic genes that induced mutations have for the fitness of a population.

If the existing, total, genetic load of unexposed human populations is due to harmful mutations that occur continuously, then induced mutations will add proportionally to that load. If, for instance, as has been estimated, as many as 25 to 40 per cent of human zygotes are eliminated for genetic reasons, then a permanent doubling of the rate of mutations by radiation would lead to elimination of 50 to 80 per cent of human zygotes. If that were the case, one might justifiably wonder whether the human species would persist or would die out from insufficient reproductive fitness. However, if the total genetic load of unexposed human populations is due largely to segregation of less-fit genotypes from more-fit heterozygotes, then the additional load from induced mutations will only slightly raise the frequency of eliminations. Induced mutation will then constitute a less-serious threat to the survival of the group.

It is not possible at present to assess the relative roles which the mutational and the segregational loads play in human populations. Many genes are known whose effect must be harmful under most if not all conditions. Few examples of definitely heterotic genes can be cited, but it may be that such genes are frequent for graded traits in polygenic systems where their existence cannot be demonstrated readily. Neel has suggested, in harmony with evidence on experimental organisms marshalled by Lerner, that some or many of the sporadic congenital malformations which occur in all populations may be multiple homozygous segregates from normal heterozygotes whose heterozygosis is the very basis of their normality. It may be a long time until the proportion of mutants with generally harmful effects to those with heterotic effects is known. Until then, we cannot confidently evaluate the full effect of induced mutations on human populations. At present, experiments on laboratory animal populations demonstrate various possibilities for the relation between induced mutation rate and fitness, but they are only first indications of what may be important in man.

Direct Studies on Man

Certain human groups that have been exposed to unusually high doses of radiation have been the subject of a number of investigations. The offspring of such individuals were scored for frequency of congenital malformations, stillbirths and neonatal deaths, birth weight, and ratio of males to females.

This last trait particularly has been regarded as an important indicator of induced damage to the genetic material. If men alone are exposed to radiation, their relatively large X-chromosomes should be broken more frequently than their small Y-chromosomes. Their X-chromosomes, also, should carry induced, lethal mutant genes, some of them dominant or partly so, in contrast to their Y-chromosomes which should be low in clearly mutable loci. Therefore, female zygotes from irradiated fathers should die disproportionately more frequently than those from nonexposed fathers, and a changed sex ratio would result. This trend toward more male births would be counteracted to an unknown degree by the losses of broken Y-chromosomes in zygotes which, instead of developing into XY males, would develop into XO females. If women alone are exposed, some of their X-chromosomes should be broken and some should carry induced lethals. This would result in greater harm to the hemizygous male zygotes than to the *XX* female zygotes, and the result would be a relative surplus of female births. If both parents are exposed, it would be expected that the effect of the mother's irradiation on the sex ratio would be the more striking; thus, after joint irradiation a lowering of the male ratio would result. These theoretical expectations concerning changes in the sex ratio of children from irradiated parents are plausible. Nevertheless, it must be said that the results of radiation experiments on Drosophila males cannot be accounted for solely by the assumption of differential frequencies of X- and Y-chromosome breakage or of induced genic lethals. Rather, the results seem to require additional mechanisms, not yet understood, for their explanation. Such unsolved aspects should emphasize the importance of caution in interpreting shifts in the human sex ratio, particularly in the case of exposed fathers.

The largest groups studied consisted of the offspring of Japanese and American radiologists and radiological technicians, of the offspring of French men and women who, for medical reasons, had received relatively high doses in the pelvic region, and of the offspring of Japanese parents exposed to the atomic explosions in Hiroshima and Nagasaki. All studies, with the exception of the last, were based on answers by the parents to questionnaires. Many parents did not return their questionnaires, as was true also for many of the unexposed control parents. This is unfortunate, since it is difficult to judge whether the persons who did answer were selected samples in the sense that they had special reasons either to report on affected children (and the sex of their children) or to not report on them.

No clear evidence has been obtained on the frequency of congenital malformations. While some data gathered by questionnaire showed a significant increase in malformations, there was no significant difference in frequency of affected offspring from exposed as compared to nonexposed parents in the largest group in which each individual had been carefully inspected: the children born in Hiroshima and Nagasaki during the period 1948–1953. For the exposed parents, 300 congenital malformations are recorded among 33,327 live born (0.89 per cent); for the nonexposed parents, 298 are recorded among 31,904 (0.92 per cent). It would be completely in error to draw from this negative result the conclusion that exposure to the atomic explosions did not induce mutations. The average dose received by survivors who became parents in later years was not very large, and the expected increase in malformations among their newborn was correspondingly small. Neel and Schull, the leaders of the genetics group of the Atomic Bomb Casualty Commission, submitted their findings to a detailed statistical treatment. It indicated that, had the frequency of malformations been actually doubled, owing to the exposure, there could still have been a 10 per cent chance of the observed frequencies not showing any difference. Furthermore, if many congenital malformations should represent segregational consequences of heterotic systems and not simple consequences of the mutational load, then the absence of an increase in affected children would be even less unexpected. However, the findings also have an important positive aspect. If the sensitivity of human genes were very high—for instance, if the doubling dose were close to its possible minimum of 3r for acute exposures—then there should probably be a significant increase in the malformation frequency of children of exposed parents. The fact that such an increase did not occur suggests that the acute doubling dose in man is perhaps at least 15r, and possibly is in the range which led, in this book, to the assumption of the figure of 50r.

In contrast to the present lack of direct evidence for the production of individually observable effects on the offspring of irradiated parents, several of the studies suggest a shift of the sex ratio in the direction expected from the induction of chromosome breakage and X-linked lethal mutations. In this respect, the surveys of offspring of French patients and of Japanese radiological technicians agree with each other as well as with the findings from Hiroshima and Nagasaki. In the latter findings, in 11 out of 12 possible comparisons there was a rise of male births from exposed fathers, and a decline in male births from exposed mothers. Most changes in the sex ratio are small and often not significant statistically, being of the order of 1 or 2 per cent. The observations are compatible with the assumption that the frequency of sex-linked, lethal mutations per röntgen induced in man is similar to that which would be expected if the sensitivity of human genes to radiation corresponded to that of the mouse. It bears repeating that the expectations of changes in the human sex ratio due to radiation are not sufficiently well grounded to warrant concluding that the observed changes are really the consequences of radiation.

Recapitulation of Some of the Uncertainties. In this chapter an attempt has been made to evaluate the effects of irradiation on human genes, on the phenotypes of individuals carrying induced mutations, and on the changes caused by such mutations in populations. Such an evaluation is bound to have only temporary validity, since there are many unknowns. In spite of this, and for the sake of concreteness, qualitative and even quantitative estimates have been presented. It is therefore appropriate to summarize some of the uncertainties involved in these estimates by asking the following questions:

1. Is the number of recoverable induced mutations proportional to the dose received after either acute or chronic exposure?
2. What is the relation between mutagenic effectiveness and intensity of radiation?
3. Are the sensitivities of human genes like those of Drosophila genes or mouse genes, or are they different from both?
4. Are the genes of men and women equally sensitive?
5. Is the number of mutable genic loci in man 5,000, 10,000, 50,000, or some other value?
6. What are the relative proportions of seriously harmful mutants to only slightly subvital mutants?
7. What is the mean penetrance of harmful human genes in heterozygotes?
8. How great is the mutational load of human populations as compared to the segregational load?
9. What is the effect of induced mutations on polygenic traits?

Definite answers to these and other questions may indeed lead to great changes in the estimates cited in the preceding pages.

The Social Consequences of Induced Mutations.   Whatever specific values will finally be determined, there is no doubt that they will represent many millions of defect-carrying genotypes and that their frequencies will be positively correlated with the amount of radiation experienced.

It may be expected that future discoveries will provide methods with which to counter the mutagenic effects of radiation. It is already known that fewer mutations are produced when the irradiated tissues are very low in oxygen, and that certain chemicals applied to irradiated animals are "antimutagenic." However, no satisfactory antimutagens, harmless to human beings, are yet available.

At present, the major contributions to doses received from man-made devices come from medical radiations that fall into the acute, high-intensity range. The benefit to the health of the individual exposed to such radiations, on the whole, far outweighs the damage to future generations, but damage there will be. Exposure due to radioactive fallout from nuclear weapons tests is only a small fraction of that due to unavoidable, natural background radiation. The contribution of fallout to genetic damage is therefore small, particularly since it involves low-intensity radiation, but fallout will still affect many individuals in the world at large. The foreseeable expanding industrial use of nuclear energy is likely to raise the level of radiation in general at a cost in the well-being of many people in future generations.

Present recommendations of national and international bodies tend to limit the mean exposure of individuals to 10r, excluding background. Such a "permissible" dose will still cause human suffering and will increase the social burden of mankind in terms of disabled or handicapped members. Such a tragic situation is not new in the history of man. When, in prehistoric times, fire was made to serve human purposes it introduced a new danger which, in spite of extensive safeguards, still kills and maims many persons every year. And modern industry has introduced serious physical and chemical hazards to workers. While every effort must be made to minimize all hazards to the present and to future generations, it must be realized that the moral problems inherent in the use of radiation are not unique.

The wartime use of atomic weapons poses the moral problems in their starkest form. The carnage of "conventional" warfare is intensified by the long-term, ill effects of radiation on generations still to be born. Nonetheless, the evils of war are sufficiently great without the use of atomic weapons to require bending all efforts to its permanent abolition.

If mankind were ever to be subjected to unrestricted atomic warfare, the genetic consequences would be far reaching. Not only would immense numbers of individuals perish from the immediate effects of explosions, but even larger numbers would be exposed to radiation from radioactive contamination of whole continents. Surviving populations living in contaminated areas would be subject to chronic irradiation that might lead to accumulation of higher doses than the 450r which constitutes an acute mean lethal dose. The effects might be very deleterious, from the standpoint of physiological changes and mutations in body cells. In regard to transmissible mutations produced in germ cells, high doses of accumulated irradiation would cause numerous genetic changes, many times above those considered in this chapter. Yet, it is likely that even such high rates would still permit the production of enough descendants with adequate reproductive fitness to avoid the extinction of the human race. Notwithstanding, this likelihood can hardly alter the horrors of the catastrophe contemplated here.

Problems

185. (a) Two employees in a radiological laboratory marry and have an albino child. Since there has been no albino in either ancestry, they ascribe the appearance of albinism to their occupational hazard. Evaluate the genetic aspects of the case.

(b) A man employed for several years in an atomic energy plant becomes the father of a hemophilic boy, the first case in the extensive family pedigrees of both his own and his wife's ancestry. Another man also employed for several years in the same plant has a chondrodystrophic dwarf child, the first occurrence of the malformation in his and his wife's ancestry. Both men attribute the abnormality of their respective children to their occupation. They sue for damages. What should be the testimony of a geneticist before the court?

186. If a large group of individuals received 100r of total body irradiation, what prospects exist for determining whether an increased number of mutations were produced? Consider separately: (i) dominant mutations, (ii) incompletely penetrant dominants, (iii) X-linked recessives, (iv) autosomal recessives.

187. A fertilizing sperm cell of an irradiated man contains a reciprocal translocation between two autosomes. (a) What will be the phenotypic effect on the developing zygote? (b) If the zygote develops into an adult female, what will be the effect on her reproduction? (c) If she has offspring, what will be their reproductive attributes?

References

In addition to the references given at the end of Chapter 23, the following should also be consulted.

Crow, J. F., 1955. A comparison of fetal and infant death rates in the progeny of radiologists and pathologists. *Am. J. Roentgenol.*, **73:** 467–471.

————, 1957. Possible consequences of an increased mutation rate. *Eugen. Quart.*, **4:** 67–80.

Fisher, R. A., 1930. *The Genetical Theory of Natural Selection.* 272 pp. Oxford University Press, London (also 1959. 2nd rev. ed. 291 pp. Dover, N. Y.).

Haldane, J. B. S., 1937. The effect of variation on fitness. *Am. Naturalist,* **71:** 337–349.

Intern. Comm. Radiological Protection and Intern. Comm. Radiological Units and Measurements, 1957. Exposure of man to ionizing radiation arising from medical procedures. An enquiry into methods of evaluation. *Physics in Med. and Biol.,* **2:** 107–151.

Lerner, I. M., 1954. *Genetic Homeostasis.* 134 pp. Oliver & Boyd, Edinburgh.

Macht, S. H., and Lawrence, P. S., 1955. National survey of congenital malformations resulting from exposure to Roentgen radiation. *Am. J. Roentgenol.,* **73:** 442–466.

Muller, H. J., 1950. Our load of mutations. *Am. J. Human Genet.,* **2:** 111–176.

————, 1950. Radiation damage of genetic origin. *Am. Scientist,* **38:** 35–59.

————, 1956. Further studies bearing on the load of mutations in man. *Acta Genet. et Stat. Med.,* **6:** 157–168.

Neel, J. V., 1958. A study of major congenital defects in Japanese infants. *Am. J. Human Genet.,* **10:** 398–445.

————, and Schull, W. J., 1956. *The Effect of Exposure to the Atomic Bombs on Pregnancy Termination in Hiroshima and Nagasaki.* 241 pp. Nat. Acad. Sci.–Nat. Res. Council, Washington.

Puck, T. T., 1959. Quantitative studies on mammalian cells in vitro. *Rev. Mod. Physics,* **31:** 433–448.

Sonnenblick, B. P. (Ed.), 1959. *Protection in Diagnostic Radiology.* 346 pp. Rutgers University Press, New Brunswick.

Tanaka, K., and Ohkura, K., 1958. Evidence for genetic effects of radiation in offspring of radiological technicians. *Jap. J. Human Genet.,* **3:** 135–145.

Turpin, R., Lejeune, J., and Rethore, M. O., 1956. Étude de la descendance de sujets traités par radiothérapie pelvienne. *Acta Genet. et Stat. Med.,* **6:** 204–216.

CHAPTER 25

HEREDITY AND
ENVIRONMENT

I. TYPES OF TWINS

The interaction of genetic constitution and environment in the production of the phenotype has been discussed at various places in this book, particularly in the chapter dealing with variations in the expression of genes. It was seen that some alleles determine the same phenotype under all external conditions, while others may produce different phenotypes under different external circumstances.

These external circumstances, which are described by the general term "environment," include all nongenetic influences, whether acting before, at, or after birth. The age-old question "How much of a specific trait of an individual is due to heredity and how much to environment?" is meaningless in this form. Since no phenotypic trait is independent of either hereditary or environmental agents, an attempt to divide into two fractions the interrelation of two agents, neither of which alone can produce a phenotype, is futile.

What the question endeavors to ask is: "How much of the variability observed between different individuals is due to hereditary differences between them, and how much to differences in the environments under which the individuals developed?" Even this formulation of the question requires further precision. It is not applicable to "the" phenotype as a whole, but only to well-definable, measurable, or classifiable components. One can easily measure the weight of a person, the length of any specific structure, the basic metabolism, the speed of reaction in finding his way through a maze, and innumerable other properties, but it is less informative to give quantitative measures to properties such as general body build, constitution, or personality. Indeed, progress in an understanding of these complex attributes is made only by determining and analyzing their separate factors. The question re-

530

garding the relative roles of heredity and environment in the determination
of differences between individuals must, therefore, be applied separately to
measurable components of the phenotype and often leads to a different answer
for each separate component.)CHD

One other point should be made. It cannot be taken for granted that the
effect of an environmental factor on the expression of one genotype can be
predicted from the known effect of the same factor on another genotype.
In some cases, the effects on both genotypes may be similar; in others, dissimilar. Thus, increase of food over the minimum necessary for maintenance
will result in higher weight both in genetically small and large individuals;
but addition of sugar to a sugar-free diet may have serious consequences for
a genetically diabetic person, while causing no disturbance in a nondiabetic.
Even opposite effects may result from two environments interacting with
two genotypes: the use of cow's milk in the diet of a child allergic to it will
cause a severe reaction, but in the diet of a nonallergic child is beneficial.
For another example, two individuals of different intellectual endowments
may both make moderate progress under limited demands from the environment, but the better endowed may thrive under high demands, while the
other may fail completely. This example implies that people with varying
intellectual endowments may vary for genetic reasons, a matter which will
be discussed in Chapter 27.

From the preceding paragraphs, it is clear that genotypes of individuals
may exhibit certain expressions in one environment and either similar or
dissimilar expressions in another environment.

Haldane has treated this problem in a generalized way. Assume that two
genotypes, A and B, exposed to two environments, X and Y, give four different phenotypes, ranked 1 (best) to 4 (poorest), and that genotype A
in environment X gives the best performance. There are, then, six different
ways, I–VI, in which the performances of A in Y and of B in X and Y can
be ranked:

	I		II		III		IV		V		VI	
	X	Y	X	Y	X	Y	X	Y	X	Y	X	Y
A	1	2	1	3	1	4	1	2	1	3	1	4
B	3	4	2	4	2	3	4	3	4	2	3	2

Thus, arrangement I signifies that genotype A performs better than genotype B in both environments X and Y, and that both genotypes A and B
perform better in environment X than Y. This arrangement would fit the
earlier example of two genotypes for large (A) or small (B) body size in
two environments, providing above-minimum (X) or minimum (Y) food
supply. The same example could also be fitted to arrangement II, in which
the genotype for large body size performs better than that for small body
size in either environment but in which the interaction of genotype and

environment leads to a poorer yield of A in Y (rank 3) than of B in X (rank 2).

The other earlier example concerning intellectual accomplishments under conditions of high or limited demands might fit arrangement IV: the "gifted" genotype A performs excellently in the highly demanding environment X (rank 1) and moderately in the less demanding environment Y (rank 2), while the less gifted genotype B fails in environment X (rank 4) but passes in environment Y (rank 3). The reader may begin to appreciate fully the implications of the table if he will formulate in words how an example concerning body size can also be fitted to arrangement III, and one concerning intellectual achievement can also be fitted to arrangements V and VI. And it may prove instructive to invent other examples and fit them to each one of the six arrangements.

If more than two genotypes and more than two environments are considered, the number of possible arrangements in performance increases greatly. Thus, three genotypes, A, B, and C, in three environments, X, Y, and Z, with genotype A in environment X having the highest rank, can be arranged in no less than 10,080 ways!

The Biology of Twinning

It is relatively easy to test the effect of nature and nurture in experimental animals or plants. Different strains can be produced, each of which is more or less isogenic and genetically distinct from the other strains; and controlled environmental variants can be applied to these strains. In some experiments, the environment will be kept constant so that the effect of genetic differences alone can be measured for each type of environment; and, in other experiments, the different genotypes will be kept constant so that the effect of environmental differences alone can be studied.

In man, isogenic strains are not available for such tests; nor is it possible, in most cases, to control at will the environment in which the phenotypic properties develop. Nevertheless, certain phenomena in man approach the ideal arrangements of experimental design. The most significant of these "arrangements" is twinning. Identical twins are isogenic and permit studies of the effect of different environments, while nonidentical twins are genetically different and permit studies of the effect of different genotypes in a similar environment.

Ever since Francis Galton (1822–1911) emphasized the importance of studying twins to obtain information on the nature–nurture problem, twin studies have played a vital role in the development of human genetics, particularly in recent decades. Before we discuss the contributions of twin studies to the nature–nurture problem, let us examine some relevant facts on the biology of twinning.

Frequency of Twins. The frequency of twin births varies in different populations: from as high as 1.79 per cent of all births in Belgium to as low as or lower than, 0.8 per cent in several South American populations and among Mongoloids. In the period 1922–1936 in the United States, 1.129 per cent of all white births, or 1 in 88.6, and 1.413 per cent of all negro births, or 1 in 70.7, were twin births. These figures are only for twin births in which at least one twin was born alive.

Identical and Nonidentical Twins.   It has long been known that there are two different types of twins. Some are so similar to each other that they are called *identical* twins; others are no more similar than sibs, and they are called *nonidentical* or *fraternal* twins. Identical twins originate from a single egg fertilized by a single sperm, while nonidentical twins come from two eggs, each fertilized by a separate sperm. The occurrence of two-egg, or *dizygotic,* twins depends on the exceptional, more or less simultaneous, release of two eggs from one or both ovaries of a woman and their subsequent fertilization. One-egg, or *monozygotic,* twins are the result of the division of a single egg into two independent embryonic structures. Monozygotic twins are genetically alike, since mitoses provide the cells of both with descendants of the same chromosomes originally carried by the single zygote. Dizygotic twins are no more alike genetically than two sibs derived from two separate eggs and two separate sperm which matured in the gonads of the parents at different times.

The theoretical question has been raised of whether it is possible that some two-egg twins would be more alike than the usual fraternal, but less alike than identical, twins. Such twins would be produced if an abnormal meiotic division of an egg gave rise, not to a large egg cell and abortive polar bodies, but to two egg cells, similar in size and fertilizability. On the average, the genetic constitution of these two cells would be more similar than that of two typical, separately formed eggs. There is no evidence for the existence of twins derived from the hypothetical, abnormal maturation of an egg cell; and it is unlikely that more than an insignificant fraction of twins, if any at all, are of this type.

Weinberg's Differential Method.   A statistical method, first conceived by Bertillon and later developed by Weinberg, permits us to find how many twins in a twin population are monozygotic and how many are dizygotic. It is based on the fact that sex is determined genetically. Unlike-sexed twins are undoubtedly derived from two separate zygotes, one XX and the other XY in constitution. Now, the number of like-sexed dizygotic twins should bear a simple relation to that of the unlike-sexed ones. In a population in which the secondary sex ratio is 1:1, dizygotic twins of the ♂, ♂; ♂, ♀; and ♀, ♀ types should occur according to the chance frequencies 1/4:1/2:1/4. This means that the number of like-sexed dizygotic male and female twin pairs, 1/4 + 1/4, would be the same as that of the unlike-sexed twins, 1/2; or, the total number of dizygotic twins would be twice that of the observed number of unlike-sexed twins. The number of monozygotic twins is obtained simply by subtracting the number of dizygotics from the total of all twins.

Since the number of monozygotics is represented by the difference between all twins and the dizygotics, Weinberg's procedure is known as the "differential method."

The sex ratio in most populations deviates from equality. Therefore, a more accurate use of the differential method employs, for the population under study, the specific values of p and q for the probability of the male and female sex at birth. The fraction of unlike-sexed twins of all dizygotic twin pairs is

$$\frac{\text{Unlike-sexed twin pairs}}{\text{All dizygotic twin pairs}} = \frac{2pq}{p^2 + 2pq + q^2} = \frac{2pq}{1}.$$

This yields

$$\text{All dizygotic twin pairs} = \frac{\text{Unlike-sexed twin pairs}}{2pq}, \tag{1}$$

and

$$\text{All monozygotic twin pairs} =$$

$$\text{Total of all twin pairs} - \frac{\text{Unlike-sexed twin pairs}}{2pq}. \tag{2}$$

By applying these formulas to the white and negro populations of the United States, it is found that the percentages of monozygotic twins among all twin births is about 34.2 per cent for whites and 28.9 per cent for negroes. In other words, about 1 out of 3 sets of twins born are identicals. For Japan, with a low frequency of 0.7 per cent, or less, of twin births among all births, the application of the differential method shows that a much larger fraction, namely, more than 60 per cent, of the twins are monozygotic. This means that the difference between the over-all frequencies of twin births among Japanese and Americans is mainly due to differences in the frequencies of dizygotics.

Age of Mother, Parity, and Frequency of Twinning.   An interesting relation exists between age of mothers and frequencies of twin births, both monozygotic and dizygotic (Fig. 210). From the ages of 15 to 39 years, the tendency of mothers to bear twins increases, relatively slightly for monozygotics but very strikingly for dizygotics. For mothers 40–44 years of age, monozygotic frequencies continue to increase but dizygotics drop sharply.

Age of mothers is highly correlated with number of pregnancies: younger women have fewer, and older women have more, children. The variability of twinning frequency is, therefore, correlated not only with age of mothers, but also with parity. It has been shown that the two factors act separately, and in the same direction, on the frequency of dizygotic twin births. No study has been made regarding their effect on the less variable rate of monozygotic births.

The curves in Figure 210 show that the statement "One out of three twin births gives rise to identical twins" is based on an average and does not take into account the great differences in expectation for different age groups of mothers. A young white mother, under 20 years, has about equal chances of having either identical or nonidentical twins, while the chance of a white mother between 35 and 39 years bearing nonidentical, rather than identical, twins is 3 to 1. It remains to be investigated whether the somewhat different proportions for negro mothers are due to inherent differences in age effect, or to differences in parity for corresponding maternal ages.

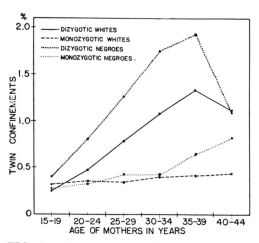

There is good evidence that the initial number of twin pregnancies of both types is much greater than the number of twins brought to term. Two embryos growing in a single uterus are in a less favorable environment than a single embryo, and rate of fetal mortality

FIG. 210. Frequency of twin confinements in relation to age of mothers in the United States, 1938. (Enders and Stern, *Genetics,* **33,** 1948.)

or stillbirth for both or one of the twins is several times higher than for single embryos. Estimates of the prenatal deaths of one of a pair of twins have been as high as from 20 to 50 per cent; and, among these deaths, the monozygotics seem to be affected two to three times as often as dizygotics.

Embryology of Twinning. The recognition of monozygotic or dizygotic origin of a given pair of twins is made by means of the *similarity diagnosis,* that is, detailed study of the phenotypes of the twins. This diagnosis is nothing more than a refinement of the inspection method often used by the layman to conclude that a specific pair is so similar as to be called identical, or another one sufficiently dissimilar as to be called nonidentical. The similarity diagnosis will be described below. It will suffice here to state that, with care, the diagnosis is so reliable that the probability of mistakes is very small.

The similarity diagnosis has been used to test another method of twin diagnosis which is based on the analysis of the afterbirth of twins and which has been employed frequently by physicians. As was described in Chapter 3, a human embryo develops from a germinal disc within an amnion, is surrounded by a chorion, and is attached to the uterus by a placenta. Since these structures, referred to as the afterbirth, are ejected from the uterus following the birth of the child, they are accessible to study.

TABLE 77. *Number of Chorions and Amnions, and Similarity Diagnosis in 132 Like-sexed Twin Births.* (Steiner, *Arch. Gynäk,* **159,** 1936.)

Afterbirth	Twins	
	Monozygotic	Dizygotic
1 chorion, 1 amnion	3	—
1 chorion, 2 amnions	29	—
2 chorions, 2 amnions	24	76

(handwritten annotation: mono {1 chorion, 1 amnion; 1 chorion, 2 amnions}, di or mono {2 chorions, 2 amnions})

Since it had long been observed that there were two chorions in some twin births but only one in others, it was believed that the number of chorions was diagnostic for two-egg and one-egg twins. Danforth, the first to use the similarity diagnosis as a check of the diagnosis based on the afterbirth, found that the latter diagnosis has only limited validity and often leads to a wrong conclusion. As is shown in Table 77, all twins enclosed in a single chorion are indeed monozygotic; but twins which are enclosed in two chorions are not all dizygotic. Among 100 twin pairs with two chorions, nearly one-quarter were shown by the similarity diagnosis to be monozygotic. Finally, the table shows that the number of amnions is of little help in diagnosis. Nearly all twins, regardless of whether they are monozygotic or dizygotic, are enclosed in two separate amnions. Only the small minority of twins which have a single amnion can be assigned to monozygosity on the basis of this embryonic finding.

Attending physicians have frequently tried to judge whether a twin birth is monozygotic or dizygotic by means of a single or double placenta rather than by means of the chorionic condition. The reason for this is that it is usually easier to determine the number of placentas than to decide on the number of chorions. Even if two chorions are present, they are often so closely joined that they may be mistaken for a single membrane. (Actual fusion of two chorions, according to Corner, "is to say the least uncommon.") The similarity diagnosis indicates that diagnosis by means of the placenta is even more unreliable than by means of the birth membranes (Table 78). All monochoric twins have only one placenta; but, as the table makes clear,

TABLE 78. *Number of Placentas and Chorions, and Similarity Diagnosis in 236 Twin Births.* (Steiner, *Arch. Guynāk,* **159,** 1936.)

Afterbirth	Twins	
	Monozygotic	Dizygotic
1 placenta, 1 chorion	32	—
1 placenta, 2 chorions	8	80
2 placentas, 2 chorions	16	100

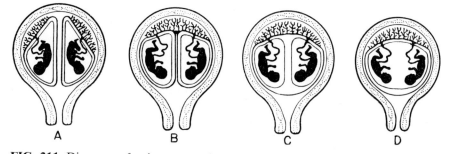

FIG. 211. Diagrams of twin pregnancies enclosed in the uterus.   A. Monozygotic or dizygotic twins with separate amnions, chorions, and placentas.   B. Monozygotic or dizygotic twins with separate amnions and chorions, and fused placenta.   C. Monozygotic twins with separate amnions, and single chorion and placenta.   D. Monozygotic twins with single amnion, chorion, and placenta. (A–C, E. L. Potter, *Fundamentals of Human Reproduction,* McGraw-Hill, 1948.)

a single placenta may also be found in dizygotic twin births, and two placentas may be found in the birth of either type of twins.

It is possible not only to determine the various kinds of afterbirths but also to derive from them information on the early stages of development of twins. An understanding of the afterbirth of dizygotic twins is quite easy. Since dizygotic twins begin as separate fertilized eggs, they of course form two separate chorions and amnions. When implantation in the uterus occurs, the two embryonic structures sink into the uterine wall, but not in any particularly well-defined region: sometimes they become implanted apart from each other, sometimes in close proximity. In the former case, two separate placentas form (Fig 211, A); in the latter, the two placentas which started separately grow together into a single one (Fig. 211, B).

Monozygotic twins owe their origin to the remarkable phenomenon of a single egg forming two separate embryos. Students of experimental embryology have succeeded in greatly clarifying the origin of one-egg twins by studies of the developing eggs of such animals as sea-urchins, salamanders, and rabbits; and descriptive embryologists have established the existence of regular monozygotic "super-twinning" in armadillos.

After the fertilized egg of a sea-urchin or a salamander has divided once, it is possible to separate the two daughter cells from each other. This can be accomplished mechanically, by means of a fine glass needle or a hair loop; or chemically, as by placing sea-urchin eggs into calcium-free sea water which changes the cell surfaces at the region of their contact so that the two cells do not remain together. The two separated cells may develop into whole animals instead of into half animals. In rabbits, Seidel has shown the possibility of monozygotic twinning in the following way. He succeeded in removing fertilized eggs from the oviduct and, when they had divided just once, killed one of the two cells by puncturing it with a needle. When the egg was

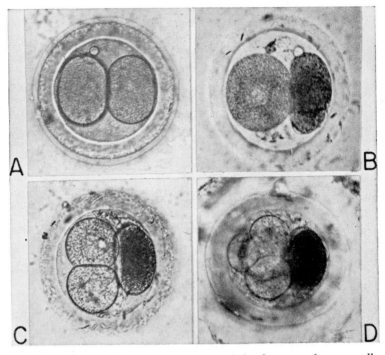

FIG. 212. Development of a rabbit from one of the first two cleavage cells of an egg.   A. Fertilized egg, at the two-cell stage, which has been removed from the uterus.   B. One of the cells (right) has been killed by being pricked with a fine glass needle.   C. The surviving cell has divided into two cells.   D. Further division has resulted in four living cells. (Seidel, *Naturw.,* **39,** 1952.)

then returned to an oviduct, the unharmed cell proceeded to develop, not into a half embryo, but into a whole rabbit—whose twin mate had been sacrificed (Figs. 212 and 213).

Twins can also be artificially initiated at a later stage in development of a single zygote. This is seen in Figure 214 where, in a multicelled stage of a single egg, salamander twins have been produced by constriction of the egg with a hair. In the nine-banded armadillo, a mammal, the single fertilized egg develops normally into a hollow cell ball which, instead of forming a single embryonic streak, forms four. Consequently, identical quadruplets are born regularly. These examples show that monozygotic twinning can be initiated early or late in development.

Apparently, spontaneous twinning of a single human egg can likewise set in at various stages. Few direct observations of these occurrences have been made, but it is not difficult to reconstruct what may happen. If the two cells of a zygote which has just divided should become separated, or if the cell ball divides during an early stage, each half will probably be able to develop into a blastocyst and differentiate an outer chorion and an inner embryonic shield and streak. Two separate chorions are thus present; and, as in dizygotic twins, implantation of the embryos in the uterus, close together or distant from each other, determines whether one or two placentas are formed. If monozygotic human twinning, similar to the process in armadillos, is initiated after the formation of a chorion, further development may occur in one of two ways. Instead of a single amniotic cavity, two such cavities may appear, each having a separate embryonic shield; or a single amnion and a single shield may appear but two embryonic streaks may form (Fig. 215). In the first case, a pair of twins will be enclosed in a single chorion but each separated in one of the two amnions (Fig. 211, C); in the latter case, the single chorion will contain a single amnion with

FIG. 213. An operated egg cell was transplanted into the uterus of the large gray female. The transplanted egg developed into the fully formed rabbit shown in the foreground. (Seidel, *Naturw.,* **39,** 1952.)

its twins (Fig. 211, D). The different types of afterbirths of twins are thus consequences of early embryonic happenings.

More than a pair of embryos may develop from a single egg. Subdivision of an early embryo into three, four, or more separate entities can lead to the formation of triplets, quadruplets, or still higher multiple births. Not all multiple births are monozygotic. Any combination of monozygotic and dizygotic multiplication may occur. For instance, human triplets may be children derived from a single egg; or from two eggs, one of which underwent twin formation; or from three separate eggs. The two well-known sets of quintuplets, in which all members survived birth, represent two extremes: the Dionnes came from one egg, and the Argentine children came from five.

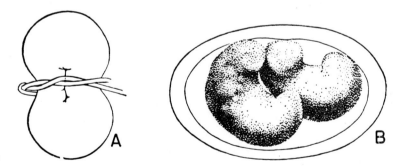

FIG. 214. Experimental production of monozygotic twins in a salamander. A. Constriction with a fine hair loop. B. The resulting twin embryos. (After Spemann, from Hartmann, *Allgemeine Biologie,* 2nd ed., Fischer, 1933.)

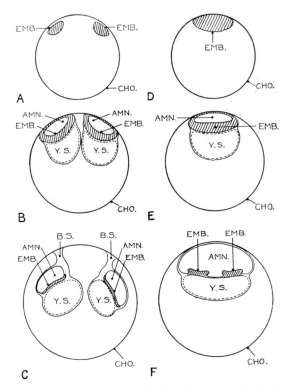

FIG. 215. Two types of single-ovum twinning in man.　A–C. By formation of two inner cell masses.　D–F. By formation of two embryos on a single germ disc. Emb. = inner cell mass (A, D), embryonic shield (B, E), embryo (C, F); Cho = chorion; Amn = amniotic cavity; Y.S. = yolk sac; B.S. = body stalk (Corner, *Bull. Johns Hopkins Hosp.*, **33**, 1923.)

Very rarely, the embryonic subdivision which normally leads to mono-zygotic twinning remains incomplete and results in an abnormal embryo in which some parts are duplicated. Experimentally, such incomplete twinning has been produced with salamander eggs by means of incomplete artificial constriction with a hair loop. The results of these partial separations are two-headed, single-bodied, or one-headed, two-bodied salamanders. In humans, also, there are known cases of incomplete twinning, ranging from duplication of some parts to nearly complete duplication of the whole body. The latter types of conjoined individuals are often referred to as Siamese twins, after a famous Siamese-born, Chinese pair of the nineteenth century.

Inheritance of Twinning Tendency. In many sibships, more than one pair of twins is found; and in numerous pedigrees, twin births appear in succes-sive generations or in the offspring of close relatives. The meaning of such recurring twinning is not obvious. To one who might regard accumulation of twin births within a kindred as evidence of an inherited tendency, it would be easy to point out that selection for oddity may give an erroneous impression. Since twin births occur in more than 1 per cent of all births, by chance alone, sibships or pedigrees which include two, or several, twin births should not be too rare. If only those pedigrees which show numerous twin births are singled out for attention, then no more weight should be attached to them than to selected pedigrees in which only males or only females have been born.

Again, the statistical approach is sounder. One of the first to study the question in this manner was Weinberg. He determined the frequency of twins among the sibs of twins or, as he called it, the *repeat frequency*. Mothers of monozygotic twins did not show a higher frequency of twin births among the rest of their children than did individuals of the general population, but mothers of dizygotic twins were found to have about twice as high a chance of having another twin birth.

A high repeat frequency, by itself, does not prove heritability of twinning; but it shows that a mother who has had twins is, in some way, different from mothers who have had only single births. The frequency could be either due to a special genetic constitution of the mothers of twins or to unknown environmental agents which make these women more susceptible to twin pregnancies than other women. To determine whether particular hereditary or environmental factors are responsible for recurring twinning, studies have been made of the frequencies of twin births in successive generations and among the relatives of parents of twins. At present, the results obtained by various investigators are not always in agreement. However, the evidence generally indicates that monozygotic twinning has no, or no greatly increased, tendency to reappear in pedigrees in which either monozygotic or dizygotic twin births occurred, but that there is a decidedly increased tendency to recurrence of dizygotic twinning. The most extensive investigation which bears out these statements was made on American twin births by Greulich (Table 79). It was shown that a significantly higher-than-average frequency of twins (approximately 3 per cent as compared to 1.2 per cent), occurred not only among the sibs of twins but also among the parents, the parents' sibs, and the offspring of the parents' sibs. The data showed an increased twinning

TABLE 79. *Frequencies of Twinning among the Children of the Sibs of Twins' Parents.* (Greulich.)

Parents of Twins	Propositi Monozygotic		Propositi Dizygotic		Per Cent Expected
	No. of Births	Twin Births (%)	No. of Births	Twin Births (%)	
Father's sibs	620	1.61	1,851	2.48	
Mother's sibs	661	1.05	2,020	2.17	1.15*
Both	1,281	1.32*	3,871	2.32*	

* The difference between 1.32 and 1.15 is not statistically significant, that between 2.32 and 1.15 is significa nt.

among the relatives of dizygotic twins but not among those of monozygotic twins (Table 79).

It is unlikely that the increased twin rates are due to hypothetical external conditions which recur in related families and favor twin births to a degree demanded by the data. The hypothesis is, therefore, held by many students, that hereditary factors are responsible for dizygotic twinning. This hypothesis finds further support in studies of families which are distinguished by significantly different frequencies of dizygotic twins.

In this respect, a Norwegian investigation by Bonnevie and Sverdrup is of importance. They found great variations in the frequencies of twins born within different family lines of several isolated agricultural communities in a valley near the Trondheim Fjord. Reliable church registers and other documents provided information on births over the past 250 years. In one pedigree, no twins occurred among 800 births; in another, 101 (or 2.85 per cent) appeared among 3,645; in still another, 107 (or 3.91 per cent) among 2,840. Averaging the twin frequency of all families in which twins occurred gave 3.25 per cent among 10,485 births. This contrasts, on the one hand, with a general twin frequency of about 1.24 per cent in these communities, which included the families with high frequencies. On the other hand, among 1,618 births of selected twin lines within the twin families, the frequency was as great as 8.23 per cent.

As a statistical phenomenon, the recurrence of dizygotic twins is different from occasional excessively frequent twin pregnancies in any one particular woman. Bonnevie and Sverdrup report a case, unrelated to their family data, of a woman who had four successive twin births, followed by four single births, then by four more twin births, and, finally, by a single birth. Most likely, the twins were all dizygotic. No other twin pregnancy occurred in the three preceding generations of this woman's ancestors. This, as well as similar cases, is apparently due to special physiological conditions causing, as a rule, double ovulations. Whether or not such an anomaly is hereditary is not known.

The genetic interpretation of typical dizygotic twinning is complicated by the astonishing results of several studies which indicate that the disposition toward dizygotic twins is also found in males. For instance, in Greulich's study of American families, it was found that the relatives of both the mothers and fathers of twins—not only female relatives (specifically, the sisters) but also male relatives (specifically, the brothers)—had increased tendencies toward twinning among their offspring (Table 79). It has been said that data showing a hereditary disposition toward dizygotic twinning in the father and his male relatives "prove too much." Indeed, it is hard to understand how the genetic constitution of the father can affect the production of two-egg twins. One possibility which has been suggested is that there is *not* an unusually high frequency of dizygotic fertilizations, but that double ovulations are much more common than is generally assumed and that the "high frequency" of dizygotic twin births is due to a high survival rate of dizygotic fertilizations. If this were so, and if the constitution of the embryo were largely responsible for its prenatal survival, then both parents could be assumed to contribute alleles favoring twin births. Evidence from ovary studies, however, does not seem to support the assumption of frequent double ovulation, although this evidence, itself, is probably not conclusive.

If the genetic basis of dizygotic twinning is a simple one, it must have very low penetrance. More likely, perhaps, it is polygenic, with incomplete penetrance as a result of nongenetic factors such as maternal age and parity. In this connection, it may be worth pointing out that even a doubling or tripling of the normal frequency of twinning, in twin kindreds, raises the probability for a twin birth by only a few per cent and still leaves an overwhelming probability that any specific birth will be a single one.

Twin Diagnosis by Means of the Similarity Method

Weinberg's differential method enables us to determine the number of monozygotic and dizygotic twins in a population of twins. In order to classify a particular twin pair in regard to their one- or two-egg origin, the similarity method of diagnosis, as elaborated particularly by Siemens and von Verschuer, is employed. The general reasoning underlying it is as follows: Two parents are, in general, heterozygous for numerous genes. If for a certain locus, one parent is heterozygous, AA', and the other parent homozygous, AA, the probability for two dizygotic twins being genetically alike is the sum of both of them being either AA or AA', which is $1/4 + 1/4 = 1/2$. If both parents are heterozygous, AA', the probability for genetic identity of dizygotic twins becomes $1/16$ (both AA) + $1/16$ (both $A'A'$) + $1/4$ (both AA') = $6/16$ = $3/8$. These probabilities for genotypic identity of the twins are also valid for phenotypic identity if the heterozygote has an intermediate or codominant phenotype and if penetrance of all genotypes is complete. If A' is dominant, then $A'A'$ and $A'A$ twins will appear alike; and the probability for phenotypically like dizygotic twins from two heterozygous parents becomes $1/16$ (both AA) + $9/16$ (both having at least one A' allele) = $10/16 = 5/8$.

All these probabilities, $1/2$, $3/8$, and $5/8$ are high, so that finding twins who appear alike in regard to the A locus will be fully compatible with their being regarded as dizygotics. If one considers that the two parents are both heterozygous not only for one locus, but for many, then phenotypic alikeness of two twins for many characters takes on a different aspect. For example, if ten loci with intermediate or codominant expression of heterozygotes are involved and one parent is homozygous for some loci and heterozygous for other loci, while the other parent is heterozygous for the first and homozygous for the second group of loci, then the probability of two dizygotic twins being phenotypically alike becomes $(1/2)^{10}$. If both parents are heterozygous for ten loci with intermediate or codominant expression in heterozygotes, the probability is $(3/8)^{10}$, or in dominance $(5/8)^{10}$. If, for another example, two loci with intermediate or codominant heterozygotes are homozygous in one parent and heterozygous in the other parent, and four loci with intermediate or codominant heterozygotes and four loci with dominance are heterozygous in both parents, the probability of dizygotic twins being phenotypically alike is $(1/2)^2 \cdot (3/8)^4 \cdot (5/8)^4$. These are very low probabilities, and they become still lower with every additional locus taken into account. To classify as dizygotics those twins who are alike in numerous genetic traits for which their parents were heterozygous would, therefore, involve an improbable assumption. On the other hand, if the twins were classified as monozygotics, then their genetic identity would correspond with their single-egg origin.

The main argument described in the preceding paragraphs can be applied even if the genotypes of the parents are unknown. If, for instance, two twins whose parents are not available for study are both recognizable as being homozygous for a pair of alleles, $A'A'$, then the parents must have represented one or another of the following combinations: $A'A' \times A'A'$, $A'A' \times AA'$, $AA' \times AA'$. The relative frequencies of the three types of marriages can be calculated if the allele frequencies p_A and $q_{A'}$ are known. Thus, if $p_A = 0.9$ and $q_{A'} = 0.1$, the probabilities of the types of marriages are 0.0001, 0.0036, and 0.0324, respectively, and the proportions of each marriage to the total of all three $(0.001 + 0.0036 + 0.0324 = 0.0361)$ are

$$
\begin{array}{lll}
A'A' \times A'A' & 0.001/0.0361 = 0.0028 \\
A'A' \times A\,A' & 0.0036/0.0361 = 0.0997 \\
A\,A' \times A\,A' & 0.0324/0.0361 = 0.8975 \\
& \text{Total} = 1.0000
\end{array}
$$

Now, the probability of an $A'A'$ child from these marriages is 1, 1/2, and 1/4, respectively. Multiplying these probabilities with the proportion of the relevant marriages, we find the joint probability of an $A'A'$ child from either one or another of the marriages as being

$$0.0028 + \tfrac{1}{2}\,0.0997 + \tfrac{1}{4}\,0.8975 = 0.2870.$$

The probability in these marriages of two $A'A'$ children from separate eggs is

$$0.0028 + \tfrac{1}{4}\,0.0997 + \tfrac{1}{16}\,0.8975 = 0.0838,$$

so that, among all those pairs of children which include at least one $A'A'$ child, the relative probability of two children from separate eggs both being $A'A'$ becomes

$$0.0838/0.2870 = 0.292.$$

This, of course, is also the probability of both partners of a dizygotic twin pair being $A'A'$. In contrast to this, the probability of both partners of a monozygotic pair being $A'A'$ if one is $A'A'$ is 1.

Let us assume that the twins are alike in four other loci and that calculations similar to those given for the A locus would yield probabilities of dizygotic twins being alike in these four loci of 0.2, 0.9, 0.3, and 0.5, respectively. Then the combined probability of dizygotic twins being alike for all five loci would become

$$0.292 \times 0.2 \times 0.9 \times 0.3 \times 0.5 = 0.007884,$$

while the combined probability of monozygotic twins being equally alike would remain 1. The odds are therefore highly in favor of monozygotic origin of the twins.

These calculations could still be improved by considering the probability of any randomly selected pair of twins being of dizygotic origin, which is approximately 0.652 (for United States whites). Furthermore, since the similarity diagnosis is applied to like-sexed twins only—unlike-sexed twins are always considered to be dizygotic—the probability should be entered of a dizygotic twin pair being like-sexed. This probability is about 0.5. Combining the probabilities 0.652 and 0.5 with that calculated from the five assumed loci, the over-all probability of the twins being dizygotic and alike in sex and five genotypes becomes

$$0.652 \times 0.5 \times 0.007884 = 0.00257.$$

In comparison, the probability of a randomly selected pair of twins being monozygotic is 0.348, with certainty of such a monozygotic pair being alike in sex and five genotypes. Thus the probability that the twins are of dizygotic origin, expressed in terms of their being either of dizygotic or monozygotic origin, is

$$\frac{0.00257}{0.00257 + 0.348} = 0.0073.$$

This is a low probability, and the probability of the pair being monozygotic is greater than 99 per cent ($1 - 0.0073 = 0.9927$).

In accord with these considerations, the similarity diagnosis ideally uses a large number of phenotypic characters based on: (1) numerous loci for which the population is highly heterogeneous, and (2) loci which have complete penetrance and uniform expressivity under all known environmental conditions. Identical, or very close, resemblance between twins in all relevant traits is taken as evidence of monozygosity, while difference in one single trait is taken as proof of dizygosity. The diagnosis is best made after the twins are at least several years old, because many traits are not well differentiated in infants.

The choice of traits used in the similarity diagnosis presents a special problem. Rather few known loci express themselves in a simple way and have various alleles sufficiently common to be useful for the classification of most twin cases. For example, since the albino allele, *a*, is so rare, the genotype, *aa*, can be used to classify twins in only a negligible number of cases. Loci which are suitable for twin diagnoses, both on account of their simple expression and the presence of different, common alleles, are those determining the various main blood groups. Making use of the known frequencies of blood-group alleles in the English population (which may be regarded as similar to many other white populations), Sheila Smith and Penrose have published probability tables for any one of the possible combinations of two sibs in respect to eight different blood-group systems. The use of these tables may be demonstrated by means of an actual example.

For blood groups, two female twins had the following phenotypic identity: B; MS; $Rh_1(CDe)$; P_1; Le^a negative; K negative; Lu^a negative; Fy^a negative. Since the relevant table gives the frequency of B children as 0.084509 and the frequency of two sibs being B as 0.040062, the probability if one of two sibs is B that the other is also B becomes $0.040062/0.084509 = 0.4741$. The probability of a dizygotic twin pair being both B is equally 0.4741. Other tables provide probabilities of dizygotic twins being alike for the other blood groups. These probabilities are listed in the upper part of Table 80, together with the initial probability of a twin pair being dizygotic and that of a dizygotic pair being like-sexed. Multiplication of all these independent probabilities yields a combined probability of 0.0183 for finding twins being dizygotic and alike in all listed traits. Since the probability for finding twins who are monozygotic and, of course, alike in all listed traits is 0.3480, the probability of the two twins being dizygotic is $0.0183/(0.0183 + 0.3480) = 0.0499$. This is close to 5 chances in 100 of the twins being dizygotic, or 95 chances in 100 of their being monozygotic. These probabilities, while highly

TABLE 80. *The Similarity Diagnosis for a Pair of Female Twins Who Are Identical in Eight Blood Groups and Similar in Two Morphological Traits.* (Changed from S. M. Smith and Penrose.)

Trait	Probability
A. Dizygotic origin	0.6520
Likeness in sex	0.5000
Likeness in B	0.4741
Likeness in MS	0.5161
Likeness in Rh	0.5400
Likeness in P positive	0.8489
Likeness in Le^a negative	0.8681
Likeness in K negative	0.9485
Likeness in Lu^a negative	0.9614
Likeness in Fy^a negative	0.6319
Combined probability of dizygotic origin and likeness in above characters	0.0183
B. Difference of ridge counts	0.2574
Difference of palmar angles	0.4977
Combined probability of A and B	0.0023
Total combined probability of dizygosity of the twins	0.0066

suggestive, are not sufficient to establish the origin of the twins with near-certainty. To reach this goal, additional traits must be considered.

Two such traits, for which tables are available, are properties of ridges on fingers and palms. For the finger pattern, counts were made of the total number of ridges in a certain area of the finger tips; and for the palm pattern, the size of an angle between two ridges was measured on both hands. The values for the two twins were as follows:

Twin	Total Ridge Count	Sum of Angles
I	143	86
II	134	88
Difference	9	2

For 52 pairs of monozygotic twins and for 101 pairs of like-sexed sibs, a total ridge-count difference of between 8 and 12 was observed in 26.92 per cent of the monozygotic twins but in only 6.93 per cent of the like-sexed sib pairs. If the sib pairs are assumed to be representative of dizygotic twins, the relative probability of such twins having a difference of between 8 and 12 is therefore $0.0693/0.2692 = 0.2574$. Similarly, from observations on 80 pairs of monozygotic twins and 310 pairs of sibs, the probability of dizygotic twins having a total difference of 1 or 2 degrees in palmar angles is 0.4977. When the two probability values for differences of ridge counts and palmar angles are multiplied with the combined probability of 0.0183 (given in Table 80), a value of 0.0023 is obtained for finding twins which are dizygotic and alike in sex and all ten traits tested. Compared with the unchanged probability of 0.3480, for finding monozygotic twins, the probability of the two twins being dizygotic is $0.0023/(0.0023 + 0.3480) = 0.0066$. There is thus a chance of more than 99 per cent that the assignment of the twins to the monozygotic class is correct.

The use of the two morphological traits, finger and palmar ridge patterns, requires further explanation. For these two traits, unlike the blood groups, the exact nature of the determining genotypes is unknown. Although family data show clear evidence of hereditary influence on ridge patterns, neither the type of gene nor the number of loci involved has been determined. Moreover, the expression of whatever genotypes are involved is somewhat variable, since even monozygotic twins are not identical in number of ridge counts or degrees of angles. What, then, justifies their use in the similarity diagnosis? It is the observation that these traits express themselves very similarly in monozygotic twins but not in sibs or in dizygotic twins. This makes it possible to attribute with greater probability a monozygotic origin to twins who are very similar in these traits.

Specific data are available on ridge counts and palmar angles from which to derive probability values for the similarity diagnosis. These data have been used in the preceding example of the two female twins. In most twin studies, the similarity diagnosis has been based on a multitude of traits for which only

TABLE 81. *Frequency, in Per Cent, of Complete or Nearly Complete Identity of Traits in Twins. (After v. Verschuer, Naturwiss., 22, 1934.)*

	Monozygotics		Dizygotics
Trait	Complete Identity	Near Identity	Complete or Near Identity
Hair color	75	23	23
Hair form	99.5	0.5	79
Eye color	86.5	13	28
Skin color	87	13	45
Shape of nose	80–85	15–20	30–35
Shape of lips	85	15	about 65
Shape of eyes	77	21	20

a few, or even no, specific data are available. Thus, Newman, Freeman, and Holzinger, who made one of the most fundamental studies on twins, used the following partial list of criteria for twin classification: striking similarity in (1) general appearance, and essential identity in (2) hair color, (3) hair texture, (4) hair form, (5) eye color, (6) pigment pattern of the iris, (7) skin color, apart from tanning, (8) amount of body down on face, neck, hands, (9) distribution of body down, (10) shape of nose, (11) shape of lips, (12) shape of chin, (13) shape of ears, (14) types of teeth, including irregularities, and (15) type and proportions of hands and fingers.

For seven of these fifteen traits, some rather crude data on complete and nearly complete identity of German twins, both monozygotic and dizygotic, are listed in Table 81. For none of the fifteen traits is the genetic basis known. Most probably, it is a complex one, due to the collaboration of genes of different, perhaps very many loci. The more loci involved in any one trait, the less likely two children, unless they are monozygotic twins, from one parental pair will inherit the same alleles. Identity, or close similarity, in so many different traits, each based on genes at several loci, will thus constitute a very high probability in favor of monozygotic origin.

The use of traits whose genetic base are not known still presumes that the traits are genetically determined, and that the penetrance and expressivity of the genotypes is identical or closely similar in monozygotic twins. What is the evidence for these assumptions? The answer to this question bares a weak spot—a bit of circular reasoning—in the theory on which the diagnosis for similarity in complex traits is based. This may be shown by the diagnostic use of one of the characters, hair color. In general, genetic determination is known from pedigree studies which show specific, but complex, relations between hair colors of parents and children, and from the well-known facts of hair-color differences between different populations. The question of this trait's uniform expressivity is answered partly by the observation that—except for direct chemical treatment of the hair!—hair color is highly independent of outside factors, and partly by the finding that the hair color of identical twins is always identical, or nearly so. But if someone inquired how the monozygosity of the twins was established, it might be found that the similarity in hair color provided *one* of the supporting arguments for monozygosity. This flaw inherent in the logical basis of the similarity diagnosis applied to genetically complex traits is, however, greatly reduced in significance by the simultaneous use of many traits, each of which has a high probability of possessing a uniformly expressed genetic determination. Since the use of many traits reduces the significance of any one trait that may be of doubtful validity, the diagnosis is probably more than 99 per cent reliable.

Some time ago, when only a few blood groups had been discovered and the similarity diagnosis was based exclusively on traits of the type just listed, an independently working serologist checked on the ABO and MN blood properties of many hundreds of twins who had been classified by means of the similarity diagnosis by a geneticist. Among the twins classified as monozygotic by the similarity diagnosis, not one pair was found to have blood groups which did not agree; and among twins diagnosed as dizygotic, the frequency of similar and dissimilar bloods was in complete agreement with the frequencies expected from pairs of ordinary sibs. A full study of the blood groups should now be regarded as a highly desirable prerequisite for any twin study, to be complemented by a similarity diagnosis, based more and more on traits such as finger ridges, for which tables of probabilities for monozygotic or dizygotic origin are available.

Tissue Grafts between Twins

In an earlier chapter, we described how pieces of skin taken from one person and grafted to another do not remain healthy but slough off after a few weeks. This histo-incompatibility is due to the different genotypes of the tis-

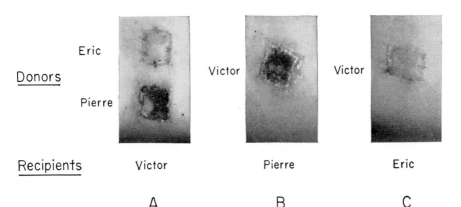

FIG. 216. Skin grafts and their fate. Pieces of skin from the identical twins Victor and Eric, grafted from one to the other were accepted by the recipients (A, upper graft; C). Grafts between Victor and Pierre, children of different parentage, did not take (A, lower graft; B). (Franceschetti, Baxmatter, and Klein, *Bull. Acad. Suisse Sc. Méd.*, **4,** 1948.)

sues of the donor and the recipient. Permanent and successful grafts can be obtained, however, if the donor and recipient are monozygotic twins. Since identical twins have all genes in common, grafts from one twin to the other are "accepted," as are grafts from one part to another part of the same body. If diagnosis of identity or nonidentity is important enough, tissue grafts can be used as the deciding criterion. This skin-grafting test was used in a famous case in Switzerland. Six years after the birth of a pair of clearly nonidentical twins, Victor and Pierre, it was observed that another boy, Eric, of another family bore a striking resemblance to Victor. The suspicion arose that a mistake had been made in the assignment of the babies, all of whom were born on the same day in the same hospital. It seemed likely that Eric was actually the identical twin of Victor, and that Pierre was a single-birth child belonging to the second family. This conclusion was proven correct when skin grafts from Victor to Eric, and vice versa, were permanently accepted (Fig. 216).

Because of the compatibility of tissues of identical twins, it has also been possible to transplant successfully, in one case, a thyroid gland and, in several cases, a kidney from a healthy individual to his identical twin whose corresponding organs had begun to fail.

Problems

188. Outline three possible sets of situations, each representing effects of your choice, of three genotypes, A, B, and C, in two environments, X and Y, which fit the following ranking arrangements, I, II, and III (1 = best, 6 = poorest):

Environment	I		II		III	
	X	Y	X	Y	X	Y
Genotype A	1	2	1	6	1	3
Genotype B	3	4	3	4	2	4
Genotype C	5	6	2	5	6	5

189. If among 10,000 twin births in Japan, there were 4,350 male pairs, 4,150 female pairs, and 1,500 pairs of mixed sex: (a) What were the numbers of monozygotic and dizygotic twins? (b) How does the ratio of monozygotics to dizygotics in this population compare with that in a white population?

190. Assume a sex ratio of 1:1. (a) What sex combinations of separate-egg quadruplets do you expect, and in what proportions? (b) Among a total of 48 American quadruplets, there were 13 with four boys, 6 with three boys and one girl, 12 with two of each sex, 7 with one boy and three girls, and 10 with four girls. How do these data compare with the expectation derived in Part a? (c) What, most likely, accounts for the deviation?

191. The afterbirth of three pairs of twins consists of: (a) 1 amnion and 1 placenta; (b) 2 amnions and 1 placenta; (c) 2 amnions and 2 placentas. Discuss the problem of monozygosity or dizygosity for each of the three pairs of twins.

192. What is the probability that: (a) 2 identical twins from MN parents will both belong to type MN? (b) 2 nonidentical twins from MN parents will both be-

long to type MN? (c) 2 girl twins are not identical if they are alike in being *B*, *MS*, and *Lu^a* negative? (To obtain the answer, use the information given in Table 80.)

193. A man (X) has a father who is an identical twin. If X is heterozygous for a very rare recessive gene, what is the probability that his offspring will be defective if he marries a first cousin who is the daughter of his father's twin brother? (Assume that all individuals mentioned have normal phenotypes and that the recessive gene enters the pedigree only once.)

194. A few marriages are known in which identical twin brothers have married unrelated identical twin sisters. Which relationship in typical families is genetically equivalent to marriages between cousins from these twin marriages?

References

Corner, G. W., 1955. The observed embryology of human single-ovum twins and other multiple births. *Am. J. Obstetr. Gynecol.* **70**: 933–951.

Dahlberg, G., 1926. *Twin Births and Twinning from a Hereditary Point of View.* 296 pp. Bekförlages A. B., Stockholm.

———, 1952. Die Tendenz zu Zwillingsgeburten. *Acta Genet. et Gemel.,* **1**: 80–88.

Galton, F., 1874. *English Men of Science: Their Nature and Nurture.* 270 pp. MacMillan & Co., London.

Gedda, L., 1951. *Studio dei Gemelli.* 1381 pp. Ediz. Orizzonte Medico, Rome.

Greulich, W. W., 1934. Heredity in human twinning. *Am. J. Phys. Anthrop.,* **19**: 391–431.

Haldane, J. B. S., 1946. The interaction of nature and nurture. *Ann. Eugen,* **13**: 197–205.

McArthur, Norma, 1953. Genetics of twinning. A critical summary of the literature. *Australian Nat. University, Social Sci. Monogr.,* **1**: 1–49.

Newman, H. H., 1940. *Multiple Human Births.* 214 pp. Doubleday, New York.

———, Freeman, F. N., and Holzinger, K. J., 1937. *Twins: A Study of Heredity and Environment.* 369 pp. University of Chicago Press, Chicago.

Rosin, S., 1947. Theoretisches zur Frage der ovozytären Zwillinge. *Arch. Julius Klaus-Stift.,* **22**: 73–84.

Siemens, H. W., 1924. *Die Zwillingspathologie.* 103 pp. Springer, Berlin.

Smith, Sheila M., and Penrose, L. S., 1955. Monozygotic and dizygotic twin diagnosis. *Ann. Human Genet.,* **19**: 273–289.

Verschuer, O. v., 1939. Twin research from the time of Francis Galton to the present day. *Proc. Roy. Soc., B,* **128**: 62–81.

Weinberg, W., 1901. Beiträge zur Physiologie und Pathologie der Mehrlingsgeburten beim Menschen. *Arch. f. Ges. Physiol.,* **88**: 346–430.

CHAPTER 26

HEREDITY AND
ENVIRONMENT

II. PHYSICAL TRAITS

We are now ready for the data which twin studies contribute to the nature-nurture problem. They are of three main types: First, a phenotypic study of the two members of identical twin pairs who are reared, as is usual, in the same family may afford information on the influence of environmental differences which exist even for such twins in the expression of identical genotypes. Second, a comparison of the degree of the environmentally conditioned differences between the two members of identical twin pairs with the degree of differences between the two members of nonidentical pairs who develop under both environmental and genetic differences may provide a clue to the relative strength of nature and nurture in the production of differences in nonidentical twins. Third, a comparison of differences between the two members of identical twin pairs reared apart in different homes with the differences between the two members of identical pairs reared together may illuminate the part played by the greater variation in environment provided by different homes as compared to that of a single home. We shall draw on material from all three types of studies in discussing various points.

A brief reference should be made to the method of "co-twin control." It is customary in the testing of methods for the improvement of health, educational, and social procedures to use both an experimental and a control group of individuals. Applying such methods to population samples, which are nearly always *selected* in one way or another, makes it difficult to ascertain whether the new methods offer advantages or disadvantages over old ones, or whether their effect is neutral. However, if groups of identical twins are used, and if one of each pair is exposed to the new procedure and the other "kept as a control," unequivocal information can be obtained.

The material for twin studies in the nature-nurture problem consists partly

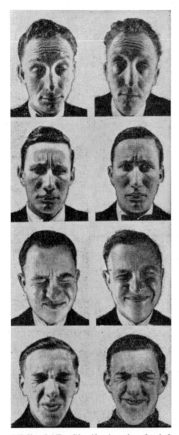

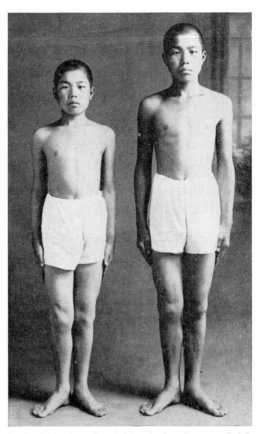

FIG. 217. Similarity in facial folds of four pairs of identical twins. (After Buehler, from Abel, *Hdbch. Erbbiol. d. Menschen*, **I**, Springer, 1940.)

FIG. 218. A pair of identical twins, aged 15. Until these twins were 5 years old, they were very similar in size. The left twin then became retarded in growth, probably from abnormal functioning of the pituitary gland. (Komai and Fukuoka, *J. Hered.*, **25**, 1934.)

of data on large samples of twins and partly of individual descriptions. From such descriptions, particularly of identical twins, facts emerge which sometimes highlight an astonishing similarity between twins (Fig. 217), and sometimes show up a striking difference (Figs. 218, 135). For a more general analysis, statistical data derived from a study of many twins are necessary. Such data provide some measure of the average difference or similarity between the two members of numerous identical pairs as compared to the average between numerous nonidentical pairs. Although the averages of the differences and correlation coefficients are among the measures used, much more refined statistical methods have also been applied to the problem.

Detailed comparisons involving identical and nonidentical twins must be based on *unselected* samples—a necessity that has only been realized in more recent years. Earlier, the data were usually based on the sum of cases culled from the scientific or medical literature. In these reports, there is often a proportion of identical over nonidentical twins in excess of that expected in a random sample. The reason for this excess may be that it seemed more worthwhile to publish cases of striking likeness of twin pairs than of unlikeness— and likeness is more frequent in identicals. But it is also true that an author may be more astonished by a striking difference between identical twins than by lack of a difference, so that he may describe cases of differences rather than of similarities. Many studies also leave some doubt about the identity or nonidentity of twin pairs. It is likely that in some cases an author classified certain pairs as identicals or nonidenticals because they agreed or differed in the trait in which he was interested, instead of diagnosing the type of twinning independently of the trait.

Concordance and Discordance

A particularly simple way of scoring differences between twins is to evaluate traits which are either present or absent. Thus, twins may be either *concordant,* that is, both possess or both are free of a particular trait; or *discordant,* in that only one of the pair possesses the trait. Concordance and discordance can also be determined for twin pairs who have been classified into the two groups "similar" and "dissimilar" for some specific trait.

The relative frequency of concordance in different groups of twins can be used for a comparison of the groups. When such comparisons involve abnormal traits, the term concordance is usually restricted to affected pairs of twins —a restriction which is really not legitimate. This may be shown by an example. Assume that a trait has 60 per cent (0.6) penetrance. Then, in identical twins of the appropriate genotype, it would be expected to be present in both partners in $0.6^2 = 36$ per cent, present in one partner only in $2 \cdot 0.6 \cdot 0.4 = 48$ per cent and absent in both partners in $0.4^2 = 16$ per cent. The true proportion of concordant to discordant pairs is therefore $(36 + 16 =)$ 52 per cent to 48 per cent, or about 1.1:1. In contrast to this, the usual method would give the proportion as 36 per cent to 48 per cent, or 0.75:1.

It would be simple to correct reported concordance figures which are based on the concordance of affected twins only by calculating and taking account of the expected concordance frequencies of nonaffected pairs. This, however, would involve assumptions concerning the independence in twin partners of the penetrance of the traits. Such assumptions are often not easily susceptible to test. In the following pages, whenever concordance frequencies are derived from affected twins only, this fact will be stated explicitly. In order to exclude a possible source of error in comparisons between identical and nonidentical twins, only like-sexed twins are generally used in such studies. Since identical twins are, of course, always like-sexed, this means that unlike-sexed nonidentical twins are disregarded.

Anatomical Traits. Of the exceedingly numerous traits studied, only a few can be discussed. Results obtained by Newman (a biologist), Freeman (a

TABLE 82. *Average Differences between the Two Members of Identical Twins, Nonidentical Twins, and Pairs of Sibs, Reared Together; and Identical Twins, Reared Apart.* (Newman, Freeman, and Holzinger.)

Difference in	Identical	Nonidentical	Sibs	Identical (reared apart)
Height (cm)	1.7	4.4	4.5	1.8
Weight (lb.)	4.1	10.0	10.4	9.9
Head length (mm)	2.9	6.2	—	2.20
Head width (mm)	2.8	4.2	—	2.85

psychologist), and Holzinger (a statistician) on height, weight, head length, and head width are listed in Table 82. (Data on mental traits obtained in the same study will be presented in Chapter 27.) These three investigators studied fifty pairs of identical twins reared together, fifty pairs of nonidentical twins reared together, nineteen pairs of identical twins who had been separated very early in life and reared in different homes, and for purposes of some comparisons, a group of fifty-two regular sibs.

Identical twins reared together (second column of the table) showed differences in all four physical traits. This is an effect of nongenetic agents—that is, the environment—which prenatally or postnatally gives rise to phenotypic differences in spite of identical genotypes. In Figure 219, these differences, for height, are shown graphically. There, the curve for the "intrapair" differences—that is, between twins—shows that 35 of the identical pairs were less than 2 cm different in height; 12 were between 2 and 3.9 cm different;

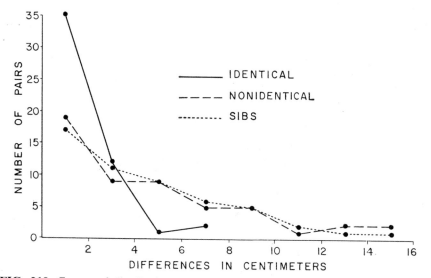

FIG. 219. Curves of distribution of differences in standing height of 50 identical twins, 52 nonidentical twins, and 52 pairs of sibs. (After Newman, Freeman, and Holzinger.)

TABLE 83. *Correlation Coefficients for Four Physical Traits in Pairs of Twins and Sibs.* (Compare with Table 82.) (Newman, Freeman, and Holzinger; and Woodworth.)

Trait	Identical	Nonidentical	Sibs	Identical (reared apart)
Height	0.932	0.645	0.600	0.969
Weight	0.917	0.631	0.584	0.886
Head length	0.910	0.691	—	0.917
Head width	0.908	0.654	—	0.880

1 was between 4 and 5.9 cm different; and 2 were between 6 and 7.9 cm different. By themselves, neither the fact that there are environmentally caused differences in physical traits of identical twins reared together nor the specific distributions of these differences are very informative. They become significant, however, when comparisons are made between these findings for identical twins reared together and the corresponding findings for the other groups of individuals. The third and fourth columns of Table 82 show that the average intrapair differences are larger in nonidentical than in identical twins for each of the four traits and also larger in sibs for the two traits for which data are available.

Moreover, as shown for height in Figure 219, the ranges of these differences and their distributions were different from those for the identical pairs reared together, but very similar for nonidentical and sib pairs. Among other details, the graphs show that only 17 and 19 nonidentical and 19 sib pairs differed less than 1.9 cm in height, as compared to 35 identical pairs reared together; and that 10 nonidentical and 9 sib pairs differed by more than 8 cm, but not a single identical pair. The much greater dissimilarity of nonidentical twins, as compared to identicals, must be ascribed to their different genotypes, in addition to environmental differences which act on them as they do on the identicals.

It is interesting to note that the nonidentical twins and the sibs are practically alike in the degree and distribution of the differences in height and weight, which were the only traits measured in pairs of sibs. Since nonidentical twins correspond genetically to ordinary sibs, their similarity in these studies not only reflects their genetic correspondence but, further, suggests that the average environmental differences which influence height and weight are not larger for two sibs born at different times than for those born together.

The fifth column of Table 82 contains the important average intrapair differences for identical twins reared apart. More will be said later about the differences in home environment in which the two members of each of these pairs lived. For most pairs, the home environments were not strikingly different. It is seen that the weight difference, 9.9 pounds, is not like that for the identical twins reared together, but is very similar to that for nonidentical and sib pairs. One may conclude that weight is a highly modifiable trait, since the different environments in which the separated twins grew up made them as unlike in weight as two genetically unlike sibs reared in the same home. Environmental differences had little effect on the other three traits, height, head length, and head width: the intrapair differences of the separated identicals are as small as those of the nonseparated.

These relations are expressed once more in Table 83, but as correlation coefficients instead of mean differences. All coefficients in the table are positive, signifying that, in general, both partners of a pair deviated from the average in the same direction. The correlations are higher between identical twins reared together than between nonidentical twins or between sib pairs. For separated identical twins, the coefficients are similar—even in the case of weight—to those for nonseparated identical twins.

Physiological Traits.   People differ not only in obvious external ways but in innumerable details of both external and internal traits. Interesting pilot studies on metabolic differences have been instigated by the chemist R. J. Williams. He tested various individuals for 31 physiological traits, including taste sensitivity to five different substances, the amounts of twelve substances in the saliva, and the presence of fourteen substances or properties of the urine. The findings were graphically represented by the length of 31 lines which radiate from a center. A hypothetical "average" individual's metabolic pattern would be one in which all 31 rays were drawn of equal length (Fig. 220, A). Actual individuals differ greatly from the average as well as from one another (B and C). Identical twins were found to be strikingly similar in their metabolic patterns (D and E). Yet, in addition to this similarity, which probably has a genetic basis, nongenetic influences can be discerned. Thus, lysine, an amino acid, was present in relatively large amounts in the saliva of one twin but in only small amounts in the other (D and E, lines 12); and the concentration of citrulline, another amino acid, was low in the urine of the first and high in that of the second twin (lines 30).

A more detailed comparison of a physiological process in twins concerned changes in blood sugar after intake of 50 grams of glucose. By analyzing samples of blood taken at intervals over a period of four hours, a curve was plotted for each individual showing the initial blood-sugar concentration, its rise, and its subsequent decline. For pairs of identical twins, most of the pairs of curves were very similar; for pairs of nonidenticals, they differed consid-

TABLE 84.   *Relations of Blood-sugar Curves in 30 Pairs of Identical and 32 Pairs of Nonidentical Twins. (After Werner, Deutsch. Arch. f. klin. Medizin, 1936.)*

Twins	Very Similar	Intermediate	Very Dissimilar
Identical	10	14	6
Nonidentical	3	9	20

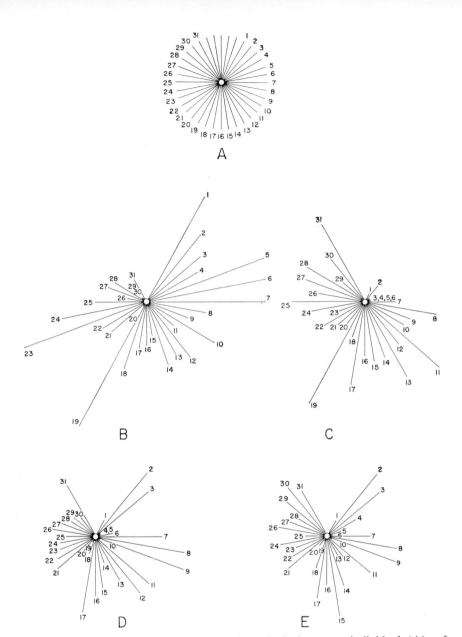

FIG. 220. The "metabolic patterns" of a hypothetical average individual (A), of two actual persons (B, C), and of a pair of identical twins (D, E). The 31 traits are taste sensitivity for: creatinine (1), sucrose (2), KCl (3), NaCl (4), HCl (5); salivary constituents: uric acid (6), glucose (7), leucine (8), valine (9), citrulline (10), alanine (11), lysine (12), taurine (13), glycine (14), serine (15), glutamic acid (16), aspartic acid (17); urinary constituents: citrate (18), an undefined "base Rf. 28," (19), an undefined "acid Rf. 32," (20), gonadotropin, a hormone (21), pH (22), pigment/creatinine ratio (23), chloride/creatinine (24), hippuric acid/creatinine (25), creatinine (26), taurine (27), glycine (28), serine (29), citrulline (30), alanine (31). (Williams.)

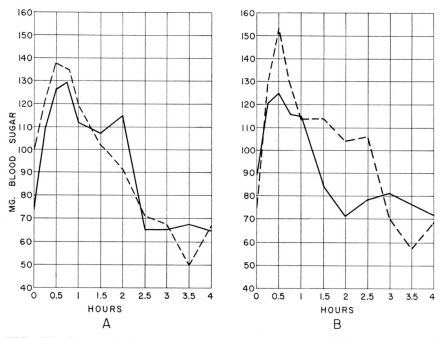

FIG. 221. Curves of blood-sugar concentration in a pair of identical (A) and a pair of nonidentical (B) twins. (After Werner, *Ztschr. f. Vererbgsl.*, **67**, 1934.)

erably (Fig. 221, A and B). Nevertheless, as seen in Table 84, for unknown nongenetic causes, even identical twins often differed in their reactions.

Two other physiological traits studied in twins are blood pressure and pulse rate. Concordance in such continuously varying traits is defined as similarity within a specified range. Thus, in the study of blood pressure, concordance meant agreement of the twins within a pressure difference of less than 5 mm mercury. It occurred in 63 per cent of identical twins (Fig. 222, upper half). This shows environmental plasticity of the trait, since, in spite of genetic identity, the rest (37 per cent) were discordant. Again, taken by themselves, these two percentages do not permit further deductions. The higher concord-

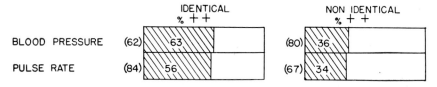

FIG. 222. Concordance and discordance in twins for blood pressure and pulse rate. The total width of each bar is equal to 100%. The diagonally lined section represents the per cent of concordance, the white section the per cent of discordance. Numbers in parentheses signify the total number of twin pairs investigated. (After Malkova, *Proc. Maxim Gorki Med.-Biol. Res. Institute*, **3**, 1934.)

TABLE 85. *Mean Difference, in Months, in Time of First Menstruation.*
(Petri, *Zeitschr. Morph. u. Anthropol.,* **33,** 1934.)

No. of Pairs	Relationship	Difference
51	Identical twins	2.8
47	Nonidentical twins	12.0
145	Sibs	12.9
120	Mother-daughter	18.4
120	Unrelated women	18.6

ance than discordance figure could be due either to a relatively strong effect of genetic identity or to the similar environment in which the twins grew up. Here, the percentages for the nonidentical twins become significant. They are nearly reversed (as compared to the identical twins): 36 per cent concordant pairs and 64 per cent discordant pairs. Clearly, the genetic dissimilarity of the nonidentical twins has contributed its share to the discordance, thus making it larger than for the identical twins.

In addition to the concordance determination for blood pressure, data are available on the mean intrapair difference of this trait as expressed in mm of mercury: 5.1 for 112 identical and 8.4 for 82 nonidentical twins. These figures are in agreement with the information on concordance and with the interpretation that heredity has a share in the determination of differences in blood pressure. Similar conclusions hold for the pulse rate (Fig. 222, lower half).

Another physiological trait whose dependence on differences in both nature and nurture has been clarified by the twin method is the beginning of female puberty as defined by the first menstruation. Here, the data are particularly satisfactory, since they permit various comparisons (Table 85). Not only is it obvious that identical twin sisters have a very much smaller mean intrapair difference than nonidentical twins, but differences between sibs, between mothers and daughters, and between unrelated women compared in pairs indicate greater environmental differences acting in different families and in different generations than those acting within the same family.

Rate of aging and longevity are collective terms which, undoubtedly, cover a great variety of physiological properties whose details and interrelations are but poorly understood. In spite of the complexity of these two traits, the twin method gives evidence of important hereditary elements in their determination (Table 86).

TABLE 86. *Intrapair Differences in Life Span of Deceased Twin Pairs Who Were More Than Sixty Years Old at Time of Death.* (Kallmann and Sander, *J. Hered.,* **39,** 1948.)

Twins	No. of Pairs of Twins	Difference in Time of Death (months)
Identical	18	36.9
Nonidentical	18	78.3

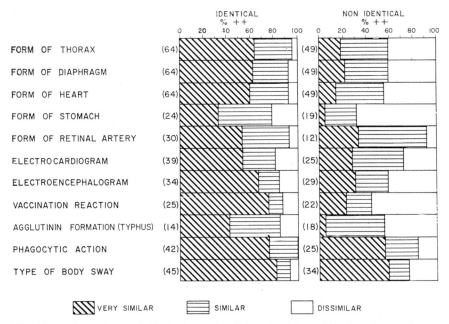

FIG. 223. Similarity and dissimilarity of identical and nonidentical twin pairs for a variety of traits. The numbers at left are the numbers of pairs considered. (After Osato and Awano, *Acta Genet. Med. Gemel.*, **6,** 1957.)

Other Traits. Twin comparisons have been carried out on so many traits that even a simple listing would be a lengthy task. In order to suggest the variety of properties investigated, Figures 223 and 224 have been abstracted from a very broad survey of Japanese twins (children and students). Figure 223 shows the similarities and differences in form of internal organs and in

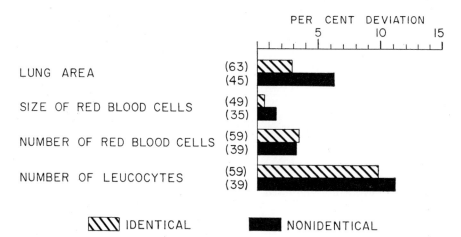

FIG. 224. Mean percentage deviation of four traits in identical and in nonidentical twin pairs. The numbers at left are the numbers of pairs considered. (After Osato and Awano, *Acta Genet. Med. Gemel.*, **6,** 1957.)

physiological reactions. Figure 224 shows the intrapair deviations, in percentage of the means, of some traits relating to lung area and blood cells. Identical twins always score closer to each other than nonidentical twins, but the difference between the two groups is great for some and smaller for other traits.

To obtain information on nongenetic factors affecting the variability of traits, some of the Japanese twins have been separated into two groups: (1) those partners who had similar birth weight, were reared together, and had a similar history of illnesses; and (2) those differing in these respects. The differences between identical twin pairs of group (1) were smaller than between those of group (2), and the same held for nonidenticals. This demonstrates the influence of environmental agents. Nevertheless, the mean differences between identicals with different history were smaller than those between nonidenticals with similar history—an indication of the strength of hereditary influences.

Pathological Conditions.   Various pathological conditions have been studied in twins. In collecting the case material, the appropriate procedures consisted of taking a sample of affected individuals and then finding out who of these had twin partners. These twin partners were then investigated in order to determine (a) whether they were identical or nonidentical twins of the propositi and (b) whether or not they were, or had been, affected by the same condition as the propositi.

The results of some of these studies, assembled in Figure 225, are striking. For the congenital deformity clubfoot, 32 per cent of identical twins are con-

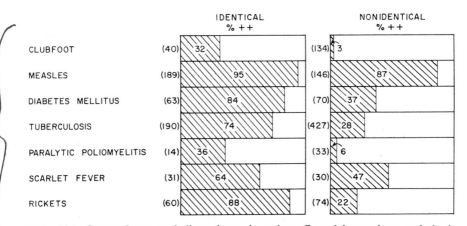

FIG. 225. Concordance and discordance in twins affected by various pathologic conditions. Percentages of concordance based on affected pairs only. (After v. Verschuer, *Ergebn. Allg. Pathol.,* **26,** 1932; *Beiträg. z. Klinik d. Tuberkul.,* **97,** 1941; and *Acta Genet. Stat. Med.,* **6,** 1956 [tuberculosis]; Idelberger, *Ztschr. Orthop.,* **69,** 1939 [clubfoot]; and Herdon and Jennings, *Am. J. Human Genet.,* **3,** 1951 [poliomyelitis]).

cordant. This rather low incidence might suggest that special prenatal circumstances are the only ones which decide whether a child will be born with, or without, the deformity. Although the importance of such prenatal variations in the outer or inner environment of the embryo is, of course, obvious from the frequent discordance of identical twins, there is still the question whether every genotype will respond to such conditions or whether a special genotype or genotypes are necessary for the formation of clubfoot. The validity of this latter interpretation is borne out by the incidence of clubfoot in the nonidentical twins: concordance here is only 3 per cent. Since concordance is so much lower in nonidentical than in identical twins, genetic nonidentity is probably the decisive factor which determines that one twin will be normal in most cases when the other is affected. Studies on clubfoot also serve to emphasize that the frequency of this trait, as well as that of most other abnormal traits, is no higher in nonidentical twins than in single-birth sibs: among the 1,525 sibs of 624 propositi with clubfoot, 46 (equal to 3 per cent) were likewise affected.

Concordance in identical twins is higher for the other conditions (listed in Figure 225) than for clubfoot, but, as before, only limited conclusions on the nature-nurture problem can be drawn as long as data of one kind alone are considered. Thus, concordance of 95 per cent in susceptibility of identical twins to measles does not necessarily imply a special hereditary inclination, with very high penetrance, for being affected by this disease. It might mean only that any two children of equal age in the same home will probably get measles if one of them comes down with the disease. That this is close to the truth is suggested by the nonidentical pairs, who have, in spite of their genetic diversity, a concordance nearly as high as that of the identical twins. Yet, there may be some special hereditary element involved, since the difference in concordance between identical and nonidentical twins, although not statistically significant, is at least in the doubtful range. The same is true for the other diseases listed, with the exception of scarlet fever, for which the number of twins studied is too small to make the difference statistically significant.

The diseases studied represent several different types of pathological conditions: diabetes mellitus is an abnormality of metabolism; tuberculosis, poliomyelitis, and scarlet fever are caused by microorganisms; and rickets is caused by a deficiency of vitamin D. What, may be asked, has the heredity-environment problem to do with the last four diseases, which so clearly seem externally conditioned? Robert Koch's discovery of the tubercle bacillus in the last century seemed, to many, to dispose forever of the idea that tuberculosis is hereditary; and the early reports of rickets "running in families," which had been interpreted as proof of the hereditary nature of the disease, seemed later to be explainable on the basis of continuous existence of poor nutritional conditions in successive generations. There is, however, no contradiction between the fact that an external agent whose presence (as in tuberculosis) or absence (as in vitamin deficiency) leads to a disease and the fact that different genotypes may make different individuals more or less susceptible to infection by microorganisms or to nutritional deficiencies.

Although many of the concordance figures clearly indicate hereditary differences in susceptibilities to diseases or to vitamin D deficiency, they give only an incomplete picture. This may be shown for tuberculosis and tumors.

Tuberculosis. A summary treatment as given in Figure 225 of the 617 tuberculous twin pairs studied in Germany, Switzerland, the United States, and Argentina obscures the fact that concordance included much greater similarity in the expression of the disease for identical twins than for nonidentical twins. In the pioneer studies of Diehl and von Verschuer, concordance for identical twins frequently signified not only that both partners were affected, but also that if one twin had a particular lobe of a lung affected, the other twin was affected in the same part and not anywhere else, or if one was infected in his kidneys the other would be attacked likewise. Concordance in nonidentical twins does not show such similarity.

Conversely, discordance in identical twins was rarely as striking as in nonidentical twins. Discordance for tuberculosis is indicative: in only 1 case out of 16 did the affected identical twin of a normal twin partner die of the disease; but in approximately one-third of the 68 cases the affected nonidentical twin died, "in spite of" normality of the other twin. Two particularly striking examples of similarity in identical twins and dissimilarity in nonidentical twins were: (1) concordance in a pair of identical girl twins, separated for years, one of whom became tuberculous on a farm at the same time that the other became affected in the city; and (2) discordance in a pair of nonidentical boys who lived under slum conditions and slept in one bed, and yet one remained healthy while the other succumbed to tuberculosis. In good agreement with these findings, Kallmann and Reisner's American data show that the degree of resistance to tuberculosis is much more similar in identical than in nonidentical pairs: defining degrees of similarity by somewhat arbitrary quantitative values, they found that identical twins are nearly six times more similar in resistance and susceptibility than are nonidenticals.

Both the German and the American tuberculous twins have been reinvestigated after the lapse of twenty and ten years, respectively. Such "longitudinal" studies are valuable for, among other things, the information they provide on the later development of the disease in the twins. Thus, among the 15 identical and 18 nonidentical German pairs who were concordant for tuberculosis in 1935, both partners of 4 identical pairs, but not a single pair of nonidentical pairs, had died from the disease by 1955. The 1955 survey also furnished important information on the possibility of complete recovery from tuberculosis. In addition to the 4 pairs of identicals who died, there were 6 initially concordant pairs in which by 1955 one twin had died but the other was in good health. In good agreement with these findings on recovery are the results of the restudy of the American twins. There is, however, no agreement on the persistence of the initially greater similarity of identical than of nonidentical twin partners. The initial differences in degree of similarity between

TABLE 87. *Percentage Frequency of Tuberculosis in the Families of 308 Tuberculous Twins.* (Kallmann and Reisner, *Am. Rev. Tuberculosis,* **47,** 1943.)

Relationship to Affected Twin	No. in Group	Percentage Affected
Unrelated general population		1.4
Spouses	226	7.1
Parents	688	16.9
Half-sibs	42	11.9
Sibs	720	25.5
Nonidentical twin	230	25.6
Identical twin	78	87.3

identical and nonidentical pairs were striking in both the German and American twins. The follow-up investigations revealed that these initial differences had persisted in the German group, but had disappeared in the American group. The causes of this disagreement have not yet been resolved.

Studies on the frequencies of a trait in twin partners as well as in other members of the families of affected twins have been particularly informative. Table 87 gives such twin-family data on the tuberculous twins of the American sample. Many instructive comparisons are possible, such as comparison of the frequencies of affected identical and nonidentical co-twins, of nonidentical co-twins and sibs, of sibs and half-sibs, of sibs and their parents and spouses, and of all these with frequencies in the general population.

The conclusion of these studies that susceptibility to tuberculosis is partly under genetic control is supported by the results of experiments in both man and animals. It has been found that the local reaction of the skin to tuberculin injection—that is, the size of the red area—varies from person to person. The difference in diameters of the spots is always small for identical pairs. The differences vary greatly for nonidentical twins and, on the average, are several times larger than for identical twins. There are also strains of rabbits which show strikingly different response to controlled infections with human-type tubercle bacilli. In some strains, death regularly ensues; in others, the disease soon becomes localized, and the restricted area of infection disappears after a time.

The conclusion that tuberculosis is partly under genetic control is much better supported by twin studies than by earlier statistical comparisons of the frequencies of infection in different groups of parents and offspring (Table 88). The frequency of tuberculosis was determined among the offspring of healthy and affected parents. It is seen that the incidence of tuberculosis is from 60 to 70 per cent higher if one parent is affected than if both parents are healthy, and more than 300 per cent higher if both are affected. Although this suggests a hereditary susceptibility, it would be difficult to disprove the hypothesis that the environment of the affected parent or parents was the decisive factor in the increased incidence of the disease among their children.

TABLE 88. *Frequency of Tuberculosis in 564 Pairs of Parents and Their 2,480 Children.* (Pearl, *Zeitschr. Rassenk.,* **3,** 1936.)

Parents		Offspring	
Affected	Number	"Unit of Incidence" *	Number
Neither	327	1	1,501
Mother	122	1.6	492
Father	88	1.7	372
Both	27	4.3	115

* 1 unit of incidence = 8.3 per cent.

Tumors. There are some genes which are clearly the basis for specific types of cancer. A simply inherited dominant gene for finger-like growths in the large intestine (polyposis) typically leads to cancer which can be prevented only by timely surgery. The dominant gene for retinoblastoma causes tumors of the retina, and the gene for the complex Zollinger-Wermer syndrome is responsible for tumors of various endocrine glands, namely, the pituitary, the parathyroids, the adrenals, and the islets of Langerhans in the pancreas. For most other types of malignant growths, no simple genetic basis is apparent, but large-scale family studies are highly indicative of a heritable component in the origin of tumors. These studies have shown two important facts about the genetics of tumors. First, the frequency of tumors of the type found in the propositi is higher among their close relatives than in the general population. Second, the frequency of tumors other than the type found in the propositi is *not* higher in their relatives than in the general population. The first fact suggests the presence of genetic factors in the origin of tumors; the second, that such genotypes are specific for different types of tumors. No genotypes seem to lead to "cancer in general."

TABLE 89. *Comparison of Observed and Expected Deaths from Breast Cancer and Other Types of Cancer in Relatives of Breast-cancer Propositi.* (After Woolf.)

Relation	Total No.	No. of Breast Cancer Deaths		No. of Deaths from Other Types of Cancer	
		Obs.	Exp.*	Obs.	Exp.*
Mother	200	4	2.1	13	16.8
Father	200	—	—	7	13.7
Sister	561	8	3.2	19	16.0
Brother	600	—	—	20	16.5
Total	1,561	12	5.3	59	63.0
Per cent	100	0.8	0.3	3.8	4.1

* The number of expected deaths is based on the frequencies in a control population.

TABLE 90. *Comparison of Observed and Expected Deaths from Stomach Cancer and Other Types of Cancer in Relatives of Stomach-cancer Propositi.* (After Woolf.)

Relation	Total No.	No. of Stomach Cancer Deaths		No. of Deaths from Other Types of Cancer	
		Obs.	Exp.*	Obs.	Exp.*
Mother	200	7	4.5	5	10.8
Father	199	6	3.8	6	7.0
Sister	654	8	7.6	32	33.8
Brother	586	23	9.3	24	21.2
Total	1,639	44	25.3	67	72.8
Per cent	100	2.7	1.5	4.1	4.4

* The number of expected deaths is based on the frequencies in a control population.

Even though significant statistically, the incidence of mammary cancer in the mothers and sisters of patients with the disease, or the incidence of stomach cancer in the relatives of affected patients, is not greatly increased. In the study summarized in Table 89, instead of the 0.3 per cent of deaths due to mammary cancer in the control group, not more than 0.8 per cent of deaths had occurred among the relatives of propositi. For cancer of the stomach (Table 90), the difference is relatively smaller still, since the control-group death rate of 1.5 per cent had increased less than twice, namely, to 2.7 per cent. These figures suggest that the genetic bases of the increased incidences of specific cancers are perhaps polygenic and that, in addition, the origin of cancers also depends on nongenetic factors which control the penetrance of the genotypes involved.

The overwhelmingly great importance of nongenetic factors in cancer is demonstrated by twin material. The data in Table 91 are based on twins encountered in unselected series only. For all three types of cancers listed, most identical twin pairs are discordant, which is proof of low penetrance of the genotypes concerned. Nevertheless, concordance is higher in the identical partners than in nonidentical twins. Although this difference in concordance approaches statistical significance only for stomach cancer, it may be pre-

TABLE 91. *Concordance (++) and Discordance (+−) for Specific Types of Cancer in Twins.* (Concordance defined in terms of both twins affected.) (v. Verschuer.)

Type of Cancer	Identical		Nonidentical	
	++	+−	++	+−
Stomach	3	8	1	23
Mammary gland	1	17	1	36
Uterus	1	15	—	21

dicted that, with studies on larger numbers of cases, concordance for other types of cancer will also prove significantly higher in identical than in nonidentical twins. For traits whose penetrance is as low as that suggested by the very low concordance of cancer in identical twins, only very large series of twins can be expected to give a clear picture. Earlier studies on cancer in twins either summarized the results of selected cases or did not deal separately with specific types of cancer. Since the frequency of malignant growths of all kinds together is high, concordance of "cancer in general" in both identical and nonidentical twins was reported to be much higher than that now established for specific types. These older data are now seen to have little meaning.

The nature of the nongenetic factors which interact with the genetic components in the causation of cancer is manifold and, to a large extent, unknown. One nongenetic factor in the origin of mammary tumors has been established: childbearing. The incidence of mammary cancers is much lower in mothers than in childless women. Madge Macklin has also furnished data which show a genetic agent in mammary cancer: the frequency of the disease is higher in childbearing relatives of affected propositi than in those of a control population. But the same study shows that the incidence of the disease is higher in childless women among the controls than in the childbearing relatives of the cancer families.

Limitations of the Twin Method

It is noteworthy that the twin method affords a recognition of a hereditary basis for phenotypic differences, but not an analysis of the genotypes responsible. The method provides no answer to the problem of whether dominant or recessive genes, autosomal or sex-linked alleles, single-gene or polygenic combinations, or one or many different genotypes are responsible for the appearance of a trait. Nor does the recognition of "nurture" as having a share in the variability of man involve, by itself, a recognition of what kinds of environmental factors are involved. These are natural limitations of the method which deals with "heredity" and "environment" primarily as collective terms.

Only occasionally can twin data be used to test some specific genetic hypothesis. If, for instance, a given trait is believed to be the result of a simple dominant gene A, then, according to Rife, the following relation should hold for the frequency of discordance among pairs of nonidentical twins. Such pairs can come from two kinds of matings: (1) $Aa \times aa$, and (2) $Aa \times Aa$. These should occur with the frequencies $4pq^3$ and $4p^2q^2$, respectively, where p and q are the allele frequencies. The frequency of discordant pairs Aa, aa from mating (1) will be $2 \cdot (1/2)^2 \cdot 4pq^3 = 2pq^3$; and of discordant pairs AA, aa and Aa, aa from mating (2), $2 \cdot (1/4)^2 \cdot 4p^2q^2 + 2 \cdot 1/2 \cdot 1/4 \cdot 4p^2q^2 = 3/2\ p^2q^2$. The sum of discordant pairs from both types of matings is $2pq^3 + 3/2\ p^2q^2$. Obviously, the value of this sum varies with the allele frequencies. It can be shown that it never rises above 28 per cent. Therefore, the finding of discordance frequencies significantly greater than 28 per cent is, by itself, evidence against simple dominant determination of a trait.

In the preceding pages, a smaller mean intrapair difference, a greater intrapair correlation, or a greater concordance in identical, as compared to nonidentical, twins has been considered the result of genetic identity of the monozygotic twins. Various students of human genetics have gone beyond this statement and have attempted to assign specific quantitative values to the shares which heredity and environment hold in the determination of the observed differences. A particularly simple way of treating the problem has been to assume that the environments under which two identical twins grow up are, on the average, neither more nor less different than the environments of two nonidentical twins. The average intrapair difference, or the discordance, of a trait for identical twins is, therefore, regarded as the measure of environmental differences in identical and nonidentical twins. Whenever nonidentical twins have greater intrapair differences or discordance than the identical twins, this excess is taken as the measure of the effect of hereditary differences between nonidentical twins. Thus, the relative strength of genetic (G) to environmental (E) factors, as indicated by studies of twins reared together, is expressed by

$$\frac{G}{E} = \frac{\text{Difference of nonidenticals} - \text{Difference of identicals}}{\text{Difference of identicals}}.$$

Objections have been raised to this partitioning of heredity and environment. It has been asked: "Are the environmental differences for identical twin partners really of the same magnitude as for nonidentical twins?" The answer is that frequently they are not. On the whole, identical twins have very similar habits. If one is robust and inclined to outdoor activities, the other shares this inclination; if one is weak and physically inactive, so is the other. If one finds pleasure in social activities, so does the other; if one prefers solitude, the other does likewise. With nonidentical twins, the situation is different. Their unlike genotypes may give a strong physique to one and a weak one to the other; and the environments they seek may differ greatly, to conform to their genetic differences. In general, it may be said that the environments in which nonidentical twins live are more different that those in which identical twins live. Since nonidentical twins live in environments that are more different, their greater discordance may in part be environmentally conditioned. Consequently, a partition of G and E according to the formula given above would lead to an exaggerated estimate of the share of heredity in the discordance of nonidentical twins.

Another objection to regarding identical and nonidentical twins as equivalent except for heredity is that identical twins, at birth, frequently exhibit larger differences in size and vigor than would be expected from their genetic identity. For instance, prenatal death of one of a pair of identicals is considerably more frequent than of one of a pair of nonidenticals. Such inequalities are probably caused by the often unequal placental blood supply, which particularly affects monochoric twins. The prenatal inequalities might also increase the intrapair differences between identical twins in typical twin investigations. Consequently, the differences in environment (prenatal) responsible for differences between identical twins may be larger than those for nonidentical twins. Neglect of such "prenatal biases" (Price) would attribute too small a share to heredity as a factor in the diversity of nonidentical twins.

Among still other doubts regarding the validity of comparisons between identical and nonidentical twins is one based on the assumption that identical twins are possibly, on the average, constitutionally inferior to nonidentical twins. This possibility is suggested by the higher prenatal mortality of one partner in identical twin pairs as compared to nonidentical pairs, as well as by the fact that the frequency of both twins being stillborn is also significantly higher for identical than for nonidentical twins. The question has been raised, therefore, whether or not identical twins who survive birth show the aftereffects of their often unfavorable prenatal environment. If so, then the higher concordance in abnormal traits found in identical twins might be based on their common inferior constitution.

To many students of these problems, the last two objections do not seem very serious. In most ways, identical twins differ so little that the result of special prenatal inequalities in environment would not seem important enough to have much weight in a general evaluation of nature and nurture. And a constitutional inferiority of no more than a minority of identical twins is apparent in the records of those twins who have survived, unharmed, the hazards of prenatal life, birth, and infancy. Much more significant is the first objection: that the postnatal environments of identical twins are more alike than those of nonidentical twins. It is difficult to estimate the effect of this difference in variability of environment. Many investigators believe that the effect on most traits is not great enough to change the conclusion that the hereditary differences and not environmental ones between nonidentical twins are the main causes of their greater trait differences.

Two factors possibly contributing to the greater similarity of the environments of identical, as compared to nonidentical, twin partners should be distinguished. One factor may be the tendency of identical partners to remain together just because they are alike. The second factor itself may be an expression of the specific, identical genotypes, which may lead the identical partners to select, independently of each other, similar environments; in contrast, the differences in genotypes of nonidentical twin partners may lead them more frequently to select different environments. As far as the second factor is involved, the differences in types of environments would themselves be expressions of the genetic situation. Therefore, instead of weakening the validity of assigning the excess in trait differences of nonidentical twins to heredity, the justification of this procedure would become strengthened.

This evaluation of the limitations of the twin method may be summarized in terms of a formula which plays a basic role in scientific plant and animal breeding. Hereditary and environmental factors are of great importance in determining the yield of, for example, corn per acre, milk per cow, or eggs per chicken. The variability of these traits is expressed in terms of a statistical concept, "variance," whose symbol is V. By referring, for a human example, to the studies on height in twins (p. 555), it is obvious that the variability of the differences is greater for the nonidentical than for the identical twins. Computation yields approximate values of $V_{nonid.} = 15.6$, and $V_{id.} = 2.1$.

The total variance of a population is the sum of three components: genetic variability, environmental variability, and the variability due to interaction of genetic and environmental factors—

$$V_{total} = V_{genetic} + V_{nongenetic} + V_{interaction}. \tag{1}$$

In twin studies the variance of the differences between partners of pairs is determined. For identical twins, this intrapair difference has no genetic component, and for any given twin pair it is due solely to nongenetic influences. For a comparison of the intrapair differences of different identical twin pairs, two components of the variance must be considered: the nongenetic intrapair differences and, in addition, an interaction variance. This is necessary since the same range of environmental agents impinging on a twin pair with the genotype A and causing its partners to differ may cause a different intrapair difference in another twin pair with the genotype B. The total variance of the differences between identical twin partners, therefore, is

$$V_{total\ id.} = V_{nongenetic\ intrapair\ id.} + V_{interaction\ id.}. \tag{2}$$

The variance in nonidentical twins is

$$V_{total\ nonid.} = V_{genetic\ nonid.} + V_{nongenetic\ intrapair\ nonid.} + V_{interaction\ nonid.}. \tag{3}$$

Only when it is justifiable to equate the nongenetic components of the total variances in identical and nonidentical twins and also to regard the interaction components as equal could equations (2) and (3) be combined thus:

$$V_{genetic\ nonid.} = V_{total\ nonid.} - V_{total\ id.}. \tag{4}$$

By substitution of $V_{genetic\ nonid.}$ in equation (3), we obtain

$$V_{nongenetic\ intrapair\ nonid.} + V_{interaction\ nonid.} = V_{total\ id.}. \tag{5}$$

Stated in words, the last two equations would signify a partitioning of the total variance of nonidentical twins into two measurable components: that due to their genetic differences alone, as expressed in (4); and that made up jointly of nongenetic differences and interactions, as expressed in (5). If one had reasons for assuming that interaction factors were negligible—that is, that the different environments had similar effects on the expression of the different genotypes—then the partitioning of the total variance would yield simply the contributions of genetic and nongenetic causes. In such a situation, it would be justifiable to say that, for instance, half of the variance of a trait in nonidentical twins is due to heredity and the other half to environment.

Even then, however, this partition applies, as stated, to the differences between nonidentical twins only, and not necessarily to differences between other sibs or between individuals in a general population. For the variance in individuals in a general population, the relative shares of nature and nurture may be very different from that for nonidentical twins, since both genetic and environmental differences from one person to the next will greatly exceed those for these twins.

These critical considerations are not intended to discredit the importance of twin investigations. They not only show that—as so often happens—a problem initially believed to be simple has turned out to be complex, but also suggest additional methods of approaching the problems of nature and nurture. By a comparison of the variance of a trait difference in pairs of sibs with that in pairs of nonidentical twins, it can be seen whether the possible greater mean difference in environment for children born to the same parents successively instead of simultaneously expresses itself in greater phenotypic variability. Similarly, a comparison of the variance in identical twins reared apart or in sibs brought up in different homes can provide information on the strength of different environments in molding a trait. Another approach to the same problem consists of measuring the variance in pairs of unrelated individuals reared in the same home instead of in different homes. Examples of some such comparisons have already been given (pages 555–557), and more will appear in the next chapter.

Problems

195. Using the data from Figure 225, test the significance of the difference in concordance between identical and nonidentical twins for the following traits: (a) clubfoot; (b) measles; (c) scarlet fever.

196. If a certain congenital human trait is concordant in 60 per cent of nonidentical twins: (a) What conclusions regarding the heredity-environment problem can be drawn from this fact? (b) What would you conclude if this trait is 93 per cent concordant in identical twins?

197. Analyze the following data and draw conclusions, whenever possible, regarding the roles of heredity and environment: (a) In a certain city, symptoms of lead poisoning are concordant in nearly 100 per cent of all pairs of identical twins; in another city, only 80 per cent of identical twin pairs are concordant. (b) The frequency of concordance for measles is practically alike in identical and nonidentical twin pairs. (c) Concordance for a disease was found in 31 out of 33 pairs of identical twins and in 1 out of 16 pairs of nonidentical twins.

198. For a certain genetic trait which has full penetrance, one-third of the affected nonidentical male or female twin pairs are concordant, but the female co-twin of an affected male is rarely concordant. What is the explanation?

References

Allen, G., 1952. The meaning of concordance and discordance in estimation of penetrance and gene frequency. *Am. J. Human Genet.*, **4:** 155–172.

Anderson, V. E., Goodman, H. O., and Reed, S. C., 1958. *Variables Related to Human Breast Cancer.* 172 pp. University of Minnesota Press, Minneapolis.

Heston, W. E., 1953. The bearing of mouse genetics on our understanding of human cancer. *Am. J. Human Genet.*, **4:** 314–331.

Kühne, K., 1936. Die Zwillingswirbelsäule. *Zeitschr. Morphol. u. Anthrop.*, **35:** 1–376.

Lurie, M. B., 1953. On the mechanism of genetic resistance to tuberculosis and its mode of inheritance. *Am. J. Human Genet.*, **4:** 302–314.

Macklin, M. T., 1959. Comparison of the number of breast-cancer deaths observed in relatives of breast-cancer patients, and the number expected on the basis of mortality rates. *J. Nat. Cancer Inst.*, **22:** 927–952.

Murphy, D. P., 1952. *Heredity in Uterine Cancer.* 128 pp. Harvard University Press, Cambridge.

Newman, H. H., Freeman, F. N., and Holzinger, K. J., 1937. *Twins: A Study of Heredity and Environment.* 369 pp. University of Chicago Press, Chicago.

Penrose, L. S., MacKenzie, H. J., and Karn, M. N., 1948. A genetical study of human mammary cancer. *Ann. Eugen.*, **14:** 234–266.

Planansky, K., and Allen, G., 1953. Heredity in relation to variable resistance to pulmonary tuberculosis. *Am. J. Human Genet.*, **5:** 322–349.

Price, B., 1950. Primary biases in twin studies. A review of prenatal and natal difference-producing factors in monozygotic pairs. *Am. J. Human Genet.*, **2:** 293–352.

Schinz, H. R., Cocchi, U., and Neuhaus, J., 1948. Die Vererbung des Krebses beim Menschen. *Arch. Julius Klaus-Stift.*, **23:** 1–232.

Verschuer, O. v., 1956. Tuberkulose und Krebs bei Zwillingen. *Acta Genet. et Stat. Med.*, **6:** 103–113.

Williams, R. J., 1951. Biochemical Institute Studies IV. Individual metabolic patterns and human disease: an exploratory study utilizing predominantly paper chromatographic methods. *University of Texas Publications, No. 5109*, pp. 7–21.

Woodworth, R. S., 1941. *Heredity and Environment.* 95 pp. Bulletin 47, Social Science Research Council, New York.

Woolf, C. M., 1955. Investigations on genetic aspects of carcinoma of the stomach and breast. *University of California Publ. in Public Health*, **2:** 265–350.

CHAPTER 27

HEREDITY AND ENVIRONMENT

III. MENTAL TRAITS

Mental activities, expressed in human behavior, are intimately related to physical activities in the brain and nervous system. Destruction of small or large components of the brain result in mental changes. Alterations in the biochemistry of nerve cells and their interactions are often accompanied by changes in behavior. Behavior also depends on the organization of the sense organs which relay to the nervous system signals from the outside world and from within the body. Moreover, it also depends on the reactions of the tissues to nervous stimuli which may elicit hormonal secretions and muscular contractions that express themselves in mental states, in movements, and in speech. Since genes exert their actions on the development of the most various types of biological structures and the functioning of innumerable kinds of biological processes, it is to be expected that they also influence those structures and functions on which mental traits depend, and that differences in genotypes may express themselves in differences in behavior.

Features of human behavior separate it widely from the behavior of even man's closest animal relatives. Nevertheless, because of the basic similarity of nervous organization in man and animals, particularly mammals, it will be helpful to survey briefly the genetics of animal behavior relevant to human genetics in order to point out both agreements and differences.

Genetics of Animal Behavior

Animal species differ not only in appearance but also in behavior. The genotype of a fertilized spider egg determines both the form of the developing spider and the activities which will lead to the spinning of the web characteristic of the species. A chicken's egg of female genotype will transform itself into a bird which, without ever having heard the sound of another hen, will produce the notes typical of its kind. A female rabbit which has never seen another rabbit prepare a home for its young will when pregnant build a rather complex nest and pluck hair from her body to line it. But not all individuals of a species will act alike. For example, birds of the same species often show variations in their song, and different dogs are known for either friendliness or aggressiveness, ability or inability to retrieve, and many other specific behavioral traits.

Intraspecific differences could be acquired by specific contacts with other animals or with human trainers, or they could be consequences of different genetic constitutions of different individuals. They could also be the results of combined action of specific genotypes and specific outside stimuli—just as the ability of a child to learn the language and behavior of his culture depends both on the human genotype which permits such complex achievements and on the specific culture in which this genotype expresses itself.

To distinguish genetic from nongenetic aspects of behavior, one must observe different individuals under identical external conditions. In higher animals, this may involve separating at birth from their mother the young to be studied. In order to repeat behavioral tests on more than one specimen, it is desirable to have available strains of animals whose members are highly alike in genotype. And to find the specific mechanisms which govern genetic differences in behavior, one must study descendants of various crosses between different strains.

The results of such studies have shown that not only nervous diseases but also differences in behavior within the normal range of variability are inherited in mice, rats, and rabbits. Among the abnormalities of behavior, one of the most intensely studied traits is a type of epileptic seizures caused by high-frequency sounds. Different rat genotypes include those that are immune to these "audiogenic seizures," that succumb to them early in life, and that succumb to them on repeated stimulation. Other inherited behavioral abnormalities include no less than six genetically different types of shaking, "waltzing," and circling in mice, a simply inherited recessive tremor and cramp disease in rabbits, and similar afflictions in deermice and chickens.

Among normal behavioral traits, one of the easiest to measure is the amount of running of mice or rats in an activity wheel. (An activity wheel records the number of revolutions enforced upon it by the efforts of the animal.) Male rats from a highly active strain averaged nine thousand revolutions per day, while males from an inactive strain averaged only one thousand revolutions. As long as certain strains of wild-type and domesticated laboratory rats were fed adequately, the wild type was no more active than the laboratory animals. On starvation diet, however, the wild rats were much more active than the domestic specimens.

Mice of 15 strains have been studied for exploratory activity, which was measured by the number of maze sections without dead ends that the mice entered. The mean scores differed from strain to strain and were distributed in a normal manner. The activity of the highest strain was 23 times that of the lowest.

"Emotionality" in mice and rats has been assessed by the number of fecal and urinary eliminations occurring under unaccustomed conditions. In a strain selected for high emotionality, approximately seven eliminations occurred in 12 trials; in a strain of low emotionality, a mean of only one-half elimination occurred under like circumstances.

Hoarding of pellets of food was likewise found to be dependent on the genotype. Rats of one strain collected about 44 pellets during a 12-day period; rats of another strain assembled fewer than 11 pellets. This hoarding occurred under conditions of food shortage, but differences in intensity of hoarding remained when a pile of pellets was placed in each rat cage and kept there at all times. Animals of the formerly low hoarding strains virtually ceased hoarding after a few days; whereas animals of the formerly high hoarding strain still collected at least 5 pellets a day for 12 days.

Strains with different behavior are sometimes distinguished by different physical traits, for instance, fur color. In the epileptic rabbits of the White Vienna genotype, for example, it has been established that the specific behavior is at least partly controlled by the gene which determines coat coloration. Another interesting example in which the appearance of a special morphological character has been shown to be due to a peculiar type of behavior is in a strain of obese mice. The cause of obesity is not simply one of an unusual food utilization but also of an inability to regulate the food (that is, calorie) intake. On a palatable diet on which other mice thrive, the obese mice overeat; on an unpalatable fare to which other mice adjust, the obese mice undereat and become then contrary to their original designation. In other cases, it seems that chance and not intrinsic factors are responsible for associations between behavioral and nonbehavioral traits.

Genetic differences in learning ability have been demonstrated by letting rats run through a maze in which alternate pathways lead either to a food supply or into blind alleys. Some genotypes enabled their carriers after a period of training to make few errors on their way toward the goal, while other genotypes enabled their carriers to succeed only after many mistakes. The original designations of such strains as either "bright" or "dull" have given way to the more cautious terms "maze-bright" and "maze-dull," since animals with high scores in maze learning may be low scoring in other learning tasks, and, conversely, low-scoring maze testers may be higher in other achievements. Learning is a highly complex phenomenon and, in rats, may be dependent on such genetically controlled variables as general activity, exploratory activity, and emotionality, as well as on many others.

A genetically controlled trait involving social interrelations concerns fighting in mice. When kept under special identical conditions, males of two different strains were opposite in aggressiveness toward a third mouse introduced into their environment, one type being strongly aggressive, the other pacific. It is noteworthy, however, that males from either strain could be easily trained to be either aggressive or peaceable. Genetic differences in sexual drive in male guinea pigs have been mentioned in the discussion of sex determination (Chap. 20).

Traits analogous to human language are the songs of birds. It is well known that different species of birds have different songs, and that within one and the same species regional variations of the song may be found. Experiments with hand-reared English chaffinches which have been kept separate from birth in a soundproof room have shown that both heredity and learning are involved in their song. The normal song has three phases, but an isolated chaffinch is able to produce only a song of about the normal length and consisting of a crescendo series concluded by a single note of relatively high pitch. All typical refinements of the song which result in the regional "dialects" have to be learned by contact with other birds of their species. Interestingly, the innate basis of the song is selective enough to insure that the bird does not normally acquire songs from any species other than its own. In contrast to this, bullfinches and greenfinches will readily learn complete songs from alien species, and certain mockingbirds seem to be genetically endowed with an ability to learn a whole range of songs of other species. The call notes of many birds, however, seem to be fixed genetically.

Final examples of carefully studied genetic control of behavior are furnished by observations made on dogs at the Jackson Memorial Laboratory at Bar Harbor, Maine. Animals of four different breeds were brought up under standardized conditions and rated for such traits as sensitivity to noises, orientation in space, reaction (as measured by change in heart rate) to the approach of the human handler, learning behavior, and type of activity developing in puppies during a period of mild restraint by the handler. Striking specific differences between breeds were found, some in degree of

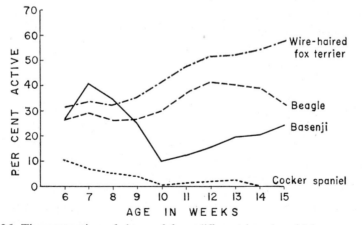

FIG. 226. The proportion of dogs, of four different breeds, which were rated as "active" when required to remain quiet during weighing on a scale. Note the initial differences in young puppies and the partial increase in these differences with age of dogs. (After Scott and Charles, *J. Genet. Psych.,* **84,** 1954.)

trait expression (for instance, length of response delay), and others of a nature which might be called alternative. Thus, predominant submissiveness was observed in a sample of cocker spaniels consequent upon restraint, in contrast to predominant aggressiveness developing under the same circumstances in a sample of wire-haired terriers (Fig. 226).

These studies on animal behavior have shown the existence of genetic controls. They have given equal evidence that behavior can be modified by varying the external conditions. Wild and domestic rats are about equally active when well fed, but not when undernourished; although differences in hoarding do not disappear completely when the nests are well stocked, they become diminished; and mice innately aggressive under one type of environment can be made pacific under another.

Studies of animal behavior have revealed the existence of critical periods during which an individual's future behavior is determined in a sometimes unalterable manner. Thus, incubator-hatched goslings who have never seen a goose will consider the human feeder whom they first see as their "mother," and will not pay any attention to their real mother. Or, a single act of ill treatment of a young dog may leave an indelible "imprint" on the animal, so that all his subsequent behavior is influenced by the experience.

Human behavior may be expected to follow rules similar to those governing animal behavior. The degree to which genetic differences in man may express themselves in mental attributes will vary from case to case, as it does in animals. However, the immensely greater learning potentialities of man may serve as a means of overcoming the effects of different genotypes. The same result may be accomplished by man's power, already large and yet still rudimentary, to manipulate the environment. Beyond such equalizing tendencies, man's special abilities may also be employed to develop the expression of different genotypes in a diversified manner so that each genotype, furnished with its "appropriate" environment, can make a maximum contribution to the well-being of the individual and society. It is obvious that the goals outlined in the preceding two sentences involve discussions and evaluations which lie far beyond the proper realm of human genetics.

Mental Disorders

The nature-nurture problem arouses unusual interest in mental traits. We shall discuss first some pathological characters and then the particularly important differences within the normal range of human mental capacities. Since geneticists have found genetic bases for many illnesses of the body, they are inclined to look for hereditary factors in the development of mental diseases. They postulate that mental phenomena have a physical basis, and they follow with high expectations the work of physiologists and biochemists who attempt to find physical or chemical properties which characterize patients with specific mental diseases. Such findings might, it is thought, reveal the underlying action of genotypes which physiologically cause abnormal states of the brain and express themselves also in abnormal mentality. A model for such correlations is the well-established case of mental deficiency (not mental disease) caused by the recessive gene for phenylketonuria, which does not permit normal metabolism of phenylalanine and, correlated with this, causes brain damage and low intelligence. Other aspects of the inter-relationship between bodily and mental states are demonstrated by the use of certain compounds which when taken by normal persons induce symptoms similar to those found in persons with psychoses, and by other compounds which when taken by mentally ill persons change them temporarily toward normality. Of course, the consideration of genetic factors in the origin of mental diseases does not exclude awareness of the gene-environment inter-action (which is the theme of the present chapter)—as it is one of the funda-mental concepts of "dynamic," physiological-developmental genetics.

Psychiatrists, and particularly those of the psychoanalytical schools, are sometimes inclined to consider only the environmental stresses in the lives of their patients. The study of mental harm done to children at very early stages, or in later periods of life, may lead to significant information on the environmental aspects of mental disease. Yet, even convincing proof of harmful psychological experiences preceding a psychosis would not neces-sarily rule out the presence of genetic components.

Theoretically, the joint efforts of geneticists and psychiatrists could yield the conclusion (1) that mental disease is invariably fated by specific geno-types; or (2) that it is equally likely in all known genotypes; or, finally, (3) that nongenetic influences lead to illness in some, but not all, genotypes. The first alternative is easily seen to be false, since identical twins are not always concordant in respect to mental illness. It is more difficult to decide between alternatives (2) and (3), complete versus partial nongenetic determination. The occurrence of increased frequencies of mental illness in various types of relatives of propositi suggests that these frequencies are due to a common genetic basis. But this interpretation can be countered by the argument that the relatives may have been exposed more frequently than unrelated individuals to precipitating external causes of the disease.

Final answers to these problems may have to depend on long-range, large-scale studies which have not yet been made. They might include the follow-up on the mental development of many infants whose prenatal life, birth, and later experiences are well recorded. When these children have become adults, will there be significant differences in the past histories of the majority who remain mentally healthy and the small minority who be-come mentally ill? Even in such detailed studies, however, it may not be easy to decide whether recorded unfavorable experiences were solely of environmental origin or whether certain individuals, owing to their special genotypes, respond in an amplified way to some not-too-rare external event.

Another decisive attack on the nature-nurture problem of mental disease would be to follow up children placed very early in adoptive homes. Will the children of biological parents who become mentally ill be no more inclined to mental illness in adoptive homes than the children of healthy biological parents? If the children of healthy biological parents are reared by adoptive parents who develop mental illness, will the children become ill more frequently than they would have if reared in homes of healthy adoptive parents?

Although there has been no definitive investigation, there are general facts which point to genetic factors in mental illness or, to express the same idea differently, to genetic factors providing resistance to mental illness. One of these facts, stressed by Kallmann, is the specificity of the disease. The two most frequent types of mental illness, to be discussed below, are schizophrenia and manic-depressive psychosis. It has been found that among the relatives of schizophrenic propositi the frequency of schizophrenia is higher than in the general population, but that the frequency of manic-depressive psychosis is not increased. Similarly, among the relatives of manic-depressives there is an increased frequency of this disease, but a normal frequency of schizophrenia. If one regarded environmental disturbances as sole causes of mental illness, one would have to assume that these disturbances are so specific in different kindreds as to produce only schizophrenia and not manic-depressive psychosis in the parents, children, grandchildren, cousins, nieces, and nephews of some propositi, and only manic-depressive psychosis and not schizophrenia in those of other propositi. This seems unlikely.

It has also been found that most of the sibs of a schizophrenic propositus are nonaffected, and that those who are affected occur in a random order among the series of sibs. These facts are expected if a genetic predisposition is involved. A purely environmental causation would, it may be assumed, result in "runs" of affected sibs which should correspond to unfavorable situations in the families and which should frequently last over prolonged periods.

A few cases are known of identical twins who were early separated from one another and who both became mentally ill. Identical twin sisters, described by Kallmann, were adopted into different homes soon after birth. The sisters had hardly any contact during the first ten years, and little contact later. At the age of fifteen, one, a factory worker, gave birth to an illegitimate child, while the other lived as a domestic servant in the sheltered home of a private family. Nevertheless, both became schizophrenic—the first shortly after the birth of her child, the second about one and a half years later. Another pair of identical twin sisters was studied by Craike and Slater. After spending the first eight and a half years in the home of a violent, often drunken father, one sister then lived in a children's home until she was nineteen; the other sister was adopted after the death of the mother, at the age of nine months, by an affectionate aunt in whose home she stayed until the age of twenty-four. The two sisters had had no personal contact or correspondence before they were twenty-four years old, though each knew of the other's existence. They were rarely together afterwards. Mutual suspicion and dislike dominated their relations. Despite very different upbringings, there was concordance in childhood neurosis, in various aspects of personality and life story, in slight deafness, and in schizophrenic illness. The psychosis of the twin with a harsh childhood was chronic and progressive, while that of the other was less severe and showed its symptoms only at intervals.

Such concordances are suggestive of a constitutional background of the disease, but they, by themselves, still are compatible with purely environmental interpretations. It lies in the nature of twin studies that the existence of nongenetic factors in mental disease, as in other traits, is proven beyond doubt whenever discordant identical pairs are encountered, but that the existence of genetic factors is not unequivocally established when the twins are concordant. In the absence of any proof to the contrary, however, it will be assumed here that greater discordance of nonidentical than of identical twins, and greater incidence of affected relatives of affected propositi, in mental disease as well as in most other traits, is in part due to genetic causes.

Schizophrenia.   The incidence of schizophrenia in the general population has been estimated as approximately 1 per cent. This disease, which frequently sets in during the third decade of life and thus has been called dementia praecox, or early insanity, is characterized by a cleavage in the

TABLE 92. *Schizophrenia among Relatives of Affected Individuals from Germany* (A, C) *and among Relatives of Affected Twins from the United States* (B). (Luxenburger, *Fortschr. Erbpathol.,* **1,** 1937; v. Verschuer, *Erbpathologie,* 2nd ed., Steinkopf, 1937; and Kallmann, 1946, 1953.)

	Morbidity Risk (%)		
	Schizophrenia		Psychopathic Condition Similar to Schizophrenia
Relation to Propositus	A	B	C
Unrelated	0.85	—	2.9
Step-sibs*	—	1.8	—
Half-sibs†	—	7.1	—
Sibs	10.8	14.2	9.7
Parents	—	10.3	—
Children	16.4	16.4	32.6
Grandchildren	3.0	4.3	13.8
Cousins	1.8	—	10.2
Nephews, nieces	1.8	3.9	5.1
Great-nephews and -nieces	1.6	—	1.9
Great-grandchildren	—	—	3.9

  * Step-sibs are genetically unrelated. They are the offspring of two spouses from their marriages to other partners.

  † Half-sibs are the offspring of one person from different marriages.

personality that, in extreme cases, may necessitate permanent institution-alization of the patient.

Large-scale studies have shown that the frequency of schizophrenia among the relatives of affected persons is higher than that of the general population (Table 92). The table shows the risk probabilities that specific relatives of a propositus will, at some time during life, have the disease. Such risk figures are usually obtained from data on relatives, which include some nonaffected individuals who have died before or during the age period when onset of the disease occurs. Obviously, the full inclusion of nonaffected individuals will bias the actual risks; thus the raw data have to be "age corrected" by the use of tables which give the age distribution for the disease. Weinberg and others have worked out the necessary methods. The frequency values of Table 92 are often called the "empiric risk" or the "morbidity risk." (The risk figure is called "empiric" because it is not based on any theory of hereditary or environmental causation of the disease, but on the statistical facts of experience.) The very much higher incidence of schizophrenia among the relatives of affected persons than in the general population is most impressive. Among the adult children of patients, for instance, the incidence is nearly twenty times higher than in general. In addition to schizophrenia itself, the frequency of similar, less serious, mental abnormalities is also greatly increased.

Twin studies from several different countries uniformly show high degrees of concordance for schizophrenia in identical twins and low degrees in non-identicals (Table 93). The differences in percentages of concordance in the different studies are due to statistical variability and to the somewhat varying criteria that are used by the different investigators for a clinical definition of the disease. The absence of concordance of the disease in 20 per cent of identical twins is evidence for nongenetic factors in the origin of the disease, but the much greater concordance frequency of identical than of nonidentical twins points to genetic predisposition.

TABLE 93. *Concordance and Discordance in Twin Pairs Affected with Schizophrenia.* (After Kallmann, 1953; Inouye, from Kamide, *Jap. J. Human Genet.,* **2,** 1957.)

	Identical		Nonidentical	
Authors	++	+−	++	+−
Luxenburger (Germany)	14	7	2	58
Rosanoff, Hardy, Plesset, Brush (U. S.)	28	13	10	91
Essen-Möller (Sweden)	5	2	4	20
Slater (England)	31	10	16	99
Kallmann (U. S.)	231	37	99	586
Inouye (Japan)	8	9	0	4
Mean concordance	80%	—	13%	—

TABLE 94. *Similarity in Type of Onset and Number of Attacks of Schizophrenia in Relatives (Singly Born Sibs and Co-twins) of Affected Twins.* (After Slater, 1953.)

		Relatives				*Relatives*	
		Sudden Onset	Gradual Onset			One Attack	Two or More Attacks
Propositus	Sudden Onset	23	8	*Propositus*	One Attack	31	13
	Gradual Onset	15	32		Two or More Attacks	8	15

It was possible to subdivide the identical pairs in Kallmann's State of New York population into two groups: one in which the partners had not been separated before the onset of the disease, and another in which the partners had been separated. The average time of separation before the onset of disease was 11.8 years, with a minimum separation of 5 years. The morbidity risk of the other twin was 85.8 per cent for those not separated, but only 77.6 per cent for those separated. This difference in concordance rate between pairs of identical twins is further evidence of some environmental agent in schizophrenia.

Is the high concordance of schizophrenia in identical twins due to the mental shock which the onset of the disease in one twin causes in the other? The data on nonidenticals show that this shock, in most cases, is not sufficient to cause the disease if the genotypes of the twins are different from each other. It is, of course, true that the mental reaction of an identical twin to the illness of his twin partner is probably different from that of a nonidentical twin, who knows that his fate is dissimilar in many other ways. It seems unlikely, however, that this difference in psychological attitude can account for the observed difference in concordance.

The theory of a genetic component in schizophrenia does not reveal the specific nature of this component. Do all schizophrenics possess the same abnormal genotype? The evidence is not clear, as is so often true for a trait whose presumed genetic basis is not fully penetrant. Phenotypically, schizophrenia appears in strikingly different forms, and some indications have been found of a tendency for similar types of the illness to occur in the relatives of an affected propositus. Other indications for specific genotypes within the general trait called schizophrenia are the similarities in number of attacks and in types of onset among related individuals (Table 94). But in spite of such suggestions of genetic diversity, it is possible to assume that a single main gene is the necessary prerequisite for schizophrenia, with minor genes in the genetic background accounting for the specific form of the illness. Kallmann has advocated the theory of a single recessive gene

TABLE 95.   *Concordance* $(++)$ *and Discordance* $(+-)$ *in Twin Pairs Affected with Manic-depressive Psychosis.* (After Luxenburger, from v. Verschuer, 1937; Rosanoff, Handy, and Plesset, *Am. J. Psych.*, **91,** 1935; Kallmann, 1953; and Slater, *Proc. 42nd. Ann. Meeting Am. Psychopath. Assn.*)

Authors	*Identical*		*Nonidentical*	
	$++$	$+-$	$++$	$+-$
Luxenburger (Germany)	3	1	—	13
Rosanoff, Handy, Plesset (U. S.)	16	7	11	56
Kallmann (U. S.)	25	2	13	42
Slater (England)	4	4	7	23
Mean concordance	77%	—	19%	—

which causes the disease with a limited degree of penetrance in homozygotes. The theory is compatible with the finding of from 10 to 14 per cent morbidity among sibs of propositi and the observation that 60 per cent or more of the children of two schizophrenic parents are affected. But, according to the theory, it is difficult to explain the observation that the morbidity risk of the children of an affected individual is similar to the morbidity risk of his sibs. Since the genotypes of the parents of an affected individual would have to be $Aa \times Aa$, $Aa \times aa$, or $aa \times aa$, his sibs would have a mean probability of more than 25 per cent of being aa; but the children of affected individuals, a majority of whom would come from marriages to AA individuals and a minority from marriages to Aa or aa individuals should be much less frequently aa than in 25 per cent of the total. Some of these observations can be better explained by the assumption of a dominant gene. Böök, in a study of a presumably highly homogeneous, isolated Swedish population, has found that a genetic scheme which best fits his findings assumes the presence of a dominant gene with about 20 per cent penetrance in heterozygotes and 100 per cent penetrance in homozygotes. Actually it cannot yet be decided whether a single factor difference or perhaps polygenic differences account for the genetic basis of schizophrenia.

Manic-depressive Psychosis.   Manic-depressive illness has an incidence in the general population of somewhat less than $1/2$ per cent. The disease is characterized by alternating emotional stages of exaggerated exaltation and depression. Empirical data on its incidence in relatives suggest inheritance with dominance involved, but no definite knowledge of the genetic details is available. Twin studies again show a strikingly higher concordance in identical as opposed to nonidentical genotypes (Table 95).

Intelligence

As important as abnormal mental properties are, both to the individual and to society, they play a minor role as compared to the variations within the normal range of mental characteristics. One of the difficulties of making studies within this range is the dearth of devices with which to measure objectively the differences in normal mental traits. The most commonly used devices for this purpose are the so-called intelligence tests. The concept of intelligence is a complex one. It includes the assumption of inherited psychological capacities, as well as the knowledge of the behavioristic activities made possible by the acquisition of the cultural tools which society makes available. *Intelligent behavior* is regarded as behavior which, on the basis of an inherited capacity, makes good use of the social inheritance, such as language and numbers or scientific and moral concepts. Intelligence tests do not directly measure intelligent behavior, but measure a particular type of behavior as defined by a given type of test. The tests are constructed so that the essentials of the test behavior will closely resemble significant elements of life behavior. How well intelligence tests do this is still a matter for investigation. Different intelligence tests score the behavior of tested individuals in different ways. The most widely used measure is the *intelligence quotient,* or I.Q., so called because it is the quotient (multiplied by 100) of the mental age of the individual as defined by the test and his chronological age. It assigns a score of about 100 as the mean value of the population and is constructed so that higher and lower scores are distributed approximately in a normal curve. Accordingly, the number of individuals who score higher or lower than average decreases with the deviation of the score from 100.

Psychologists have subdivided the mental abilities of man into distinct so-called primary abilities, such as ability to visualize objects in space, to memorize, or to reason inductively. It has been found that two individuals with the same I.Q. may be very different in their endowment of primary abilities. In the future, intelligence studies on the nature-nurture problem will have to be concerned with primary abilities rather than over-all scores. Unfortunately, to date, most objective data on intelligence are available only in terms of I.Q. scores.

The nature-nurture problem regarding intelligence is immediately posed by the earlier statement that intelligent behavior implies both inherited capacities and acquisition of external cultural tools. Differences in intelligence-test behavior among individuals may be due to differences in their genetic endowment, to differences in their opportunities for acquiring the tools of society, and to complex interrelations between the genetic and environmental differences. In general, the tests have been constructed with the endeavor to make them independent of environmental differences within a given society—none of the tests can be applied to different societies—so that differences in test behavior would be due to differences in genotypes.

A complete independence from nongenetic influences is impossible, however. Human intelligence behavior always occurs within a cultural organization, so that the idea of an absolutely "culture-free" intelligence test has intrinsic limitations. What this idea really implies is the desirability of "culture-fair" tests—that is, tests which minimize the effect of cultural differences of groups within a given society. Thus, one may attempt to reduce the influence on test scores of the fact that the upbringing of some individuals may motivate them less than others to score as high as they can. Or one may reduce the influence on test scores of the verbal skill required to score well, since much of this ability depends on home background. One difficulty in such procedures is that there may possibly be some genetic control of motivation or of verbal skill, and efforts to eliminate nongenetic factors may also eliminate the genetic ones.

The opportunities for acquiring information helpful in obtaining high scores are not simply different in different homes. Subtle differences have been detected in individuals' attitudes toward gaining knowledge and making use of it in intelligence tests. A certain eagerness for the intellectual success of their children, as it is frequently found among middle-class parents, provides an attitude favorable to test success; whereas lesser stress on intellectual achievement, as is often characteristic of lower socioeconomic homes, may fail to prepare the emotional background on which a high test performance must be based. However, bright and dull children often occur in the same family, and in any layer of the population. Socioeconomic level and cultural status, though important, are not the only factors interacting in intelligence-test performance.

There are examples of improvement or deterioration in intelligence scores of individuals under the influence of particularly favorable or unfavorable circumstances. Such examples are important because they may show which factors in the environment influence the expression of the genotypes involved in test behavior, but they have no bearing on the question of whether or not there are genetic differences among individuals that determine such behavior.

Correlations between Different Mental Traits. When the same individuals are tested for two or more different primary mental abilities, it is usually found that scores for one test are positively correlated with scores for another. Such positive correlations could be due to three main causes acting singly or in combination: (1) environmental influences which lead to similar scores for various tests, (2) variations in some underlying, general genetic factor which tend to make test scores similar for different mental abilities, and (3) the possibility that the past history of the population has brought together in the same individuals those alleles of different genes which determine similar levels of test performance for their respective abilities. According to an analysis by Dempster, both genetic and nongenetic components seem to be involved in the observed correlations.

Feeble-mindedness. Before going into the evidence on the nature-nurture problem within the normal range of intelligence, let us briefly discuss the borderline phenomenon called feeble-mindedness, or mental retardation. Intelligent behavior of different individuals, both in life and in tests, varies greatly and continuously from very high, through average and low, to very low. The individuals in the lowest group on the scale of behavior, which include the so-called idiots, have to be permanently cared for in institutions. A somewhat higher group, which grades into low "normal" intelligence, still contains individuals incapable of independent life. These individuals need special schools or institutions in which their limited capacities are trained and put to use. Persons belonging to this group are called "feeble-minded," or "mentally retarded." They comprise several per cent of the population of Western societies. In terms of I.Q., feeble-minded individuals are, with some variations, defined by scores in the range from 50 to 70.

External causes, particularly prenatal and birth injuries to the brain, may be responsible for idiocy and feeble-mindedness, but there is no doubt that genetic factors are also frequently responsible for mental deficiency. One such case is mongolism, and another phenylketonuria, where a single-gene difference causes mental defect. But, contrary to earlier belief, most of the genetics of feeble-mindedness fits a polygenic interpretation. As in the inheritance of stature, measured intelligence in a population shows continuous variation from very low to very high. Feeble-minded individuals in general seem to possess an accumulation of alleles at many loci which assign these persons to the lowly endowed "tail" of the frequency distribution of mental ability.

Evidence for this interpretation of mental defect comes from family data in which the mental abilities of children from different types of parents are compared (Table 96). Certainly, the positive correlations between frequencies of defective offspring and defective parents are not free of the environmental factor. Defective parents are likely to provide less favorable opportunities for mental development than nondefective. Nevertheless, it is true that the great majority of mental defectives comes from the great majority of parents who are not defective (Table 97). Although this does not exclude the possibility that the environment provided by "normal" parents

TABLE 96. *Offspring of Various Types of Parents Ascertained by Their Having Had a Mentally Defective Child.* (After Halperin, *Am. J. Mental Deficiency,* **50,** 1945.)

		Children		
Parents	No.	Average or Above (%)	Inferior* (%)	Defective* (%)
Average × Average	18	72	5	22
Average × Inferior	59	64	33	3
Inferior × Inferior	252	28	57	15
Inferior × Defective	89	10	55	35
Defective × Defective	141	4	39	57

* Approximate I.Q. range of "inferiors," 70–85; of "defectives," 50–70.

TABLE 97. *Parental Origin of 1,194 Mentally Defective Children.* (After Penrose, 1938.)

Parents*	Propositi	
	Dull to Feeble-minded	*Imbeciles and Idiots*
Superior × Superior	—	1
Superior × Normal	4	5
Normal × Normal	316	481
Normal × Dull	126	70
Normal × Feeble-minded or Dull × Dull	73	40
Normal × Imbecile or Dull × Feeble-minded	38	16
Dull × Imbecile or Feeble-minded × Feeble-minded	11	13

* The mean I.Q. of the superior parents was estimated as 122, that of the normal, dull, feeble-minded, imbeciles and idiots as 100, 78, 56, 34 and 12, respectively.

may in these cases still be responsible for the mental defect of their children, such an assumption hardly qualifies as a general explanation. It is also unlikely in view of the following observations. When the mental defectives are separated into two groups, the feeble-minded and the imbeciles and idiots, it is found that the mean I.Q. of the sibs of the feeble-minded is lower than that of the sibs of the imbeciles and idiots (Fig. 227). If unfavorable nurture were the cause of the more severe defects, one would expect it to cause low intelligence of the sibs too. In reality, the sibs of the imbeciles and idiots have a rather normal average and a normal distribution except for a small peak of defectives like the propositi. In contrast, the sibs of the less abnormal feeble-minded average about twenty points lower than normal, although an assumed unfavorable nurture in their homes would have had the effect of making the propositi only feeble-minded, not imbecilic or idiotic. One must agree with Roberts and other investigators in concluding that both types of mental defectives often have abnormal genotypes, and that imbecility and idiocy are primarily caused by single recessive genes, but feeble-mindedness is the result of polygenic genotypes.

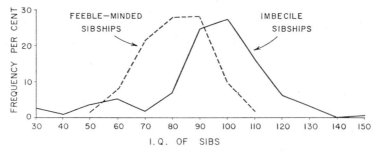

FIG. 227. Frequency distributions of the I.Q.'s of 562 sibs of feeble-minded and imbeciles of the I.Q. range 30–68. (Roberts, 1952.)

TABLE 98. *Concordance* (++) *and Discordance* (+−) *in Twin Pairs Affected with Feeble-mindedness.* (Rosanoff, Handy, and Plesset, *Psychol. Monog.,* **48**, 1937; Juda, *Zeitschr. Neurol.,* **66**, 1939; Yoshimasu, from Kamide, *Jap. J. Human Genet.,* **2**, 1957; and Smith, from v. Verschuer, *Erbpathologie,* 2nd ed., Steinkopf, 1937.)

	Identical		Nonidentical	
Authors	++	+−	++	+−
Rosanoff, Handy, Plesset (U. S.)	115	11	42	51
Juda (Germany)	60	—	76	73
Yoshimasu (Japan)	14	1	3	—
Smith (Denmark)	14	2	1	14

Twin studies illuminate aspects of the nature-nurture interrelation in feeble-mindedness (Table 98). Some discordance is found in identical twins (in spite of their like genotype), and much more discordance is found in nonidenticals; but, in addition, in the data of Rosanoff and his associates, there is still greater discordance between sibs. The difference in discordance between the nonidenticals and the sibs cannot be attributed to differences in the genetic diversity of the two groups. Since postnatal factors seem to have had little influence in the feeble-mindedness studied by these authors, factors in the prenatal environment and at the time of birth must be regarded as underlying the differences in discordance. Apparently, nongenetic prenatal and perinatal influences sometimes lead to feeble-mindedness and, obviously, have a higher chance of affecting twins concordantly than of affecting two sibs born at different times.

Even within the range of normal intelligence, twins fare slightly less well than single born. Their I.Q. scores average four points or more lower than those of non-twins, probably due primarily to such biological factors as prematurity and lower birth weight which affect a minority of twins. The relatively more frequent occurrence of twin births to older mothers also tends to correlate positively twinship with larger family size, which itself is known to reduce test performance of children (see p. 641).

The last of the studies listed in Table 98 throws further light on the question of prenatal or natal influences on mental defects. All cases in which there was an obvious environmental cause for feeble-mindedness had been excluded. As a result, concordant pairs of nonidentical twins had become very rare, in contrast to the high frequency of concordance in pairs of identical twins. The question may be raised whether the greater concordance for mental defect of identical twins, as compared to nonidenticals, could also be accounted for by prenatal or birth factors which influence monozygotic twins more heavily. There is no evidence to justify such an assumption. Even though identical twins are somewhat more endangered in early life than nonidenticals, that difference seems insufficient to account for the great difference in concordance.

Word Blindness. A considerable number of individuals of normal or superior intelligence experience difficulties in reading and writing, called

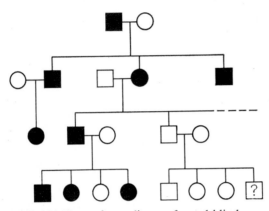

word blindness, or dyslexia. In some, this defect can be traced to special illness; in others, no specific cause can be determined for it. Pedigree data have been interpreted in terms of a single dominant gene, with nearly complete penetrance (Fig. 228). Of three identical twin pairs, all were concordant, in contrast to two discordant pairs out of three nonidenticals. A trait

FIG. 228. Part of a pedigree of word blindness. The youngest child in the last sibship had not yet reached the age of possible manifestation. (After Hallgren, *Acta psychiat. neurolog., Suppl.* **65,** 1950.)

such as word blindness is frequently not easy to diagnose with certainty—a fact which leaves some doubt regarding its genetic basis. But the existence of specific mental inabilities caused by certain genes is by no means unlikely.

Normal Intelligence-test Behavior. Twin studies on normal differences in intelligence have been carried out by several investigators. The most extensive study (Table 99) was that of Newman, Freeman, and Holzinger, which also served us earlier for a discussion of nature and nurture in regard to some physical traits. The average I.Q. difference in fifty identical twin pairs reared together was 5.9 points, that in fifty-two nonidentical twin pairs reared together 9.9 points, the latter being practically the same as that for forty-seven pairs of sibs, which was 9.8 points. The difference between the two kinds of twins is greater than the scores suggest. If one corrects

TABLE 99. *Mean Differences in Binet I.Q. and Correlation Coefficients between Twins and Paired Sibs.* (Woodworth, after Newman, Freeman, and Holzinger.)

I.Q.	Identical (reared together)	Non-identical	Sibs	Identical (reared apart)†
Mean differences	5.9	9.9	9.8	8.2
Corrected mean differences*	3.1	8.5	—	6.0
Correlation coefficient	0.881	0.631	—	0.767

* See text.

† See p. 592.

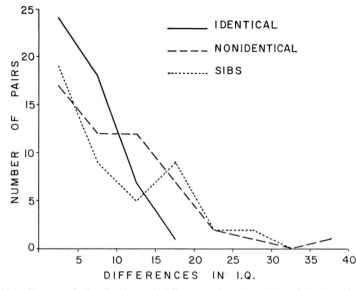

FIG. 229. Curves of distribution of differences in Binet I.Q. of 50 identical twins, 47 nonidentical twins, and of 52 pairs of sibs. (After Newman, Freeman, and Holzinger.)

the scores for chance errors in measurement, the true mean differences between the I.Q.'s of identical twins is reduced to about 3.1 points and that between nonidenticals to 8.5 points. It is apparent from a comparison of these two means that heredity plays an important role in the determination of the I.Q. differences between nonidentical twins.

Environmental differences, prenatal or postnatal, are not without effect, even on the I.Q. scores of identical twins reared together. The uncorrected *average* difference of I.Q. scores, 5.9 points, is small, but the distribution of the fifty different values for the fifty pairs of identical twins (Fig. 229) shows that eighteen pairs had differences between 5 and 10 points, seven between 10 and 15 points, and that one pair differed by about 17 points. Further light on the nature-nurture influence on intelligence is provided by the studies summarized in the following section on twins reared apart, adopted children, and children raised in orphanages.

Identical Twins Reared Apart.   The usual procedure for studying the genetics of intelligence and achievement would be to compare the scores of parents and children and other related individuals. Pedigrees of the Bach kindred show an accumulation of great musicians, of the Bernoullis a series of famous mathematicians, of the Darwins a group of distinguished scientists; but a Beethoven, a Gauss, or a Franklin stands alone in eminence among his relatives. Passing from the study of individual families to statistical data, Galton in his book *Hereditary Genius* (1869) showed that the proportion of outstanding men was much greater among the relatives of outstanding

Englishmen than in the English population at large. On a still broader scale, positive correlations were found by many investigators between the school performances of parents and children or other individuals closely related to one another. All these facts could be explained on the basis of heredity. Since it is possible that some unusual achievements depend on the presence of single genes, the appearance of the responsible trait in various members of a kindred would be likely. It is possible that other unusual achievements have a polygenic basis, so that the unique combination assembled in a genius has little chance of being present again in someone else. But, clearly, in no human cultural achievement can the influence of nongenetic factors be denied, and no reliable conclusions can be drawn from the facts even though they may suggest genetic participation.

The comparison of I.Q. scores in identical and in nonidentical twins, as seen above, offers advantages over more general procedures. Additional information is available from studies of the test performance of identical twins reared apart. A pair of such twins was first studied intensively by H. J. Muller, who recognized the special significance of testing individuals with identical genotypes who had been subjected from infancy, or at least from early life, to the environments of different homes. Newman, Freeman, and Holzinger reported on nineteen more cases of separated twin pairs. A few additional pairs have been discovered by other investigators. For the nineteen separated twin pairs, the raw mean difference in I.Q. was 8.2, and the adjusted difference was 6.0 points (Table 99). These average differences lie between the mean differences of identicals reared together and of non-identicals. Similarly, the correlation coefficient for identical twins reared apart was intermediate. The conclusion may be drawn that the environmental differences provided by the separate homes were able to double the usual I.Q. differences between individuals with like genotypes, but that the I.Q. differences between twins of unlike genotypes, even if raised in the same home, were still greater.

As always, averages tell only an incomplete story. A detailed consideration of each pair of identical twins reared separately reveals that, in general, the home environments of the twin partners did not differ greatly. In most cases, both twins were brought up in either rural or urban communities; and both had similar kinds and lengths of formal schooling. For fifteen of the nineteen twin pairs, it may be said that only moderate intrapair variation existed in the educational, social, and physical environment. The remaining four pairs had been subjected to such differences as "one with two years of regular schooling only, the other with completed college education" (Case 11, Table 100); or "one reared on a farm, and completing grade school, the other reared in a town, and completing high school" (Case 4); or "one reared in the home of a somewhat shiftless, often unsuccessful, man of various semiskilled occupations, the other in the home of a well-to-do physician" (Case 7). If the intrapair differences scored in intelligence tests of the various separated twins are compared with the environmental dif-

TABLE 100. *Identical Twins Reared Apart.* (Woodworth: after Newman, Freeman, and Holzinger; Muller; Gardner and Newman; Saudek.)

| Case Number | Sex | Age at Separation (mos.) | Age at Testing (yrs.) | Environmental Differences in | | | I.Q. Difference |
| | | | | Schooling (yrs.) | Advantages* | | |
					educational	social	
11	♀	18	35	14	37	25	24
2	♀	18	27	15	32	14	12
18	♂	12	27	4	28	31	19
4	♀	5	29	4	22	15	17
12	♀	18	29	5	19	13	7
1	♀	18	19	1	15	27	12
17	♂	24	14	0	15	15	10
8	♀	3	15	1	14	32	15
3	♂	2	23	1	12	15	−2
14	♀	6	39	0	12	15	−1
5	♀	14	38	1	11	26	4
13	♂	1	19	0	11	13	1
10	♀	12	12	1	10	15	5
15	♂	12	26	2	9	7	1
7	♂	1	13	0	9	27	−1
19	♀	72	41	0	9	14	−9
16	♀	24	11	0	8	12	2
6	♀	36	59	0	7	10	8
9	♂	1	19	0	7	14	6
Muller	♀	1	30	9	?	?	−1
Gardner, Newman	♀	1	19	0	2	?	−3
Saudek	♂	1	20	0	?	?	±4

* The differences in educational and social advantages are estimated, and are in "points," with a maximum possible of 50. From the case material, each of five judges rated the environmental differences between every pair of twins on a scale of ten points, and the figure given in the table is the sum of these five ratings. A minus sign before an I.Q. difference means that the twin who received the higher rating for educational advantages obtained the lower I.Q.

ferences to which they had been subjected, some interesting correlations become apparent. More extensive schooling and general educational advantages resulted in higher scores than those attained by the less favored, genetically identical twin. Much of the average difference is accounted for by only four twin pairs, those for whom the difference in amount of schooling was largest. It seems, then, that only considerable differences in environment can bring out a great difference in I.Q. scores of identical twins.

Table 100 not only contains data on the separated identical twins, but also includes estimated ratings of the social advantages of the more favored twin. There is some correlation between social advantage and higher I.Q., but it is smaller than that between educational advantage and I.Q. An example is provided by the pair of twins referred to above, one of whom was reared in a low-income home, the other in the home of a well-to-do physician. These boys were thirteen years old when tested and had an equal number of years of schooling. In spite of the estimated social advantages (27 points) for the adopted son of the physician, his I.Q. score was practically identical to (in reality 1 point lower than) that of his brother. How dangerous it is to generalize from findings in this complex field of human behavior is shown by a pair of English twin brothers who were separated early and who lived under considerably different social environments, though their formal schooling was alike. In this case, the twin who experienced the poorer environment was 19 points higher in I.Q. than his partner. One is inclined to ask with Gates, "Did adverse conditions sharpen his mind?"

In summary, the twin studies on intelligence-test behavior show: (1) modifiability of the I.Q. score under the influence of differences in environment and (2) greater similarity in I.Q. of identical twins, whether reared together or in different homes, than that of nonidentical twins reared in the same home. The second fact demands an interpretation in genetic terms: differences in intelligence scores of nonidentical twins are partly due to differences in their environments and partly to hereditary differences.

The same conclusions seem to be justified by twin studies in which some of the primary mental abilities that are part of general intelligence have been analyzed separately. It has been estimated that from less than one-half to more than three-quarters of the variance of scores in tests for different primary abilities in nonidentical twins may be accounted for by genetic influences, and the rest by environmental ones. However, the detailed shares of heredity and environment in the variability of intelligence are still subject to future evaluation.

Differences in the scores of unrelated individuals of a population, of course, are also due to both environmental and hereditary variables. But it is even more difficult with unrelated persons than with nonidentical twins to ascertain the specific shares of nature and nurture responsible for degrees of differences between individuals. It is clear, however, that persons with "good" inheritance have a better chance of having parents with "good" inheritance than persons with "poor" inheritance, and that there exists either a "beneficial" or a "vicious" principle of accumulation: "good" heredity of the parents generally provides "good" environment, and "bad" heredity generally provides "bad" environment.

The share of heredity and environment, whatever it may be, at any stage in history or any locality, is not fixed. Sometimes, the poorer the environment, the more may environmental differences account for differences between individuals. Thus, where only the wealthy can give their children schooling, differences in cultural intelligence between individuals are environmentally conditioned to a much greater extent than where general education is available to everyone, so that differences in inherited capacities are more decisive for score differences than are differences in educational opportunities. The hereditary component of differences between men may sometimes be clearly apparent only because environment has been leveled upward.

Adopted Children.   Twin studies on the nature-nurture aspects of mental traits are complemented in an important way by studies on adopted children. If a group of children is divided in a random manner into several samples, the average genetic endowment of the children in each sample should be the same, within the limits of statistical error. If the children of one sample are then placed in adoptive homes of one kind, and the children of each other sample into adoptive homes of other kinds, then the effects of different kinds of adoptive homes on the development of the children can be compared. (It should be noted that the original studies usually refer to adopted children as "foster" children. In modern usage, "foster" does not convey the meaning that a child has been legally adopted and permanently placed in an adoptive home.)

It is not easy to find series of adopted children in which no open or hidden selective placement has been practiced because the presumably better-endowed children are usually placed in the better adoptive homes. Selective placement seems to have been minimal in a group of adopted children from Chicago. The sample is small, but agrees in what it shows with other, larger samples which perhaps included some selectively placed children. The adoptive homes were classed as "good," "average," and "poor" (the last term does not mean unfavorable home environment, but one less favorable than the other two). Had there been no influence of home environment, it would have been expected that the average scores of the samples of children in the three classes of homes would have been alike. It was found, however, that the mean I.Q. scores of the adopted children were strikingly related to the quality of the adoptive homes: 45 adopted children in good homes scored, on the average, 112 points; 39 adopted children in average homes scored, on the average, 105 points; and 27 adopted children in poor homes scored, on the average, 96 points. These figures clearly demonstrate the modifying influence of home environment on intelligence-test behavior.

Other studies on adopted children afford an opportunity to judge the hereditary component of the I.Q. score. If heredity has something to do with I.Q. performance, then adopted children should be less similar to their adoptive parents than the "own" (biological) children of a control parent group. For a group of adopted children in Minnesota homes, which were graded in various ways, there was a continuous decrease in mean I.Q. with descent in occupational status of the father from professional to the relatively unskilled occupations (Table 101). This decrease, which reflects the environmental effect on test performance, covered a rather narrow mean range, from 113 to 108. In the control group of own children, there was also a steady decline in mean I.Q. corresponding to the occupational status of the father, but the range is more than three times greater, namely, from 119 to 102. This latter range shows a much more pronounced correlation with the father's occupational

TABLE 101.   *Mean I.Q. of Adopted Children and "Own" Children in Homes of Different Occupational Categories.* (Leahy, *Psychol. Monog.*, **17**, 1935.)

Occupation of Father	Adopted Children		Control ("Own") Children	
	Number	Score	Number	Score
Professional	43	112.6	40	118.6
Business, management	38	111.6	42	117.6
Skilled trades and clerical	44	110.6	43	106.9
Semiskilled	45	109.4	46	101.1
Relatively unskilled	24	107.8	23	102.1

status than the narrower range of the adopted children. Specifically, it is significant that for the upper occupational groups the own children scored higher than the adopted children, but for the lower occupational groups the adopted children did better than the own children. It seems reasonable to conclude that the differences between the scores in adopted and in own children are due to the fact that the latter resemble their parents more than do the adopted children because they inherited part of their parents' genotypes.

Similar conclusions have been reached in more recent studies on the trend of parent-child resemblance in intelligence during the development of the child. Over a period of twelve years, Skodak and Skeels measured the performances of a group of children adopted during their first months of life, and correlated them with measures of the education or actual I.Q. scores of (1) the biological mothers and fathers, and (2) the adoptive mothers and fathers. Up to the age of two years there was essentially no correlation between the child's performance rating and that of either the biological or the adoptive parents—a finding which agrees with the results of other studies involving only biological parents. With increasing age of the children, there was a steep rise in correlation between I.Q. of the child and the biological parents; this correlation reached values of approximately 0.3 around four years of age, after which it increased only slightly more. In contrast to these significant positive correlations between measured or estimated intelligence of children and biological parents, the correlations between intelligence of the children and their adoptive parents remained insignificantly small. These data strongly suggest that intelligence performance depends in part on the children's genetic endowment from their biological parents, and is to a high degree independent of the educational status or intelligence performance of their adoptive parents.

Orphanage Children.   The presence of a genetic component in intelligence is also apparent from a British study on the relation between the occupational status of the parents, particularly the fathers, and the test performances of illegitimate children brought up away from their parents in a relatively uniform environment. These children were under the care of "Dr. Smith's Home," a large and important charitable institution. They had been separated from their mothers before the age of one year, and on the average at six months. Until they were between five and six years old, the children were boarded out individually in the approved and inspected cottage homes of agricultural laborers "of the better type." Thereafter, for about ten years, they lived together in the headquarters of the institution, where they also attended school. The identity and social status of the biological parents remained entirely unknown to the children, and their placement in the cottage homes as well as their treatment in Dr. Smith's Home was unrelated to their parental background. These long-established procedures of the institution furnished an opportunity for a study of the intelligence scores of the children as related to the status of their biological parents. An ideal way of studying the relationship would have been to compare actual tests of the parents with those of their children. This was not possible, since the parents were not available. Instead, the *mean* scores of children from various occupational layers had to be used. One investigation of this type has already been cited for control children (Table 101), and other studies have borne out the general trend of decreasing test performance with progression from professional to less skilled occupational status of fathers. If the higher mean scores of children from the upper occupational groups were not exclusively due to better environmental opportunities but also to genetic causes, then the scores of the children in Dr. Smith's Home should show a similar relationship to the occupational status of the parents.

The children were classified, according to occupations of parents, into five groups: group A included not only professional people but also elementary school teachers and farmers (from the country gentlemen to the working farmers); group B, tradesmen, clerks, and highly skilled artisans; group C, skilled and semiskilled workers; group D, unskilled workers; group E, a very arbitrary mixture of dock laborers, peddlers, gypsies, and paupers. Both groups A and E were represented by only a few children.

The children were tested individually by the Stanford-Binet test and in groups. The scores of both tests, for boys and for girls, showed positive cor-

TABLE 102. *Mean I.Q. Scores, Obtained by Averaging Individual and Group Tests, of Children in Dr. Smith's Home, Classified into Five Groups According to Status of Parents.* (After Evelyn Lawrence.)

| | Boys | | Girls | |
| | Mean I.Q. | | Mean I.Q. | |
Group	Score	Number	Score	Number
A	99.0	4	105.0	1
B	104.2	15	100.1	18
C	101.1	41	97.1	25
D	96.5	23	92.8	25
E	98.0	1	—	—

relations with the occupational status of either father or mother. Examples relating the average scores derived from a combination of the individual and group tests of boys and of girls to the average socioeconomic status of the two parents are given in Table 102. Although there are two minor exceptions to the positive correlation between test performance and status of parents, in general the positive relationship is clearly apparent. In spite of a relatively uniform foster-home and orphanage environment, which was unrelated to the status of the parents, the mean performances of the children of parents from different socioeconomic groups showed the same ranking which would have been expected had the children been brought up in the homes of their biological parents. The range of mean scores of children from the five different groups (A–E) in Dr. Smith's Home is narrower than the range of mean scores of children from similar classes living with their parents. Although this greater similarity is a reflection of the less differentiated environment, the fact that, in spite of this, there is still a significant correlation between mean scores and parental classes is evidence that intelligence performance is partly governed by genetic endowment. Some might be inclined to assume that the prenatal environment of an illegitimate child, and its environment during the first half-year before acceptance into Dr. Smith's Home, would affect the later test performance and be correlated to the status of the *mother*. But such a supposition, according to present knowledge, is without foundation and, in any case, could hardly account sufficiently for the correlation between test scores and the occupational status of the *father*.

Personality Characteristics

Intelligence tests are not the only means by which mental traits have been evaluated. Many tests of temperament, emotional behavior, and specific abilities have been devised. Other evaluations of personality have been based on intense examination and observation of twins assembled in special summer camps over periods of months.

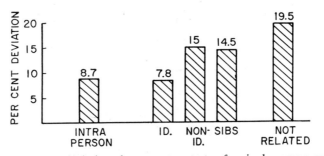

FIG. 230. Percentage deviations between two tests of a single person and between partners of various twin pairs for a joint index of personal tempo, involving speed of knocking (an act of willing) and speed of metronome ticking (an act of perception). (After Frischeisen-Köhler.)

Personal Tempo.   When individuals seated at a table are asked to knock on it at a speed which is "natural" to them, different individuals have been observed to perform at markedly different speeds. Similar differences are found when people are asked to decide the speed of the ticking of a metronome that seems to them just right. The "personal tempo" thus determined is rather constant for each individual. On the average, tests of identical twins do not differ more from one another than repeated tests of the same individual (Fig. 230). Nonidentical twins are much more different from one another, their differences being similar to those between ordinary sibs. Unrelated persons differ still more than sibs. If the personal tempo is one component of what has been called the "natural velocity of the psychological life," then these tests provide important evidence that it is influenced by inheritance.

Orientation in Space.   This behavioral trait involves the ability to orient oneself toward a specific known place after one has been led, blindfolded and with cotton plugs in one's ears, in various ways within an experimental room. In a series of observations on forty pairs of identical twins and forty pairs of nonidentical twins, concordance in orientation in space was defined as an agreement within seven degrees in the angular deviations from the right direction. Identical twins were found to be concordant at least twice as often as nonidenticals.

Psychomotor and Sport Activities.   Studies have been made of average differences in sport attainment by twins (Fig. 231) and determinations of the time when twin infants begin to sit up and when they begin to walk (Table 103). The time of first sitting up seems little affected by the greater similarity of identical, as compared to nonidentical, twins, since the figure of 82 per cent concordance for the former is not statistically significant, when compared with the 76 per cent for the latter. However, for the beginning of walking, in

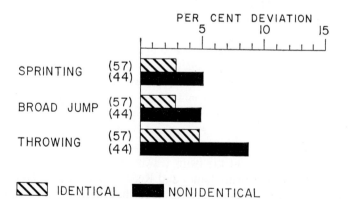

FIG. 231. Mean percentage deviations in sport performances of twin partners. The numbers at left are numbers of pairs considered. (After Osato and Awano, *Acta Genet. Med. Gemel.*, **6**, 1957.)

TABLE 103.   *Concordance* $(++)$ *and Discordance* $(+-)$ *for Beginning of Sitting Up, and of Walking, in Infant Twins.* (Bossik, *Proc. Maxim Gorki Med.-Biol. Res. Institute,* **3,** 1934; and v. Verschuer, *Ergebn. Inn. Med. u. Kinderheilkd.,* **31,** 1927.)

Beginning of	Twins	Per Cent		No. of Pairs
		$++$	$+-$	
Sitting up	Identical	82	18	63
	Nonidentical	76	24	59
Walking (v. Verschuer, Germany)	Identical	69	31	39
	Nonidentical	35	65	31
Walking (Bossik, U.S.S.R.)	Identical	67	33	97
	Nonidentical	30	70	97

two different studies, the concordance of 67 and 69 per cent for identicals outranks concordance of only 30 and 35 per cent for nonidenticals. (It is remarkable how closely the results of the two independent investigations agree with each other.)

A Genetic Component of Language?   Different languages make use of widely different sounds, and the variety of sounds which an infant of any race is able to produce is greater than that finally employed by the child in his native language. Why does any one language use only a specific fraction of the many possible sounds? Darlington has argued that the different genotypes which control the development of the organs of speech must limit the ease with which races and individuals can produce the various sounds. Therefore, a specific language is a reflection of the genotypically controlled phonetic preferences of the people who created it. However, this view has not been substantiated by other than very circumstantial evidence.

Other Personality Traits.   Tests have been devised to study such traits as tender-mindedness, general neuroticism, will power, dominance, energetic conformity, and submissiveness. Some of these traits, such as the first three, seem to be predominantly environmentally determined; others seem to be dependent to different degrees on both nature and nurture.

Two examples of performances in the Downey Individual Will-Temperament Test for identical twins reared apart are reproduced in Figure 232. The sums of the twelve scores of the twins Edwin and Fred are 70 and 63—both higher than those of the twins James and Reece, which are 58 and 57. A different over-all pattern of scores also distinguishes the two pairs. Thus, Edwin or Fred reaches the top score of 10 for three traits (freedom from load, speed of decision, and resistance to opposition) for which the high scores of either James or Reece are only 3, 6, and 8. On the other hand, James and Reece both score 10 for "finality of judgment," for which Edwin and Fred score 7 and 8.

On the whole, the differences between the responses of James and Reece are smaller than between those of Edwin and Fred. This, however, is in contrast to the life experiences and social adjustments of these individuals. Edwin and Fred have had extremely parallel lives: similar occupations and similar positions in society. James and Reece had very diverse social environments and very different schooling and education (James had the better environment). James has had steady occupation and a respected place in society, but Reece has not been steadily employed and has several times been in conflict with the law. It seems that the will-temperament tests give an answer less representative of life behavior than the intelligence tests. The individual case histories, on the other hand, often show a striking similarity in basic personality traits between identical twins, including those reared apart. (The reader will find fascinating descriptions of the life histories of separated twins in Newman, Freeman, and Holzinger's book.)

The most elaborate study to date of the over-all personality and development of twins is that of Gottschaldt in Germany. He assembled ninety pairs of twin children in special camps and made detailed observations and tests. Thirteen years after the initial work he was able to relocate seventy of the

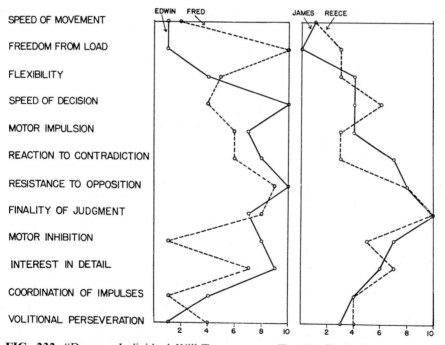

FIG. 232. "Downey Individual Will-Temperament Test Profiles" of two pairs of identical twins reared apart. The individuals were scored, on a scale from 0 to 10, for their responses to tests which measure aspects of the twelve Will-Temperament factors listed at the left. (After Newman, Freeman, and Holzinger.)

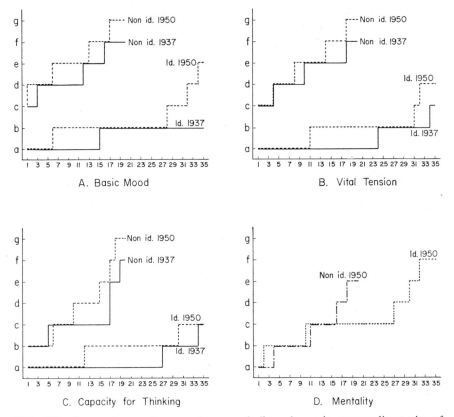

FIG. 233. Comparisons of concordance and discordance in personality traits of twin partners studied in 1937 and, again, in 1950. The letters from a to g represent a scale from full concordance to striking discordance; the numbers signify the numbers of pairs of a given concordance rating. (Gottschaldt, *Zschr. f. Psychol.*, **157**, 1954.)

twin pairs and evaluate their development during the intervening period, which included the disaster of World War II and its aftermath. Figure 233 shows some of the results. Many mental traits, such as those defined as basic mood, vital tension (which includes the personal tempo), capacity for thinking and abstraction, show not only greater similarity between identical than nonidentical partners, but a persistence of the trends from childhood to adulthood, in spite of separation of the twins and, sometimes, of greatly different life experiences. Some other traits, such as social-personal superstructures of the personality ("mentality") as expressed in judgments of ethical and social values, do not show much greater similarity between identical than nonidentical partners. Such studies confirm that, by and large, identical twins are much more similar than nonidentical twins. They also provide insight into the shaping of the personality structure by the forces of nature and nurture.

Body Types and Personality.   Attempts to relate physical appearances to mental traits are of great antiquity. One modern classification of body types is (1) pyknic, with strong development of head and trunk, and inclination to obesity; (2) athletic, with strong skeletal and muscular development; and (3) asthenic, with relative thinness but normal growth in height. A similar classification by Sheldon, based on extensive series of measurements, assigns each individual to a "somatotype"—endomorph, mesomorph, or ectomorph. These are roughly similar to the pyknic, athletic, and asthenic types, and their ideal numerical designations on a seven-point scale are 7–1–1, 1–7–1, and 1–1–7.

It has been found that certain mental diseases occur more frequently in some body types than in others. Schizophrenia is more common in ectomorphs, and manic-depressive states in endomorphs. Lack of knowledge of genetic bases for the physiques defined by somatotyping stands in the way of a clear interpretation of relationships between mental illness and body type. The same is true, perhaps even more so, for the apparent relations between normal types of personalities and somatotypes. Without doubt, the nature-nurture interaction is significant in these relationships. The degree of severity of manic-depressive psychosis in pairs of identical twins is positively correlated with degree of obesity—and normal temperaments, too, are not unrelated to bodily states.

Although some investigators regard attempts to correlate over-all mental and physical constitutions as futile, they do expect that fruitful correlations will eventually be made between well-defined "single" characters of behavior and physique or, ultimately, biochemistry. It is probable that important information will be contributed by both approaches in the future.

Criminal Behavior.   The case for an inborn tendency toward ill behavior has been strikingly stated by Prospero in Shakespeare's *The Tempest*. He says of Caliban:

> A devil, a born devil, on whose nature
> Nurture can never stick; on whom my pains,
> Humanely taken, all, all lost, quite lost . . .

Such a view is denied by many. In their opinion, since the law is a kind of externally imposed special environment, there is no point in raising the question of whether or not some individuals are genetically criminals. It is certainly true that different social orders will be correlated with different kinds and incidences of crime. Nevertheless, an inquiry into the nature-nurture of criminality is concerned with a legitimate genetic problem—namely, whether in a given social order, with its specific laws, hereditary factors predispose some individuals more than others to criminal acts.

The results of twin studies carried out by different investigators, in the United States, in different parts of Germany, and in Holland, are summarized in Table 104. The high concordance of a criminal record in pairs of identical

TABLE 104. *Concordance* $(++)$ *and Discordance* $(+-)$ *in Twin Pairs Involved in Criminality.* (Kranz, *Lebensschicksale Krimineller Zwillinge,* Springer, 1936; Lange, 1929; Legras, *Psychose en Criminaliteit bei Tweelingen,* 1932; Rosanoff, Handy, and Plesset, *Psychiat. Monog. I,* State of Calif. Dept. of Instit., 1941; Stumpfl, *Die Ursprünge des Verbrechens,* Thieme, 1936; Borgström, *Arch. Rassenbiol.,* **33,** 1939; and Yoshimasu, after Kamide, *Jap. J. Human Genet.,* **2,** 1957.)

Authors	Identical		Nonidentical	
	$++$	$+-$	$++$	$+-$
Lange (Germany)	10	3	2	15
Rosanoff, Handy, Plesset (U. S.)	35	10	6	21
Legras (Holland)	4	0	0	5
Kranz (Germany)	20	11	23	20
Stumpfl (Germany)	11	7	7	12
Borgström (Finland)	3	1	2	3
Yoshimasu (Japan)	14	14	0	26
Total (number)	97	46	40	102
Total (per cent)	68	32	28	72

twins is obviously not due to a "bad home background" alone, since concordance in nonidentical twins is comparatively much lower—and nonidentical twins also share a common home background.

The full degree of concordance is shown only very incompletely by the numbers given in the table. The individual life histories (in the detailed, sympathetic accounts of each pair, by Lange and Kranz) disclose that concordance in identical twins signifies not only that both were, at one time or another, in prison, but that the type of crime or crimes was very similar. And discordance in identicals often consisted in only a slight difference in behavior or, in case of great differences, was probably based on specific birth injuries. Concordance in nonidenticals, on the other hand, usually signified conflicts with the law for rather diverse, and generally deep-seated, causes. In this connection, the greater contrast between the identical and nonidentical twins in Lange's material than in Kranz's should be pointed out. Kranz included many individuals in his studies, who had only one criminal encounter with the law; whereas Lange included a greater number of repeated offenders. From these two studies it appears that the causes which lead a person only once toward a criminal offense are less dependent on his genotype—and more on nongenetic "chance"—than those which make him a chronic criminal.

The high concordance of identical twins for many traits which have been determined to have a hereditary basis may incline one to attribute the greater concordance in criminality of identicals as compared to nonidenticals to the identity of their genotypes. It may be assumed, however, that the greater similarity in the environment of identical twins plays an important role in this behavioristic trait. If nongenetic chance leads one twin into a criminal offense, would not the similarity of the environmental experiences of his identical partner also lead him to a similar crime? Conversely, if nongenetic chance leads one twin into an offense, would not his nonidentical partner, who is less likely to share his specific environment, be spared the conflict with the law? The facts on criminality in twins actually show only that identity in genes plus the close similarity in social experiences, at least in early childhood, are more likely to bring both identical twins into prison than two nonidenticals who have nonidentity of genes plus less similar social experiences. On the basis of present data, one cannot exclude the possibility that the higher concordance for criminality of identical twins is mainly, or even exclusively, the result of their more similar social experiences; nor can one exclude the opposite possibility that their higher concordance is mainly the result of their identical genotypes. Studies on criminal twins reared apart from birth are needed to clarify this important question.

If the present evidence is insufficient to indicate reliably that criminals are "born," it does point to a genetic component for the type of crime committed, if a crime is committed at all. The personality traits which distinguish people and which seem to have a genetic basis will partly determine whether a criminal is an embezzler, a burglar, or a murderer. This is indicated by the similarity in types of crimes committed by identical twin partners, as well as by the similarity in personalities even of those identical pairs of whom only one partner has had conflicts with the law.

Nature–Nurture Studies

Discussions of the nature and nurture problem of mental traits have often been more heated than is usual for scientific arguments. Heredity and environment have been regarded as opposing concepts, and an attempted demonstration of the influence of either one has been considered to imply the nonexistence of the other. Some students who are impressed by the facts of genetics have tried to "explain away" results which seem to show the effect of environment; and some students who find evidence for the effect of environmental factors have tried to discount results which speak in favor of heredity. The difficulties of obtaining perfectly controlled experimental setups in man are so large that it is indeed possible to find loopholes in the conclusions of virtually every study. Because of the nearly unavoidable imperfections in the studies on nature and nurture, arguments have sometimes been based on a position which, with overwhelming probability, will prove untenable.

There is nothing unusual in the recognition that differences in mental traits between different individuals are due to both heredity and environment. There is no a priori limit which the geneticist can place on the power of specific environments in leading any genotype to highest expression. The concept of different genetic endowments may even be more helpful in the task of developing a variety of suitable environments than an assumption of lack of genetic differences, which might induce people to search for a single, standardized "best" environment.

Results such as those reported in this chapter frequently justify an optimistic attitude, in spite of the fatefulness which the term heredity seems to imply. If the concordance of 80 per cent among identical twins for schizophrenia, as opposed to only 13 per cent in nonidenticals, emphasizes the influence of heredity, it is, nevertheless, highly important that in 20 per cent of identical twins, one of them was spared by the disease. If we can find out why the same genetic constitution in 20 per cent of the twin partners did not express itself by the symptoms of mental illness, we can hope to use our knowledge in saving still more individuals with these genotypes from breakdown. Instead of regarding the results of nature-nurture studies as static, they can serve the dynamic purpose of continuously fitting more suitable environments to the different genotypes.

The astonishing basic similarity, if not near-identity, of genetically identical twin pairs in both mental and physical traits contrasts with the absence of any such close similarity in the genetically nonidentical twin pairs, and remains as strong support for the view that neither in body or in mind are men born alike.

Problems

199. Assume that a mental disease depends on a gene A' which is 20 per cent penetrant in heterozygotes and 100 per cent penetrant in homozygotes.

(a) What frequencies of affected would be expected in the following matings: $AA \times AA'$; $AA \times A'A'$; $AA' \times AA'$; $AA' \times A'A'$.

(b) If the allele frequency of A' were $q = 0.02$, what would be the sum of the frequencies of all marriages of two affected spouses? What would be the mean frequency of the disease among the offspring of these marriages?

(c) What would be the answers to Parts a and b, if improved nongenetic circumstances would reduce the penetrance of the heterozygotes to 10 per cent and that of the homozygotes to 60 per cent?

200. Assume the existence of three pairs of alleles, A and A', B and B', and C and C', which act cumulatively in respect to mental endowment so that "average" individuals carry from 0 to 2 "prime" alleles, "inferior" individuals from 1 to 4, and "defectives" from 3 to 6. Apply this model, in a qualitative way only, to the data in Table 96.

201. Among 278 sibs of criminals, Stumpfl found 103 who had a criminal record. This corresponds to 1 criminal out of 2.7 sibs of criminals. Among 62 nonidentical twin partners of criminals, Stumpfl and Kranz found 30 offenders. This corresponds to 1 criminal out of 2.1 nonidentical twin partners of criminal twins. It has been suggested that the last-named higher frequency of criminals (1 in 2.1) as compared to the first-named frequency (1 in 2.7) is due to the greater environmental similarity for twins than for ordinary sibs. (a) What is the statistical significance of the data? (b) What bearing has the answer to the preceding question on the suggested explanation for the different frequencies?

References

Böök, J. A., 1953. A genetic and neuro-psychiatric investigation of a north-Swedish population, with special regard to schizophrenia and mental deficiency. *Acta Genet. et Stat. Med.,* **4:** 1–100.

Cattell, R. B., Blewett, D. B., and Reloff, J. R., 1955. The inheritance of personality. A multiple variance analysis determination of approximate nature-nurture ratios for primary personality factors in Q-data. *Am. J. Human Genet.,* **7:** 122–146.

Cowie, V., and Slater, E., 1959. Psychiatric genetics. *Recent Prog. Psychiatry,* **3:** 1–53.

Darlington, C. D., 1947. The genetic component of language. *Heredity,* **1:** 269–286.

———, 1953. *The Facts of Life.* 467 pp. Allen & Unwin, London.

Eells, K., Davis, A., Havighurst, R. J., Herrick, V. E., and Tyler, R. W., 1951. *Intelligence and cultural differences: A study of Cultural Learning and Problem-Solving.* 388 pp. University of Chicago Press, Chicago.

Frischeisen-Köhler, I., 1933. *Das persönliche Tempo. Eine erbbiologische Untersuchung.* 63 pp. Thieme, Leipzig.

Fuller, J. L., and Thompson, W. R., 1960. *Behavior Genetics.* Wiley, New York.

———, and Scott, J. P., 1954. Genetic factors affecting intelligence. I. Heredity and learning ability in infrahuman mammals. *Eugen. Quart.,* **1:** 28–43.

Ginsburg, B. E., 1958. Genetics as a tool in the study of behavior. *Perspectives in Biology and Medicine,* **1:** 397–424.

Hall, C. S., 1951. The genetics of behavior. In S. S. Stevens (Ed.). *Handbook of Experimental Psychology.* Chapter 9. Wiley, New York.

Hirsch, J., 1958. Recent developments in behavior genetics and differential psychology. *Diseases of Nerv. Syst.,* Monogr. Suppl. **19:** 1–7.

Honzik, M. P., 1957. Developmental studies of parent-child resemblance in intelligence. *Child Development,* **28:** 215–228.

Kallmann, F. J., 1946. The genetic theory of schizophrenia. *Am. J. Psychiatry,* **103:** 309–322.

———, 1953. *Heredity in Health and Mental Disorder.* 315 pp., Norton, New York.

Lange, J., 1929. *Verbrechen als Schicksal.* 96 pp. Thieme, Leipzig. (Translation: *Crime and Destiny.* 250 pp. 1930. Boni, New York.)

Lawrence, E. M., 1931. An investigation into the relation between intelligence and inheritance. *Brit. J. Psychol.,* Monogr. Suppl. No. **16:** 1–80.

Malan, M., 1941. Zur Erblichkeit der Orientierungsfähigkeit im Raum. *Z. Morphol. Anthropol.,* **39:** 1–23.

Newman, H. H., Freeman, F. N., and Holzinger, K. J., 1937. *Twins: a Study of Heredity and Environment.* 369 pp. University of Chicago Press, Chicago.

Penrose, L. S., 1938. A clinical and genetic study of 1280 cases of mental defect. *Medical Research Council, Spec. Rep. Ser. No.* **229:** 1–159.

———, 1954. *The Biology of Mental Defect.* 303 pp. Sidgwick & Jackson, London.

Richter, C. P., 1954. The effects of domestication and selection on the behavior of the Norway rat. *J. Nat. Cancer Inst.,* **15:** 727–738.

Roberts, J. A. Fraser, 1952. The genetics of mental deficiency. *Eugen. Rev.,* **44:** 71–83.

Sheldon, W. H., 1940. *Varieties of Human Physique.* 347 pp. Harper, New York.

Shields, J., 1958. Twins brought up apart. *Eugen. Rev.,* **50:** 115–124.

Skodak, M., and Skeels, H. M., 1949. A final follow-up study of one hundred adopted children. *J. Genet. Psych.,* **75:** 85–125.

Slater, E., 1953. Psychotic and neurotic illnesses in twins. *Medical Research Council Spec. Rep. Ser. No.* **278:** 1–385.

Tabah, L., and Sutter, J., 1954. Le niveau intellectuel des enfants d'une même famille. *Ann. Human Genet.,* **19:** 120–150.

Woodworth, R. S., 1941. *Heredity and Environment.* 95 pp. Bulletin 47, Social Science Research Council, New York.

CHAPTER 28

SELECTION AND GENETIC
POLYMORPHISM

In a large population in which each allele present has an equal chance of being transmitted to the next generation, no change in the corporate genetic endowment takes place from generation to generation. If random mating is followed and the reproductive rates of all different genotypes are alike, then not only do the initial allele frequencies remain constant (except for minor chance fluctuations) but also the proportions of individuals who are homozygous or heterozygous for any given locus are constant. There will be, of course, no absolute identity in successive generations. The number of recombinations of the many loci represented by more than one allele is so great that only a small fraction of all possible genotypes is actually found at any given time, even in a large population; thus, different generations contain different samples of the theoretical array of genotypes. By and large, these changes from generation to generation are without trend. Therefore, it may be said that in general the genetic constitution of a large population does not change basically under random mating and equal reproductive rates for different alleles and for different genotypes.

In Chapter 22 on the occurrence of mutations we saw that an equilibrium in the constitution of a population will be preserved even if mutations tend to shift allele frequencies, as long as selective forces balance such mutation pressure. If the frequencies of mutations or the strength of selection change, then alterations in the allelic frequencies take place from one generation to the next and, consequently, the genetic make-up of the population changes. Genetic variations in populations without changes in allele frequencies are also possible if the mating structure becomes reoriented. If, in an originally random-mating population, assortative mating sets in, the proportions of homozygous and heterozygous genotypes will no longer obey the Hardy-

Weinberg Law but will shift in a predictable fashion. Or, if in a population originally subdivided into genetically different isolates a breakdown of the isolates occurs and random mating becomes established, the alleles will be redistributed until they obey the Hardy-Weinberg proportions.

In the evolution of living forms, selection has played an important role. The preferential survival of certain alleles and certain combinations of alleles has led to the establishment of new types of plants and animals. However, selection is not solely an instrument of change; it is also a means of stabilization. If a species is once genetically well fitted for survival in its environment, the majority of new alleles originating by mutation and of new genic combinations will likely have a lower selective value than those alleles and combinations already present. Consequently, selection will tend to purge the species of genetic novelties. A striking example of the conservative role of selection is the equilibrium between mutation and selection. Recurrent mutations which confer lowered reproductive fitness on their bearers are constantly eliminated from the population. Nevertheless, with recessive mutants, even complete lack of fitness of the homozygotes permits a considerable accumulation of the unfavorable mutant in heterozygous individuals.

It has often been considered that, under the influence of civilization, the role of natural selection in human populations has been greatly reduced, and that it is destined to decrease further. Does not civilization, through charitable care and medical skill, reduce or eliminate selection against the less fit by improving his chances of reproduction? Clearly, this question is answered in the affirmative. Nevertheless, there is evidence that natural selection in man is presently active to a far greater degree than the obvious elimination of extreme deviants.

Selection against Heterozygotes Relative to Homozygotes

One of the first demonstrations of striking selective events in man concerned the Rh alleles. As we have seen, erythroblastosis fetalis, which until recently was often fatal, acts against some of the heterozygous children born to Rh-negative mothers and Rh-positive fathers.

Considering only the Rh_o antigen of the Rh system, and representing its genetic counterpart by R and that of its absence by r, we may say that with each hemolytic fetus lost, one R and one r allele are eliminated. This selection against heterozygotes has important consequences. If a population possesses equal numbers of the two alleles ($p_R = q_r = 0.5$), no change in the general make-up of the population will occur, since removal of equal numbers of the two alleles obviously does not alter the allelic frequencies (Fig. 234, A). However, equal frequencies of the two alleles are not found in any human population, and even if such an equality existed at one time, it would soon be disturbed by small chance deviations. Any such inequality would automatically result in still greater inequality since a loss of heterozygotes would mean removal of equal numbers of the two alleles from the unequal numbers

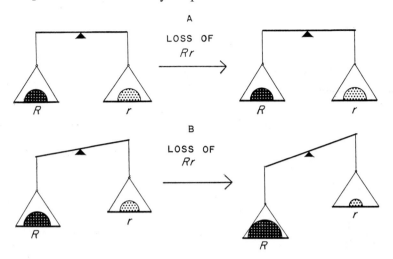

FIG. 234. Selection against heterozygotes. A. In a population in which the alleles *R* and *r* are of equal frequencies, loss of *Rr* children owing to erythroblastosis fetalis will not disturb the equilibrium. B. In a population in which *R* is more frequent than *r*, loss of *Rr* children will shift the allele frequencies toward greater inequality.

present. Consequently, in each generation the imbalance of the two allelic frequencies would become greater (Fig. 234, B) until, finally, the rarer allele would be completely lost. In most populations the frequency of *R* is considerably higher than that of *r*. Therefore, in these populations the *r* allele should eventually be lost. In some races such completion of allelic shift seems to have been reached; for example, the Mongoloids do not possess the *r* allele. No human race is known in which the *R* allele has been lost, but its absence in chimpanzees may possibly represent the end result of selection against heterozygosity in that species.

In the Caucasoid and in some other races, both *R* and *r* persist. In view of the selection against heterozygotes, the presence of *both* alleles requires a special explanation, since the process of "running out" of the rarer allele should, in the course of evolutionary time, have already been completed.

An explanation, proposed by Wiener and Haldane, suggests that, prehistorically, there were some populations with more *R* than *r* alleles, and other populations with more *r* than *R* alleles. Selection, and perhaps chance deviations, resulted in elimination of the rarer allele, so that nonpolymorphic races, some isogenic for *R* and others isogenic for *r*, became established. Then, in the course of migrations, miscegenation occurred between *RR* and *rr* people, which resulted in the appearance of groups such as the present Europeans, who are polymorphic for *R* and *r*. Using certain plausible assumptions, Haldane has calculated that selection against heterozygotes in Europeans would require some 600 generations, or 15,000 years, to reduce the frequency of the Rh-negative individuals from the present 14 per cent to 1 per cent. It can also be shown that the present allelic frequencies may be the result of a hypothetical mingling of a large number of RR with a smaller number of rr individuals about 10,000 years ago, followed by a decrease of r alleles due to selection against heterozygotes. The finding that the Basques have more r than R alleles has given some support to such an assumption. These people have often been regarded as remnants of a very early European race. Possibly, the original European population was isogenic for rr, the immigrants belonging to an RR race.

These suggestive speculations do not take into account possible population dynamics which might greatly delay or even reverse the decrease of the r allele in spite of selection against some of the heterozygotes. One such mechanism might be mutation from R to r, thus replacing all or part of the r alleles lost. This hypothesis will be discussed later in this chapter.

Spencer has suggested another mechanism counteracting selection against heterozygotes. Parents of children lost from erythroblastosis tend to "replace" these children by creating new ones until the number of viable children born is equal to that of the average in the population. This, of course, is usually possible only if the father is heterozygous Rr. The viable children will all be rr and will thus replace the loss of r alleles caused by the death of their Rr erythroblastotic sibs.

A third possibility is that, relative to the homozygotes, selection favors those heterozygotes who come from compatible matings or those who have survived the dangers of incompatibility. Still other possibilities would be selection for rr homozygotes, or combinations of the various factors.

At present there is no evidence for any of these mechanisms except perhaps the second—compensation for lost children. If replacement were absent or were inadequate to make up for losses, then the mean number of living children from Rh-negative women should be lower than that from Rh-positive women, since a fraction of the children of the former would succumb to hemolytic disease. On the contrary, if the mean number of living children from Rh-negative women is equal to, or greater than, that from Rh-positive women, compensation or even overcompensation may be assumed to have taken place. Glass has found indications that both types of relations exist in women of the Baltimore population. Among negro women, the (incompleted) families of Rh-negative mothers consisted of only 2.20 living children, as compared to 2.41 living children of Rh-positive mothers; whereas among white women, Rh-negative mothers had 1.45 living children as compared to 1.37 living children of Rh-positive mothers. It is significant that the Rh-negative white women compensated for the losses due to Rh incompatibility, but the Rh-negative negro women did not replace such losses or did so only partly. The reason for this seems to be a sociological one: the average family size in the negro groups is larger than in the white group. The effective control of family size in the latter group permits an adjustment, if desired; whereas less control in the former group leaves less freedom for adjustment.

The lack of evidence for factors other than compensation to counteract

the results of selection against Rr heterozygotes does not mean that such factors do not exist. It can be proven that even very weak counterselection in
favor of the surviving heterozygotes, or of homozygotes, would greatly affect
the course of populations. Depending on the degree of counterselection, the
changes in allele frequencies which would follow from selection against heterozygotes alone would be slowed down or shifted in the opposite direction. Proof
for the existence of such hypothetical, very weak counterselection requires
large-scale inquiries, which have not yet been made. Similarly, proof for the
existence of mutations from R to r is difficult to provide.

Future studies will undoubtedly contribute to our insight into the dynamics
of human populations which are subjected to selection against heterozygotes.
A fact of general importance is already known and deserves understanding.
It concerns the following question: Could opposing forces of selection against
heterozygotes and in favor of replacing the rarer of the lost alleles balance
each other so completely that the population would not change in its allele
frequencies? The answer, as shown by Haldane, is in the negative. In order
to follow the argument, we investigate first, in somewhat greater detail than
before, the fate of R, r populations with different allele frequencies.

The Frequency of Mortality from Rh Incompatibility.   Obviously, there
can be no losses of heterozygotes when either $p = 1$ or $q = 1$. If we neglect
slight corrections for the fact that a population with selective loss of some
heterozygotes does not fully fit the Hardy-Weinberg Law, then for other
values of p and q the proportion of incompatible mother-offspring combinations is p^2q^2 from marriages of rr women to RR men plus pq^3 from marriages to Rr men. The sum $p^2q^2 + pq^3$ is equal to $pq^2(p + q)$, and since
$(p + q) = 1$, equal to pq^2. Substituting $(1 - q)$ for p, the proportion of
incompatible combinations, expressed in terms of the frequency q for the r
allele, is $q^2(1 - q)$. Actually, as seen earlier, only a small fraction of offspring from incompatible combinations is lost. If this fraction is taken as 0.05
(1 out of 20)—and owing to medical provisions the fraction is now decreasing—we can express the frequency of loss of heterozygotes by a curve, as
shown in Figure 235. The percentage of mortality rises from zero for $q_r = 0$
to a maximum for $q_r = 0.67$, then declines rather steeply to zero for $q_r = 1$.
An average population of European descent with $q_r = 0.4$ corresponds to
point I on the curve. If selection against the heterozygotes alone were determining the future of the R allele frequencies, the allele frequencies q_r in successive generations would move toward the left. A Basque population with
$q_r = 0.6$ corresponds to point II on the curve. Here the allele frequency q_r
would move toward the right.

The Fraction of Alleles Lost.   The graph of Figure 235 gives us the relation between allele frequency and loss of fetus. It is instructive to consider the
relation between allele frequency and loss of R and r alleles. If a population
loses $0.05 \, q^2(1 - q)$ of its zygotes as a result of selection against Rr hetero-

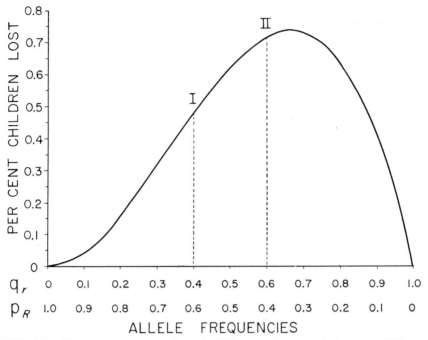

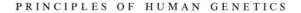

FIG. 235. The per cent mortality of children owing to Rh incompatibility as related to the frequencies p_R and q_r under the simplified assumption of two alleles only. Only 5 per cent of children from incompatible mother-child combinations are assumed to be lethal. I: Position of many Caucasian populations. II: Position of a Basque population. (After Haldane, 1942.)

zygotes, then it loses with them 0.05 $q^2(1 - q)$ of its alleles, equally divided between the R and r alleles. However, the proportions of the R and r alleles lost are unequal for any values of q other than 0.5. The fraction of the existing, $(1 - q)$, R alleles lost is 0.05 $q^2(1 - q)/(1 - q) = 0.05\ q^2$, and that of the existing, q, r alleles is 0.05 $q^2(1 - q)/q = 0.05\ q(1 - q)$.

Curves expressing these relations between allele frequency and fraction of alleles lost are shown in Figure 236, A. The curve for the R allele shows no loss when all alleles of the population are R and shows exponentially increasing relative losses the rarer R becomes. This is easily understandable, since the frequency of Rh-negative women increases with the square of the allele frequency q, so that R-carrying men have a correspondingly increasing chance of producing incompatible heterozygotes.

The curve for the r allele has a different appearance. It, too, begins with no loss when there are only R alleles present and rises at first with increasing number of r alleles. It reaches a maximum for equal frequencies of R and r $(q = [1 - q] = 0.5)$ and then declines at the same rate at it rises until there are no losses again when only r alleles are present. This symmetrical curve also is easily understandable. With low frequencies of r alleles, most of them will exist in heterozygotes, and only part of the small fraction of *rr* homozygotes will be involved in the loss of *r* in the offspring of Rh-negative women. The more *r* alleles that exist, the higher will be the number of *rr* women, but, simultaneously, the number of Rh-positive men will decrease and with it decreases the fraction of *r* alleles lost. The differences between the curves for the fraction of *R* and *r* alleles eliminated are due primarily to the following fact: *R* is a dominant and is potentially subject to selection against incompatible heterozygotes when singly present in a parent; whereas *r* is a recessive which can meet selection only when doubly present in a parent.

Interesting as the two curves for the relation of allele frequencies and allele losses are, their true significance for the population is apparent only when they are considered jointly. It is obvious that a population whose *R* and *r* alleles are of equal frequency loses not only equal *numbers* of *R* and *r* alleles in fetal deaths but also equal *fractions* of the existing alleles. Selection against the *Rr* heterozygotes in populations with unlike frequencies of *R* and *r* results in unlike fractions of loss of the two kinds of alleles. Figure 236, B, shows the ratios of the fractions of *r* to *R* losses for all allele frequencies. This curve is simply the ratio of fractional *r* loss, $0.05\ q(1-q)$, to *R* loss, $0.05\ q^2$. It begins with a very high relative loss of *r* alleles. At $q = 0.1$, still nine times as many *r* alleles are lost, in proportion to those present, than are *R* alleles. The disproportionately high losses of *r* alleles decrease with increasing allele frequency q until, at $q = p = 0.5$, equality of relative losses is reached. With q larger than 0.5, the new inequality of relative losses is to the detriment of the *R* alleles.

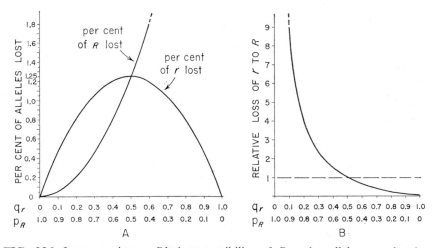

FIG. 236. Losses owing to Rh incompatibility of *R* and *r* alleles as related to their frequencies. Only 5 per cent of children from incompatible mother-child combinations are assumed to be lethal.   A. The per cent losses of *R* and *r* alleles.   B. The loss of *r* alleles relative to that of *R* alleles. (As in Fig. 235, the presence of only two alleles has been assumed.)

Selection against Heterozygotes and Mutation. Let us now assume that the population I in Figure 235 is not subjected solely to selection against heterozygotes, but that mutations from R to r take place at such a rate as to balance exactly the relative loss of r alleles in erythroblastotic mortality. This would require a rather high mutation rate, since the relative loss of r alleles in heterozygotes is considerable. Theoretically, however, a mutation rate could be calculated which would furnish the required balancing gain of r alleles. *But* the population could not persist with unchanged allele frequencies for more than a generation, and once changed even slightly it would by necessity deviate further in future generations. The reasons for this interesting behavior will be given in general terms.

If the frequency of r were q in the first generation and the balancing rate of mutation to r were u, chance would bring it about that the allele frequency q_r in a future generation would not be exactly the same as in the beginning. If, for instance, q_r became slightly higher, then the frequency of mortality of heterozygotes would rise and the relative loss of r alleles from the population would be lower than that prevailing at the original allele frequency. The *rate* of replenishing mutations would of course not change, though the *number* of mutations from R to r would decrease slightly, since with increased frequency of r alleles less R alleles would be present. A quantitative treatment of the interplay between selection and mutation under these circumstances yields the following result. The initial chance increase of the frequency of the r allele would lead to a predictable further increase in the next generation, since mutations to r would then be more numerous than selective losses of r. This situation would persist over successive generations until the frequency of q_r became 0.5. At this stage, loss of r alleles would be balanced by loss of R alleles, but mutations to r would continue. Therefore, the frequency of q_r would rise above 0.5. Once r alleles were more numerous than R alleles, the frequency of the former would increase, owing to selection against heterozygotes, even without mutation to r. Given such mutations, the increase would be accelerated, and the population would tend toward the stable equilibrium $q_r = 1$.

Had chance originally led to an allele frequency q_r of population I slightly below the initial one, then, the detailed treatment shows, the allele frequency would decrease still further in successive generations. Mutations would be insufficient in number to make up for the selective loss of r alleles. The successive shifts of q_r would not tend to lead to the extreme value of $q_r = 0$ but would cease at about $q_r = 0.257$. At this point, there would be a stable equilibrium between the postulated mutation rate and selection, so that the mutation rate which would have supported the (postulated but unstable) initial equilibrium at $q_r = 0.4$ would not only balance the relative loss of r alleles but also tend to overcome any further chance deviations of q_r: a slight increase of q_r is immediately followed by greater selective loss of r alleles, and a decrease by greater gain.

We have seen that the present situation of a typical Caucasoid population, in respect to its frequencies of the R allele, cannot be regarded as one of a stable equilibrium brought about by selection against heterozygotes balanced by mutation. Similarly, compensation by an increase in numbers of pregnancies of Rh-negative mothers who have lost offspring because of Rh incompatibility does not lead to a stable situation except for the two "trivial" equilibrium points of $q_r = 0$ and $q_r = 1$. A mathematical treatment shows that for a given degree of compensation per family there is a third equilibrium point somewhere between the two extremes just mentioned, but that any chance deviation of the allele frequency from this point leads to further deviation in the same direction. The point of unstable equilibrium acts thus as a "repulsive" point to gene frequencies, which move away from it in either direction.

Still other objections can be raised to assuming that selection against Rh heterozygotes in incompatible mother-child combinations may be in equilibrium at present with such possible, postulated situations as selection for those heterozygotes which are viable, or as selection for rr homozygotes. While these types of selective advantages would of course tend to counteract the relatively higher loss of r (than of R) alleles, a slight random change in the initial frequency of q_r would destroy the balance between selection against the incompatible heterozygotes and selection for other types. It appears, then, that the frequency of the R alleles is changing among Caucasoid populations. The direction in which this change goes is not obvious. The percentage of Rh mortality of heterozygotes was greater before modern medical help was available than it is at present, and without effective control over family size, compensation must have been absent or weak. With the exception of the Basques, this must have meant a change of R frequencies toward a lower value of q_r. With lowered mortality, the selective loss of r alleles has been slowed; the degree of compensation suggested by the sample of whites from Baltimore was more than sufficient to counterbalance the loss. If this relation holds for white populations in general, then the frequency q_r is actually on the increase. If medical advances should someday eliminate all losses from Rh incompatibility, no further systematic changes of the allele frequencies would be expected, unless presently unknown attributes of the different alleles would lead to selection independent of incompatibility. We shall soon learn about such attributes in the ABO blood groups. Before proceeding to this and other topics, it may be well to remember that the preceding treatment of Rh groups as if they were based on only two instead of many alleles is a great oversimplification.

Selection against heterozygotes resulting from maternal-fetal incompatibility occurs not only for the R allele but also for other blood-group genes. The very powerful selection against $I^A I^O$, $I^B I^O$, and $I^A I^B$ offspring in certain mother-child combinations has been reported earlier (Chap. 17, p. 345). According to Matsunaga, in Japan selection against these heterozygotes leads to approximately 1 out of 5 early terminations of pregnancy, in potentially incompatible combinations, mainly by abortion, and, occasionally at later stages of pregnancy, by hemolytic disease. Other data, however, suggest a considerably lower selective force.

As in the selection against Rh heterozygotes, selection against ABO because of mother-child incompatibility should lead to successive decreases in the frequencies of the rarer alleles. In all populations the allele I^O is more frequent than is any other I allele, so without opposing forces all populations should tend toward $r_0 = 1$. Such opposing forces are now known, as will be seen in a later section of this chapter.

It will be remembered that incompatibility for the ABO blood groups protects against the effects of Rh incompatibility. Since the frequencies of ABO incompatible matings vary in different populations, the effect of the strength of selection against Rh heterozygotes must also vary. Thus, in negroes, in whom the frequencies of the I^A, I^B, and I^O alleles lead to potential ABO incompatibility in mother-child combinations more often than they do in whites, more protection against Rh losses would be provided. Nevertheless, it may well be that still other genes tend to change the force of selection against Rh heterozygotes in the two populations, for instance by controlling the severity of the hemolytic disease.

In whites and negroes selection against Rh heterozygotes will simultaneously favor selection for I^A and I^B over I^O alleles, since I^A and I^B are less frequently involved than is I^O in the loss of the ABO-compatible, but Rh-incompatible fetuses. In Mongoloids, in whom most combinations are Rh compatible, the loss of I alleles would be proportional to ABO incompatibility, uninfluenced by Rh incompatibility. The relation between selection against heterozygotes in the Rh and ABO blood groups is a reminder that our treatment of selective forces represents only a first approach to the much more complex situation in the total genic systems of individuals and populations.

At present, selection against heterozygotes in man has been demonstrated only in cases of antigenic incompatibilities. It will be important to investigate whether other situations occur in which A^1A^2 heterozygotes are inferior to both A^1A^1 and A^2A^2 homozygotes. There are indications of such occasional relations in other organisms.

Selection for Heterozygotes Relative to Homozygotes

The vigor of hybrids, as compared to that of their parental stocks, has long been known in animal and plant breeding. The often-quoted example of the mule, the result of a cross between the horse and the donkey, is a case in which the individual vigor of the hybrid is accompanied by nearly complete sterility, that is, absence of reproductive fitness. The most famous, modern example of heterosis is hybrid corn, which combines both greater individual vigor and higher reproductive fitness than its pure-bred parents possess. Part of this high selective value of hybrids is due to the superior fitness of heterozygous constitutions at various loci over that of the corresponding homozygotes. A variety of phenomena in diverse animals and plants has likewise been interpreted as intrinsic superiority of heterozygous genotypes.

A remarkable theory of selection for human heterozygotes has come from studies of the three genotypes $Hb_1^A Hb_1^A$, $Hb_1^S Hb_1^A$, $Hb_1^S Hb_1^S$, which possess normal hemoglobin, a mixture of normal and sickle-cell hemoglobin, and sickle-cell hemoglobin, respectively. Great differences in the frequency, q_S, among different African tribes have been noted, and groups of people with high, medium, and very low frequencies of the Hb_1^S allele have also been found in southern India, Greece, and Italy. Following a suggestion by Beet, Allison pointed out that the frequency, q_S, of the allele for sickle-cell hemoglobin in different populations is positively correlated with the frequency of malaria in these populations. The hypothesis was therefore suggested that red blood cells of $Hb_1^A Hb_1^S$ heterozygotes are more resistant to infection by the malarial parasite than are those of $Hb_1^A Hb_1^A$ homozygotes. Since $Hb_1^S Hb_1^S$ homozygotes have a very low reproductive fitness—the majority succumb early to sickle-cell anemia—the presence of malaria in an area would selectively favor $Hb_1^A Hb_1^S$ heterozygotes over both kinds of homozygotes. A small experiment, in which volunteers of the genotypes $Hb_1^A Hb_1^A$ and $Hb_1^A Hb_1^S$ submitted to infection with the so-called subtertian variety of malaria (caused by the protozoan parasite *Plasmodium falciparum*), showed a decidedly greater disease resistance among the heterozygotes than among the normal homozygotes. Other work suggests a similar greater resistance of the $Hb_1^A Hb_1^S$ heterozygotes to anemia caused by hookworm infection. There are still unanswered questions concerning the relation between the sickle-cell gene and malaria. The following discussion assumes that the basic thesis of heterozygote superiority is correct.

We have seen that selection against heterozygotes typically leads to a reduction of frequency, or a disappearance, of one or the other of the two alleles in the population. An opposite effect is produced by selection in favor of heterozygotes. To start with an extreme model, if both homozygotes, AA and $A'A'$, are lethal or sterile, so that the only parents are AA' heterozygotes, then the population would obviously contain equal numbers of A and A' alleles and would be stable. This is so, since the fertile offspring of the AA' parents would consist of AA' genotypes only. In other words, the population would forever retain both A and A' alleles, and their frequencies would be equal. The same result would be obtained if selection against AA and $A'A'$ were not complete but if both homozygotes could have offspring in equal numbers, though fewer than those of the heterozygotes. At the time of fertilization the proportions of AA, AA', and $A'A'$ zygotes would follow the Hardy-Weinberg Law, $p^2:2pq:q^2$, in spite of later selection against survival or fertility of the homozygotes. With p initially equal to q, the loss of equal numbers of AA and $A'A'$ parents or their gametes would not change the proportion of A and A' alleles.

An important property of a selective system which favors heterozygotes is: Whatever the initial allele frequencies are in a population, the population

TABLE 105. *Selection for Heterozygotes during One Generation.*

Population	AA	AA'	$A'A'$	Total Individuals	Alleles
POPULATION I					
Initial proportions					
($p_A = 0.5$; $q_{A'} = 0.5$)	0.25	0.50	0.25	1.00	2.00
Selective values	$\frac{1}{2}$	1	$\frac{1}{2}$		
Proportion after selection	0.125	0.5	0.125	0.75	1.50
Initial proportion in next generation	0.25	0.50	0.25	1.00	2.00
POPULATION II					
Initial proportions					
($p_A = 0.4$; $q_{A'} = 0.6$)	0.16	0.48	0.36	1.00	2.00
Selective values	$\frac{1}{2}$	1	$\frac{1}{2}$		
Proportion after selection					
($p_A^1 = 0.433$; $q_{A'}^1 = 0.567$)	0.08	0.48	0.18	0.74	1.48
Initial proportion in next generation	0.187	0.491	0.322	1.00	2.00

will tend toward a single stable proportion of the alleles. The equilibrium point is determined solely by the strengths of selection against the two homozygotes. Two examples will clarify these assertions. Assume that the selective value of both AA and $A'A'$ homozygotes is one-half that of the AA' heterozygotes, and consider two different populations, I and II, in which the initial allele frequencies are as follows: population I, $p_A = 0.5$, $q_{A'} = 0.5$; population II, $p_A = 0.4$, $q_{A'} = 0.6$ (Table 105). Random mating in population I will produce zygotes in the proportions 0.25:0.5:0.25. After selection, the effective proportions are changed to 0.125:0.5:0.125. The allele frequencies, however, remain as they were before selection, namely,

$$p_A = (2 \cdot 0.125 + 0.5)/1.5 \text{ and } q_{A'} = (0.5 + 2 \cdot 0.125)/1.5 = 0.5.$$

Population I is thus at equilibrium.

In population II, however, random mating will produce zygotes in the proportions 0.16:0.48:0.36, which after selection become 0.08:0.48:0.18. The allele frequencies are now

$$p^1_A = (2 \cdot 0.08 + 0.48)/1.48 = 0.433,$$

and

$$q^1_{A'} = (0.48 + 2 \times 0.18)/1.48 = 0.567.$$

Population II is therefore not in equilibrium. Its allele frequencies have moved from the initial values of $p_A = 0.4$ and $q_{A'} = 0.6$ toward $p_A = q_{A'} = 0.5$. Further progress toward these equilibrium values would be made in successive generations. It is obvious that the reverse change in allele frequencies would occur if population II initially possessed a $p_A = 0.6$ and a $q_{A'} = 0.4$. In one generation, p_A would change to $p^1_A = 0.567$ and $q_{A'}$ to $q^1_{A'} = 0.433$ and thus would have tended toward $p_A = q_{A'} = 0.5$. In selection for heterozygotes, the equilibrium point thus serves as a "point of attraction" for deviating allele frequencies, in contradistinction to selection against heterozygotes where we found it to be a "point of repulsion."

Only rarely will the selective disadvantages of the two homozygous types, relative to those of the heterozygotes, be of equal degree, as assumed in the last examples where the fitnesses of AA and $A'A'$ were both one-half. If the homozygotes differ in fitness, then the equilibrium point will not be at $p_A = q_{A'} = 0.5$ but will be shifted toward a frequency which is higher for that allele whose homozygote is fitter. If, for instance, in a malarial environment the fitness of $Hb_1^A Hb_1^A$ individuals were 0.8, relative to a value of 1 for $Hb_1^A Hb_1^S$, and if the fitness of $Hb_1^S Hb_1^S$ were only 0.1, then a stable equilibrium would be represented by allele frequencies of approximately p_{Hb_1A} 0.82 and $q_{Hb_1S} = 0.18$. For the simple formulas from which these equilibrium values have been obtained, the reader may be referred to Li's *Population Genetics*.

Selection for heterozygosis may also account for retention in many populations of the gene for thalassemia. It has also been considered whether selection for heterozygosis may play a stabilizing role in polygenic inheritance. For many traits intermediate phenotypes may be of selective advantage. For example, it is known that the frequency of infant death at or within a month of birth is higher for the lightest as well as for the heaviest babies than it is for middle-weight babies. Although it is true that birthweight is determined to a large degree by factors other than the genotype of the child itself, its genotype does play a certain role and it is likely that the intermediary classes contain more heterozygotes for the unknown number of loci involved than do the extreme classes. However, as was first pointed out by Fisher, selection for intermediate phenotypes in polygenic traits is not a stabilizer of allele frequencies since such selection may favor both heterozygotes, e.g., $AA'BB'$, and homozygotes, e.g., $A'A'BB$ and $AAB'B'$. Nevertheless, if selection were effective not for intermediate phenotypes in general but specifically for heterozygous genotypes within them, stability may be attained.

If, among the group of intermediate individuals, selection for reproductivity should favor those with polygenic heterozygous genotypes, a trend toward stabilization of allele frequencies would be established. Such a hypothesis of selective advantage involves heterosis from the standpoint of reproductive but not of mental performance. As an alternative one might assume that the genetic component of high mental performance tends to consist of heterozygous genotypes. In this case the low reproductive fitness of high mental performers would signify selection not for, but against, heterozygotes. As seen earlier, this type of selection is not a stabilizer of allele frequencies. It is likely that the genetic basis for high mental performance is different in different individuals. Favorable mental performance in some individuals may be correlated with a variety of homozygous genotypes for a variety of loci; in other individuals, with heterozygous genotypes at a variety of other loci; and in still other individuals, with a variety of combinations of homozygous and heterozygous genotypes. Until we know more about the genetic control of mental performance, we can only work out models from which the trend of the endowment of hypothetical populations can be deduced. The actual processes occurring around us will undoubtedly remain obscure for a long time.

Genetic Polymorphism

The existence in a population of more than one allele at a given locus leads to the appearance of more than one genotype. In the past such genetic polymorphism was often accepted as a fact which did not pose any unusual problem. Indeed, the existence of rare dominant or recessive alleles which cause the appearance of clearly abnormal phenotypes can be understood as a consequence of mutation of the normal allele and of selection which keeps the abnormal allele at a low equilibrium level. With the coexistence in populations of frequent alleles, none of which seems to have an obviously abnormal effect, the situation is different. Examples such as those of the I^A, I^B, I^O alleles, or those of the alleles for so many other blood groups, or of the presence of the two taster alleles T and t, the secretor alleles Se and se, and many others, could hardly be regarded as the result of the opposing mutation-selection processes. It is true that the Hardy-Weinberg equilibrium would lead to permanence of the proportions of genotypes, once the presence of two or more alleles at a locus was established. Even nonrandom mating, with its resulting different proportions of genotypes, would not change the frequencies of the different alleles.

Nevertheless, several questions remained. How did the high frequencies of the different alleles become established in the different populations? Why did the same allele occur in different frequencies, for instance, I^O as low as, or slightly less than, 0.5 and as high as 1.0, or t as low as 0.80 and as high as 0.97? Why, also, did not chance often lead to complete loss of an allele from a population when, as must have happened frequently in the pre-historic past, famine, disease, or war decimated the different, mostly small, human groups? Answers to these questions that were based on such unlikely assumptions as very high mutation rates and striking differences in these rates in different populations were not satisfactory.

There is another set of facts which requires explanation. As widely as allele frequencies may diverge from one population to another, they are usually limited to a range which is narrower than the possible range of 0.0 to 1.0. This is clear from the two examples of I^O and t given in the preceding paragraph.

A striking demonstration of the limited variability of allele frequencies is provided by a detailed study of I^A, I^B, and I^O. In Figure 237, the allele fre-

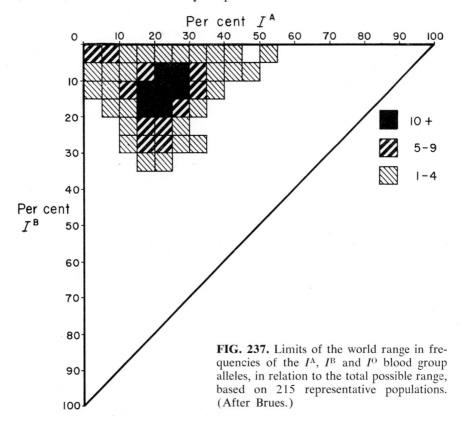

FIG. 237. Limits of the world range in frequencies of the I^A, I^B and I^O blood group alleles, in relation to the total possible range, based on 215 representative populations. (After Brues.)

quencies of 215 different populations are graphed within the possible ranges of I^A and I^B frequencies (and thus also according to their frequencies of I^O, since p + q + r = 1). It is seen that of the whole possible range of gene frequencies, represented by the triangle, only about one-fifth is actually occupied by existing populations. Moreover, even within the occupied range, the populations are not equally distributed; the majority is concentrated in a restricted area.

R. A. Fisher and E. B. Ford have long insisted that the existence and persistence of normal genetic polymorphism must be the result of selective processes which, although less striking than in obvious genetic anomalies, are powerful enough to account for the observed facts. Selection for heterozygotes, originally known only for a few animal cases, seemed to be the most obvious mechanism which would account for the retention of two or more frequent alleles in a population, but it was also foreseen that additional selective forces may be acting on the homozygote.

Selective Attributes of the ABO Blood Groups.   Early attempts had been made to demonstrate selective advantages of one or another of the ABO blood groups, particularly by investigating whether some diseases were less frequent in members of one of the groups than in members of the others. None of these studies seemed to yield convincing evidence.

After the discovery of the role played by the *R* genes in the origin of hemolytic disease of the newborn, it became known that unfavorable antigenic mother-child interactions may also be caused by ABO incompatibility. However, such interactions appeared to be rare.

Waterhouse and Hogben, after considering data from various sources, showed that considerably fewer A children are born to O mothers from A fathers than to A mothers from O fathers. This suggested early and stringent selection (by death of embryos) against $I^A I^O$ heterozygotes in incompatible mother-child combinations. Later work, partly reported in Chapter 17, confirmed these findings. Since selection against heterozygotes at the high strength implied in the data would lead to a rapid change of allele frequencies in the course of generations, and since such facts as the present similarity in allele frequencies of related populations who became separated from one another historically seemed to contradict a rapid change of allele frequencies, it seemed necessary to postulate opposing selective forces. Thus, to consider only one possibility, a high selection in favor of increased reproductivity of the surviving $I^A I^O$ heterozygotes could theoretically overcome the effect of selection against some of the $I^A I^O$ embryos. More recently, indications of differential fertility of women belonging to different blood groups, which might compensate for losses of alleles in incompatible unions, have actually been found. In addition, Alice Brues has worked out a theoretical model of a system of balanced selective effects which could explain the limitations on the present range of ABO frequencies (as shown in Fig. 237) and their relative stability in successive generations.

The data on differential fertility are still difficult to evaluate. It is therefore the more significant that since 1951 an increasing series of studies has fully established a correlation between the ABO blood groups and a number of diseases. Usually these investigations proceeded as follows. A large number of patients suffering from a specific disease were classified according to blood group. The percentages of the different blood groups among the patients were compared with those among a control group of persons not affected by the disease. For patients with diseases such as cancer of the breast, the bronchus, the colon, or the rectum, or with abnormally high blood pressure, the blood-

TABLE 106. *Percentages of ABO Blood Groups in 7,112 Patients with Duodenal Ulcers and in 83,126 Controls, from Eight Different Research Centers.* (Roberts, 1956–1957.)

Group	Ulcer (%)	Control (%)
O	55.51	47.32
A	34.07	39.81
B	7.93	9.60
AB	2.49	3.27

TABLE 107. *Relative Incidence of Duodenal Ulcers in Patients of Different ABO Blood Groups.* (Same data as in Table 106.) (Roberts, 1956–1957.)

Persons of Group:	Compared with Persons of Group:	Relative Incidence
O	A	1.37
O	B	1.42
O	AB	1.54
A	B	1.04
A	AB	1.12
B	AB	1.08

group frequencies were not significantly different from those for the controls. But with certain other diseases there were significant differences. Among more than 7,000 sufferers from duodenal ulcers, 55.51 per cent belonged to blood group O; whereas among more than 83,000 persons of the control groups, only 47.32 per cent belonged to blood group O (Table 106). Correspondingly, the incidence of the A, B, and AB blood groups was lower in the disease sample than in the control. It is possible to express these facts in terms of relative incidence of duodenal ulcer. In Table 107 it is seen that a person belonging to blood group O has from 37 to 54 per cent more likelihood of developing ulcers than have persons belonging to groups A, B, or AB. It is also seen that there is no significant difference in the relative incidence of the disease among the A, B, and AB patients and controls. Consequently, a single, meaningful comparison gives the incidence of duodenal ulcers in group O relative to the sum of incidences in the three other

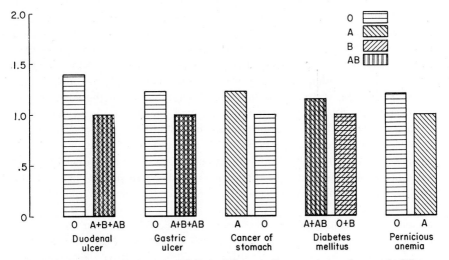

FIG. 238. Relative incidence of five different diseases in patients of different blood groups. (After Roberts; and Bentall, *Acta Genet. Stat. Med.,* **6,** 1956–1957.)

groups. This relative incidence is 1.40, which implies a 40 per cent increase in the likelihood of the disease in group O as compared to other than O individuals.

A similar disadvantage of belonging to blood group O is seen in the increased incidence of gastric ulcer in this group (Fig. 238). On the other hand, O individuals are favored in regard to cancer of the stomach, sugar diabetes, and pernicious anemia—diseases which have an increased relative incidence in members of blood group A.

It is important to realize that the established correlations between ABO blood groups and various diseases do not necessarily imply that the possession of a certain blood-group allele increases the likelihood of contracting the illness. Before assuming such a causal relationship, one must exclude the possibility that the patients do not belong to a subpopulation, i.e., a partial isolate, in which both the specific blood-group allele and the disease happen to be more frequent than in the control group. This point is still under study. It seems unlikely that such isolates would exist in all of the different cities and the countries from which the data have been used and which include England, Scotland, France, Norway, Denmark, Portugal, Switzerland, and the United States.

A direct approach to the problem has also been made by studying the relative incidence of duodenal ulcers, in respect to the blood groups, not between patients and a general control population but between patients and their own sibs. In such a comparison a genetic stratification in respect to blood groups of patients and controls is obviously excluded unless it is causally related to the disease. So far, the data available have shown that the relative incidence of the disease among patients and their healthy sibs differs according to blood-group frequencies in the same general way it does among patients and unrelated controls, but these differences are less striking and statistically not significant. The weight of these findings is limited, since sib studies rely on much smaller samples than do population studies. This smallness is responsible for the fact that while patients and sibs do not diverge significantly from identity of blood-group frequencies, they also do not differ significantly from distributions predicted on the basis that there are true differences in the relative frequencies of affected and healthy individuals!

The meaning of the relations between ABO blood groups and disease, for the dynamics of human population, is not simple. Some diseases, such as cancer of the stomach, mainly affect persons past the reproductive age and therefore should influence the proportions of alleles in successive generations only slightly. Other diseases, such as duodenal ulcers, frequently affect younger people. Although this condition is rarely fatal, it may possibly have a more pronounced effect on the frequency of reproduction, that is, the transmission of alleles. Duodenal ulcer is also correlated with the nonsecretor allele, *se,* of the secretor locus and thus should be a selective agent concerning this gene.

It must be realized that the effective strength of many of these selective processes is limited. Even if there is a higher relative incidence of a certain blood group among patients suffering from a certain disease, it is obvious that only a small fraction of all individuals contract the disease and that in only some of these persons may the relative fertility be influenced. It is the smallness of some of the selective differences and their partly opposing trends which accounts for the good agreement, found in so many populations, of the ABO blood-group frequencies with the Hardy-Weinberg proportions.

The incidences of the diseases mentioned depend on complex and partly unknown environmental factors. For instance, in some diseases the type of food consumed seems to play a role, and the occurrence of duodenal ulcers is obviously correlated with psychological stress. These various interactions will have to be fully explored before all aspects of the polymorphism of the ABO blood groups are understood.

PTC Tasting and Goiter. A curious relation exists between the ability to taste phenylthiocarbamide (PTC) and certain types of the thyroid disease called nodular goiter. Among affected persons a significantly higher frequency of nontasters has been found than among nonaffected. PTC is chemically related to substances which produce goiter, and one is led to speculate on selective forces involving disease in determining the polymorphism at the T, t locus. A deeper understanding of this problem is still to be attained.

Selection and Disease Resistance. One of the important group-selective processes which must have occurred in historical times was selection for resistance to infectious diseases. The accumulation of people in cities and densely populated areas facilitates the spread of disease and the occurrence of epidemics, and it is likely that the great toll of deaths taken by epidemics in former times led to selective elimination of genetically susceptible persons. The many historical incidences in which isolated native populations became seriously endangered by such diseases as measles and tuberculosis, through contact with the relatively resistant Caucasoids, indicate differences in susceptibility which seem to have originated by earlier exposure of, and consequent selection among, the Caucasoids. To account for the low frequency of alleles for disease resistance in unexposed populations, Haldane has suggested that these alleles may have had minor, but unknown and unfavorable, effects on the reproductive fitness of their carriers. If this is true, one might foresee a future in which incidence of alleles conferring resistance to various diseases might decrease again, since modern chemotherapy and antibiotic drugs abolish selective consequences of most infectious illnesses.

Direct evidence of selection in human populations would be provided by data on successive generations of interbreeding populations. If it could be shown that allele frequencies change from one generation to the next, and if chance could be excluded as the cause of such changes, then the existence of "directional" selection would be proven. Absence of allele-frequency changes, however, does not constitute evidence against selection. Selection for heterozygotes is a stabilizing process. The interplay of selection for and against certain homozygotes and heterozygotes (for which examples were given in the associations between blood groups and diseases and mother-child incompatibilities) may likewise result in relative constancy in allele frequencies. Within a single generation the results of selective processes should become apparent if one compares allele frequencies of different age groups, of reproducing versus nonreproducing groups, and of the degree of fertility of different subgroups. Only a beginning has been made in the analysis of these important genetic-demographic phenomena.

Problems

202. (a) What percentage of all pregnancies is potentially subject to selection against Rr heterozygotes in each of seven different populations with the following frequencies of r: 0.01; 0.1; 0.4; 0.5; 0.6; 0.9; 0.99? (b) If selection actually eliminated one-tenth of all children from potentially incompatible mother-child combinations in the above seven populations, what mutation rates, and from which allele to the other, would be required to maintain an (unstable) equilibrium?

203. List all those mother-child combinations which are compatible for ABO and all those which are potentially incompatible. (a) From the data of Table 26, determine for various populations the frequencies of the maternal genotypes and of the incompatible sperm types. (b) Calculate and compare with one another the total frequencies of potentially incompatible combinations.

204. In a certain population, selection during childhood favors the heterozygotes AA' so that the adult population consists of: 10 per cent AA, 10 per cent $A'A'$, and 80 per cent AA'. Assume that this population intermarries with another one of equal size consisting of $A'A'$ individuals only. If the selective processes continue to be active in the mixed population, what will be the allele frequencies after equilibrium?

205. Carry population II of Table 105 through a second generation of selection. What are the allele frequencies $p_{A''}$ and $q_{A''}$? What are the initial proportions of the three genotypes in the following generation?

206. Assume that, in comparison with normal reproductive partners of AA' individuals, AA are reduced in fitness by a specific disease to 0.9 and $A'A'$ to 0.8. (a) Starting with a population in which there are 24 per cent AA and 22 per cent $A'A'$, what will be the percentages in the following generation? (b) What will be the percentages in the second generation?

References

Allison, A. C., 1955. Aspects of polymorphism in man. *Cold Spring Harbor Symp. Quant. Biol.*, 20: 239–255.

————, 1959. Metabolic polymorphisms in mammals, and their bearing on problems of biochemical genetics. *Am. Naturalist*, 93: 5–16.

Brues, Alice M., 1954. Selection and polymorphism in the A-B-O blood groups. *Am. J. Phys. Anthrop.*, n.d. 12: 559–597.

Glass, B., 1950. The action of selection on the principal Rh alleles. *Am. J. Human Genet.*, 2: 269–278.

Haldane, J. B. S., 1942. Selection against heterozygosis in man. *Ann. Eugen.*, **11:** 333–340.

———, 1944. Mutation and the Rhesus reaction. *Nature,* **153:** 106.

Levine, P., 1958. The influence of the ABO system on Rh hemolytic disease. *Hum. Biol.,* **30:** 14–28.

Li, C. C., 1955. *Population Genetics.* 366 pp. University of Chicago Press, Chicago.

Matsunaga, E., 1956. Selektion durch Unverträglichkeit im ABO-Blutgruppensystem zwischen Mutter und Fetus. *Blut,* **2:** 188–198.

———, 1959. Selection in ABO polymorphism in Japanese populations. *J. Med. Ed.,* **34:** 405–413 (also *Am. J. Human Genet.,* **11,** 2 Part 2: 405–413).

Neel, J. V., 1951. The population genetics of two inherited blood dyscrasias in man. *Cold Spring Harbor Symp. Quant. Biol.,* **15:** 141–155.

Roberts, J. A. Fraser, 1956–57. Association between blood groups and disease. *Acta Genet. et Stat. Med.,* **6:** 549–560.

———, 1957. Blood groups and susceptibility to disease. *Brit. J. Prevent. & Soc. Med.,* **11:** 107–125.

CHAPTER 29

SELECTION IN
CIVILIZATION

When Charles Darwin, in the middle of the last century, pointed out the great role which natural selection of certain genetic types has played in the evolution of animal and plant species, it was soon realized that modern man may be subjected to similar selective influences. As a result, two slightly different considerations were advanced, complementary to each other. One dealt with changes in natural selection which civilization has brought about. Darwin stressed that, in the ruthless struggle throughout the millennia of evolution, the genetically less fit had a poorer chance of reproducing its kind than had the more fit. The question arose: Had not civilization created an ominous situation in which the survival not only of the fittest but of many unfit was possible, thus leading to an increase in the undesirable genetic constitutions? But, in contrast to this pessimistic view, another idea fired the imagination toward hopeful prospects: Could not man take into his own hands the future genetic fate of his species? Could he not be more efficient and successful than nature, and by the use of his knowledge, improve the genetic qualities of future generations of men? Francis Galton, who early recognized the importance of twin studies for human genetics, also recognized the social implications of genetic changes in man. He coined the word *eugenics*, meaning hereditary well-being, to cover the whole "study of agencies under social control, that may improve or impair the racial [meaning hereditary] qualities of future generations, either physically or mentally."

Preventive and Progressive Eugenics.   In accordance with its two aspects, the field of eugenics has often been subdivided into two branches called "negative and positive eugenics." Instead of these terms, we shall use the designations preventive and progressive eugenics. The first is concerned with

630

combating the increase or the presence of alleles which produce undesirable phenotypes; the second, with furthering the increase of alleles which cause desirable phenotypes or, at least, guarding against the decrease of such alleles. In so far as specific alleles often do not produce undesirable or desirable results in every genetic background, eugenics may also include the combating of undesirable, and the furthering of desirable, allelic *combinations*. In a sense, the two branches of eugenics are identical, since decrease of un-desirable genic constitutions implies increase of desirable ones and vice versa. In practice, the distinction between preventive and progressive eugenics rests on a difference in emphasis and on the definition of desirable and undesirable genetic constitutions, in relation not so much to each other but, rather, to an average "norm." In preventive eugenics, attention is concentrated on un-desirable, subnormal traits; in progressive eugenics, on desirable, supernormal ones. Trends which improve the genetic endowment of a population are called *eugenic;* and those which entail a deterioration, *dysgenic.*

Frequencies of Defective Traits.   Although the frequencies of strikingly subnormal traits are not known precisely, the total number of affected indi-viduals in the United States amounts to many millions (Table 108). Of course, only in some of these individuals are the subnormal conditions due to hereditary causes: many physical and mental abnormalities are the result of accidental injuries and infectious diseases, and the group of feeble-minded individuals includes an unknown large number of persons whose subnormal intellectual status is partly due to social handicaps. Nevertheless, the sum of genetically defective persons is very large. The estimates in Table 108 are in line with somewhat better, but still not fully reliable, figures from other countries, for instance, Germany and Sweden (Table 109). Some differences in the relative frequencies of the various defects are due to the fact that the criteria for registering a person as crippled or feeble-minded are not uniform from country to country.

If it were possible to decrease the number of afflicted individuals born in each generation, obviously a great reduction in human suffering would be

TABLE 108. *Estimated Defectives in the United States Per 100,000,000 Births.**

Type of Defect	Number
Congenital malformations	1,000,000
Congenital blindness	30,000
Congenital deaf-mutism	30,000
Diabetes mellitus†	1,000,000
Feeble-mindedness†	2,000,000

* How many of these individuals are genetically defective is unknown except in the cases of deaf-mutism. There the number given is exclusive of defects which are probably due to non-genetic causes.

† Defects not apparent at birth.

TABLE 109. *Estimated Defectives in Germany and Sweden.** (After v. Verschuer, 1937, and Dahlberg, 1947.)

	Germany		Sweden	
Type of Defect	No. of Affected	Affected per 1,000	No. of Affected	Affected per 1,000
Blindness	30,000	0.5	6,000	1.0
Deaf-mutism	42,000	0.7	5,400	0.9
Crippleness	90,000	1.5	66,000	11.0
Feeble-mindedness	900,000–1,200,000	15–20	17,400	2.9
Schizophrenia	48,000	0.8	—	—
Manic-depressive psych.	24,000	0.4	—	—
Insanity	—	—	27,000	4.5
Epilepsy	18,000	0.3	4,200	0.7

* Estimated population for Germany 60,000,000; for Sweden 6,000,000. How many of these individuals are genetically defective is unknown.

achieved. Besides eliminating the suffering most experienced by those directly involved—the affected individuals, their nearest relatives, and their associates—such a reduction would benefit society at large.

It is customary in this connection to emphasize the monetary public expenditures required for the care of defective individuals. Some decades ago, a number of studies were published of kindreds in the United States who, in the course of generations, had produced a large number of mentally subnormal and socially undesirable individuals. The "Jukes" and the "Kallikaks," which are literary names assigned to these kindreds, became household words in the discussion of eugenics. The recurrence, generation after generation, of various types of criminality and mental deficiency was taken as proof of the hereditary nature of these traits. It is now recognized that the methods used in gathering these family histories were highly uncritical and that, therefore, these studies give a distorted picture. Moreover, even if the data were unbiased, no valid conclusions about the genetic component of the traits in these families can be drawn, since it is impossible to separate the part played by genetic factors from the influence of the very unfavorable social environment which persisted generation after generation.

It is often stated that the physical defectives and, especially, the "insane," are on the increase in Western nations. If this implies that the absolute numbers of such persons are increasing, this may well be so, since populations as a whole are increasing. A statement of this kind is meaningful only when it refers to the *relative* frequency of defectives in a population. When the facts are stated in relative terms, it is indeed found that the relative number of patients *in institutions* has steadily increased, but the reasons for this rise are by no means obvious.

A rise in the number of institutionalized individuals is furthered by a change in social attitudes and an increase in opportunities for social care.

Whereas, formerly, the mentally ill were kept at home, they are now sent to hospitals. Better diagnosis and better methods of obtaining full reports also result in adding to the census of defectives. In regard to the latter factor, an example may be cited. In Sweden, with its highly developed census system, 4,349 epileptic individuals were registered in 1940. However, a calculation of the number of epileptics in Sweden based upon medical examination of all men of conscription age placed the total of epileptics in that year at about 12,000, indicating that the census had unearthed less than 40 per cent of the actual number of epileptics. Apparently, the accuracy of the census data depended on the willingness of people to divulge the relevant information to the authorities; and this willingness was far from satisfactory. Dahlberg, to whom we owe this example, concluded that "there is plenty of room for an increased frequency through improved registration, even if the actual frequency of hereditary epilepsy were to decrease appreciably."

One more factor may be mentioned, which enters into an interpretation of increased frequencies of certain defects. A number of pathological conditions, among them Huntington's chorea and certain types of mental derangements as well as organic diseases like cancer and diabetes mellitus, tend to make their appearance in the later periods of life. The prolongation of man's average life span through medical and social progress has resulted in a greater number of persons affected with such illnesses.

We have seen that the breakdown of isolates—an aspect of modern civilization—will reduce the frequency of the many types of defects caused by homozygous recessive genotypes. Facts demonstrating this genetic trend have not been observed, since they are, at present, overshadowed by the factors described above, which may simulate an increase in genetic defectives. It must be remembered that a reduction in the frequencies of defective recessive homozygotes due to the breakdown of isolates does not signify a reduction in the frequencies of the recessive alleles. The number of homozygotes per generation is higher within the isolates than in the total population after over-all panmixis. But the absolute number of defective homozygotes produced over many generations is the same for both types of population structure. Furthermore, after the breakdown of isolates, new mutations from normal to recessive alleles will have a lower chance of being counterbalanced by selection against the homozygotes than before. This will lead to increasing allele frequencies until, very gradually, a new equilibrium is reached in which the increased frequency of the recessive allele is matched by an increased frequency of homozygous defectives.

Medical Progress and Rise in Frequency of Abnormal Genes. Apart from factors which lead to increased registration of defects (independently of any change in the actual frequencies), it must be assumed that the frequencies of alleles for certain defective conditions have risen. One of these is diabetes mellitus. Since the discovery of insulin, in 1922, the life expectancy and general health of diabetic persons have improved greatly and their ability to reproduce has been strengthened considerably. This ability has probably led to a higher frequency in the present generation than in earlier ones of the alleles which control the diabetic status. Direct evidence for this supposition is difficult to obtain, since comparable census data on diabetics in different generations are not available, particularly in view of the varying nutritional and social circumstances which influence the occurrence of the defect in an individual.

Other traits which used to reduce the likelihood of reproduction of affected individuals are harelip and cleft palate. These traits often appear together, since they may have a common embryological basis—the failure of lateral anatomic parts to grow together. Formerly, many infants severely affected by cleft palate died soon after birth on account of difficulties in feeding or as consequence of respiratory infections. Of those who survived and had less severe degrees of the defect, a number developed speech defects and minor malformations which reduced their chances of marriage or induced them to abstain from parenthood. Modern surgery has not only succeeded in keeping alive many affected newborns formerly doomed to death but frequently leads to aesthetically highly satisfactory repair of the congenital defects. In all probability, a rise in the frequency of the alleles controlling harelip and cleft palate has taken place in recent times.

Still another example of the fact that progress in medical procedures often results in the propagation of alleles which would otherwise be subject to selective elimination is the disease congenital pyloric stenosis. Occurring in from 2 to 4 of 1,000 live births, this condition is caused by constriction fibers at the opening of the stomach into the small intestine, owing to an extensive overdevelopment of the circular muscles. Before 1912, newborns who were affected with a severe form of the disease did not survive beyond infancy; but in that year an operation was devised which eliminates the condition, permitting the affected individuals to attain adulthood and have children. Although the genetic details are not fully clear, there is no doubt of an important genetic component for the disease, probably a dominant gene with reduced penetrance.

Diabetes mellitus, harelip and cleft palate, and pyloric stenosis are relatively common defects. There are many others which are rarer when appraised singly, but which together add up to a considerable total for which medical knowledge and surgical skill have made possible not only survival but a normal life, including greatly increased chances of reproduction. This increased fitness of the bearers of abnormal genes, together with a presumably unchanged rate of mutation from normal to abnormal, is bound to lead to a higher accumulation of abnormal alleles responsible for the hereditary classes of such defects.

Differential Reproduction and Intelligence

One sphere of eugenic concern which requires a special discussion is the future of the intellectual endowment of populations. The topic is closely linked

TABLE 110.   *Number of Children Born to Native White Women, Aged 45–49, in the United States in 1940.* (Cook, 1951.)

Schooling Completed (yrs.)	No. of Women	Children per Woman	Approx. No. of Adult Daughters	Gain or Loss (%)
Grade school				
0	31,720	3.95	57,096	+80
1–4	148,440	4.33	292,427	+97
5–6	270,960	3.74	448,094	+65
7–8	1,038,220	2.78	1,308,157	+26
High school				
1–3	455,440	2.37	491,875	+8
4	417,260	1.75	333,808	−20
College				
1–3	184,000	1.71	143,520	−22
4+	112,540	1.23	63,022	−44

to the facts of differential reproduction (often referred to as differential fertility), within many populations, particularly of the Western world. If, for instance, the population of the United States is subdivided into different categories according to occupation, educational background, income, or in other ways, it is found that the average number of children per family is different for the different groups. There is a high correlation between factors used in the various classifications; for instance, longer periods of schooling are more common in the higher-income groups. The striking fact regarding the number of children in the different categories is that the average decreases as the socioeconomic status increases. Table 110 gives

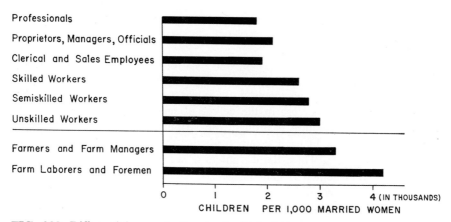

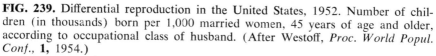

FIG. 239. Differential reproduction in the United States, 1952. Number of children (in thousands) born per 1,000 married women, 45 years of age and older, according to occupational class of husband. (After Westoff, *Proc. World Popul. Conf.*, **1**, 1954.)

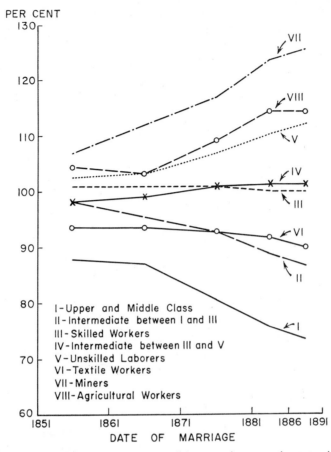

FIG. 240. Differential reproduction according to socioeconomic status in England and Wales during the last half of the nineteenth century. The vertical axis indicates percentage of replacement rate. (Notestein, from Osborn, *Preface to Eugenics*, Harper, 1940.)

the number of children born to native white women from forty-five to forty-nine years old in 1940, arranged according to the amount of schooling of the mother. With only one exception, there was a steady decrease in the number of children with increase in the degree of schooling of the mother. The significance of this relation is brought out strikingly if expressed as gain or loss of adult women in each group from the generation of the mothers to that of the daughters. Thus, the daughters of women with from 1 to 4 years of schooling represented a gain of 97 per cent over their mothers, while those of women who had completed college were only 56 per cent as numerous as their mothers—a loss of 44 per cent. In another form, and for a more recent period, the differential reproduction in the United States is shown in Figure 239, which lists the number of children born to married women forty-five years old and over, arranged by occupational class of the husband. The upper series of bars shows that couples in the professional class had an average of 1.8 children, while the average for unskilled workers was 3.0, with a steady increase between these extremes except for a drop in the clerical and sales group. The lower two bars, relating to farmers and farm laborers, demonstrate that the reproductive patterns of these groups differ from those of the other occupational classes; but, again, the reproductive average of the economically better-situated is lower than that of the poorer ones. That a similar reproductive differential of different occupational levels occurs in other countries is shown in Figure 240 for England and Wales and in Figure 241 for Ireland. In Ireland, the reproductive differential among occupational levels is smaller for Catholics than for the rest of the population, but the trend is the same nevertheless, except for the rural groups.

While there is no doubt regarding the existence of differential reproduction, it should be pointed out that the data presented do not give a full picture of the situation. The number of children born to married women is of course a prime factor in considering the reproductive attributes of a population—that is, its fertility—but there are others which also enter into the situation, such as death before reproduction, frequency of unmarried individuals, and length of generation. Information on differentials in these factors is incomplete, and an accurate evaluation of differential reproduction must await the gathering of more information.

The facts of differential reproduction of groups within a population are, of course, independent of the absolute birth rate of a population as a whole. In the period before World War II, the birth rate in many Western countries

FIG. 241. Number of children (in thousands) born per 1,000 married women in Ireland, according to occupational classes (1946 census data). Sold bars = Catholics; open bars = others. (After McCarthy, *Proc. World Popul. Conf.,* **1,** 1954.)

was insufficient to replace the number of parents. Since that time, the various national birth rates have increased significantly. Whether a population is decreasing, stable, or increasing, differential reproduction of subgroups will determine what proportion of the future population will be derived from each subgroup.

The degrees of differential reproduction of various subgroups are not constant. Although a check on reproduction by control of conception, abortion, and infanticide has been practiced regularly or intermittently for several thousand years by the most diverse peoples, the striking differentials in Western countries among different socioeconomic classes seem to be of relatively recent origin. Birth control became an important social practice in the second half of the nineteenth century, but at first it was restricted largely to the upper and middle socioeconomic layers, resulting in a decrease of their reproductive rates. The differential use of birth-control measures in itself was a cause of differential reproduction. In addition, the survival rate of infants and children was greatly increased by improvement in public health generally, so that the effective reproductive rate increased among the layers which did not practice birth control: more of their numerous children became adults. The changes in relative reproductive rates which occurred in England between 1851 and 1891 (Fig. 240) are evidence of these trends in the use of contraception and in mortality rates.

In recent decades there has been a narrowing of the gaps in reproductive differentials among different groups in several countries. In the United States the mean number of children born to a woman whose husband belonged to the professional group dropped by 1.8 from 1910 to 1952, but the drop for the same period was even greater for the unskilled workers, namely, 2.3 (Fig. 242). These data are based on women with completed fertility and only partly indicate the more recent reproduction trends. A hint of the latter is obtained when one compares the number of children under five years of age

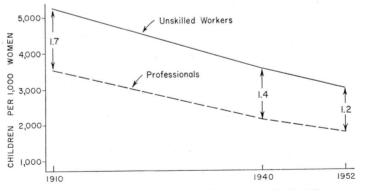

FIG. 242. Number of children (in thousands) born in the United States per 1,000 women of completed fertility in 1910, 1940, and 1952 whose husbands were unskilled workers or professionals. (After Westoff, *Proc. World Popul. Conf.,* **1,** 1954.)

TABLE 111.   *Number of Children Under Five Years of Age per 1,000 Women, Aged 15–49, According to Years of School Completed by Mother.* (Westoff, *Proc. World Pop. Conf.* **1**, 1954.)

Schooling Completed (yrs.)	1940	1947	Change (%)
Grade school			
0–5	405	508	+25
5–6	405	477	+18
7–8	339	422	+24
High school			
1–3	292	396	+36
4	218	323	+48
College			
1–3	197	306	+55
4+	153	271	+77

per 1,000 women in 1940 and 1947, arranged according to years of school completed by the mother (Table 111). The differential in 1940 ranged from 153 for the mothers who had completed college to 405 for the least-educated ones; whereas in 1947 the range had become restricted to the interval from 271 to 508. All groups showed an increased number of children under five years old, but this increase was only from 18 to 25 per cent for mothers with grade-school education, in contrast to 55 and 77 per cent for mothers who had attended college.

The decrease in the differential reproduction in recent decades is probably due to a variety of causes. The spread of contraceptive practices to the lower socioeconomic groups has resulted in an over-all lowering of their formerly high rate of reproduction. The recent increase in reproductivity among all groups—the postwar "baby boom"—has led to a particularly striking increase of births among the groups which formerly had the lowest reproductive rate. In view of the complexity of the biological and especially social factors involved in the human reproductive rate, it is hazardous to predict future trends.

Little is known about reproductive differentials within socioeconomic groups. Some data indicate that the most successful members of the upper groups (success being estimated in various ways) are more reproductive than the less successful ones. The reasons for this higher rate may be, at least partly, related to the favorable financial status of these successful families, which permits the bringing up of more children under good conditions without straining unduly the personal and material resources of the family.

No studies have been made which give information on the reproductivity of different subgroups within the groups of middle or lower socioeconomic statuses. It seems likely, however, that the correlation between success and rate of reproduction is negative. In the upper subgroups of the groups of middle or lower status with their relatively small financial resources, the desire to provide for one's children the most favorable conditions may lead to particularly stringent birth limitation.

Differential reproductivity is a phenomenon not only within individual countries but also among the different racial groups of the earth as a whole. One of the most striking examples on a large scale is provided by the reproductive rate of European Caucasoids and their descendants on other continents relative to that of the rest of mankind. In the seventeenth century they made up approximately 20 per cent of the world's population; in 1940 they represented nearly 40 per cent of all people. It appears that an opposite trend —a relative increase of Asian and African races—has set in more recently.

I.Q. Scores in Various Socioeconomic Groups. The differential reproduction of groups of different socioeconomic statuses is of no concern to the human geneticist if the genetic endowments of the different layers of the population are alike—that is if, by and large, the same allele frequencies for all loci hold for all the different groups. If, on the other hand, different layers differ in their corporate genetic make-up, then differential reproduction constitutes a selective agent in favor of increasing alleles in a population layer which reproduces at a higher rate than the rest. Differential reproduction thus would lead to permanent changes in the genetic constitution of the population as a whole.

It is not possible, at the present time, to state with certainty whether different socioeconomic groups are genetically differentiated. The difficulties of research in this important field are great. The concept of socioeconomic levels itself is subject to various definitions involving occupation, social prestige, amount of income, education, etc.; nor does a simple scale of such levels represent actualities satisfactorily. Although there is a correlation between size of income and occupation or educational level, there are also great overlaps in income among different occupations, so that, for instance, many skilled workers have larger incomes than many professional men, particularly in the younger age groups.

Difficulties of definition are, however, minor in comparison to those involved in finding out whether different groups are, or are not, genetically alike. Mental traits, as we have seen in Chapter 27, differ greatly in expressivity, according to environmental conditions in the widest sense of the term. Undoubtedly, much of the variability in mental traits among different socioeconomic levels is, therefore, attributable to differences connected with the different environments represented by these socioeconomic levels. Psychological tests which measure mental differences are very imperfect indicators of the genetic nature of such differences, since psychologists have not yet succeeded in devising tests which are equally intelligible and equally challenging to individuals who have grown up in different social surroundings.

TABLE 112. *Mean I.Q. of Children (18–54 Months Old) of Fathers of Different Occupational Levels, United States.* (After Goodenough, from Osborn.)

Occupational Level	Mean I.Q. of Children
Professional	125
Business, clerical	120
Skilled	113
Semiskilled	108
Unskilled	96

It has also been pointed out earlier that even a culture-free test would not necessarily yield the measure of genetic endowment. What is wanted is a determination of such endowment in terms of its expression in a given culture but as free as possible from influences of nongenetic—for instance, socioeconomic—factors within the culture.

Intelligence tests of the children of parents belonging to different socioeconomic levels show a rather consistent phenomenon (Tables 112, 113; see also Table 101, Control Children): a decline of the mean scores as one descends from groups of higher to those of lower socioeconomic levels. In attempting an interpretation of this fact, we must take into account a general relation between test score and number of sibs. Various studies have shown that a negative correlation exists between these two variables: the more sibs, the lower the test score of a child (Fig. 243). Numerically this correlation is rather small, approximately -0.3, thus indicating that whatever is responsible for the inverse relation between I.Q. score and size of sibship contributes only a minor fraction to the total variability. Given the differential reproduction of different socioeconomic groups, the decrease in mean test score as one

TABLE 113. *Occupations of Fathers and Intelligence-test Scores of Children, Aged Eleven, Scotland.* (Maximum possible score 76.) (Maxwell, in Scottish Council for Research in Education, 1953.)

Occupational Level	Mean Score of Children
Professionals, large employers	51.8
Small employers	42.7
Salaried employees	47.7
Nonmanual wage earners	43.6
Skilled manual wage earners	37.2
Semiskilled manual wage earners	33.2
Unskilled manual wage earners	31.1
Farmers	36.2
Agricultural workers	32.3

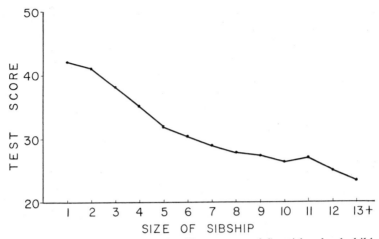

FIG. 243. Mean scores in a group intelligence test of Scottish school children of sibships of different sizes. (Maximum possible score 76.) (After Thomson, in Scottish Council Res. Educ., 1949.)

descends the sequence of socioeconomic levels, therefore, is at least partly an expression of the negative correlation between score and size of sibship.

Notwithstanding its low value, the existence of this negative correlation raises the question of its causes. Do the children in small sibships score higher because their parents have (1) "better-than-average" genes and (2) fewer children? Or is it because their parents are more intelligent for nongenetic reasons and (1) therefore provide more favorable environments and (2) have fewer children? Or is the smaller number of sibs itself solely responsible for the higher scores? If the last two possibilities were actually true, then the negative correlation between intelligence score and size of sibship would have no genetic basis and differential reproductivity no genetic consequences. Parents from different socioeconomic groups would be assumed to have, on the average, the same mental endowment, and their children would have the same mean endowment. Only the more favorable social environment of some groups, as expressed either independently of size of sibship or by size of sib-ship or by both, would be the cause of the higher scores of children in those groups. If, however, the first-named possibility were proven, namely, that endowment of the parents is responsible for their children's scores, then the negative correlation under discussion would involve selection against the better-endowed groups since size of sibship is small.

It has indeed been found that the environment provided in homes of different socioeconomic levels is reflected in differences in test score. One example was furnished by the mean scores of adopted children and the occupational status of their adoptive fathers: the higher the occupational level, the higher the score (Table 101, Adopted Children). Another example is the fact that mean test score is inversely related not only to size of sibship but also to average number of persons occupying a room. Thus, in a Scottish survey of 1947 (to be described below in detail), the mean scores in a test (whose range of possible scores was between 0 and 76) were 47.3 for children from homes with the lowest occupancy rate (less than 1 person per room), 39.3 for children from homes with from 1 to 2 per room, and 34.2 for children from homes with from 2 to 3 per room; the same trend held for still higher occupancy rates. ("Occupancy rate," which is often dependent on size of family and size of home, is, to some degree, an indication of socioeconomic status; but even within a particular occupancy rate there is a negative correlation between test score and size of sibship [Fig. 244].)

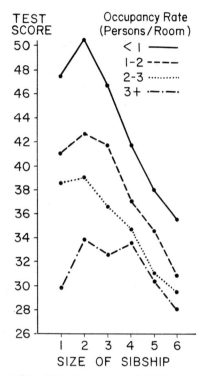

FIG. 244. Mean group-intelligence-test scores in sibships of different sizes according to occupancy rate. (After Maxwell, in Scottish Council Res. Educ., 1953.)

In spite of the undeniable nongenetic component of intelligence-test performance, the data discussed earlier concerning the differences between test scores of "own" and adoptive children (Table 101) and the differences among the test scores of children placed under common institutional care (pp. 596–598) suggest strongly that environment is not the sole agent—that there *are* mean differences in the genetic endowment of the different socioeconomic groups.

The objection has been raised that the assumption of the existence of genetic differences among different socioeconomic groups is sociologically undesirable and dangerous. It is indeed true that often, in the past, proponents of eugenic measures were biased by class prejudice. Since these individuals usually were members of the upper or upper middle class, they tended to ascribe their favorable socioeconomic position almost exclusively to their assumed good genetic endowment and to regard the plight of the lower classes as an unavoidable consequence of their assumed poor genotypes. In more recent times such extreme opinions have rarely been voiced, but some modern writers, among them Darlington, have continued to advocate the basic thesis. Usually there is no denial any more that much of the difference in intelligence-test performance by members of different groups is due to nongenetic factors and that there is a very great overlap in the range of performance among different groups. If, however, as seems very likely to me, there are also genetic causes, then such causes must be accepted regardless of the misuse to which the resulting conclusion about intelligence may be subjected. A fact cannot be denied on the grounds that it may be misused.

TABLE 114. *Distribution by Occupational Level of Fathers of Scottish School Children, Aged Eleven, Scoring 60 or More in a Group Intelligence Test.* (Maximum possible score 76.) (Maxwell, in Scottish Council for Research in Education, 1953.)

Occupational Level	No. of Children	Scoring 60 or More (%)	Scoring 60 or More (N)
Professionals, large employers	221	29.9	66
Small employers	330	10.0	33
Salaried employees	236	18.6	44
Nonmanual wage earners	556	11.3	63
Skilled manual wage earners	2,392	5.6	133
Semiskilled manual wage earners	1,190	2.6	31
Unskilled manual wage earners	1,132	2.1	24
Farmers	142	5.6	8
Agricultural workers	428	3.3	14
Total	6,627	6.3	416

I.Q. Scores within a Socioeconomic Group.   A detailed analysis of the scores of individuals in a population shows that within each socioeconomic level, the scores vary much more than do the mean scores among the different levels. An example of the overlap of test performance of children from different occupational levels will illustrate this situation. Table 114 lists the percentages and numbers of Scottish children who were in the upper 6.3 per cent of the performance range. It is seen that children with high scores occurred in all occupational classes, but that the percentage frequency decreased with each descending class, reflecting the decrease in the mean score of each class. Nevertheless, the largest number of high scorers came from the skilled manual wage earners, who formed the largest group of parents, and less than 16 per cent of all high scorers—66 out of 416—came from the class of professionals and large employers, who formed one of the smallest groups.

The fact that there is a wide spread in I.Q. scores within each socioeconomic group undoubtedly mirrors to some extent the great environmental differences among homes and the different opportunities within any one group. But it must also be assumed that the spread in I.Q. scores is partly due to hereditary differences, which express themselves in varying capacities even within a particular group.

The same conclusion is indicated if the investigation is restricted to the subnormal categories of intelligence. Several studies have shown that the frequency of feeble-minded children was considerably higher in the lower socioeconomic groups than in the upper ones. There is thus an association between low mean I.Q. score of a socioeconomic group and high frequency of *very* low I.Q. scores among their children. This association undoubtedly has an environmental component, in that the cultural environment of a lower socioeconomic status may be more prone to relegate a child of low intellectual potentialities to the feeble-minded group; whereas the environment provided by a higher socioeconomic status might shift the same child into the range of better I.Q.'s.

It seems unlikely, however, that such environmental factors are solely responsible for the higher rate of feeble-minded children in the lower levels. It is more likely that, frequently, certain recombinants of genotypes which are involved in low I.Q. scores in the parents result in genotypes among the children which relegate them to the range of feeble-mindedness. In addition, it is probable that the expressivity of genetic constitutions involved in low scores may vary from feeble-mindedness on upwards, so that the same genotype which, in a parent, permits a score short of feeble-mindedness may cause some of his children to fall into the latter category.

Genetic Differentiation and Social Mobility.   To reach the probable conclusion that there are genetic differences in intellectual endowment of the different socioeconomic levels is one thing, but to arrive at a specific determination of the type and magnitude of these differences is quite another. Undoubtedly, the differences are not absolute in the sense that any socioeconomic layer of a population is in the exclusive or greatly preponderant possession of alleles which control intelligence. There are no sharp boundaries between the different layers, since an appreciable number of individuals in each generation rise from a lower to a higher socioeconomic status, while another number fall from a higher to a lower one. Some of these shifts may be thought of as being due to genetic segregation—of better genotypes in the lower levels and of poorer genotypes in the upper levels. But even if this interpretation should be true, there is a lag caused by the socioeconomic environment into which individuals are born, which keeps many with better genetic endowment from rising, and others with poorer endowment from falling.

Given a wide range of genotypes within each layer of a population, it is to be expected that, in the course of generations, a society with high social mobility will favor within each socioeconomic group an accumulation of specific, similar genotypes. In contrast to this, a society with little mobility should retain a wider range of genotypes in each of its "castes." There are no methods available at present to test these expectations, but it is worthy of some consideration that a society which tends to give equal opportunity to all may by this very endeavor also tend to create genetically differentiated classes.

One may obtain some insight into the origin of genetic differences among layers of a population by considering a "model" studied by Dahlberg. Dahlberg assumed the existence of a population consisting of only two layers, or classes—an upper one, A, of 5 per cent in each generation; and a lower one, B, of 95 per cent—and an initial frequency of a recessive trait aa of 1 per cent in both classes. He then postulated a transfer of aa individuals from class B to class A and calculated what relative changes in class A would

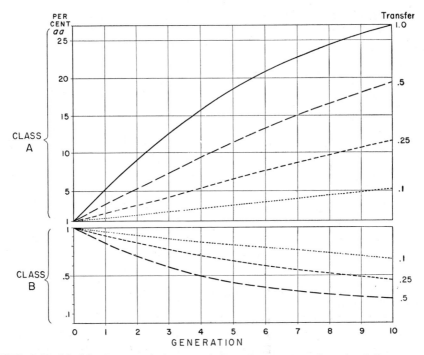

FIG. 245. Model of a population consisting of an upper class A of 5 per cent and a lower class B of 95 per cent with initially 1 per cent *aa* individuals in each class. The curves show the percentage frequencies of *aa* individuals in successive generations after transfer of 0.1, 0.25, 0.5, and 1.0 of all *aa* individuals from B to A has taken place. (After Dahlberg.)

result (Fig. 245). If, in each generation, 10 per cent of the *aa* individuals in class B transfer to class A, then the frequency of *aa* in class A is doubled (2 per cent) after approximately two generations, and it rises to more than 5 per cent after ten generations. If the society permits a greater mobility of *aa* individuals from class B to A, then obviously the increase of *aa* persons in class A proceeds faster. For example, if 50 per cent of the *aa*'s in class B transfer to A in each generation, the frequency of *aa*'s in A will be tripled in one generation and become nearly twentyfold after ten generations. This rather striking enrichment in *aa* individuals of the small class (A) by transfer of *aa* individuals is at the cost of only a minor depletion of the *aa* individuals in the larger class (B): As shown in Figure 245, with a 10 per cent transfer, the increase in *aa*'s in class A after ten generations, from 1 to more than 5 per cent, is accompanied by a decrease in class B of only from 1 to 0.7 per cent; and with a 50 per cent transfer, the nearly twentyfold increase in class A involves a decrease to only slightly less than one-half in class B.

Tendencies toward a genetic differentiation within a population are strengthened in various traits, including intelligence-test performance, by positive assortative mating. In such matings, the intellectual correlation between spouses has been found to be of the order of $+0.55$. Opposing tendencies also exist: genetic heterogeneity within each layer of a population is maintained by marriages between individuals belonging to different levels, particularly since such marriages are often entered into without regard to the intellectual similarity or dissimilarity of the spouses.

Statistical methods have been devised for determining the degree of "heritability" of complex traits such as egg production in poultry or milk yield in cattle, which depend on many gene loci and on an intricate interaction between heredity and environment. The future application of these methods to the results of intelligence tests in human populations should add to our knowledge. However, these methods are not suitable for an individual analysis of specific genotypes—whether they possess dominant, recessive, or intermediate alleles; whether a few or many loci and whether two or many alleles at one locus are involved. Moreover, it should be stressed once more that the intelligence scores cited do not differentiate between the different mental "factors" involved in intelligence, but measure, as one psychologist wrote, "conglomerates of heterogeneous abilities combined in unknown (and varying) proportions."

The Presumed Dysgenic Effect of Differential Reproduction.   Whatever the genetic details, and as important as knowledge of them is for complete understanding, one fact is already apparent: If there are genetic differences between the different socioeconomic layers, then differential reproduction will result in selective increase of some, and decrease of other, allelic frequencies in the population as a whole. Since differential reproduction favors a high rate for the presumably intellectually more poorly endowed groups and a lower rate for the better-endowed groups, a deterioration of the genetic endowment of the population should result.

Attempts have been made to calculate expected changes in I.Q. scores of successive generations. Using the observed mean scores in different socioeconomic levels and the observed reproductive differentials among these levels, various authors arrived at estimates for the decrease in I.Q. for the population as a whole, from one generation to the next. These estimates vary from about one to around five points on the I.Q. scale as the rate of decrease. The uncertainties—such as the degrees of heritability of the mean I.Q. scores characteristic of the different socioeconomic groups—which entered into these calculations are great.

Since these estimates, there have been some actual studies to determine what, if any, decline in mean intelligence scores occurs. The most extensive study is the Scottish Mental Survey. In 1932, more than 87,000 eleven-year-old Scottish school children, constituting more than 90 per cent of all Scottish eleven-year-olds, were given, in groups, a verbal intelligence test; and in 1947 the same test was administered to a similar population of children totaling more than 70,000. In addition, smaller samples of children were given individual intelligence tests of the Binet type. The results of the group test showed

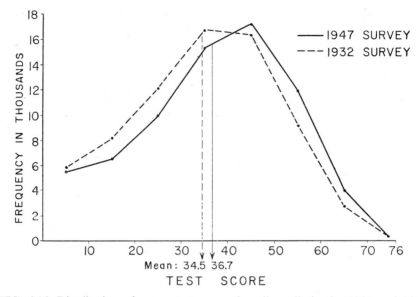

FIG. 246. Distribution of group test scores for all pupils in the 1932 and 1947 Scottish survey. (Maxwell, in *The Trend of Scottish Intelligence,* University of London Press, 1949.)

an increase—not a decrease!—in the mean score of the 1947 population over that of the 1932 population: in 1932, the mean score was 34.5; in 1947, it had risen to 36.7 points. This difference is equivalent to about two points on the I.Q. scale (Fig. 246).

Interestingly enough, the improvement in test performance was not the same for boys and girls. The mean score of the former changed only from 34.5 to 35.9, while that of the latter rose from 34.4 to 37.6. No significant change in the Binet test performance had occurred from 1932 to 1947. Figure 246 shows not only that the mean scores of the group tests had improved but that the whole curve of scores in 1947 had shifted to a level higher than that of 1932. Thus, it is clear that the predicted decline in intelligence-test performance had not taken place among Scottish children. Similar studies in England led to results similar to those in Scotland.

The interpretation of these facts is not obvious. It is unlikely that the observed rise was due to genetic improvement of the population. No selective mechanism for such an improvement is readily envisaged, nor is it likely that such a mechanism would have led to the rather strikingly greater rise for girls. One might therefore be inclined to speculate that some nongenetic factor, such as differences in sibship size of the 1932 and 1947 groups, greater familiarity with mental testing ("test sophistication"), or earlier maturation was responsible for the over-all rise in group test performance.

Do the results of the Scottish Survey, then, disprove the validity of the theoretical forecasts of a diminishing genetic endowment of populations due to differential reproduction? Two different answers have been given by those who accept the likelihood of genetic differences among socioeconomic groups. One answer suggests that the predicted decrease in endowment may actually have taken place but that it was masked by improvement in performance due to nongenetic circumstances. If nongenetic circumstances can lead to higher scores from one generation to the next without a change in genetic endowment, then, it is argued correctly, suitable nongenetic circumstances can lead to higher scores even in the face of genetic decline. Thus, the Scottish Survey may not have led to a decision on the hypothesis of decreasing genetic endowment.

Another answer, proposed by Penrose, denies the need for expecting a decline in innate intelligence. His reasoning has been demonstrated by a greatly simplified model. Assume that intelligence depends on a single pair of genes and that the genotype AA makes for superior, AA' for intermediate, and $A'A'$ for very low performance. Assume further that complete assortative mating of like genotypes occurs and that the $A'A'$ individuals are sublethal weaklings who do not reproduce. Assume finally that the proportion of AA to AA' persons is 90:10 and that their birth rates are 1.89 and 4.00, respectively. Then, as shown in Table 115, the 90 per cent of $AA \times AA$ marriages will yield 170 AA children only, while the 10 per cent of $AA' \times AA'$ marriages will yield 10 AA, 20 AA', and 10 $A'A'$ children. The proportion of the AA and AA' individuals in the F_1 generation then becomes 180:20, identical with the 90:10 proportion of the parental generation.

In this model the birth rate of the superior group is lower than that of the intermediate group, but the relative loss of the A gene owing to insufficient replacement by the AA class is counteracted by the lack of replacement of A' by the $A'A'$ class. The stability of the allele frequencies in this model population obviously rests on reproductive selection for heterozygotes. While intellectually only of intermediate grade, reproductively the heterozygous state is postulated to confer on its bearers the advantage of heterosis.

The assumption of a compensation for low reproductivity of the superior group by low fertility of the inferior group is not wholly artificial. Very in-

TABLE 115. *A Hypothetical Population Segregating for a Single Pair of Alleles Determining Intelligence Performance.* (Completely assortative mating, and highest reproductive fitness of the heterozygotes.) (After Penrose, 1954.)

Type of Marriage	Frequency (%)	Relative Birth Rate	F_1		
			AA	AA'	$A'A'$*
$AA \times AA$	90	1.89	170	—	—
$AA' \times AA'$	10	4.00	10	20	(10)
Proportion of future parental pairs from F_1			90	10	—

* Sublethals.

ferior mental ability often is associated with reduced fertility or complete infertility. In reality, the genetics of mental endowment are of course vastly more complex than the model suggests. Penrose has succeeded in devising elegant schemes in which heterosis for higher fertility of heterozygotes at many polygenic loci yields an equilibrium of allele frequencies.

An analogy to the pattern of relationship between socioeconomic level and intelligence-test score has come to light in the Scottish Survey. Very similar relations exist between height or weight of children and sibship size and occupational class as between intelligence scores and the latter two categories. Therefore, decline in height and weight was to be expected. On the contrary, the height of Scottish pupils of a given age has increased during the period covered by the Survey. Indeed, it has done so since 1910 and is still increasing. This apparent paradox may be explained by environmental improvement whose results masked an actual decrease in genes for greater height, possibly in combination with a heterotic mechanism as was offered in explanation of the intelligence-test results. It is perhaps even more likely that there are no consistent genetic differences for height among different occupational classes, so that a decline should not have been expected.

The fear of a genetically controlled decline of intelligence may have been unwarranted. But even if "gene erosion" is not a serious problem at present, a progressive eugenic program may someday—when we know more than we do now—be concerned with increasing the proportion of favorable genotypes instead of being satisfied with maintaining the current fraction of unfavorable ones. At present, a more pressing problem—one whose solution is bound to yield immediate, tangible results—is the improvement of social circumstances which prevent large numbers of individuals from developing their innate abilities to the highest degree.

The Possible Eugenic Effect of Differential Reproduction. Apart from the problem of whether the present differential reproduction among different socioeconomic groups has a dysgenic effect on intelligence, the question may be raised whether there are desirable gene-controlled mental traits whose frequencies may be positively correlated with reproductive differentials. Although the upper socioeconomic layers of Western societies apparently have a relatively high frequency of genetic constitutions favoring intelligence, they seem to be no better off than other strata in their frequency of alleles which lead to idiocy. Could there be yet a third type of genetically controlled mental trait, for which the upper groups are relatively deficient but which constitute assets to the individual and to society? An unequivocal answer to this question cannot be given, because it would involve consideration of many factors whose exact role is unknown and some of which are inherent contradictions of others.

The first difficulty arises in defining a desirable trait. Emotional stability might be one such trait, but its presence in all individuals would eliminate the appearance of many types of genius which, though often characterized by emotional instability, enrich civilizaton. Altruism may be another desirable trait, but acquisitiveness and the egocentric ambitions of individuals, while often producing misery, have also led to advances which have contributed to the welfare of society at large. It will be hard to agree on definitions of desirable traits—but it is clear that the goal does not lie in uniformity.

Even if some agreement could be reached, a second difficulty is that we have no measures of the genetic component which determines the variability of men in regard to these traits. The social plasticity of man is very great, and different societies and groups within societies mold the attitudes of their members in most diverse ways. Thus, psychological studies have shown that environmental influences can develop cooperativeness or aggressiveness in the same individuals; but this phenomenon does not preclude the possibility that certain genetic components, as yet unknown, may bring out one or the other trait more readily than do certain others.

In this connection, we may refer here once more to the relevant evidence from two genetically different strains of laboratory mice (see p. 576). Under certain conditions, the males of one strain react peaceably to a strange male mouse, while the males of the second strain are highly aggressive toward a stranger. Yet special training can transform both strains of mice, within a few days, either into peaceable or fiercely combative individuals.

Preventive and Progressive Eugenic Measures. Eugenicists have proposed various measures to counteract the decrease in the intensity of natural selection against alleles which cause severe physical and mental abnormalities, and against the presumed dysgenic effects of differential reproduction in Western societies. In order to reduce the frequencies of undesirable genotypes, it is suggested that genetically defective individuals be prevented from reproducing; while, in order to increase the frequencies of favorable alleles, individuals with better-than-normal endowments should be given incentives to have more children.

Specific measures which would lead to a reduction in the number of undesirable genotypes include dissuasion from procreation, prevention of procreation by segregation of the two sexes, or sterilization (not by castration, but by surgical interruption or removal of part of the egg or sperm ducts—an operation which does not affect the physiology or the sexual drive of the individual but only makes the passage of the gametes impossible). In some states, segregation or sterilization can be enforced legally. Another preventive procedure is the medically induced abortion of the fetus if the genetic constitution of either parent makes it highly probable that a severe, incurable defect would appear. Laws permitting induced abortions on eugenic grounds have been passed in several Scandinavian countries.

In addition to these preventive measures, which would apply mainly to certain severe defects, the eugenics program lists provisions for education on the genetic basis of human traits and encouragement of birth control in the lower socioeconomic groups in order to reduce their, supposedly dysgenic, high rate of reproduction.

Progressive measures consist partly in the enlightenment of public opinion by emphasizing the desirability that a larger share of future generations be provided by parents who are best endowed genetically. It is hoped that presentation of the presumed facts will often lead to more children per family in the upper socioeconomic levels. In part, progressive measures consist, also, in improving the social and economic conditions which discourage genetically well-endowed parents from having more children. Sufficiently large subsidies, in the form of higher salaries, greatly reduced taxes, or special bonuses for parents of more than a specified number of children, or community help in the upbringing of the children, are among the methods suggested. However, it is seldom proposed that parents from specific groups be singled out for these premiums, because such a procedure would certainly result in great individual injustices. It is hoped, rather, that the measures would induce those persons who make genetically desirable parents to have more children, and that the less desirable ones who already have a large number of children would not be induced to have still more.

Quantitative Aspects of Selection

We have stressed the tentative nature, if not the often complete lack, of knowledge about the genetic basis of many differences among human beings. Even if the information were more complete, we would still require detailed investigation of the consequences of selective agents on the genetic and phenotypic composition of later generations. In the following pages, a number of theoretical situations will be discussed, in which selection of varying strengths for or against various genotypes is postulated. Some important applications to problems of human genetics will follow from the results of these considerations.

Selection against a Dominant Genotype.   The simplest situation is that of selection against a single factor, autosomal, dominant genotype (DD or Dd) or, conversely, selection for a recessive genotype (dd). In the case of a rare dominant allele, practically all persons carrying it are heterozygous, so that we may restrict our discussion to a population consisting of only Dd and dd individuals. If the dominant allele is fully penetrant and causes its phenotypic effect to occur before the individual reaches the age of reproduction, then suppression of reproduction of all affected individuals will lead to the elimination of the dominant condition from the next generation (Fig. 247, broken line), except for new mutations from the recessive to the dominant allele. (The possibility of mutations, while significant, will not be considered in the remainder of this chapter.)

If, on the other hand, selection, in terms of suppression of reproduction

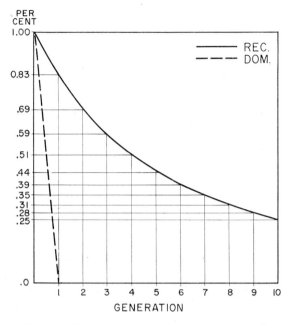

FIG. 247. Complete selection against a rare dominant genotype (broken line) and against a recessive genotype (solid line). Initial frequency of the selected genotype is 1 per cent. The reduction in frequency of the genotypes is shown for ten successive generations of selection.

of *Dd* individuals, acts on only some of these individuals either because penetrance is incomplete or for other reasons, then a fraction of affected persons will appear in successive generations. If, for instance, half of the carriers of a dominant allele are selected against, while the other half reproduces at the rate of the genetically normal population, the number of carrier individuals will be reduced to one-half in the first generation following selection, to one-quarter in the second, and, in general, to $(1/2)^n$ of the original number, where n equals the number of generations (Fig. 248, broken line). If selection affects not the specific fraction of $1/2$ of all affected individuals but a fraction k, then the number of affected individuals in n generations, after the onset of selection, is k^n.

Partial selection in which only a fraction k of the relevant individuals are prevented from reproducing is only a special case of a great variety of partial-selection systems. From the genetic point of view, it makes no difference, for instance, whether the fraction k of the individuals are sterile and the rest fully fertile, or whether all these individuals are fertile but leave only a fraction k of children, as compared to the average quota of genetically normal persons. This latter possibility is often approached when an inherited abnormality results in the death of affected individuals before the age when reproduction normally ceases.

Complete selection against a single dominant factor is thus 100 per cent effective in a single generation, and even partial selection accomplishes much. For example, with a selection factor of one-half, the number of dominants is reduced to a little more than one-tenth of the original number in three generations and has practically disappeared in ten generations. If all dominant chondrodystrophic dwarfs or all individuals with neurofibromatosis did not reproduce, then the unhappiness caused by the birth of affected individuals in these families would be eliminated in one generation. For dominant inherited diseases like Huntington's chorea, which often sets in after the reproductive age has been attained, the reduction of the disease through nonprocreation by phenotypically affected persons will follow the exponential decrease represented by k^n. Even with such incomplete penetrance of a dominant allele, a nearly complete elimination in one generation could be accomplished if *all* children who had an affected parent remained childless regardless of whether they were phenotypically normal or affected. This procedure would involve not only the *Dd* individuals, who might later become diseased, but also their *dd* sibs, who are genetically normal. Such a situation is fraught with tragedy. A person who knows for certain that he is the carrier of a genotype which leads to a very serious disease later in life will usually not wish to risk the chance of producing potentially affected children, but the personal sacrifice in remaining childless will appear very heavy in the case of an individual who does not develop the condition later in life, thereby knowing that he was free from the dreaded allele. The discovery of methods of distinguishing between a *Dd* and a *dd* individual when both still appear normal would obviously be of great benefit, especially to the *dd*'s (see pp. 671–675).

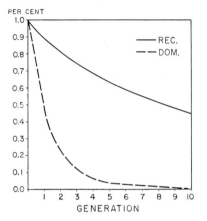

PER CENT

REC.
DOM.

GENERATION

FIG. 248. Selection of 50 per cent for ten successive generations against a rare dominant and a recessive genotype. (After Koller, *Ztschr. Konstitl.,* **19**, 1935.)

Selection against a Recessive Genotype. Selection against a homozygous, single-factor, autosomal genotype (*dd*) or, conversely, selection for a dominant genotype (*Dd* or *DD*) is less effective than the type of selection just discussed. This is due to the fact that many *dd* individuals have heterozygous (*Dd* × *Dd*) parents who are phenotypically normal and thus not directly subject to selection.

If, with full penetrance, the frequency of *dd* is q_0^2 before the onset of selection, and if *no* affected person reproduces, the number of *dd* individuals in the next generation can be easily calculated from the frequency q_1 of the *d* alleles in the reproducing population. The total frequency of the reproducing population is the sum of the *DD* and *Dd* individuals, equal to $p_0^2 + 2p_0q_0$,

while that of the d alleles in this population is one-half of the frequency of
the Dd persons, that is $p_0 q_0$. The proportion of d among all alleles after disregarding the nonreproducing dd persons is thus

$$q_1 = \frac{p_0 q_0}{p_0^2 + 2p_0 q_0} = \frac{q_0}{p_0 + 2q_0},$$

which, because $p_0 = 1 - q_0$, becomes

$$q_1 = \frac{q_0}{1 + q_0}. \tag{1}$$

Therefore, the frequency of dd in the new generation amounts to

$$q_1^2 = \left(\frac{q_0}{1 + q_0}\right)^2. \tag{2}$$

The significance of formula (2) becomes apparent if some specific values
for the initial frequency q_0^2 of dd individuals are used. If, for instance, this
frequency is 1 per cent, then, after one generation of complete selection against
the affected individuals, q_1^2 amounts to 0.83 per cent. If the initial frequency
is 0.83 per cent, selection in one generation will reduce it to 0.69 per cent;
if the initial frequency is 0.01 per cent, the reduction will lead to 0.0098 per
cent.

These figures show two main facts: (1) the lowering of the frequency is
only a fraction of any initial frequency, and (2) the relative efficiency of selection against recessives becomes less with a decrease of the initial frequency.
This latter point is well illustrated by a comparison between the first and last
examples. The reduction from 1 to 0.83 per cent represents a lowering of the
frequency of dd by 17 per cent of the initial frequency, while the reduction
from 0.01 to 0.0098 per cent represents a lowering by only 2 per cent.

This decrease in the effectiveness of selection against recessives with a
lowering of the initial frequency is of great significance if one considers the
results expected from selection continued over many successive generations.
In order to calculate the frequency of dd after any given number of generations of selection, use may be made of a simple relation which gives the allele
frequency q_n after n generations. Since, after one generation of selection, according to equation (1),

$$q_1 = \frac{q_0}{1 + q_0},$$

after two generations

$$q_2 = \frac{q_1}{1 + q_1}.$$

Substituting q_1 by the above fraction, we obtain

$$q_2 = \frac{\dfrac{q_0}{1 + q_0}}{1 + \dfrac{q_0}{1 + q_0}} = \frac{q_0}{1 + 2q_0},$$

and, in general,

$$q_n = \frac{q_0}{1 + nq_0}. \tag{3}$$

If we apply formula (3) for ten successive generations to a population with an initial *dd* frequency of q_0^2 equal to 1 per cent, we obtain the results plotted in Figure 247 (continuous line). It is seen that the reduction of frequency of *dd* becomes less in each successive generation and that, after ten consecutive generations of complete selection, it is still one-quarter of the initial frequency of 1 per cent. To reduce it to one-tenth, that is, 0.1 per cent, would require twenty-two generations, and the number of generations to reduce it further by factors of 10 are 68 generations to reduce the frequency from 0.1 to 0.01 per cent, 216 generations to reduce it from 0.01 to 0.001 per cent, and 684 generations to reduce it from 0.001 to 0.0001 per cent.

The dependence of the efficiency of selection against recessive homozygotes on their initial frequency is shown in Figure 249, in which the results of selection continued for ten generations are shown for eight different populations

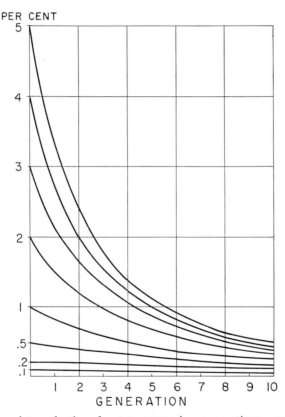

FIG. 249. Complete selection for ten successive generations against recessive genotypes occurring initially at frequencies of from 0.1 to 5 per cent. (After von Hofsten, *Hereditas*, **37**, 1951.)

with initial frequencies of *dd* ranging from 5 per cent down to 0.1 per cent. It is easily seen that progress in elimination of *dd* is faster when the initial frequency is higher, and that, because of the slower progress in the population with the lowest initial frequency, the fiftyfold difference in *dd* carriers at the onset has been reduced to less than ninefold.

If selection against recessives is *not* complete but reduces the average reproduction of *dd* individuals to some fraction of the normal rate, then obviously the effect of the selective process is even less than that discussed above. Elimination from reproduction of one-half of the *dd* individuals cuts an initial frequency of 1 per cent down to 0.91 per cent in the next generation, and, in ten generations, a reduction to little less than one-half of the initial frequency is accomplished as compared to the decrease to one-quarter with full selection. These facts may be visualized by a comparison of the two continuous curves in Figures 247 and 248.

Instead of the results of selection being expressed in terms of reduction of phenotypes, they may be given in terms of reduction of allele frequencies. Corresponding to the decrease of homozygous recessives after complete selection in one generation from an initial frequency of q_0^2 to q_1^2 as shown in Equation (2), the decrease in allele frequency is from q_0 to q_1. In our first example, where q_0^2 was 1 per cent and q_1^2 was 0.83 per cent, the decrease in allele frequency is from $q_0 = 0.1$ to $q_1 = 0.091$. Thus, the loss of the recessive allele amounts to only about 9 per cent of the initial allele frequency in contrast to the more severe reduction of 17 per cent in the frequency of homozygous recessive individuals.

The application of these calculations to human populations is easily seen. Selection, partial or complete, against recessives, reduces the number of affected persons in future generations; but the amount of this reduction per generation is low even for the comparatively common genotypes with a frequency of only 1 per cent, and it drops sharply for rarer conditions.

Selection would be more effective if it included not only the homozygotes themselves, but also certain of their close relatives whose genotypes may be known. Thus, the children from marriages of an affected and a normal person are all heterozygotes; or, to use another example, two-thirds of the normal-appearing sibs of affected persons are heterozygotes. Reducing the reproduction of such relatives, in addition to reducing that of the affected individuals, would lead to greater reduction of the allele frequency from generation to generation; but the immediate effect would be very small, since, in the case of rare alleles, most marriages of heterozygous persons are with homozygous normal ones. It is true, however, that for any two heterozygotes who do not reproduce, two recessive alleles are eliminated, which, on the average, is equivalent to the nonoccurrence, at some future time, of one affected person.

Selection against a Sex-linked Genotype.   We shall omit a detailed discussion of selection against sex-linked alleles, dominant or recessive. Such selection resembles, but is not identical to, selection against autosomal dominant alleles. This property of selection against sex-linked recessives follows from the fact that sex-linked recessives have the same phenotypic effects as do dominants in the hemizygous male. For this reason, selection against sex-linked alleles is rather highly efficient.

In spite of their selective disadvantage, deleterious sex-linked recessives may occasionally spread in a population and be transmitted for many generations. Hemophilia, for instance, which used to eliminate many affected males before they reached the reproductive age, is found in high frequency in several isolates in different parts of the world. It would be possible to eradicate most of the existing alleles for hemophilia in one generation if the following individuals refrained from having children: affected men (h), daughters of affected men (Hh), and sisters of affected men (one half HH, other half Hh). This would leave some h alleles in Hh women whose fathers were normal and who did not have affected brothers. It should be noted, however, that the selection scheme outlined involves the abstention from procreation by some women who do not carry the h allele.

Selection against a Two-factor Polygenic Genotype. A particularly important group in a consideration of selection are polygenic cases, since they

TABLE 116. *Selection against $A^2A^2B^2B^2$. Types and Frequencies of Marriages Which May Give Rise to $A^2A^2B^2B^2$ Offspring.*

Genotypes of Marriages	Frequency of Marriages*	Frequency of $A^2A^2B^2B^2$ Offspring
$A^1A^2B^1B^2 \times A^1A^2B^1B^2$	$\dfrac{4q^4}{1-q^4} \cdot \dfrac{4q^4}{1-q^4} = \dfrac{16q^8}{(1-q^4)^2}$	$\dfrac{q^8}{(1-q^4)^2}$
$A^1A^2B^1B^2 \times A^2A^2B^1B^2$	$2 \cdot \dfrac{4q^4}{1-q^4} \cdot \dfrac{2q^4}{1-q^4} = \dfrac{16q^8}{(1-q^4)^2}$	$\dfrac{2q^8}{(1-q^4)^2}$
$A^1A^2B^1B^2 \times A^1A^2B^2B^2$	$2 \cdot \dfrac{4q^4}{1-q^4} \cdot \dfrac{2q^4}{1-q^4} = \dfrac{16q^8}{(1-q^4)^2}$	$\dfrac{2q^8}{(1-q^4)^2}$
$A^2A^2B^1B^2 \times A^2A^2B^1B^2$	$\dfrac{2q^4}{1-q^4} \cdot \dfrac{2q^4}{1-q^4} = \dfrac{4q^8}{(1-q^4)^2}$	$\dfrac{q^8}{(1-q^4)^2}$
$A^2A^2B^1B^2 \times A^1A^2B^2B^2$	$2 \cdot \dfrac{2q^4}{1-q^4} \cdot \dfrac{2q^4}{1-q^4} = \dfrac{8q^8}{(1-q^4)^2}$	$\dfrac{2q^8}{(1-q^4)^2}$
$A^1A^2B^2B^2 \times A^1A^2B^2B^2$	$\dfrac{2q^4}{1-q^4} \cdot \dfrac{2q^4}{1-q^4} = \dfrac{4q^8}{(1-q^4)^2}$	$\dfrac{q^8}{(1-q^4)^2}$
Total frequency of $A^2A^2B^2B^2$ offspring:		$\dfrac{9q^8}{(1-q^4)^2}$

*$q = p_{A^1} = q_{A^2} = p_{B^1} = q_{B^2}$. The frequencies of the different genotypes have been adjusted to the size of the population after the $A^2A^2B^2B^2$ group has been excluded. This size equals $(1 - q^4)$. For example, the frequency of $A^1A^2B^1B^2$ individuals is $4q^4$ in a population of $(1 - q^4)$, or $4q^4/(1 - q^4)$.

account for the inheritance of quantitative characters. Some examples of selection for and against certain polygenic combinations will be considered.

We shall begin with the assumption that there are two independently inherited pairs of alleles—A^1, A^2 and B^1, B^2—and that the genotype $A^2A^2B^2B^2$ is phenotypically distinguishable from all others. This condition is fulfilled, not only if A^2 and B^2 are recessives, but also under a variety of other conditions, for instance, if A^2 and B^2 have equal and additive effects and the heterozygotes are intermediate between the homozygotes.

The genotypes of the population are $A^1A^1B^1B^1$, $A^1A^2B^1B^1$, $A^1A^1B^1B^2$, $A^2A^2B^1B^1$, $A^1A^1B^2B^2$, $A^1A^2B^1B^2$, $A^2A^2B^1B^2$, $A^1A^2B^2B^2$, and $A^2A^2B^2B^2$. If selection is directed against $A^2A^2B^2B^2$ and if it is assumed, for the first example, that the allele frequencies of A^1, A^2, B^1, and B^2 are alike ($p_{A^1} = q_{A^2} = 0.5$; $p_{B^1} = q_{B^2} = 0.5$), then the initial frequency of $A^2A^2B^2B^2$ individuals is $(q_{A^2})^2 \cdot (q_{B^2})^2 = (0.5)^4 = 0.0625$, or 6.25 per cent. If selection completely eliminates the $A^2A^2B^2B^2$ class from reproduction, all $A^2A^2B^2B^2$ individuals in the next generation are from the types of marriages, and in the frequencies, indicated in Table 116.

The sum of all new $A^2A^2B^2B^2$ individuals amounts to 4 per cent, a considerable reduction from the initial frequency of 6.25 per cent and the same as that in selection against single factor recessive inheritance with an initial frequency of aa individuals of 6.25 per cent. This statement can be verified by calculating the value of q_1^2 according to equation (2) on page 655. If $q_0^2 = 0.0625$, q_1^2 becomes 0.04.

It might be thought, after this result, that the effect of selection against a double homozygous two-factor combination is identical to that against a recessive single factor homozygote. This, however, is not true. As will be shown in the following pages, selection against the $A^2A^2B^2B^2$ class continued after the first generation is increasingly less effective than is selection against an aa class. The effect of selection in polygenic inheritance cannot be judged adequately by its immediate result.

For a second example that demonstrates the effects of continued selection, it will be assumed that the initial frequency of the $A^2A^2B^2B^2$ class is 1 per cent and that the allele frequencies q_{A^2} and q_{B^2} are alike. The assumed frequency of $A^2A^2B^2B^2$ is equivalent to a q_0^4 of 0.01, from which it follows that $q_{A^2} = q_{B^2} = 0.31623$ and $p_{A^1} = p_{B^1} = 0.68377$. After one generation of complete selection against the $A^2A^2B^2B^2$ class, the frequency of new individuals of this genotype is reduced to 0.83 per cent. In order to calculate the further reduction after another generation of complete selection, we could draw up a table similar to Table 116, in which the frequencies of the relevant genotypes would have to be entered in terms of the allele frequencies, p_1 and q_1, established after the preceding selection. If this tabulation is carried out, it is found that the frequency of the $A^2A^2B^2B^2$ class has decreased to 0.735 per cent in the second generation. This is a smaller reduction than that for a single factor recessive, aa, in which the frequency of the affected type by the second generation goes down to 0.694 per cent. The results to ten generations of continued selection against $A^2A^2B^2B^2$ individuals are given in Figure 250 (broken line), as well as the results of selection against a single factor recessive, *aa*, for comparison (continuous line). It is seen, that after ten generations, the $A^2A^2B^2B^2$ genotype still recurs in 0.455 per cent of the individuals, in contrast to 0.25 per cent of the *aa* class.

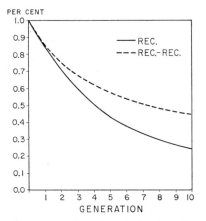

FIG. 250. Complete selection for ten successive generations against a double homozygote (broken line). Solid curve shows complete selection against a homozygote. (After Koller, *Ztschr. Konstitl.,* **19,** 1935.)

In a manner similar to that indicated above, we may calculate, among other examples, the results of selection in two-factor inheritance if the phenotypes against which selection is directed are controlled by *dominant* alleles.

Equilibrium after Selection against a Two-Factor Polygenic Genotype. It was stated above that "the effect of selection in polygenic inheritance cannot be judged adequately by its immediate result." In single factor inheritance with random mating, a change in an allelic frequency immediately results in the establishment of a new equilibrium. This is an expression of the Hardy-Weinberg Law. It was Weinberg himself, however, who realized soon after his discovery of the situation relating to one gene pair, that for multiple pairs, if the equilibrium were disturbed, a new equilibrium would be established only gradually (pp. 169ff.).

The previously treated $A^2A^2B^2B^2$ class in two-gene-pair genotypes may serve as an example of the contrast between the apparent immediate result of selection in the first generation and a "comeback" in later generations. It was seen that, after one generation of selection, this class is reduced from an initial frequency of 6.25 to 4 per cent, and from an initial frequency of 1 per cent to 0.83 per cent. We shall determine the allele frequencies q for A^2 and B^2 after one generation of selection and from these the frequency, $q_1{}^4$ of the type $A^2A^2B^2B^2$, at equilibrium.

Since selection removed all $A^2A^2B^2B^2$ individuals, which occurred with the frequency $q_0{}^4$, the new allele frequencies for A and B become

$$q_1 = \frac{q_0 - q_0{}^4}{1 - q_0{}^4}. \tag{4}$$

The value of q_1 calculated according to this formula for each of the two examples has been entered in Table 117, as well as the value for $q_1{}^4$, which gives the equilibrium frequency of the $A^2A^2B^2B^2$ against which complete selection had occurred for one generation. The last column of the table shows that the initial success of selection, which lowered $A^2A^2B^2B^2$ from 6.25 to 4

TABLE 117.   *Immediate Effect and Equilibrium Effect of One Generation of Selection against* $A^2A^2B^2B^2$.

Initial Frequency of		Frequency After One Generation of Selection of		Frequency of $A^2A^2B^2B^2$ After Selection and After Equilibrium
$A^2A^2B^2B^2$ (q_0^4)	Alleles (q_0)	$A^2A^2B^2B^2$	Alleles (q_1)	(q_1^4)
0.0625	0.5	0.04	0.46667	0.04743
0.01	0.316	0.00826	0.30932	0.00915

per cent, does not continue undiminished, since the frequency of $A^2A^2B^2B^2$ rises to the equilibrium value of 4.7 per cent. Similarly, the initial lowering of the $A^2A^2B^2B^2$ class from 1 to 0.83 per cent is partly reversed by the later rise to 0.91 per cent; that is, the comeback in this case is approximately one-half of the originally lost frequency!

Even more significant is a comparison between q_0, the initial, and q_1, the new, allele frequency of A^2 and B^2 after selection (see the second and fourth columns of Table 117). In the first example, the reduction in allele frequency is from 0.5 to 0.47; and in the second, from 0.32 to 0.31. These very slight changes are a consequence of the genetic situation which makes the overwhelming number of all individuals of these populations carriers for at least one of the alleles A^2 and B^2. Selection against these alleles reaches only the fraction q_0^4 of the population (the $A^2A^2B^2B^2$ individuals), while the alleles A^2 and B^2 present in the rest of the population, $(1 - q_0^4)$, remain untouched. With the exception of the class $A^1A^1B^1B^1$ (p_0^4), all genotypes in the population which are not subjected to selection carry either A^2 or B^2, or both. Therefore, the sum of all carrier classes, S, is

$$S = 1 - p_0^4 - q_0^4. \tag{5}$$

In a population in which $A^2A^2B^2B^2 = 6.25$ per cent, $p_0 = q_0 = 0.5$; therefore, S is 87.5 per cent. In a population in which $A^2A^2B^2B^2 = 1$ per cent $(q_0 = 0.316, p_0 = 0.684)$, S is still as large as 77.1 per cent.

The comeback phenomenon in two-gene-pair inheritance is obviously not restricted to cases in which selection ceased after one generation. In order to show its existence and extent for another example, Figure 251 is provided; it gives the changes in the frequencies of two phenotypes after complete selection had acted for four generations and then ceased.

Polygenic inheritance is usually based on many more than two pairs of genes. The foregoing discussions, modified accordingly, apply likewise to inheritance involving three or more pairs. Since, in a population, the frequency of individuals who are carriers of at least one of the alleles concerned in selection increases with the number of loci, the speed with which selection permanently accomplishes specific results decreases with increasing number of loci.

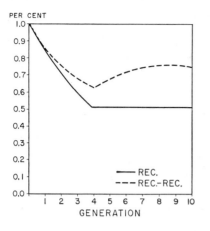

PER CENT

FIG. 251. Complete selection for 4 successive generations, and cessation of selection during the following 6 generations. For the first 4 generations, the curves relating the frequency of various genotypes to the sequence of generations are identical with the ones in Figure 250. For the ensuing 6 generations, during which selection has ceased, the curves show either no change in frequency of genotype (Rec.) or a rise (Rec.-Rec.). (After Koller, *Ztschr. Konstitl.,* **19,** 1935.)

The numerical data presented for selected cases of polygenic inheritance are examples of the kind of information needed for a detailed understanding of the effect of differential reproduction in man upon the phenotypic and genotypic composition of later generations. The model examples used in our discussion cannot be regarded as adequate representations of the as yet unknown genetic situation in such traits as performance in intelligence tests or of other genetic components which are believed to participate in the assignment of individuals to different socioeconomic layers. It already seems plausible, however, that genetic changes brought about by selective agents are small from one generation to the next, and that the effectiveness of selection cannot be judged adequately from a consideration of phenotypic changes. The loss of alleles involved in specific phenotypes against which selection acts is smaller than the reduction in frequency of the phenotypes, because the population at large represents a great reservoir of these alleles.

Opposing Forces Influencing the Effectiveness of Selection

The efficiency of selection has been discussed for populations which, at the beginning of the selective processes, were in equilibrium. It is, however, quite common for specific alleles or combinations of alleles to occur in relatively high concentration in pockets of the population. As we have seen earlier, such conditions are brought about by isolation of subpopulations. Moreover, regardless of the population structure, the allelic distributions will not fulfill the equilibrium demands if assortative mating takes place. Thus, the positive assortative mating which exists in regard to body height and intelligence must result in increased frequencies of homozygotes relative to the heterozygotes.

The efficiency of selection is *increased* if there is a relatively high concentration of alleles in isolates, or if the frequencies of homozygotes or of selected polygenic combinations is higher than in panmixis. This can easily be seen in positive assortative mating, which accumulates, relative to random mating, too many alleles in homozygous or specific polygenic combinations. Consequently, selection against such homozygotes eliminates a larger proportion of the alleles than it does in a population at equilibrium. If alleles are concentrated in an isolate, the situation is similar: more alleles will appear in homozygous or specific polygenic combinations than if the concentration of these alleles is diluted over the whole population. Again, therefore, there is a larger number of individuals who will be subject to selection.

In another respect, the effectiveness of selection may often be *lower* than predicted at first. If an inherited trait has a certain frequency in a random-mating population, it must be ascertained whether the appearance of the trait is due to alleles at the same locus in each affected individual or whether it is caused by different loci. If the former is true, then the observed frequency of the trait enters directly into the calculations of the result of selection, in the manner which has been worked out in the various cases discussed in this chapter. If the trait is the result of two or more different genotypes controlled by different loci, then the effect of selection has to be considered separately for each genotype.

This may be shown by an example. Assume a population in which 1 in 10,000 individuals is blind for genetic reasons, that is, a frequency of 0.0001. If the blindness of all individuals were due to the same homozygous recessive allele, then one generation of selection against the trait would, according to equation (2) (p. 655), reduce its incidence to 0.00009803. On the other hand, if there were ten different and equally numerous genotypes, each of which produces blindness, then the initial frequency of any one of them would be one-tenth of 0.0001, or 0.00001. Selection, for one generation, against one homozygous genotype would reduce it to 0.000009937, so that the frequency of the sum of all individuals affected with any one of the ten genotypes is 0.00009937. If this figure is compared with the one derived under the assumption that hereditary blindness depends on a single homozygous recessive genotype, it is seen that selection against the trait has led to a reduction of only 0.63 per cent of the original frequency when one of ten different genotypes is responsible, as compared to 1.97 per cent when a single genotype causes the trait.

This hypothetical example is probably representative of numerous actual situations, since it has been shown that, often, similar or apparently identical hereditary phenotypes are the result of diverse genetic constitutions. If it is true that selection against certain traits is often *more* effective on account of isolate concentration or assortative mating, than would be expected from random mating, it is equally true that selection is often *less* effective than expected on account of the genetic heterogeneity of many traits. Which of the two opposing forces is stronger will vary from case to case. The recognition that selection acts very slowly against all but single factor dominant genotypes remains the fundamental result of our considerations.

Eugenics and the Slow Action of Selection. This slowness of selective processes against recessive single factors and against polygenes is both a blessing and a curse. It is a fortunate feature, since it forms a powerful buffer against sizable, undesirable effects of selection, as in differential re-production, which is directed against intellectually well-endowed groups. It is an unfortunate feature, since selective measures aimed at eliminating undesirable traits are rendered relatively ineffective. In either respect, the population at large serves as a huge reservoir for alleles from which the desirable and undesirable genotypes can be reconstituted.

If the hopes and fears of the eugenics movement seem greatly exaggerated in the light of a numerical treatment of the problems, it should not be forgotten that the idealism which concerns itself with the genetic fate of future generations has a sound core. To say that the loss of supposedly desirable genotypes in one or even many generations of differential reproduction is small does not mitigate the fact that it *is* a loss which may be regrettable and, possibly, even have serious consequences. To state that reproductive selection against severe physical and mental abnormalities will reduce the number of the affected from one generation to the next by only a small percentage does not alter the fact that the small percentage may represent tens of thousands of individuals. Conversely, even a slight increase of desirable genotypes, through progressive eugenic measures, would be a social gain.

Eugenics and the Control of Environment. Eugenic selection and dysgenic selection are concerned with genetic constitutions which, under present physical, mental, and social circumstances, may lead to desirable or undesirable phenotypes. Since many genotypes express themselves differently under different environmental conditions, it is theoretically possible that new kinds of environments can influence the developmental reactions of those genotypes which now lead to undesirable phenotypes so that desirable phenotypes result. Thus, a certain genotype formerly led to the serious disease diabetes mellitus by causing a deficiency in internally produced insulin, but now an individual with that genotype can lead an almost normal life by means of insulin injections. Or, it may be assumed that one genotype gives its carriers, in their specific educational and social environment, a lower I.Q. than that which another genotype gives to individuals in a different environment. In spite of the genetic circumstances, it might be possible to bring the carriers of the "lower" genotype to the same high achievement as the carriers of "higher" genotypes, provided that a particularly appropriate environment were furnished. A successful search for environments best suited to the development of desirable phenotypes may accomplish sometimes less, at other times as much, and at still other times more improvement of humanity than does genetic selection in a static environment. Provision of favorable environments involves a task equivalent in importance to selection for genotypes which, under present conditions, lead to better phenotypes than others or selection against genotypes which, under present conditions, lead to poorer phenotypes.

It is often asked if the institution of special environments as compensation for deficient gene function does not necessarily lead to a weakened constitution of mankind. If this question means that man thus becomes more dependent on his environment than he would be if natural selection were allowed to operate— with the eventual elimination of deficient genotypes— the answer is in the affirmative as far as the specific trait is concerned. Such dependence on special environments, however, did not start with the advent of civilization. When, in earliest evolutionary times, "animals" first developed, a then new kind of dependence on environment arose, since animals are incapable of synthesizing their protoplasm from inorganic sources and have to rely on other organisms for food. When, much later, man's ancestors lost most of their mammalian body hair, another, but this time minor, step was taken. Man had to rely on fur from other mammals and on fire to keep his temperature at the necessary physiological level.

Man's greater dependence on specific outside sources has not been equivalent to degeneration. On the contrary, dependence has often resulted in greater freedom from the restrictions of the external world. The loss of ability to use inorganic material for food became correlated with the evolution of nervous systems and sense organs which make possible the many autonomous adjustments of animals. The dependence on clothing and fire enabled man to occupy regions of the globe where formerly he could not have survived. The passing of the primitive stages in which each man was, to a large extent, independent of the help of others gave rise to the complex interdependence of men in modern civilization. This new dependence has released man from the physical and mental starvation of earlier times. It is true, however, that man's freedom from many limitations imposed by the external world and even by his own genotypes can persist and be enlarged only if he retains and extends his control over environment and over himself.

Man's ability to create new environments has its limits. It is important to realize that many undesirable traits, such as severe myopia and harelip and cleft palate, against which selection was formerly strong and which have tended to become selectively neutral, may continue to remain disadvantageous for a long time. Although we can correct rather well for myopia by appropriate eyeglasses, harelip and cleft palate often require difficult and repeated surgery. Too much reliance on medical and surgical progress may lead to an ever-increasing number of persons whose normal functioning is made possible only by the performance of major operations, by the permanent use of artificial limbs or other functional aids, by lifelong provision of complex, special diets, or by regularly repeated blood transfusions. At some stage, it seems, preventive eugenic measures will become truly urgent.

The tasks of human genetics concern the present as well as future generations. Genetic counseling is largely devoted to individual problems, although the social implications of any specific advice usually are not disregarded. Eugenic thinking, with its emphasis on the well-being of mankind as a whole, has influenced legislation in various countries in selective immigration, sterilization of selected groups of people, and other measures.

Much of eugenic counseling in the past was based on inadequate knowledge and prejudice, and has been harmful. With increasing knowledge, wise planning will be possible in the future. Then, genetic and eugenic counseling will become the foundation of man's direction of his own biological evolution. Although eugenic problems are not as immediately urgent as the pessimists believe them to be, their ultimate importance can hardly be overestimated.

Problems

207. A dominant allele A has a frequency of 0.01. A recessive allele, b, at another locus, has a frequency of 0.1. (a) What is the frequency of persons affected with the dominant trait? (b) What is the frequency of persons affected with the recessive trait? (c) If none of the affected reproduce, how many dominantly affected persons will appear in the next generation (barring mutation)? (d) If none of the affected reproduce, how many recessively affected persons will appear in the next generation (barring mutation)?

208. In a population of 100,000,000 people, 40,000 are afflicted with a disease caused by a homozygous recessive gene. If these individuals are kept from reproducing and if the size of the population remains constant, what will be the number of afflicted individuals in the next generation?

209. In population I, 50 per cent of all individuals are heterozygous for a dominant gene D, which is penetrant in one-half of all cases. The other 50 per cent are dd. No marriages of $Dd \times Dd$ occur. In panmictic population II, 25 per cent of all individuals are homozygous for a recessive gene a, which is fully penetrant. (a) After one generation of complete selection against the affected individuals in populations I and II, which population will have a larger number of affected? (b) After many generations of selection, which population will have a larger number of affected? (Give reasons for your answers.)

210. With the use of equation 3 (p. 656), determine the frequency of dd individuals after 5, 20, and 50 generations if their initial frequency is (a) 4, (b) 0.25, and (c) 0.04 per cent.

211. With the use of equation 3 (p. 656), show how the numbers of generations required for various reductions in frequencies of dd listed on p. 656 were obtained.

212. Assume that the frequency of a sex-linked affliction in men is 1 in 10,000 and of carrier women 1 in 5,000. (a) If affected individuals ceased to reproduce, what would be the frequency of affected men in the next generation? (b) What would be the frequency of carrier women? (c) What would be the frequency of affected men in the second generation? (d) What would be the frequency of affected men in the tenth generation?

213. Figure 242 shows that the difference in number of children born to mothers of two different groups decreased from 1,700 in 1910 to 1,400 in 1940 and to 1,200 in 1952. How much greater was the fertility of one group than the other group in each of the three periods? (The less fertile group had 3,600, 2,200, and 1,800 children respectively.) Compare the trend shown by your answer with the trend of decreasing absolute differences between the two groups.

214. Assume that the genotype A^1A^1 leads to an average test score of 90, A^1A^2 to 100, and A^2A^2 to 120. A population consists of two equal-sized absolute isolates, I and II. In I, the frequency of the allele A^1 is 1/2; in II it is 1/4.

(a) What is the average score of isolate I? Of isolate II? Of the whole population?

(b) If all individuals in I reproduce at an equal rate, which is twice that in isolate II, what will be the average score of the whole population in the next generation?

(c) In isolate II, if the A^2A^2 individuals reproduce at a rate which is 50 per cent greater than either the A^1A^1 or A^1A^2 individuals, what will be the average score of isolate II in the next generation?

(d) If the individuals of isolate I reproduce at a rate which is twice as great as either the A^1A^1 or A^1A^2 individuals in isolate II, and if in isolate II the A^2A^2 individuals reproduce at a rate 50 per cent greater than either A^1A^1 or A^1A^2 individuals, what will be the average score of the whole population?

215. In the preceding problem, what will be the average score of the whole population after complete breakdown of the isolates and random mating if: (a) The initial population becomes panmictic? (b) The populations defined in Parts b, c, and d, respectively, become panmictic?

References

Boyne, A. W., and Clark, J. R., 1959. Secular change in the intelligence of 11-year-old Aberdeen schoolchildren. *Hum. Biol.*, **31:** 325–333.

Burlingame, L. L., 1940. *Heredity and Social Problems*. 369 pp. McGraw-Hill, New York.

Cook, R. C., 1951. *Human Fertility: The Modern Dilemma*. 380 pp. Wm. Sloane, New York.

Crow, J. F., 1958. Some possibilities for measuring selection intensities in man. *Hum. Biol.*, **30:** 1–13.

Dahlberg, G., 1947. *Mathematical Methods for Population Genetics*. 182 pp. S. Karger, New York.

Dunn, L. C., and Dobzhansky, Th., 1952. *Heredity, Race and Society*. Rev. ed. 143 pp. A Mentor Book, New American Library, New York (see also a critical review: Cook, R. C., and Lush, J. L., 1947. Genetics for the millions. *J. Hered.*, **38:** 299–305).

Haldane, J. B. S., 1924. *Daedalus*. 93 pp. Dutton, New York.

Kiser, C. V., 1942. *Group Differences in Urban Fertility*. 284 pp. Williams & Wilkins, Baltimore.

Osborn, F., 1951. *Preface to Eugenics.* Rev. ed. 333 pp. Harper, New York.

Penrose, L. S., 1954. *The Biology of Mental Defect*. 303 pp. Sidgwick & Jackson, London.

——, 1955. Evidence of heterosis in man. *Proc. Roy. Soc., B.,* **144:** 203–213.

Scottish Council for Research in Education, 1949. *The Trend of Scottish Intelligence*. 151 pp. University of London Press, London.

——, 1953. *Social Implications of the 1947 Scottish Mental Survey*. 356 pp. University of London Press, London.

Siemens, H. W., 1952. *Grundzüge der Vererbungslehre, Rassenhygiene und Bevölkerungspolitik*. 13th ed. 210 pp. J. F. Lehmann, Munich.

Sutter, J., 1950. *L'Eugénique*. 254 pp. Institut National d'Etudes Démographiques. Travaux et Documents, Cahier no. 2, Presses Universitaires de France, Paris.

Verschuer, O. v., 1937. *Erbpathologie.* 2nd ed. 244 pp. Theodor Steinkopf, Dresden und Leipzig.

CHAPTER 30

ASPECTS OF MEDICAL GENETICS

Medical genetics is that branch of human genetics which is directly concerned with the relationship of heredity to disease. Of course, there is no sharp line of demarcation between basic work in genetics and possible applications to medicine. In fact the only Nobel prizes in medicine and physiology awarded to geneticists—T. H. Morgan (1933); H. J. Muller (1946); and G. W. Beadle, E. Tatum, and J. Lederberg (1958)—were in recognition of pure research with the fly Drosophila on the chromosome theory of inheritance and on the production of mutations by X-rays, with the mold *Neurospora* on genetically controlled biochemical reactions, and with the bacterium *Escherichia* on sexual processes.

The chromosome theory of inheritance, now the foundation of pedigree analysis and population genetics, has recently shown its value in the field of human cytogenetics with the discovery of abnormal chromosome constitutions in inherited syndromes (Klinefelter, Turner, mongolism). Radiation genetics has become of utmost importance in the use of nuclear energy for the diagnosis and treatment of disease and to society in general in the determination of radiation effects on future generations. Biochemical and microbial genetics have likewise furnished concepts and tools for the tasks of the modern physician. Conversely, the medical profession's interest in blood transfusion and immunology has led to the fundamental discoveries of blood groups and their genetics, and the concern with sickle-cell anemia has culminated in the elucidation of the molecular structure of different hemoglobins as determined by different alleles.

The present chapter will briefly survey specifically medical aspects of human genetics, many of which have been discussed elsewhere in this book. For a discussion of medicolegal problems, see Chapter 12.

Genetic Heterogeneity of Diseases.   Clinical studies of individuals affected with some defect or disease have frequently shown that a presumed single disease is in reality a group of different diseases with similar manifestations.

Mental defect, for instance, may have any one (or more) of many underlying causes, both nongenetic and genetic. The clinician is able to distinguish some of the different kinds of inherited mental defect as part of various syndromes (e.g., Tay-Sachs disease, mongolism) or by biochemical differentiation (e.g., phenylketonuric feeble-mindedness). The geneticist has contributed evidence for heterogeneous causes of diseases by finding single-gene recessive inheritance in some kinds of mental defect (Tay-Sachs disease, phenylketonuria), gross chromosomal imbalance in another (mongolism), and polygenic determination in still others ("undifferentiated" mental deficiency). In diabetes insipidus, one of two different physiologic disturbances is responsible for the abnormally high excretion of water: a primary deficiency, or absence, of a pituitary hormone; or an abnormal primary function of the kidney tubules. The geneticist has only partly been able to discover heterogeneity of causes for this disease, since both types of abnormal water metabolism may be inherited in the same X-linked way, though presumably through genes at different loci. However, the genetic heterogeneity of diabetes insipidus goes beyond the X-chromosome, for extensive pedigrees showing dominant autosomal inheritance are also on record.

With other diseases, either the genetic evidence suggests that for apparently the same disease different mechanisms may be involved in different kindreds, or it at least supports the finding of differences by the diagnostician. For example, retinitis pigmentosa, a retinal disease that may lead to blindness, is inherited in autosomal fashion in some kindreds and in X-linked fashion in others. In addition, there are dominant as well as recessive genes for both autosomal and X-linked types. It may be that the pathology of this disease is basically different in the genetically different types, but full knowledge is still lacking. Genetic heterogeneity is also revealed by linkage studies. The heterogeneity of recombination values between the Rh blood groups and elliptocytosis (p. 277) implies the existence of at least two different gene loci involved in this abnormality of the red blood cells and therefore, presumably, of at least two different, but still unknown, physiological mechanisms which lead to the disease.

The finding of genetic heterogeneity of an abnormality may be fundamental to the discovery of the specific steps in its development. And knowledge of how the defect is inherited may later help in its prevention or cure.

Disease Resistance.   In many diseases, external agents are clearly the major causes. This is pre-eminently true of infectious diseases produced by bacteria, fungi, viruses, and animal parasites. But external agents are also instrumental in diseases due to malnutrition, such as degeneration of the liver owing to alcoholism; psychosomatic diseases, such as gastric or duodenal ulcers, which are related in some degree to mental stress; and some types of mental illness. It has become increasingly apparent, however, that humans differ in their genetic susceptibility to nongenetic causes of disease. This is not surprising in view of the successes of plant and animal breeders in raising organisms resistant to various conditions: rust-resistant wheat, cold-resistant fruit trees, wilt-resistant watermelons, typhoid-resistant poultry, and cattle resistant to tick-borne diseases. We have already cited genetic evidence for human susceptibility to infectious agents in general, as in hypogammaglobulinemia; or to special pathogenic agents, as in tuberculosis and poliomyelitis; to ulcers; and to mental illness. Genetic predisposition to certain types of tumors has also been demonstrated—with full or high penetrance in special types such as polyposis of the colon and neurofibromatosis, or with presumably low penetrance in the more common types of cancer. Such predisposition may ultimately be shown to be susceptibility to an external agent, should the virus theory of the origin of cancer be generally substantiated.

Genetic differences in susceptibility to certain drugs are also known. An X-linked gene is responsible for the severe anemia of susceptible persons who have eaten raw *fava* beans or have taken primaquine or chemically related drugs. There are also rare kindreds with individuals in whom the compound suxomethonium, a short-term muscle relaxant used in anesthesia, may cause a serious, protracted paralysis of the respiratory muscles. The abnormal reaction of the affected individuals is due to their genetically determined deficiency of the enzyme pseudocholinesterase, which is severe in some (homozygotes?) and moderate in others (heterozygotes?). In these individuals, suxomethonium is broken down too slowly and exerts its effect on the muscles for a dangerously long time. We may also refer again to the genetic variability of rickets, the deficiency disease. Most people are protected against this disease by moderate intake of vitamin D, but some individuals, who are "resistant" to vitamin D, require excessive amounts.

Evidence of drug resistance, presumably by spontaneous mutation, has been obtained in the somatic cells of mice and rats. Tumor tissues which are perpetuated by transplantation from one animal to another may be highly susceptible to various chemotherapeutic agents such as A-methopterin or 6-mercaptopurine, which are lethal in certain concentrations. But within an originally homogeneous line of tumor cells, some cells may develop that are resistant to, or even dependent upon, the normally destructive chemicals. Normal tissue cells grown in tissue cultures have also been found to develop drug-resistant strains, which result from a spontaneous, presumably genetic change in a single cell that occurs before administration of the drug. The drug itself is solely instrumental in killing the majority of nonresistant cells but selectively sparing the mutant resistant ones.

These striking phenomena had been discovered earlier in microorganisms, particularly in bacteria. Among millions of bacterial cells killed by such agents as sulfa drugs, penicillin, and streptomycin, a few survived—resistant to, or even dependent upon, the usually lethal compounds. For some of these microorganisms, hybridization or equivalent methods have proved that spontaneous genic mutations resulting in drug resistance or dependence, and subsequent selection by application of the drug, were responsible for the new strains.

The genetic involvement in resistance to infectious agents is thus twofold: genes are involved in the host's ability to resist the microorganism; and genes are involved in the resistance of the invading microorganism to the host's natural or therapeutic countermeasures.

The Recognition of Carrier States. It would seem that, by definition, individuals who are heterozygous for a "recessive" gene, A^2, are not distinguishable from the homozygous dominant A^1A^1. However, dominance and recessivity are relative terms, in the sense that their recognition depends on one's ability to distinguish the three phenotypes corresponding to A^1A^1, A^1A^2, and A^2A^2. When A^1A^2 is indistinguishable from A^1A^1, then A^2 is correctly called a recessive; but when refined observations disclose two different phenotypes produced by the two genotypes, then the designation of A^2 as a recessive is no longer fully valid. It is nevertheless customary in human genetics to speak of A^2 as a recessive if A^2A^2 causes a phenotype strikingly different from that of A^1A^1 and if the heterozygote A^1A^2 seems to resemble the normal A^1A^1.

The often arbitrary use of the terms dominance and recessivity is illustrated in the case of sickle-cell anemia. The genotype $Hb_1{}^SHb_1{}^S$ leads to a severe, often fatal illness, while both $Hb_1{}^AHb_1{}^A$ and $Hb_1{}^AHb_1{}^S$ produce a normal, nondefective phenotype. In terms of the anemic effect, $Hb_1{}^S$ is a recessive. However, a study of red blood cells which have been subjected to low oxygen pressure reveals absence of sickling in $Hb_1{}^AHb_1{}^A$, severe sickling in $Hb_1{}^SHb_1{}^S$, and an intermediate degree of sickling in $Hb_1{}^AHb_1{}^S$. Finally, at the molecular level, the two alleles in the heterozygote act codominantly, leading to the production of a mixture of hemoglobins A and S.

Many geneticists have attempted to discover differences between normal homozygotes and apparently normal heterozygotes for recessive genes that cause defects in homozygotes. Such discoveries would strengthen genetic hypotheses of recessiveness by providing direct proof of the heterozygosity of both parents of defective children. More important, as emphasized by Neel, these findings would be of general significance for human genetics in various other ways. An understanding of the interplay, in human populations, of mutation and selection for and against heterozygotes and homozygotes would be furthered if direct observation could distinguish between all genotypes. Also, the recognition of genetic factors in malformations would be facilitated if one could identify not only grossly abnormal types which may be based on homozygous genotypes but also transition stages between normal and abnormal which may have a heterozygous genetic basis. And, in genetic counseling, it would represent a great step forward if it were possible to distinguish between the heterozygous and homozygous normal sibs or

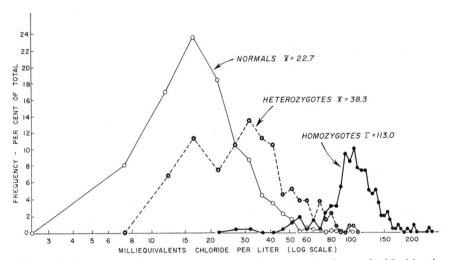

FIG. 252. Cystic fibrosis of the pancreas. The concentrations of chlorides in sweat of 665 normal, 133 heterozygous, and 259 affected individuals. $\bar{x}$ = mean concentration. (After an original graph of Shwachman, Steinberg, Dooley, and M. Stern.)

other relatives of homozygous recessive affected individuals, since one could give advice founded on certain knowledge instead of on probability.

The search for recognizable phenotypic criteria of the heterozygous carrier state has been successful in numerous genotypes. For some genes it is now possible to distinguish unequivocally individuals of all three genotypes, but for most genes the overlap in phenotypic expression makes it difficult to distinguish some of the heterozygotes from the normal homozygotes. An

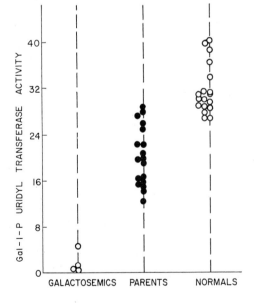

FIG. 253. Galactosemia. Determinations of the activity of the enzyme Gal-l-p uridyl transferase in 18 homozygous normal individuals, 18 heterozygous parents of affected children, and 4 homozygous affected persons. The activities are expressed as microliters oxygen uptake per volume for 0.3 cc packed and hemolyzed red blood cells. The affected individuals whose activity was measured as above zero had been given a transfusion of normal blood some time before the test. (After Kirkman and Bynum, *Ann. Human Genet.*, **23**, 1959.)

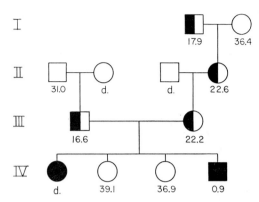

FIG. 254. Galactosemia. A pedigree giving the enzyme activity for individuals of four generations in terms explained for Figure 253. Black-and-white symbol = low activity; solid black = galactosemia; d = dead. (After Kirkman and Bynum, *Ann. Human Genet.*, **23**, 1959.)

example is the disease cystic fibrosis of the pancreas, which is fatal in children homozygous for the recessive gene involved. The sweat of affected individuals has an increased concentration of chlorides, but in a small fraction of those affected the chloride concentration is low enough to be within the range of that in certain homozygous normal individuals with relatively high concentration. On the whole the concentration of chlorides in the sweat of heterozygotes is midway between that of the normal and the affected homozygotes, but all three distributions overlap greatly (Fig. 252).

In the rare congenital disease galactosemia, the abnormal homozygotes are fully separable from the heterozygotes, but there is some overlap in the degree of a specific biochemical activity of heterozygotes and normal homozygotes (Fig. 253). Affected individuals seem to lack completely the enzyme α-D-galactose-l-phosphate uridil transferase, which is necessary for the normal metabolism of the sugar galactose. Heterozygotes generally have between 60 and 70 per cent of the enzymatic activity of normal homozygotes. The pedigree shown in Figure 254 gives details of the enzymatic state of the parents,

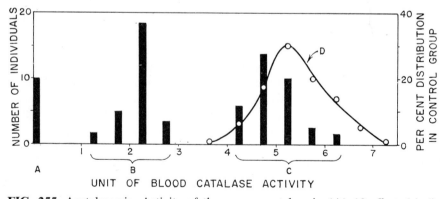

FIG. 255. Acatalasemia. Activity of the enzyme catalase in (A) 10 affected individuals, (B) 30 relatives with low activity, and (C) 36 relatives with normal activity. The curve (D) represents the percentage distribution of activity in 206 controls. (After Nishimura, Hamilton, Kobara, Takahara, Ogura, and Doi, *Science*, **130**, 1959.)

sibs, and other relatives of two affected individuals. It may be added that the amount of overlap between homozygotes and heterozygotes depends on the type of test. The galactose "tolerance test" determines the amount of milk sugar lost from the blood after intake of a given amount of the substance. The more direct tests (whose results are listed in Figs. 253 and 254) measure the enzymatic activity either in liver tissue obtained by surgery or in red blood cells.

One more example demonstrates success in completely separating the phenotypes of all three genotypes. A very rare gene, in homozygous individuals, leads to the absence in the blood of catalase, an enzyme found in considerable amounts in most individuals. The catalase content of the blood of heterozygotes is intermediate, without overlap, between that of the two homozygotes (Fig. 255).

It is not known whether the alleles for galactosemia and for acatalasemia that do not cause the appearance of the appropriate enzymes do not function at all or whether they control the production of some specific substances which are enzymatically inactive for the reactions studied. In other genotypes, the presence of both the normal and the abnormal allele is phenotypically expressed by the presence of a characteristic molecular material. This is true for the various alleles concerned with hemoglobin structure, which in heterozygotes act codominantly. It is also true for many, but not all, of the Rh alleles. Thus, r' determines antigenic properties which react with anti-rh$'$ serum, and r'' determines antigenic properties which react with anti-rh$''$. In the heterozygote $r'r''$, antigens reacting with both antisera are present. In contrast, R^1 and r' seem to be distinguished not by their control of different antigens but by the presence in R^1 and absence in r' of a reaction of red blood cells against an anti-Rh$_0$ serum. Correspondingly, the heterozygous carrier of r' (R^1r') is not phenotypically distinguishable from the homozygote R^1R^1 by the presence of a specific antigen-antibody reaction. Recent work on antibodies labeled with a radioactive isotope has shown, however, that the blood cells of the heterozygote bind fewer antibodies than do those of the homozygote. Nonoverlapping distributions of bound antibody have been observed in the two genotypes, so that the important question of whether the father of an erythroblastotic child is homozygous or heterozygous for the responsible Rh-positive allele can now be decided by a blood test.

The term "carrier state" can be extended to cover phenotypes controlled by homozygous or heterozygous genotypes with incomplete penetrance. Sugar diabetes, if dependent on homozygosis for a recessive gene, often may not be expressed in the suitable genotype. Tolerance tests for sugar can distinguish between genetically normal and genetically susceptible individuals. For Huntington's chorea, which is caused in heterozygotes by a dominant allele and usually develops in middle age or later, the attempt to discover at an early age which of the children of an affected parent are carriers of the gene has thus far been unsuccessful. It is easy to predict that determining the carrier state will be possible someday, but it is hard to decide how at that time the gratifying certainty of some individuals that they and their future children will remain healthy should be weighed against the disturbing certainty of other individuals that they will develop the disease and against the knowledge that, should they have offspring, half of their children will suffer the same fate.

The phenotypic recognition of carriers of defect-causing genes will often permit taking preventive measures. A homozygous galactosemic infant when fed milk develops an enlarged liver, cataract, and mental deficiency, but it thrives on a diet free of galactose or lactose. A heterozygous carrier develops normally on the usual milk diet; but one may ask whether, in view of his reduced enzyme activity, a reduction of galactose intake might be beneficial. A person who is genetically susceptible to sugar diabetes may be able to remain nondiabetic by controlling his carbohydrate intake. Frequently, knowledge of the biochemical mechanism by which a specific gene causes a defect will enable the physician to supply the patient with the material which his body is unable to produce in sufficient amounts. The treatment of diabetes with insulin to compensate for the lack of production in the patient's pancreas is an outstanding example of therapy for a genetic defect.

Genetic Counseling.   The use of genetic knowledge in counseling has been discussed in various places in this book: autosomal inheritance (Chap. 6), X-linkage (Chap. 13), linkage (Chap. 15), and consanguinity (Chap. 18). Well-established information on simple genetic control of traits, together with the knowledge of gene frequencies in a population, may often be adequate to provide a basis for detailed advice.

In most cases, however, it is necessary to study the specific family pedigree in order to determine the type of inheritance involved. While there are a few inherited defects whose genetics seem to be the same in all known kindreds, the heterogeneity of many genetic traits should prohibit the mechanical interpretation of pedigree data according to simplified textbook statements.

When the genetic situation is not fully understood, or hardly understood at all, counseling must become less specific, although the availability of empiric risk figures may still allow useful predictions. Thus, regardless of what hypothesis one favors on the causation of schizophrenia, the established frequencies of the disease among various types of relatives of a propositus furnish yardsticks for counseling (Table 92, p. 581). It is true, however, that empiric risk figures only report what has happened in the past and do not interpret the events. Different circumstances, genetic and nongenetic, may, in the future, greatly change such figures, particularly if whole classes of defects were lumped together in the past but can later be separated into individual types. While it is important to know, for instance, the incidence of congenital malformation in relation to the age of the mother or in sibs subsequent to one or more malformed children, such information is of limited help in predicting the fate of future pregnancies in a particular family.

Genetic counseling goes beyond advising individuals. Besides its fundamental role in evaluating the significance of mutations, both spontaneous and induced, for problems of public health (Chap. 24), genetic counseling contributes information on the constitution of the populations of different areas and of mankind as a whole. We may not now have sufficient knowledge to counsel wisely on genetic problems of entire populations, but the time for such counsel is bound to come.

The fact that even individual counsel involves problems that extend beyond the immediate case may be illustrated by a fatal infantile paralysis due to a rare recessive gene (see p. 125). A heterozygous couple first had two affected children before a normal child was born. Although this child had a normal phenotype, there was a probability of only 1/3 that he would be free from the recessive allele and 2/3 that he would be heterozygous. It may be questioned whether it was advisable to produce a third child, since the probability of his carrying the defective gene was so high. Two considerations would be taken into account: the welfare of the child himself, and that of the population at large. Though the child would remain physically normal, his mental well-being in adult life would be affected by the possibility of his own offspring being paralytic. The chances for such an event, however, are negligible, since the disease is very rare and the probability of his marrying a carrier not great. As to the welfare of future generations of the population: it is true that the undesirable gene may thus be perpetuated, and at some later date, a homozygous condition may again be produced. Such conflicts between the happiness of one generation and the possible unhappiness of a later one are not rare in practical problems of human genetics. The decision, in such cases, is not the task of the scientist, as such, but of the individual or society. Moreover, the optimist may foresee the discovery of a remedy!

A similar decision, between short- and long-range effects, must be faced in counseling heterozygous carriers of a specific deleterious recessive whether or not to avoid marrying each other. Such action would eliminate the appearance of affected children in the first generation. But in time, the frequency of heterozygotes will gradually increase either because new mutations from the normal to the defect-carrying allele are not balanced by elimination of mutant alleles, owing to low fitness of homozygous recessives, or because the frequency of the mutant allele is increased as the result of heterotic fitness of heterozygotes. Given sufficient time, the population would tend to consist of a growing majority of heterozygotes, and avoidance of heterozygous marriage partners would become difficult—if not impossible! It may be argued with merit that the time needed for the majority of the people to become heterozygous is so immense that the problems of preventing the development of the defective phenotype from homozygous genotypes may be solved long before this eventuality. The extreme formulation of the problem has been made in order to point out the kinds of effects which any choice of alternatives will entail.

The Problem of Having Affected Children. Prospective parents with a defective history in their family often ask the consultant geneticist whether it is genetically advisable to have children. The only objective statement that can be made will be in terms of probability. Assume, for example, that the chance of an abnormal child of the type in question being born is calculated to be 1 out of 50. Whether it is deemed advisable to have children, particularly in view of the fact that the chance for a normal child is, after all, 49 out of 50, will depend on the severity of the trait in question and on the inclination of the prospective parents to take the risk.

Secrecy Concerning Genetic Defects. The strong tendency to hide knowledge of hereditary defects in one's family is a reflection of the belief that a hereditary "taint" belongs in the same category as a moral offense. In addition, it is not only a feeling of shame which induces many people to keep genetic facts secret but also the fear that the marriage prospects of their children may be decreased. There is, of course, no reason for being ashamed of genetic constitutions, which fate, and not the individual, has decreed. Perhaps the knowledge that many more individuals than is generally supposed are carriers of some unfavorable genes—indeed, that probably all people are such carriers—will gradually help to reduce the feeling of shame or guilt.

Most important, however, is the fact that the consequences of hiding the truth may be worse than their open discussion. This may be illustrated by a family, known to the author, in which Huntington's chorea occurs. Only after one of the parents developed Huntington's chorea was it revealed to him that his mother had had the disease and had succumbed to it. His adult children realized that there was a 50 per cent chance that they, too, would suffer from it. The psychological load of this knowledge is, necessarily, extremely heavy. Had the parent known earlier, he could have refrained from having children, thereby averting great suffering in a later generation. In circumstances like these, secrecy itself is culpable, for it may have more serious consequences than the truth.

Aspects of Genetic Advice. The responsibility of a genetic counselor does not end when he has made as accurate a diagnosis as possible. He must, in transmitting his information to the individual concerned, take into account the psychological effect of unfavorable prospects. He must weigh the possible chance of defect against the probability that other, favorable traits may at least partly compensate for genetic misfortune. He must remind his questioner that, often, weakness itself is made a source of strength by man's ability to conquer difficulties: A man with malformed hands may become a distinguished artist; and a paralytic, a world leader. Even with the most menacing genetic diseases, such as certain nervous deterioration which may set in later in life, the adviser may suggest that probably years of normal activity lie ahead, and that medical science may still discover means of preventing or curing the illness. The genetic counselor, then, is in the same position as the physician who has diagnosed the prospects of a patient suffering from a serious, and perhaps at present incurable, disease. It is not sufficient to tell the truth; it is necessary to tell it humanely.

The Rising Importance of Genetics in Medicine. In recent times the relative importance of genetics in medicine has greatly increased. The incidence of infectious and environmentally caused deficiency diseases, which once formed a very large part of medical ills, has been, and continues to be, sharply reduced in many parts of the world. In proportion, the share of genetically determined defects, susceptibilities, and aging processes takes on more and more significance. Knowledge of the role of heredity in disease not only is compatible with hope for control but is one of the foundations on which such control can be erected.

References

In addition to the references below, consult the list of treatises on human genetics at the end of Chapter 1.

Articles on Human Genetics Counseling (apart from the books by Hammons, Reed, and Scheinfeld, and Chapter 11 of Roberts) appear frequently in *Eugenics Quarterly* and *J. Génétique Humaine.* See also "Panel Discussion: Genetic Counseling," 1952, *Am. J. Human Genet.,* **4:** 332–346.

Anderson, R. C., 1951. Genetics and medical practice. *Journal-Lancet,* **71:** 49–52.

————, and Reed, S. C., 1954. The likelihood of recurrence of congenital malformations. *Journal-Lancet,* **74:** 175–176.

Childs, B., and Sidbury, J. B., 1957. A survey of genetics as it applies to problems in medicine. *Pediatrics,* **20:** 177–218.

Dice, L. R., 1952. Heredity clinics: their value for public service and for research. *Am. J. Human Genet.,* **4:** 1–13.

Franceschetti, A., and Klein, D., 1954. Le dépistage des heterozygotes. *Analecta Genetica,* **1:** 50–78.

Fraser, F. Clarke, 1954. Medical genetics in pediatrics. *J. Pediatrics,* **44:** 85–103.

Gartler, S. M., 1953. Elimination of recessive lethals from the population when the heterozygote can be detected. *Am. J. Human Genet.,* **5:** 148–153.

Haldane, J. B. S., 1949. Disease and evolution. *La Ricerca Scientifica,* Suppl. **19:** 3–11.

Hammons, H. G. (Ed.), 1959. *Heredity Counseling.* 112 pp. Hoeber-Harper, New York. (This is a slightly changed version of: Heredity Counseling Symposium, *Eugen. Quart.,* **5:** 3–63, 1958).

Hutt, F. B., 1958. *Genetic Resistance to Disease in Domestic Animals.* 198 pp. Comstock Publ. Assoc., Ithaca.

Law, L. W., 1958. Some aspects of drug resistance in neoplasms. *Ann. New York Acad. Sci.,* **71:** 976–993.

Lehmann, H., and Simmons, P. H., 1958. Sensitivity to suxomethonium apnoea in two brothers. *Lancet,* II: 981–982.

Motulsky, A. G., 1957. Drug reactions, enzymes, and biochemical genetics. *J. Am. Med. Assn.,* **165:** 835–837.

Neel, J. V., 1953. The detection of the genetic carriers of inherited disease. In A. Sorsby (Ed.). *Clinical Genetics.* Chapter 3, pp. 27–34. Butterworth & Co., London.

Reed, S. C., 1955. *Counseling in Medical Genetics.* 268 pp. W. B. Saunders, Philadelphia and London.

Roberts, J. A. Fraser, 1959. *An Introduction to Medical Genetics.* 2nd ed. 263 pp. Oxford University Press, London.

Scheinfeld, A., 1956. *The Human Heredity Handbook.* 276 pp. Lippincott, Philadelphia.

Stormont, C., 1958. Genetics and disease. *Adv. in Veterinary Sci.,* **4:** 137–162.

Strong, L. C. (Ed.), 1958. Genetic concept for the origin of cancer. *Ann. New York Acad. Sci.,* **71:** 807–1241.

CHAPTER 31

GENETIC ASPECTS
OF RACE

There is no full agreement among students of the systematics of animals and plants as to what constitutes a "species." In general, however, separate groups of organisms are regarded as belonging to different species if they are more or less *reproductively isolated,* a term which signifies limitation or lack of interbreeding under natural conditions.

The criterion of reproductive isolation is independent of the more obvious structural differences among organisms. While many groups of structurally different organisms do not cross with each other, there are also numerous examples of reproductive isolation in spite of very small or nonobservable morphological differences, as well as of strikingly different populations without reproductive isolation. Such populations are able to retain their differences because of geographical or other isolating factors.

Often, two strikingly different groups of organisms inhabiting different regions are connected by a more or less continuous series of intermediate types. Despite the range of variability, all these organisms form one single unit, differentiated into subgroups which, in different regions, replace each other. Even members of the subgroups which are most distinct morphologically can, in many cases, interbreed freely if brought into contact. Many systematists call the large group a *species,* and the groups out of which the species is composed its *subspecies.* There are species which are not subdivided into subspecies; others in which only two or a few subspecies can be distinguished; and still others, sometimes called *polytypic species,* in which a great many subspecific types exist, each of which inhabits a different region.

A taxonomic observer of mankind, using the criteria which have just been described, would classify man as a single species subdivided into numerous subspecies. There is no doubt about the existence of morphologically dif-

ferent groups of mankind; these form the various races studied by the physical anthropologist. Undoubtedly, too, there are many intermediate populations
among the different groups, forming either a more or less continuous chain
of connections or consisting of "hybrid swarms"—the products of interbreeding and consequent segregation of genetic traits derived from different races
which were once separated and later came into contact.

As in other polytypic species, the subdivisions of mankind are not all of
equivalent rank. There are major races, as the Mongoloids and the Caucasoids, for example, and minor variants, as the Mediterraneans and the
Alpines, and many groups of intermediate taxonomic rank. Because all
degrees of differences occur between human populations, there is no generally
accepted system of classification. The term human race will be defined later
in this chapter, and it will be seen that there are no sharp genetic criteria
by which to distinguish different degrees of racial differences. As far as is
known, members of every human race can successfully hybridize with members of every other. These phenomena—morphological and reproductive—
have led the taxonomist since Linnaeus' time, two centuries ago, to assign a
single species name, *Homo sapiens,* to all mankind.

Genetics of Racial Diversity

It is one thing to recognize the existence of racial diversity and another
to define it in terms of the underlying genetic facts. We shall attempt the
latter after familiarizing the reader with specific examples of types of genetic
diversity among human groups. Our discussion assumes that racial diversity
has a genetic basis and is not exclusively conditioned by environment. This
premise is undoubtedly true for many of the differences among groups which
are studied by the physical anthropologist. Color of skin and hair; shape of
hair, nose, and lips; amount of body hair; prominence of cheekbones, and
large differences in stature and in many other traits are highly independent
of the climatic, nutritional, or cultural environments in which human beings
are reared. Whether or not there are mental differences of genetic nature
among races will be discussed in the next chapter.

Genetic analyses of the main differences between human races are few
and incomplete. Such differences are probably based on differences at several
if not many loci. Some examples are the dark pigmentation of the Negroids
and the lighter of most of the Caucasoids; the kinky hair of the former and
the straight or wavy hair of the latter; the different configurations of lips,
noses, eyelids, and other facial features among Mongoloids, Negroids, and
Caucasoids; and the differences in body build of African Pygmies, Hottentots,
and Polynesians.

Results of crosses between members of the different races consist mostly
of data on first-generation hybrids. The phenotypes of such hybrids are
mixtures of dominant and intermediate expression of individual traits. Thus,

the hair type of first-generation mulattoes is similar to that of the negro parent, while the pigmentation is intermediate between negro and white.

It is not correct to use the words dominance, recessiveness, or intermediateness in a genetic sense for these first-generation hybrid phenotypes. The genetic terms were coined for the types of expression of heterozygous allelic pairs in comparison to the homozygotes (A^1A^2 as compared to A^1A^1 and A^2A^2). Whether the distinguishing racial traits are based on allelic differences at single loci will remain unknown until later generations have been studied. Most of the limited number of such studies are fragmentary, but it is safe to say that, in general, the genetic differences underlying opposite traits are polygenic. Thus, while the kinky hair of the negro appears in first-generation negro-white hybrids, in later generations a whole array of different hair types is found. First-generation children from marriages between American Indians and negroes frequently show the straight hair of the former, but, again, various grades and types of hair occur in later generations. The polygenic determination of pigmentation differences between whites and negroes has been discussed earlier (Chap. 18). The discussion of the inheritance of quantitative characters given there is relevant to the majority of the main racial character.

Another difficulty in the genetic interpretation of phenotypic differences among races is the possibility that different genotypes have resulted in similar phenotypes. Thus, the absence of crosses between such groups as African negroes and the small groups of negritos in Southern India, Malaya, Java, and the Philippines leaves an open question of whether their similar characteristics of skin color and hair type have the same genetic basis or are the phenotypically similar products of different genotypes.

Antigenic Differences. In order to avoid such uncertainties, anthropologists in recent decades have studied racial differences in genetically well-defined characters, particularly blood groups and types of hemoglobin. Two discoveries of general importance have resulted from these studies: (1) there are striking differences in the frequencies of various alleles in different races and racial variants; and (2) these differences are usually merely relative. Most human groups have the same array of alleles at the different loci, even if in different proportions. Table 118 shows that the blood-group alleles I^{A1}, L^{Ms}, L^{Ns}, R^o, R^1, R^2, and probably P and Fy^a are found in all six human groups listed. Several other alleles, such as r', r'', R^z, and Lu^a, which are rare wherever they occur, may well be present even in those races for which they have not yet been recorded.

There are, however, some alleles which are common in some races and apparently absent in others: I^{A2} is restricted to Basques, other Caucasoids, and Negroids; I^B appears in these groups as well as in Asian Mongoloids but not in American Indians and Australian aborigines (Australoids); and r has a high frequency in Basques, other Caucasoids, and Negroids and a low frequency in Asian Mongoloids but is lacking in American Indians and Australoids.

The major races have long been differentiated from one another on the basis of their external physical characters. It is significant that the study of blood groups leads to a similar classification. Wiener, Boyd, and Mourant have pointed out that most people can be classified into six "serologic races," which coincide fairly well with the differentiation according to external physical characters. Caucasoids are characterized by possession of I^{A2} as well as I^{A1}, high frequency of r, and total or near absence of Di^a; Negroids, by possession of I^{A2} as well as I^{A1} and high frequency of R^o; Asian Mongoloids, by absence of I^{A2}, low frequency of L^{MS} and L^{NS}, and high frequency of R^1 and Fy^a;

TABLE 118.   *Frequencies, in Per Cent, of Various Blood Group Alleles in Six Racial Groups Belonging to Three Major Races.* (After Boyd; Mourant; and Wiener and Wexler.)

Genetic Loci	Caucasoids		Negroids	Mongoloids		Australoid
	Basques	Others		Asian	Amer. Indian	
I^{A1}	20	20–30	10–20	15–25	0–55	20–45
I^{A2}	3	4–8	5	0	0	0
I^B	0–3	5–20+	10–20	15–30	0	0
L^{MS}	55	20–30	7–20	4	15–30	0
L^{Ms}		30	30–50	56	50–70	26
L^{NS}	45	5–10	2–12	1	2–6	0
L^{Ns}		30–40	30–50	38	5–20	74
r	48–53	30–40	10–20	0–7	0	0
r'	1–3	0–2	0–6	0	0–17	13
r''	1	0–2	0–1	0–3	0–3	0
R^0	1	1–5	40–70	0–5	0–30	9
R^1	38–42	30–50	5–15	60–76	30–45	56
R^2	5–7	10–15	6–20	20–30	30–60	20
R^z	0	0–1	0	0–0.5	1–6	2
P	?	40–60	50–80	15–20	20–60	?
Lu^a	?	2–5	0–4	?	0–10	0
Fy^a	?	40	<10	90	0–90	?
Di^a	?	0+	0	1–12	0–25	0

NOTE: The frequencies given are sometimes based on a single or a few samples. The ranges are based on from two to many samples. Altogether, the data are somewhat selected and intended to show general trends only. For details, consult the original sources.

American Indians, by absence of I^{A2}, I^B, and r and low frequency of L^{NS}; and Australoids, by absence of I^{A2}, I^B, L^{MS}, L^{NS}, and r and high frequency of L^{Ns}. The Basques of Spain and southern France belong physically to the Caucasoid race, though they are to some degree culturally and linguistically separate. (It is believed that they are the remnant of an early European population which has been largely replaced by later arrivals.) Serologically the Basques are distinguished by very low frequency of I^B and high frequency of r.

Table 118 shows also that within each racial group there is often great variability of allele frequencies. We shall later discuss some aspects of these very interesting and equally complex variations.

Differences in Hemoglobin Types. There are some striking associations between racial groups and incidences of alleles for certain types of hemoglobin. One of the most significant is the high frequency of the allele for hemoglobin C in Equatorial West Africa and its virtual absence elsewhere. The allele for sickle-cell hemoglobin is found in wider groups of African negroes as well as in various Mediterranean people and a few Asian groups, and the gene for thalassemia is restricted to Mediterraneans and dispersed populations of Asia. The very rare presence of these alleles in northern and western Europeans and their descendants in the United States is perhaps the result of past intermarriages with Mediterraneans. We will return to the distribution of hemoglobin types in the final chapter of this book.

Other Differences in Allele Frequencies. The genetic "polymorphism" of blood-antigen types is certainly representative of a great number of other traits. The genetic basis of some of these polymorphic characters is more or less well known, but information on racial differences is limited. Among these traits are type of singing voice, "secretor" property, pattern of finger ridges, and ability to taste phenylthiocarbamide (PTC).

The proportions of people with basso or soprano voice decrease from northern to southern Europe. Assuming the correctness of Bernstein's theory of the inheritance of singing voices in Europeans by means of a pair of alleles (see also p. 318), the gene frequency for the basso-soprano allele in the geographical range studied has been calculated. It was concluded to have a maximum of 61 per cent along the northwest coast of Germany and a minimum of about 12 per cent in Sicily. Although this specific interpretation of the polymorphism of singing voice has to be abandoned, there is undoubtedly a genetic basis for it, and differences in allele frequencies must account for the different frequencies of types of voice in different populations.

The frequency of the gene Se (for secretion of the ABH substances into body fluids) is approximately 50 per cent in Caucasoids, only 38 per cent in American negroes and probably less in African Negroids, and rises to nearly 100 per cent in American Indians.

A final example concerns the ability to taste PTC. The frequency of tasters

TABLE 119.   *Racial Variations in Ability to Taste Phenylthiocarbamide.*
(Valls, 1958.)

Racial Group	No. Tested	Tasters (%)
Australoids	152	51
American whites	>6,000	65–75
Egyptians	208	76
American negroes	>3,000	91
African negroes	>1,000	91–97
Chinese	>200	89–94
American Indians	>1,000	90–98

ranges from only 63 per cent among Arabs to 98 per cent among American Indians; expressed in terms of nontasters, these numbers are 37 and 2 per cent (Table 119). In view of the recessive nature of the allele for nontasting, we obtain a range of allelic frequencies from over 0.6 to 0.14. While there is little doubt about the hereditary nature of the taste-polymorphism, it is too early to assume that the differences in frequencies of tasters are the result of differences in the frequency of the t allele only. The somewhat variable frequency of the trait among whites and its sex modification in many racial groups suggest that when the frequency of modifying genes is studied, the interracial variability may be found to depend, at least in part, on genes at other loci.

There are some data on differences among races in frequencies of red-green color blindness and ability to smell hydrocyanic acid, but the evidence is insufficient for making valid comparisons.

The finding of so many relative differences in the frequencies of alleles suggests that even apparently absolute differences in traits between two races may be dependent on alleles which occur in both of them. If the differences in skin color between Negroids and Caucasoids are based on a polygenic system involving five or more loci, then it would be possible to account for the dark pigmentation of the African Negro by the presence of alleles for darkness with frequencies of, say, 99 per cent and presence of alleles for lightness of 1 per cent. Inversely, the Caucasoids may possess the alleles for darkness in frequencies of 1 per cent and those for lightness of 99 per cent. With such large, but not "all-or-nothing," differences in allele frequencies, practically all members of one group would be dark and practically all of the other group light.

A Genetic Definition of Race

We are now ready to approach the problem of a genetic definition of race. Let us begin with a discussion of a dictionary definition:

> **"Race.**   A division of mankind possessing constant traits, transmissible by descent, sufficient to characterize it as a distinct human type; a permanent variety of the genus *Homo*. . . ."

It will be seen immediately that this definition does not fit the anthropological concept of race. All people belonging to blood group O constitute a division of mankind fulfilling the specifications outlined; yet, this group of O people is composed of individuals from all anthropological subdivisions of man. Or, if a more superficially obvious character, e.g., albinism, were chosen, it would be true that albinos constitute a division of mankind according to the definition given, but individual albinos differ from each other in the most diverse respects.

It may be wondered whether the difference between anthropological races and "artificial" groups, such as those cited above, is essentially dependent upon the number of genic differences involved. This is not likely to be the case, although it is unknown how many loci are involved in racial differentiations. Whatever the number of the loci differentiating two specific races, the number will be different for another pair of races. Phenotypically, nearly or fully Caucasoid segregants are rarer among the offspring of first-generation hybrids between Caucasoids and Negroids than among the corresponding offspring of Causasoid-Mongoloid crossings. This suggests that a smaller number of genic loci is involved in the phenotypic differences between the latter two races. Whatever the number of loci concerned in the determination of these interracial differences, it would probably be possible to select groups of individuals within any one of the anthropological races which are distinguished by as many, or even more, intraracial genic differences. Yet, while the term race is applicable to Caucasoids and Mongoloids, it would not be applicable to two groups within the Caucasoids or Mongoloids which were defined artificially by the sum of alternative genotypes (and phenotypes) in regard to blood groups, hair color, eye color, taster ability, hair type, form of nose, mouth, etc., etc.

The dictionary definition would be improved if the following italicized words were added:

> **"Race.** A division of mankind, *inhabiting a limited geographic area or areas, and . . .*"

The addition would then make the definition applicable to the majority of cases. However, there would be important exceptions. For example, gypsies are characterized by a number of physical features which separate them racially from typical Caucasoids; yet, they inhabit the same geographic areas as the latter. The same is true for the "racial minorities" all over the globe. Nor are the exceptions restricted to minorities. In some areas of the southern United States, Caucasoids and Negroids are present in equal proportions.

These exceptions all have in common an element closely related to geographic distribution. In the past, gypsies and other fractions of geographically coexistent populations were limited to geographic areas different from those of the rest of the population with whom they now live together. Should we, then, improve the definition further by adding a reference to the historical background which originally involved geographic separateness? Again, this would not satisfy the facts completely. There is good evidence that many of the now existing minor racial types are the results of past mingling of originally geographically separated races. Thus, the Japanese are believed to be the offspring of Malayan, Mongolian, and, perhaps, Polynesian immigrants into Japan who have intermarried among one another and also with the aboriginal Ainus. Knowledge of this hybrid origin does not run counter to the recognition of the Japanese as a single, somewhat distinct racial group.

What, then, is the difference between a country where gypsies and other racial types occupy the same territory, and Japan, where descendants of different races, too, live in the same geographical region? The difference results from the two different systems of mating. In respect to gypsies, barriers exist which lead to preferential marriages of gypsies with gypsies, and of nongypsies with nongypsies. Among the Japanese, on the other hand, mating barriers between the originally separate races have largely disappeared. The anthropological term "race" thus becomes allied to the genetic term "isolate."

A genetic definition of race must take into account the fact that all populations consist of individuals who are heterozygous for many loci and many alleles. There is no "pure" race—a designation which, in genetic terms, would signify homozygosity and isogeneity of all individuals.

The study of blood-group genes has shown that races often differ only in the relative frequencies of alleles, and this phenomenon may be true for most loci. A race, then, is a group of individuals whose corporate genic content, sometimes called the *gene pool,* differs from that of other groups. The members of a race retain the differences, more or less, over the course of generations because geographic or cultural isolation results in only a small amount of genic exchange between them and members of other races.

We may now summarize our discussion by the following definition:

> **"Race.** A geographically or culturally more or less isolated division of mankind whose corporate genic content (gene pool) differs from that of all other similar isolates."

Does this definition coincide with the everyday concept of race? The definition includes this concept but goes beyond it. It fits the anthropological characterization of the major groups of mankind as well as of the minor racial types, since they are all endowed with different genic contents and are more or less isolated from one another by geographic or social barriers. In addition, the genetic definition considers as "races" different groups of individuals who are fully or partly isolated but whose genic contents are so slightly different from one another that our language has no word to characterize these groups as separate entities. For example, during World War II, it was found in northern Wales that the ABO frequencies of blood donors with Welsh family names differed from those of donors with non-Welsh names (Table 120). There were more O and B individuals and fewer A and AB among the Joneses, Williamses, Robertses, and other people with Welsh surnames than among the people with English names. The differences in allele fre-

TABLE 120. *Percentage Frequencies of ABO Blood Groups among Donors with Welsh and Non-Welsh Family Names.* (Roberts, *Ann. Eugen.,* **11,** 1942.)

Men and Single Women Donors with	No. of Individuals	O	A	B	AB
Welsh family names	909	52.7	35.0	9.7	2.6
Non-Welsh family names	1,091	46.6	42.0	8.3	3.2

quencies for both sexes are significant. Obviously, then, the genic content of the group of Joneses, Williamses, etc., is distinct from that of the rest of the population among whom they live, a difference which can only be due to some genetic isolation between the two groups. Yet, we would hardly call the Joneses, Williamses, etc., a different race.

The dictionary definition cited earlier tries to circumvent the difficulty by inserting the specification that the traits which are possessed by a race should be "sufficient to characterize it as a distinct human type." Unfortunately, however, the definition does not clarify what is to be regarded as "sufficient" for this purpose.

The difficulty is inherent in the facts of nature. There exists a continuous series of degrees of difference in the genic content of isolates, from the slight differences between the Welsh isolate and the population of which it is a part to the obvious differences among the major races of the anthropologists. The biological phenomenon is the same, irrespective of the size of the difference. The basic genetic similarity of all differences among isolates results in arbitrary decisions as to when to apply the term race and when to regard its use as inappropriate. A problem of this kind is frequently met. Natural bodies of flowing water of different width and depth are called brooks, creeks, streams, and rivers. No sharp definition can be drawn up to separate these different terms from one another, although there is no doubt about which term to apply to the Mississippi or, conversely, to a very narrow and shallow current.

There is not only a wide range of genic diversity between different groups but also many degrees of isolation. Absolute isolation of different human groups hardly exists, since contacts between such groups have always resulted in some interbreeding. The degree of isolation, itself, is variable not only from group to group but also with time. In historical periods of mass migration, barriers to interchange of genes have always been decreased. Technical developments in modern transportation, which facilitate and increase contact between formerly geographically isolated groups, have led to equivalent results. Global wars, too, with their shifting of large military forces into foreign areas, have contributed to the breakup of genetic isolation, either through legally sanctioned marriages or from illegitimate unions.

Frequencies of Specific Genotypes in Different Races. Let us assume that two races possess n loci, A^1A^2, B^1B^2, $C^1C^2 \cdots N^1N^2$, each of which occurs in two allelic forms, with the frequencies p_{A^1}, q_{A^2}; p_{B^1}, q_{B^2}; p_{C^1}, $q_{C^2} \cdots p_{N^1}$, q_{N^2} in race I and the frequencies p'_{A^1}, q'_{A^2}; p'_{B^1}, q'_{B^2}; p'_{C^1}, $q'_{C^2} \cdots p'_{N^1}$, q'_{N^2} in race II. In both races, there will be individuals who are homozygous or heterozygous for either one of the alleles of any one locus. Consequently, an N^1N^1 individual taken from race I cannot be assigned to his race on the basis of his constitution at the one N locus. However, a priori, the probabilities of his belonging to race I or II may be different, the proportion of the expected frequencies of N^1N^1 individuals in the two races being $(p_{N^1})^2$ and $(p'_{N^1})^2$, respectively.

If we assume that the allele frequencies p and q for every locus are 1/10 and 9/10 in race I, and that the allele frequencies p' and q' for every locus are 9/10 and 1/10 in race II, the probability that an N^1N^1 individual will occur in race I becomes $(p_{N^1})^2 = 1/100$, and that he will appear in race II $(p'_{N^1})^2 = 81/100$. Thus, the probabilities that an N^1N^1 individual will be a member of race I or II differ from each other in the proportion 1:81, so that the probability that an N^1N^1 individual belongs to race I is 1/82 and to race II is 81/82. If an individual's genotype were known to be $A^1A^1N^1N^1$, his chance of occurring in race I would be only $(1/100)^2 = 1/10,000$ as opposed to the chance $(81/100)^2 = 6,561/10,000$ of his occurring in race II. Therefore, the probability of an $A^1A^1N^1N^1$ belonging to race I and not to race II is 1 out of 6,562. Clearly, the more loci known, the more reliable may be the assignment of an individual to his race. However, not only is there a small uncertainty, even in favorable cases, but there are genotypes which have rather similar probabilities or even an equal probability of belonging to either race. Among these genotypes are the complete heterozygotes. The probability of a person being heterozygous for n loci is $(2pq)^n$ in race I, and $(2p'q')^n$ in race II. In our example where $pq(1/10 \cdot 9/10)$ is equal to $p'q'(9/10 \cdot 1/10)$, there would be an even chance that an A^1A^2, $B^1B^2 \cdots N^1N^2$ individual would belong to either race.

In general, gene frequencies in two races will not be as "symmetrical" (1/10:9/10 vs. 9/10:1/10) as in our two assumed populations. Consequently, it will usually be possible to discriminate with a high probability between the two possibilities. It must be emphasized, however, that these calculations apply only to races that are absolutely isolated genetically and not to races between which there is some degree of miscegenation. Particularly between the minor anthropological subdivisions, intermarriages are frequent, or have been so in the past. For example, in the course of many centuries, the Nordic, Alpine, and Mediterranean racial variants of Europe have interchanged genes freely. Consequently, allele frequencies for different loci are probably rather similar in these racial subtypes. The result is that it is often difficult to place a given individual in one or another of these groups. Indeed, such an attempt may become meaningless, since segregants from the same parental pair may show phenotypes characteristic of different minor racial divisions.

In view of the imperfections of any definition of the term race and particularly in view of the fateful misuses of the term, some geneticists are inclined to strike the word race from modern vocabulary, substituting words like "population" or "ethnic group." Since, however, the word race will probably remain in our language, it has been retained in this book and is used, without value judgment, in its scientific sense.

References

Boyd, W. C., 1950. *Genetics and the Races of Man.* 453 pp. Little, Brown, Boston.

Cold Spring Harbor Symposia on Quantitative Biology, 1950. Origin and evolution of man. *Cold Spring Harbor Symp. Quant. Biol.,* **15:** 1–425.

Mourant, A. E., 1954. *The Distribution of the Human Blood Groups.* 438 pp. C. C. Thomas, Springfield, Ill.

Rosin, S., 1956. Die Verteilung der ABO-Blutgruppen in der Schweiz. *Arch. Julius Klaus-Stift.,* **31:** 17–127.

Valls, A. Medina, 1958. Estudio antropogenetico de la capacidad gustativa para la fenitiocarbamida. *Fac. Cienc. Univ. Madrid.* 67 pp.

Wiener, A. S., and Wexler, I. B., 1958. *Heredity of the Blood Groups.* 150 pp. Grune & Stratton, New York.

CHAPTER 32

GENETIC ASPECTS
OF RACE MIXTURE

W henever history brought together two or more races in the same territory, unions of persons of different races occurred. This interbreeding, called *miscegenation* (from the Latin *miscere* = to mix, *genus* = race), proceeded sometimes at a slow pace and at other times rapidly. Often, complete "amalgamation" or "assimilation" of the different groups was the end result. Before the particulate nature of the hereditary material was understood, it was thought that such joining of the germ plasms of the races would result in a new, homogeneous population. The recognition of the existence of separate genes has, of course, changed this expectation. Recombination of the different alleles brought into the gene pool of a mixed population results in the production of numerous diverse genotypes in proportions that are predictable if the allele frequencies are known.

Segregation of allelic differences brought into a mixed population should increase its variability, as compared with the variability within each parent race. However, a comparison of the variability of the mixed population with that *between* the parent races shows a decrease in variability, since statistical measurements of variability are less dependent upon the rare extreme variants of a group than upon the distribution of the majority around the mean. Expressed differently, the *intra*racial variability within the mixed group is less than the *inter*racial variability before mixture.

The specific application of these considerations to human miscegenation on a population scale depends on the number of loci, on the phenotypic expression of polygenic genotypes, and on the relative sizes of the two parent races involved in any specific crossing.

In a population derived from negro-white mixtures, a trait like skin color shows a greater variability than is found in the parental races. Other traits may be less variable. In fact, it has often been found that many traits do not vary appreciably more in the mixed population than within the parental groups. There are several ways in which this low variability may be interpreted. Perhaps the most probable explanation, advanced by H. J. Muller, is that if the intraracial variability of a character in each of the two parent races is due to numerous recessives of individually rather low allele frequencies, and if these genes are at different loci in the two races, then the variability of the mixed race would be lower than that of either of the parent races. This is a consequence of the relative lowering of each allele frequency due to "dilution" (by intermarriage) of the concentration of alleles present in one, but not in the other, race. This dilution results in a lower frequency of homozygous recessives in the new isolate and, thus, in a lower number of phenotypes which vary from the mean. Opposite in effect to this lowering of the variability is the segregation of interracial differences. It is not to be expected that the two factors affecting variability, dilution and segregation, will always compensate for each other completely. Hence, a mixed race may show increase of variability in some traits, decrease in others, and no, or little, change in still others. That the changes in variability observed in mixed populations of negro-white, Tahitian-white, or Hottentot-white intermarriages have been small may be taken as an indication that the differences between individuals within the parental groups are of magnitude comparable with the differences between the groups.

Negro-White Miscegenation in the United States

One of the most important examples of miscegenation, both because of the number of individuals involved and because of its contemporary historical significance, is that between the white and negro populations of the United States. Neither group was racially uniform, in the sense that neither consisted of a single random-mating isolate, but the whites stemmed mostly from western and central Europe and thus, probably, were less differentiated into genetically different groups than the negroes, who came from widely separated parts of Africa. The slight initial genic isolation between the white subgroups has had a strong tendency to disappear, although geographic and religious factors, as well as new immigration, have retarded their complete amalgamation. The different negro subraces, likewise, underwent a process, by intermarriages, of gradual transformation into a single Negro race.

Superimposed on these two separate processes of amalgamation within each of the two major races, miscegenation has occurred and continues to occur. Negroes, whites, and American Indians have been involved in this miscegenation, but the discussion will be restricted to negroes and whites, since the over-all contribution of the American Indians to the gene pool of the other groups has been very small. This is proven by comparisons of the frequencies of blood-group alleles among the three groups.

The Colonial period and the succeeding decades before the emancipation of the negro slaves was the most significant period of miscegenation. Miscegenation, primarily between white men and negro women for more than a hundred years, had led to the existence of a very large number of first-generation hybrid mulattoes. Although half their genes were derived from whites and half from negroes, socially the mulattoes were classified together with negroes, as "colored" people. Accordingly, they married either with each other or with negroes who had no white ancestors. The result of this system of mating at first was an infiltration of "white" genes into the colored population without an appreciable reciprocal gene flow from negroes to whites. Lately, as a result of the segregation of alleles concerned with the more obvious characters which differentiate whites from negroes, colored parents have produced children whose skin pigmentation, hair type, and facial features are similar enough to those of whites for them to "pass" for whites. The segregants undoubtedly carry various combinations of less obviously recognizable genes of negro derivation than those responsible for the traits mentioned above. They also contain heterozygously recessive alleles concerned with some of the more obvious differences between whites and negroes, as well as alleles which, in specific combinations with alleles at other loci, determine genotypes characteristic of negroes. Consequently, individuals who have "crossed the color line" and have "white" children represent a channel through which various genes derived from negroes flow into the white population. Thus, the initially one-sided gene flow, from the white to the negro population, has developed into a mutual exchange of genes.

The frequency of white or near-white segregants is probably higher than would be expected from random mating within the negro population. There is a tendency for positive assortative mating among negro individuals; for example, lightly pigmented persons preferentially marry light ones. This mating preference favors the reconstitution of homozygosity for pigmentation alleles derived from the Caucasoid race; that is, it favors the production of individuals who function in the transfer of genes from the negro to the white population.

The process of extraction of alleles for light pigmentation from the negro population and the return, by means of "crossing the color line," of these light alleles to the white population from which they were derived is bound to continue—with the result that the negro population will be drained of those alleles or combinations of alleles which make for the more striking anthropological white phenotypes, particularly light pigmentation. It may be expected, therefore, that the American negro population, whose mean coloration is lighter than that of the original Africans, will gradually darken again due to selective "back-migration" of white genes.

This process will be counteracted by continued miscegenation, legitimate or illegitimate, between whites and negroes. The time span of a human generation is not negligible if it is measured against historical periods of one or two centuries. For whites and negroes in the United States, this time span certainly has been much too short to result in a complete breakup of genic isolation. Possibly, in the future, miscegenation will increase, or continue long enough, so that a single random population will finally be produced. It is more likely that selective mating of whites with whites and negroes with negroes will uphold the relative genic isolation between the two groups for a long time, but that an inconspicuous gene flow in both directions, as described, will continue.

What will the final consequences of these processes be, in terms of the over-all genic differences which existed between the original whites and negroes? There will be a tendency toward equalizing the frequencies of any one allele in the white and negro groups, except for those genes which are concerned with the most obvious racial characters. This equalization of numerous allele frequencies will proceed fastest for loci which are not chromosomally linked to those genes for which racially assortative mating exists, as for genes concerned with pigmentation. Even for loci linked to them, crossing over will tend to establish an equilibrium in which the original racial linkage combinations will occur no more frequently than exchange combinations. The result will be that the white and negro populations will become similar for most allele frequencies for which they were different before miscegenation and will remain different only in those probably fewer loci which contribute in an appreciable degree to superficial diversity of Caucasoid and Negroid individuals.

The gradual breakup of isolation for most genes has an important bearing on the genetic evaluation of segregants in future generations. Apart from genes causing obvious phenotypic differences, the least African-like members of the white group will belong to the same array of genotypes and with equal probability distribution as the most African-like members of the negro group. Even at the present time, the skin pigmentation of white-negro segregants is but a poor indicator of their total genotypes.

The Consequences of Miscegenation

Many persons regard miscegenation as undesirable. So far as it focuses attention on sociological problems arising from unsolved difficulties in the attitudes of races toward one another, the question of the undesirability of miscegenation does not fall within the province of the biologist. Nor is it the geneticist's task to evaluate the historical consequences of a gradual disappearance of the diversity of cultures as a possible result of extensive racial intermingling. Nor are the psychological conflicts which may confront an individual whose parents belong to two racial groups with widely different cultures of primary genetic concern. The opinion is often expressed, however, that there are biological reasons for the undesirability of racial hybridization. The most important arguments for this opinion center around views concerning (1) the breakup of well-adapted racial genotypes; (2) the origin, in the first or later generations, of disharmonious gene combinations; and (3) the superiority of certain races over others. We shall take up these arguments in the order given and further divide our discussion by considering physical characters first and mental ones later.

Physical Traits

Racial Adaptations.   It is indeed possible that some of the major racial physical characters are the result of selective forces which acted against certain genotypes in one isolate and favored their appearance in others. Such adaptations may be in response to environmental (ecological) factors. With pigmentation, which has often been cited in this connection, two different and opposing selective forces are known: an advantage, in that dark pigmentation provides a shield against strong sunlight, which may cause burns; and a disadvantage, in that, as a shield, it may decrease the amount of vitamin D which is formed in the body from ergosterol by natural irradiation. The darker pigmentation of the inhabitants of tropical regions thus may be regarded as an adaptive protection against intense sunlight, and the lighter pigmentation of northern people as an adaptation which permits enough of the less intense light rays to penetrate the skin and help manufacture vitamin D. Other traits also have been interpreted as ecologically adaptive. The long, narrow nose of Caucasoids is thought by some anthropologists to allow for warming up cold outside air before it enters the lungs, while the shorter and broader nose of Africans seems more suited to their evenly warmer surroundings. The lean physique, with its long arms and legs, of inhabitants of deserts, whether in North or South Africa or in Australia, seems to be an adaptation to the heat of these regions, since the relatively large amount of body surface provides for more cooling evaporation than compact bodies.

It is difficult to prove the correctness of such interpretations, but it seems likely that some, even if not all, racial characters represent adaptations to the specific environments in which the major races evolved. It is questionable, however, whether the value of these adaptations is still as great as it may have been in the past. Technological developments, particularly those of the last century, have so greatly changed man's environment and his ability to cope with it (and greater changes are bound to come) that adaptations to former environments are becoming largely obsolete; i.e., they lose their positive selective value. If this is so, then the breakup of formerly adaptive racial genotypes is of little concern.

Regardless of whether many racial characteristics are of ecological adaptive significance, the proper working of any human body depends on the harmonious adjustment of its different parts and functions. We may speak of this adjustment as *internal adaptiveness*. The blood-pumping function of the heart must be fitted to body size; the size and activity of the different glands of internal secretion must be delicately related to one another; the proportions of limbs to trunk and of various bones to one another must be fitted within the limits of normality. It may be wondered whether different human races contain different gene combinations which provide, within each race, the necessary internal harmony. If this were so, the breakup of former racial isolates would justifiably be a matter of concern. It appears, however, that internal adaptiveness should not be conceived as the ability of an organism to fit together, in a harmonious way, separately determined parts. Rather, the sizes and the degrees of function of organs are genetically provided with a wide range of possible expressions, and the specific expressivity that will result is dependent on developmental interrelations. The marvelous ability of an organism to regulate—that is, to respond in an adaptive way to a great variety of conditions—is responsible to a large degree for internal adaptiveness. If one kidney is removed, the other kidney compensates for the loss by increasing its activity; or, if a bone is broken and heals in an abnormal fashion, it rebuilds internal structure in a new manner best fitted to cope with the different mechanical stresses imposed on it. It may be assumed, similarly, that, in general, a developing human being will form during his embryogeny and later an internally adaptively balanced system, regardless of the gene combinations he inherits from his ancestral race or races.

Disharmonious Gene Combinations.   The regulatory abilities, or developmental homeostasis, of organisms makes the occurrence of disharmonious phenotypes rare. It is, however, conceivable that different parts of the body may sometimes be genetically determined in a sufficiently independent manner so that actual incongruities may arise. Such disharmonies occur occasionally when different species of animals or plants are crossed with each other. Disharmonies have also been described within a single species, namely, in crosses of widely different breeds of dogs. Thus, some hybrids between a short-legged, slender-bodied dachshund and a long-legged, heavy St. Bernard have the short legs of the first and the large body of the second breed, so that the body drags on the ground.

As instructive as this example is in showing the limits of regulatory development, it is hardly comparable to human race crosses. The dachshund is a disproportionately dwarfed animal, corresponding to chondrodystrophic human dwarfs and not to naturally occurring human races. Differences between human races seem to be dependent, not on a few genes which independently determine striking properties of parts, but rather on polygenic combinations of which each single gene affects to a small degree one or more characters, so that the various allelic combinations of the system are able to direct development toward a reasonably harmonious system. This seems to be the explanation for the fact that no well-substantiated examples of disharmonious constitution resulting from miscegenation have been reported.

In this connection, a very special case may be recalled: the Rh incompatibility between pregnant Rh-negative mothers and their Rh-positive embryos. If two isolated human races existed, one isogenic for the allele R, the other for r, the pathological phenomenon of Rh-determined erythroblastosis fetalis would not be known in either race. If the two races intermarried, many disharmonious mother-child combinations would appear, resulting in a disease which might then be called typical for miscegenation. There are races—the

Mongoloids, for example—which have a frequency for the allele r of nearly 0.0. No known race has an r allele frequency of 1.0, but intermediate frequencies occur. These differing allele frequencies account for the apparent absence of Rh erythroblastosis in Mongoloids and presence in Caucasoids.

Let us imagine the immigration of whites into China and of Chinese into a country inhabited by whites, and the miscegenation of the immigrants with the native race. In China, no erythroblastosis fetalis will occur in the first generation of intermarriages between Chinese women and white men, since all Chinese women are Rh positive and not subject to Rh iso-immunization. However, in the marriages between white immigrant women and Chinese men, the disease will affect some of the children, since about 16 per cent of white women are Rh negative and can be iso-immunized by fetuses, all of whom have inherited the R allele from their fathers. In later generations, the relative frequency of erythroblastosis in the population of China, now of mixed Chinese-white origin, will be less than in the first generation, since the frequency of the r allele and, therefore, of rr women will be lower than among the original whites due to the decreased frequency of r after dilution with the R allele of the original Chinese. Still, the frequency of the r allele will be higher than it was before the white immigrants came. Hence, rr women will result as expected from random mating, and some of them will have erythroblastotic pregnancies. Thus, from the point of view of the Chinese, and judged purely from Rh incompatibility, miscegenation will have had permanently bad effects.

The results will be very different in the "white country" with its Chinese immigrants. None of the Chinese women married to white men will add to the fetal disease, but Chinese men married to white women will cause the appearance of a higher frequency of erythroblastotic children than among marriages of white men and white women. In later generations, the frequency of the r allele in the white population, now of mixed white-Chinese origin, will be *lower* than before the RR immigrants came; the frequency of rr women will be correspondingly less, and the incidence of the disease will be lower. Thus, again, judged purely from Rh incompatibility, miscegenation will be found to be permanently beneficial.

Racial "Superiority." The argument that certain races are superior to others and that miscegenation involving the superior type is bound to destroy its excellence has rarely been used in connection with purely physical characteristics. While it is likely—though not established—that some races have a better genetic endowment than other races in regard to normal eyesight, hearing acuity, endurance of extreme temperature, longevity, and so on, it is improbable that some races contain many or all of these desirable traits and that others lack most or all of them. It would be difficult to give an objective rating to races, because they form different combinations of genic endowments—some resulting in many excellent phenotypes of one kind, and others in less frequent excellent phenotypes of another kind.

The same difficulty in evaluating relative superiority exists in regard to what has sometimes been called *race pathology,* the study of diseases in relation to race. It has been found that certain diseases are nearly unknown in some races and that the frequency of other diseases varies from race to race. Environmental differences may account for many such variations. Moreover, where a genetic basis is well established, differences in the frequencies of the disease-conditioning alleles often account for the observed racial differences. Examples of such differences, cited earlier in this book, are thalassemia, which is mostly restricted to people of Mediterranean racial background, and sickle-cell anemia to negroes. The frequency of erythroblastosis fetalis depends on the highly variable frequency of the different *R* alleles in different races. Other more or less well-substantiated examples are the rare occurrence of scarlet fever among Mongoloids and Negroids as compared to Caucasoids, and the less severe course of the disease when it does appear in the former races; the less frequent occurrence of tuberculosis among Jews as compared to members of many other racial variants; and the more frequent occurrence of infantile amaurotic idiocy among Jews as compared to Caucasoid non-Jews.

Public health statistics contain further data on different frequencies of various diseases in different racial groups, and the causes of some of these diseases are known to have a genetic component. Frequently, however, the penetrance of this component is dependent, to an unknown degree, on complex external circumstances, such as social status and its interrelation with housing, nutrition, type of occupation, etc. It would, therefore, be premature to draw general conclusions regarding differences in racial frequency of pathogenic alleles.

The examples given for racial differences in hereditary diseases should not overshadow the large number of diseases for which no striking difference exists. One of the most extensive compilations on the subject is Komai's two-volume *Pedigrees of Hereditary Diseases and Abnormalities Found in the Japanese Race,* which comprised probably all such pedigrees ever published in Japan up to 1943. The list is similar to a recounting of a great number of the frequent and the rarer abnormalities well known among Western peoples: albinism, ichthyosis, harelip, arachnodactyly, hemophilia, diabetes mellitus, cataract, blue sclerotics, partial and total color blindness, Huntington's chorea, amaurotic idiocy, deaf-mutism, and many others. In contrast to genes which differentiate the normal characters of Japanese from those of Caucasoids, most of the alleles for pathological traits are found in both groups. Specific allele frequencies are not known, however, and it is likely that quantitative differences exist in the incidence of alleles involved in the different diseases. It is also possible that some hereditary, apparently identical diseases or abnormalities in the two racial groups may be caused by genes at different loci.

If two different races possess different frequencies of certain pathogenic alleles, miscegenation will result in a decrease of the allele frequency in the mixed population, as compared to the frequency in the original race which has the higher incidence. As we have seen earlier, for recessive traits, this will result in a lower *total* frequency of the affected homozygotes. Miscegenation, then, like the breakup of isolates within racial groups, will result in a reduction of pathological conditions. This may be illustrated by an example for sickle-cell anemia. If, in a racial isolate of 1,000,000 people, the frequency of $Hb_1{}^S$ is 6 per cent, then $0.06^2 \cdot 10^6 = 3{,}600$ individuals are affected by the homozygous disease. Should miscegenation occur with another isolate consisting of 9,000,000 people in whom $Hb_1{}^S$ is virtually absent, then after panmixis only 360 affected individuals would be produced.

Heterosis. Hybridization between different species or breeds of animals or plants often results in increased size, productiveness, and resistance to diseases or other unfavorable conditions of the environment. This phenomenon has been referred to as *the stimulating effects of hybridity, hybrid vigor,* or *heterosis.* The causes of heterosis may be diverse in different crosses, or different causes may be jointly effective in a single cross. Indeed, full clarification of the phenomenon of heterosis has not been obtained, but two main theories seem to contain important elements of truth, as demonstrated by experimental tests.

One theory, in simplified form, is that vigor results from the collaboration of many loci; that different species or breeds are not likely to carry all the favorable alleles at the various loci concerned; and that, therefore, hybrids may combine in their genotype favorable alleles from both parents. If these favorable alleles are dominant, then their effect in the first-generation hybrids will be apparent as increased vigor. Theoretical examples of genotypes fitting this explanation have been given in Chapter 18 on polygenic inheritance, the simplest case being a pair of *AAbb* and *aaBB* parents and their *AaBb* hybrid. The other important theory concerning causes of heterosis assumes that heterozygosity of single loci may result in increased vigor as compared to the vigor of the constituent homozygotes; in other words, the heterozygous constitution AA' may confer on an organism a more vigorous phenotype than either AA or $A'A'$.

The first of the two theories depends on the existence of dominant genes for vigor. Such dominance has been well established in specific cases—for example, by Mendel, in peas, for an allele for tall, over dwarf, size. Similarly, in mice, normal size is dominant over pituitary dwarfism. Although no conclusive evidence is available, it is possible that normal breeds may differ in both dominant and recessive genes for vigor. If two isogenic breeds are, respectively, *AABB* and *aabb* where A is a dominant and b a recessive allele for increased vigor, then the hybrids, *AaBb*, would show no change in vigor if the A allele for increased and the B allele for decreased vigor balance each other (Fig. 256, I). If dominant genes for vigor are in excess over recessives, heterosis will result (Fig. 256, II); and if the recessive genes for vigor are in excess (or, to say it differently, if dominant genes for decreased vigor are

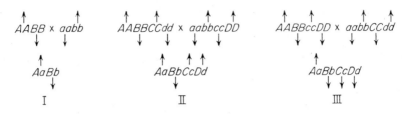

FIG. 256. Three crosses between strains which differ in several loci concerned with increased or decreased vigor. Because of compensating effects of dominant and recessive genotypes at these loci, it is assumed that all strains are equally vigorous. Upward arrow = increased vigor; downward arrow = decreased vigor. I. If *A* increases and *B* decreases vigor, then the vigor of the hybrid is like that of the parents. II. If *A*, *C*, and *D* increase, and *B* decreases vigor, then the vigor of the hybrid is increased. III. If *A* increases, and *B*, *C*, and *D* decrease vigor, then the vigor of the hybrid is decreased.

in excess of those for increased vigor), then the offspring of hybridization will be less vigorous than either parent (Fig. 256, III). The breakdown of human isolates within a given race, as well as miscegenation between major racial groups, may well result in no change of some traits, improvement of others, and deterioration of still others.

The same may be true if the second theory of heterosis holds. In addition to increased vigor of heterozygotes for a single locus, mutual interference in the action of two alleles may result in decreased phenotypic effectiveness. Very often, heterozygosity for single loci has no perceptible effect.

Heterosis and Human Stature. It is well known that the average body size has increased during the past century in various European countries, the United States, and Japan. Part of this increase undoubtedly is the result of improved external conditions. In addition, it has been suggested that the breakdown of isolates has furnished a genetic basis for heterosis. The most impressive study is that by Hulse on various physical measurements of the descendants of villagers from the Swiss district of Ticino. Because the villages in this mountain district are rather isolated from one another, a very high percentage of marriages has been between individuals within the same village. As a result of this inbreeding, many inhabitants of a given village have specific traits, such as big noses, which distinguish them from inhabitants of other villages. Hulse has compared the offspring of parents from the same village (endogamous marriages) with those of parents from two villages (exogamous marriages). Each of the two groups of offspring could be further subdivided into (1) those who remained in their native area, (2) those who had emigrated to California, and (3) those who were born in California of immigrant parents. It is noteworthy that these data show a decided influence of the environment, in that the men born in Switzerland were about 4 cm shorter than those born in California (Table 121). More important than this, however, is the fact that, in all three subdivisions, the mean stature of the exogamous group was approximately 2 cm greater than that of the endogamous one, the over-all difference being statistically significant. As with stature, several other physical measurements gave larger mean dimensions for the exogamous than for the endogamous group. It is likely that a common cause underlies these differences: a prolonged period of bodily growth in the children and young adults of exogamous parentage. This is interesting in view of the findings by Morton that the birth weight of Japanese infants from nonconsanguineous, exogamous marriages was not greater than that from consanguineous, endogamous ones. It is possible that these offspring might differ in size in adulthood, after completion of growth.

An interpretation of the Swiss data in terms of heterosis is based on the assumption that the individuals who enter into exogamous marriages are not genetically different from those who marry endogamously. As far as is known, this is true.

The inhabitants of the different Swiss villages are, of course, all members of the same racial group. It is not known whether heterosis also occurs in interracial matings, but it would seem likely.

TABLE 121.   *Mean Stature, in Centimeters, of Adult Male Offspring of Exogamous and Endogamous Marriages of Swiss Natives or Their Descendants.* (Hulse, 1958.)

Subgroup	Exogamous	Endogamous
(a) Swiss	168.51	166.21
(b) Emigrants	168.71	166.90
(c) Californians	172.33	170.50

Mental Traits

There is no doubt that racial differences in psychological traits exist. Attitudes vary among different races, and their study is the object of special sciences, such as social anthropology. It is clearly true that psychological attributes of races are greatly influenced by the particular historical, cultural, and sociological environment. It is difficult enough to define an over-all social psychology, but even when some valid approximation can be made, it seems to apply only to specific historical periods, or, if the race occupies different parts of the globe, only to specific regions. Differences in group psychology are also well known in different social layers of populations presumably rather genetically homogeneous.

As we have seen in Chapter 27, the study of the hereditary components of mental differences among individuals is still in its infancy. Progress is slow, mainly because of the lack of tools for accurately measuring mental traits independent of the environmental factors which are known to influence them. No determination of allele frequencies concerning normal mental attributes in different races has been made, nor will such a determination be possible until specific genes can be singled out for study. At present, all inferences regarding differences in the mental endowment of different races remain conjectures. Nevertheless, such conjectures are justifiable, provided that their hypothetical nature is kept in mind.

Biological arguments against miscegenation as it concerns mental traits assume that there are basic mental differences among races and that these are at least partly determined by different genetic endowment. Such discussions emphasize the first two arguments which were discussed in connection with physical traits, namely, the breakup of well-adapted racial genotypes and the origin of disharmonious gene combinations, as well as the third, the supposed existence of superior races. "The psyche," writes von Verschuer, "is a more sensitive reagent [than the body]. Disharmony of genes, therefore, will probably become apparent more easily in psychological than in physical disturbances." He adds, significantly—and scientifically—"There exists, however, a lack of really convincing data." An opposite point of view is held by other writers, who doubt the existence of well-adapted and of disharmonious gene combinations which affect mental traits. This opinion is guardedly expressed by Dobzhansky and Ashley Montagu: ". . . genotypic differences in personality traits, as between individuals and particularly as between races [are probably] relatively unimportant compared to their phenotypic plasticity. Instead of having his responses genetically fixed, as in other animal species, man is a species that invents its own responses, and it is out of this unique ability to invent, to improvise his responses, that his cultures are born." These authors, as well as others, stress evolutionary factors which "in all climes and at all times have favored genotypes which permit greater and greater educability and plasticity of mental traits. . . ." In other words the range of expressivity of genotypes concerned with mental traits is considered to be unusually wide.

The consequences of this point of view for miscegenation are, obviously, that there is no specific racial adaptiveness in mental traits, but that mental harmony is potentially present in all human beings. This also means that mental disharmonies resulting from hybridization should not be ascribed to genetic causes.

The two points of view are, of course, not mutually exclusive. Stressing possible genetic factors in racial mental differences does not deny plasticity, and stressing plasticity leaves room for genotypic differences. Even though we lack exact knowledge, we may still be rather confident of the existence not only of great plasticity, which is an obvious phenomenon, but also of genotypic differences in racial endowment. Mental traits are correlated with material physical factors, among which the organization of the nervous system and the hormonal constitution are the most important. Delicate and far-reaching interrelations may mold the psychology of each individual in conformity with all aspects of his physical make-up. Since genic differences influence all parts of the body and since differences in allele frequencies have been established for various genes in different races, one may expect some genetic influence on mental traits. The important problem is how great this influence is in differentiating races mentally. How does it compare with the inherent plasticity of mental traits, which may diminish or obliterate phenotypic expression of genotypic divergence; and how does it compare with external factors, which cause different expressions of like genotypes in different individuals and different groups?

In an attempt to answer this question, the facts of history are often cited. The cultural achievements of different races are very diverse, and such differences in achievement are taken as proof of different genetic endowments of mental traits. In such discussions, particularly, the concept of a scale of racial superiority is employed, the measure being achievements in such fields as mechanical inventions, abstract thought, social and political organization, religious creativity, and accomplishments in architecture, sculpture, music, and other arts. The scientist and the historian alike regard established differences in achievement as very inadequate evidence of genetic causation. Not only each individual but, even more, societies seem to be similar to electronic amplifier systems, in which the relation between intake and output is most complex. The development of any society is intricately conditioned by history. The fortuitous appearance or lack of appearance of some external circumstances which provide stimuli of just the "right" intensity to specific cultural endeavors may, with all probability, determine the most divergent future developments. Similarly, the appearance or lack of appearance of a specific influential individual at a specific moment may possibly decide the course of a culture, although here, as in the case of external circumstances, opinion cannot point to controlled experiments in history.

In this connection an opinion voiced by Lord Raglan is relevant: "It has been said against the African Negroes that they never produced a scientist; but what kind of a scientist would he be who had no weights and measures, no clock or calendar, and no means of recording his observations and experiments? And if it be asked why the Negroes did not invent these things, the answer is that neither did any European, and for the same reason—namely, that the rare and perhaps unique conditions which made their invention possible were absent!"

Remote indeed seems the time when a reliable statement can be made regarding a possible genetic component in the cultural achievements of different races.

Apart from the statement itself, it is pertinent to ask whether an objective scale of superiority is possible if we take into account cultural achievements which defy a simple hierarchy of values, such as European Gothic art as compared to Chinese T'ang art; if we consider simultaneously excellence in different fields, such as Roman law and Buddhist thought; and if we include negative values, which stem from ruthless acquisitiveness, coercion, and intolerance.

If, for the sake of argument, it is assumed that the different achievements of different races have some genetic foundation, it is, without doubt, true that variation in individual endowment shows a very wide range in every race. Although methods of testing the hypothesis are lacking, it may be assumed that the ranges of mental endowment of individuals of different races overlap greatly. Therefore, it would probably be possible to find individuals in each race who are mentally superior to the majority of individuals in their own and in every other race.

A genetic explanation of the proposed wide overlap would suggest the existence not of absolute differences in the presence or absence of specific alleles among races but of differences in allele frequencies. In addition, it would involve the assumption that many loci are involved in mental endowment. Such a genetic basis may lead to various kinds of racial differences, namely, variations in mean endowment, in relative frequencies of specific endowments, and in range. How such variations would be mirrored in racial achievement will be estimated differently by different men. What importance should be ascribed to differences in the average endowment of two groups, as compared to differences in the frequency of a few exceptional individuals? How important are variations in the frequency of a large, better-than-average group? How great is the drain on a group's achievement if the distribution of grades of endowment is biased too heavily on the poorer side? To ponder questions like these not only shows our inability to answer them rationally, but, even more, brings to light the inadequacy of an approach which attempts to analyze the history of cultures in terms of allele frequencies.

Confronted with the lack of decisive evidence on the genetic consequences of miscegenation for physical and mental traits, the conservative will still counsel abstention, since the possible ill effects of the breakup of races formed in the course of evolution will not be reversible; whereas the less conservative will regard the chance of such ill effects as small and will not raise his voice against the mingling of races which, from a very long-range point of view, is probably bound to occur anyway. It should not be forgotten, however, that the problem of race is only partly genetic; men will have to consider the biological, sociological, and ethical problems when they attempt to plan for the future.

References

Alvarez, J. J., 1951. Studies on the A-B-O, M-N, and Rh-Hr blood factors in the Dominican Republic, with special reference to the problem of admixture. *Am. J. Phys. Anthrop.,* **9:** 127–148.

Benedict, Ruth, 1934. *Patterns of Culture.* 291 pp. Houghton-Mifflin, Boston. (Reprinted 1946. 272 pp. Penguin Books, New York.)

Coon, C. S., 1954. Climate and race. *Ann. Rep. Smithsonian Inst.,* **1953:** 277–298.

————, Garn, S. M., and Birdsell, J. B., 1950. *A Study of the Problems of Race Formation in Man.* 153 pp. C. C. Thomas, Springfield, Ill.

Dobzhansky, Th., and Montagu, M. F. Ashley, 1947. Natural selection and the mental capacities of mankind. *Science,* **106:** 587–590.

Glass, B., 1955. On the unlikelihood of significant admixture of genes from the North American Indians in the present composition of the Negroes of the United States. *Am. J. Human Genet.,* **7:** 368–385.

Howells, W. W., 1955. Universality and variation in human nature. *Yearb. Anthrop.,* **1955:** 227–236.

Hulse, F. S., 1958. Exogamie et hétérosis. *Arch. Suisses d'Anthrop. Gén.,* **22:** 103–125.

Penrose, L. S., 1955. Evidence of heterosis in man. *Proc. Roy. Soc., B.,* **144:** 203–213.

United Nations Educational, Scientific and Cultural Organization, 1952. *The Race Concept.* 103 pp. UNESCO, Paris.

CHAPTER 33

THE ORIGIN
OF HUMAN DIVERSITY

We have seen that men differ widely in their genetic constitutions. Let us now examine some of the causes of human polymorphism and polytypy. These two kinds of human diversity require separate treatment, since it is one problem to explain why one individual differs from another, and another problem to determine why a racial group has genetic similarities within it which distinguish it from other groups.

The primary phenomenon in all genetic diversity is the existence of different alleles. These different alleles at any given locus may be thought of as having common genic ancestry, in the sense that they were derived by mutation from each other or from some common ancestral allele. The occurrence of mutations, in the broadest sense of the term, is the necessary condition for evolutionary changes; and the evolution of man from his primate ancestors undoubtedly was dependent on this process.

Polymorphic Loci in Man and Other Primates

It is beyond the scope of human genetics to analyze the evolution of *Homo sapiens* from nonhuman and early human types to modern man. It may be asked, however, whether the genic diversity of modern man is a recent acquisition or whether it is part of his prehuman inheritance. If it were found that none of the animal primates possessed genetic polymorphism of the kinds found in man, it would be reasonable to conclude that man's polymorphism is a new acquisition. But an opposite finding—namely, of polymorphism in other primates—would not necessarily justify the conclusion that man's polymorphism is directly inherited from his ancestors. Genes are mutable and man might possess different alleles, not only because he inherited them from his ancestors, but also because his "original" allele at a given locus may have mutated to the various alleles now present. In a more subtle sense, such a situation might still be interpreted to signify that man's polymorphism is a part of his primate inheritance: the assumed mutation of one early human allele to other alleles which also occur in nonhuman primates would mean that the polymorphism of man and other primates is the result of the common property of the locus to give rise to similar alleles.

Polymorphism in Blood Antigens.   The best—and also so far nearly the only—traits for a comparison between the genic variability of man and other primates are antigenic properties. By immunological techniques similar to those employed in determining the antigenic constitution of humans, it is possible to investigate whether or not substances identical or similar to specific human antigens occur in other animals. The results of such tests on the four species of apes and two species of monkeys for the ABO antigens are summarized in Table 122. All four blood groups occur among these primates, but different species do not present the same picture. All four blood groups are present in Java monkeys, but chimpanzees seem to lack the B antigen group, and orangutans, gorillas, gibbons, and Rhesus monkeys do not contain group O. Among Rhesus monkeys, only group B was found.

The absence of certain groups in the animals available for these investigations does not, of course, prove that individuals which belong to the missing groups do not exist. They may still be found, particularly since, in some of the species, only a few individuals have thus far been tested. There seems little doubt, however, that chimpanzees either lack group B completely or at least have a very low frequency for it, since the pooled data of several investigators add up to more than one hundred individuals. Similarly, the absence of group O in orangutans and gorillas suggests, at least, a rarity of this group, since not one out of nearly twenty individuals was found to contain O.

Tests of other primates, and of nonprimate animals, have shown either

TABLE 122.   *Presence* (+) *or Absence* (−) *of ABO Blood Groups among Primates.* (After Wiener and others.)

Species*	O	A	B	AB
Man	+	+	+	+
Chimpanzee	+	+	−	−
Orangutan	−	+	+	+
Gorilla	−	+	+	−
Gibbon	−	+	+	+
Rhesus	−	−	+	−
Java	+	+	+	+

* Some of the animals listed comprise more than one species

the absence of the blood-group antigens or the presence of antigenically related, but not identical, substances. In this connection, an interesting fact has been discovered, which indicates the caution necessary in accepting some of these data as final. In some species, including the gorilla, the antigens are absent from the red blood cells but are present in tissues, body secretions, and the urine.

If one accepts the reasonable assumption that identical antigens in different, related species owe their presence to identical genes, then one may conclude that the antigenic polymorphism of man regarding his ABO constitution is an old heritage. None of the now-living species of apes is known to contain all four blood groups, and only one, the chimpanzee, includes individuals of group O. This is the most frequent human group.

Tests have also been carried out with various primates for the presence of the M and N antigens which are presumably based on alleles L^M and L^N. Orangutans, gibbons, and all of several species of Old World monkeys investigated possess M-like antigens, but lack antigen N. Most New World monkeys tested contained neither. Chimpanzees' blood gave reactions indicating the presence of antigens very similar to human M and N, but both of these substances were present in all individuals. Should further work fail to disclose separate M and N phenotypes, it would have to be concluded that either two (or more) separate isogenic loci, *M* and *N,* are concerned with the production of both antigens, or that a single locus, *L,* isogenic for an allele L^{MN}, is responsible for the presence of the two antigens. Thus, in spite of the suggestive fact that the chimpanzee is the only known primate, apart from man, which possesses an N-like antigen, the genetic basis may not be alike in the two species.

The Rh antigens of man owe their name to the fact that the Rhesus monkey contains a similar substance. Information on apes other than the chimpanzee is lacking. The blood of all of nearly thirty chimpanzees tested reacted regularly with human anti-rh' (anti-C) and anti-rh" (anti-E) sera. Most of the blood samples failed to react with anti-Rh$_o$ (anti-D), and thus correspond to the blood of *rr* humans (cde). Some reacted to anti-Rh$_o$ in an intermediate manner similar to that of the human "variants of R^o" (cD^{u}e) described on page 197.

Polymorphism in Taster Ability.   Polymorphism in a nonantigenic trait, ability to taste phenylthiocarbamide, is met in other primates as well as man. Out of 28 chimpanzees in British zoos, 20 showed by their unambiguous reactions that they were tasters, while 7 were obviously nontasters (one animal "was too shy to be tested"). Among the 3 orangutans available, 2 were tasters and 1 was a nontaster. Other species were represented by one or two specimens only, some being tasters and some not.

In summary, the information suggests that genic polymorphism is a common property of the primate stem and not a property of man alone. This conclusion is in agreement with the results of genetic studies of many other animals and plants: polymorphism is a general phenomenon.

The Origin of Racial Diversity in Man

The racial diversity of man is, presumably, the result of evolutionary processes which occurred after the species *Homo sapiens* had evolved from prehuman ancestors. The later divergence of humans into racial groups is a phenomenon of *microevolution,* the evolution of genetically distinct populations within a single species. The nature of microevolution in general has been the subject of many studies since the 1920's, when the theoretical work of J. B. S. Haldane, R. A. Fisher, and Sewall Wright introduced mathematical genetic concepts into the study of populations, and Tschetverikoff and his followers began to study experimentally the genetic diversity of populations (rather than of individuals) of Drosophila and other organisms.

The prerequisite for any evolutionary change in a population is the presence of different genotypes. This presence depends on the existence of different alleles at various loci. The existence of different alleles is brought about by mutation from one allele to another. Mutation, whether of intragenic nature or of chromosomal-aberration type, is thus the basic condition necessary for the origin of racial diversity.

The mechanism of Mendelian recombination creates an immense amount of genetic variations from even a small number of mutated genes. For example, if a population is initially homozygous and isogenic at the two loci $A^1A^1B^1B^1$ and if mutations occur from A^1 to A^2 and from B^1 to B^2, then recombination can result in 9 different genotypes: $A^1A^1B^1B^1$, $A^1A^1B^1B^2$, $A^1A^1B^2B^2$, $A^1A^2B^1B^1$, $A^1A^2B^1B^2$, $A^1A^2B^2B^2$, $A^2A^2B^1B^1$, $A^2A^2B^1B^2$, and $A^2A^2B^2B^2$. Four of these genotypes are homozygous, and five are heterozygous. With mutations at n loci from one allele to another, recombination can produce 3^n genotypes, of which 2^n are homozygous; and with m multiple alleles at each of n loci, the total number of combinations becomes m^n. Even if n, the number of loci concerned, were as low as 100, and m, the number of alleles per locus, as low as 5, the term $m^n = 5^{100}$ would be so large that the possibilities of genetic newness become inexhaustible.

The origin of genetic newness produced by mutation and recombination is, in itself, not sufficient for an evolutionary phenomenon. In an industrial society, it is one thing to make a technological invention, and another to insure its widespread use and persistence. Similarly, evolutionary history consists of two different processes: one, the origin of newness; the other, the more or less permanent establishment of the innovation in all or many members of a population.

Mutation, Nonrecurrent and Recurrent.   As a first hypothesis on the establishment of evolutionary newness, we might consider mutation a method not only for *originating* newness but also for *establishing* it. Without recourse to secondary processes, like selection, could not the mere occurrence of a mutation lead to its permanent presence in the population? In the analysis of this problem, it is well to separate singular—that is, nonrecurrent—mutational events from recurrent mutations.

The chance that a single mutation will become established is very small. Assume that, in a population containing the A^1 allele only, one gamete is produced which contains the mutant allele A^2, so that an A^1A^2 individual appears. Assume, also, that the number of individuals remains the same, so that each individual of one generation is represented, on the average, by one individual in the next generation—though some individuals will leave no progeny at all; others, one or two; and still others, many. If the A^1A^2 individual reaches maturity and becomes one of the parents of the next generation, he may have one or more children, who, themselves, become parents of the succeeding generation. As a result of segregation, he forms two kinds of gametes, A^1 and A^2, in equal numbers. If he has one child, it may or may not receive the new A^2 allele; if he has two children, chance may give A^2 to both, to only one, or to neither. In general, for any given number of children there are specific probabilities of all (n) or (n − 1) or (n − 2), etc., down to no child receiving the A^2 allele. It is thus seen that the new allele A^2 may not occur again in the next generation, or it may recur only once or more than once. If it does not recur, then the evolutionary potential of the mutation has obviously been cut off. If it recurs in single number, the chance that it will be extinct by the next generation is like that of the original A^2 allele. If it recurs in several individuals, its total chances of survival—that is, continued existence in later generations—are, of course, improved, but the likelihood persists that any one of the A^2 alleles present in an A^1A^2 individual will become extinct in the next, or a later, generation. Fisher has calculated the probabilities of survival of a mutation which appears only once and in a single individual (Table 123). It is seen that the chance of survival of a single mutation is very small indeed. For example, there are only 153 out of

TABLE 123. *Probability of Survival of a Mutation Appearing in a Single Individual.* (No selective advantage or disadvantage.) (Fisher.)

Generations	Probability of Survival
1	0.6321
3	0.3741
31	0.0589
63	0.0302
127	0.0153
1,000	Approx. 0.0010
10,000	Approx. 0.0001
40,000	Approx. 0.000025

TABLE 124. *The Minimum Numbers of Surviving Descendants of a Mutant Allele Which Appeared First in a Single Individual and Did Not Become Extinct.* The second, third, and fourth columns give the minimum numbers of surviving alleles determined by the probabilities 0.1, 0.01, and 0.001. (No selective advantage or disadvantage.) (Fisher.)

Generations	0.1	0.01	0.001
50	58	116	174
100	116	232	348
500	578	1,160	1,738
1,000	1,160	2,320	3,480
10,000	11,600	23,200	34,800
40,000	46,400	92,800	139,200

10,000 chances—or 1 in 65—that A^2 will exist after 127 generations; and, after 40,000 generations, these chances will decrease to only about 25 out of 1,000,000—or 1 in 40,000.

However, these probabilities are not infinitely small; and if the allele A^2 survives at all, it may be found in small, or even in rather large, numbers. Just as chance may lead to nonoccurrence or extinction of the A^2 allele, conversely, chance may result in an increase. The survival of any specified number of A^2 alleles derived from the original A^2 can be expressed in terms of specific probabilities. Table 124, which affords some insight into these relations, lists the probabilities that a minimum specified number of survivors will be found, provided that survival has taken place at all. Thus, as the second column shows, there exists a probability of 1 in 10 that 58 or more A^2 alleles will appear in the descendants 50 generations after the occurrence of the original single A^2, provided that at least one A^2 allele escaped extinction. After 100 generations, at least twice as many alleles possess the 10 per cent chance of having become established (again provided that at least one has survived). After 1,000 generations, there is a 10 per cent chance of finding 1,160 or more A^2 alleles, and, as seen in the final column, a rarer but still finite probability of 0.1 per cent of finding 3,480 or more A^2 alleles. After 40,000 generations, the numbers of A^2 alleles corresponding to the various probabilities have increased further.

We have seen that the survival and the establishment in fairly large numbers of a unique mutation are improbable, but not impossible, events. If we assume that many thousands of loci which might give rise to unique mutations exist, it follows that most of these new alleles never become established but that an occasional one may escape extinction. As a general phenomenon, however, it is very unlikely that the present diversity of man is the result of singular, nonrecurrent mutations.

Most mutations are not singular events, but recur at an appreciable rate. Such recurrent mutations have a much better chance of becoming established. For each specific mutational event, in a recurrent change of A^1 to A^2, the prospects are identical to those listed in Tables 123 and 124. Recurrent mutation, however, may greatly increase the number of opportunities for establishment of A^2. If, in each generation, a large enough number of individuals carry the A^1 allele and a large enough number of generations are considered, numerous A^2 alleles will be produced, and the probability that at least one of them will survive and even become established in appreciable numbers will be greatly increased. If mutation from one allele to another occurs recurrently and at numerous loci, most of the single mutations at any one locus will never be established and even none of the many recurrent mutations at any one locus may become established. Some mutations at some loci, however, will escape extinction and may, indeed, even become numerous.

When mutation is unidirectional—from A^1 to A^2, but not from A^2 to A^1— then recurrent mutation may not only initiate the establishment of A^2 but even lead to the complete replacement of A^1 by A^2. In the course of time, all the A^1 alleles will be transformed into A^2 alleles. If, however, mutations in both directions occur, then the A^2 alleles will produce A^1 alleles, and an equilibrium will be reached: the A^1 alleles will give rise to just as many A^2 as the A^2 alleles give rise to A^1. The equilibrium frequency will be determined by the relative rates of the two mutation processes. Although there is no available information on the existence in man of mutations in both directions, evidence from plants and other animals indicates that such reversible mutations may occur in man as well. In all these cases, mutation pressure alone from recurrent mutations will not lead to isogeneity of the new allele in the population.

Selection. If the primary process of creating genetic variability (mutation) does not, in general, carry the "evolutionary reaction" $A^1 \rightarrow A^2$ to completion, what processes do accomplish evolutionary changes? Two main processes are recognized: natural selection, and genetic drift. Natural selection is the principle emphasized by Charles Darwin. Applied in terms of modern genetics—and given genetic variability—natural selection has retained its status as the most important agent of evolution. If certain genotypes endow their bearers with higher reproductive fitness than is found in others, then the alleles responsible for such relatively "better-adapted" types will be represented in higher proportion in the succeeding generations than the alleles responsible for reproductively less fit—that is, relatively more "poorly adapted"—types. "Better" or "worse" adaptation is used here in the general, and strictly objective, sense of reproductive fitness.

Selection, even to a slight degree, can be a powerful agent for shifting allele ratios from one extreme to another, and thus can lead to the establishment of new genotypes. If a new dominant A^2 allele allows A^2A^1 individuals to produce one thousandth more offspring in each generation than an equal number of A^1A^1 individuals, then it can be calculated that it takes fewer than 10,000 generations to change a population with only a fraction of a

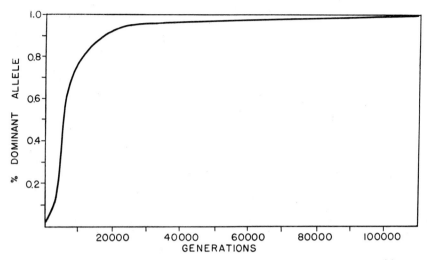

FIG. 257. Effect of selection for a dominant allele. Selective advantage of bearers of the allele, 1 in 1,000. The allele increases rapidly from an initially low frequency. After having reached a frequency of approximately 0.9, the allele's further increase is very slow and at a decreasing rate.

per cent of A^2 alleles to one with 50 per cent A^2 (Fig 257). To raise the frequency of A^2 from 50 to 90 per cent requires fewer than another 10,000 generations. The final increase toward complete replacement of A^1 by A^2 is, however, very slow, as shown by the curve which approaches 100 per cent A^2 asymptotically. The reason for this lies in the fact that, with high frequency of A^2, most individuals will be A^2A^2 and A^2A^1, and only very few will be A^1A^1. Therefore, the effect of selection against A^1A^1 becomes negligible, while the reproduction of A^2A^1 individuals results in perpetuation of A^1 alleles in the population.

As stated, these figures apply to dominant alleles which endow their bearer with a selective advantage, and no difference is postulated for the selective advantage caused by heterozygous A^1A^2 or homozygous A^2A^2. With recessives, selection is effective only in homozygotes. This means that a rare recessive, which only occasionally appears in homozygous form, is nearly free of selective influences. Only when a recessive has become frequent enough to result in the production of an appreciable number of homozygotes will selection become effective. The effect of selection on the frequency of a recessive allele is illustrated in Figure 258. There is an extremely slow increase in the frequency of the allele a as long as it is rare, and a steep rise in its frequency once it has become common.

We have seen that mutation pressure alone is very inefficient in establishing new alleles. We now find that selection is relatively efficient in increasing the number of advantageous dominant alleles and that this is also true for recessive alleles, provided they are present in appreciable numbers. If selective advantages are of the order of 1 in 100 or higher, instead of 1 in 1,000,

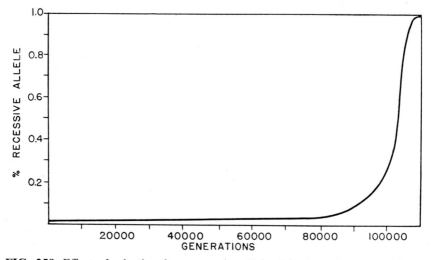

FIG. 258. Effect of selection for a recessive allele. Selective advantage of homozygotes, 1 in 1,000. The allele increases very slowly from an initially low frequency, but relatively rapidly after it has attained an allele frequency of approximately 0.1.

then the rate of increase in the frequency of the new alleles is greatly enhanced.

Concerning recessive alleles, the efficiency of selection is low as long as they are still rare. But, as we have seen in earlier discussions, many so-called recessives are likely to have a slightly dominant effect in heterozygotes, so that their response to selection resembles that of dominants more than that of complete recessives.

It is remarkable that the coexistence of mutation pressure and selection in nature results in greatly increased speed of evolutionary changes. Where it requires many millions of generations of selection to double the frequency of a from 0.00001 to 0.00002, pressure produced by mutation from A to a at the rate of 1 in 100,000 will accomplish the same result in a single generation.

Thus, both mutation and selection may play roles in the establishment of new recessive alleles. At one stage, mutation is the more important and, at another stage, selection. If details are to be worked out, one must, of course, consider separately autosomal and sex-linked alleles; differentiate between the mutants with dominant, recessive, or intermediate effects; and consider, furthermore, whether a genotype at the locus under discussion has selective advantages in all genetic backgrounds or only in certain specific ones. Still more important is the consideration that a selective advantage in one environment may not be, and often is not, an advantage in another environment; for instance, heavy pigmentation of the skin may be selected for in southern regions and selected against in northern regions.

In general, it must be emphasized that selection affects simultaneously the whole gene pool rather than the alleles at single loci. An individual selected for his reproductive fitness transmits assemblages of alleles which differ from those of individuals with lower fitness.

Sometimes the relatively high reproductive fitness of an individual may depend primarily on the specific alleles he carries at a certain single locus. In this case, the assemblages of alleles at other loci that he transmits are selected by the chance which brought them together with the specific alleles at the single locus. More often, his relatively high reproductive fitness will be the result of an interaction of the alleles at the single locus with those at many other loci. When this is true, the assemblage of alleles which he transmits has a tendency to be "coadapted" within itself. In either case, the evolution of diversity as a result of selection constitutes evolution of new gene pools.

Genetic Drift.   Selection, by definition, is powerless in the establishment of new neutral alleles—that is, those which confer neither reproductive advantage nor disadvantage on individuals who carry them, and which, therefore, leave in later generations, neither relatively more nor fewer alleles than the original allele. Whether or not neutral alleles exist cannot be demonstrated at present but there must be many isoalleles whose selective differences approximate zero. It is of great importance to realize that a process, *genetic drift,* has been recognized which is powerful in leading to the establishment of nonadaptive, neutral characters, or even slightly unfavorable traits, and which must be taken into account, together with mutation and selection, as an evolutionary agent.

Let us introduce genetic drift by the following hypothetical situation. Assume that each of 160 isolated islands with exactly identical environmental conditions is settled by a man and woman, all of the genotype A^1A^2. Let each couple have two children, one of each sex, who, on reaching maturity, will become the ancestors of the subsequent populations of the 160 islands. Assume, finally, that the alleles A^1 and A^2 are of equal selective value. What will be the genic composition of each of the 160 populations? As a first approximation, we might be inclined to state that whatever the specific composition might be, it would be alike in all 160 groups, since it was postulated that the original genotypes were identical, the environments are identical, and the selective values for the two contrasting alleles are the same.

This answer is false, as will now be shown. The two original parents $A^1A^2 \times A^1A^2$ will have children of the genotypes A^1A^1, A^1A^2, and A^2A^2 in the expected proportions $1/4:1/2:1/4$. Since we postulated that there were to be only two children, chance will result in:

both A^1A^1	in $\frac{1}{16}$,
both A^1A^2	in $\frac{1}{4}$,
both A^2A^2	in $\frac{1}{16}$,
one A^1A^1 and one A^1A^2	in $\frac{1}{4}$,
one A^1A^1 and one A^2A^2	in $\frac{1}{8}$, and
one A^1A^2 and one A^2A^2	in $\frac{1}{4}$ of all cases.

Any one of these six different situations may arise in each one of the 160 islands. And considering the various probabilities, the most likely result will be that 10 islands will have only two A^1A^1 children, 40 islands only two A^1A^2, 10 islands only two A^2A^2, and the remaining 100 islands will be divided into three different groups each with two children of different genotypes.

The genic constitution of the later populations will obviously depend on the genotypes of their second-generation ancestors. To consider the extreme first, the 10 island populations descended from the two A^1A^1 individuals will contain only A^1A^1 people, while the 10 other island populations descended from the two A^2A^2 individuals will contain only A^2A^2 people. Thus, polytypy for neutral differences in genotype will have arisen, not by mutation pressure or by selection but by the play of chance. This happening, as in these two groups of 10 islands, has been called "chance loss" of an allele (A^2 in the first, and A^1 in the second group) or, conversely, "chance fixation" of the other allele (A^1 in the first and A^2 in the second).

The same process of allelic loss and fixation may occur in the course of later generations in any one of the other 140 islands. On some of the islands, the two children of the original parents still represent two A^1 and A^2 alleles. On others, instead of two of each kind, a shift by chance will already have resulted in the appearance of three A^1 and only one A^2 alleles. On still others, one A^1 and three A^2 alleles will appear. As long as both types of alleles occur in succeeding generations, chance may shift their ratio back and forth in either direction. Whenever chance leads to fixation of one and loss of the other allele, an irreversible situation will have been established (barring mutation).

The speed of this process of genetic drift of the ratio of A^1 and A^2 alleles depends on the size of the population "N" (more specifically, the part of the population which actually becomes parents in each generation). With two parents and two maturing children, as in the island examples, 1/8 of all populations undergo complete loss and fixation for one locus within one generation. With more parents, the chances of loss and fixation become lower, since it will be less frequent that the children of all of the parents will have lost the same allele. Rather, some of the children will have lost A^1 and others A^2, with the over-all result that both alleles persist in the population. Yet, there always remains a small but finite chance, even with large populations, of complete loss of one allele and fixation of the other.

The size of the population not only is decisive for the speed of drift, which, results in loss and fixation of alleles, but also plays a similar role within the reversible range of shifting gene ratios, that is, within the range where both alleles are still present. When populations are small, the speed of drift is high, and often of striking degree from one generation to the next; but when populations are large, drift proceeds slowly and is mostly of slight degree. This is shown diagrammatically in Figure 259. The upper part shows allele ratios attained in successive generations in a population with large

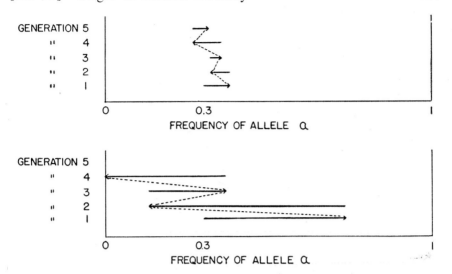

GENERATION 5
    "   4
    "   3
    "   2
    "   1

0   0.3   I
FREQUENCY OF ALLELE a

GENERATION 5
    "   4
    "   3
    "   2
    "   1

0   0.3   I
FREQUENCY OF ALLELE a

FIG. 259. Changing allele frequencies under the influence of drift. *Upper part:* Drift in a large population. Starting with the frequency of 0.3, the allele *a* increases slightly after one generation, and its frequency continues to fluctuate moderately in successive generations. *Lower part:* Drift in a small population. Again starting with a frequency of 0.3, the allele *a* drifts violently. After four generations, drift leads to the extinction of *a*.

numbers of parents, and the lower part shows the same for a small population.

It might appear that the concept of genetic drift contradicts the Hardy-Weinberg Law, which demands an equilibrium, that is, a constancy of allele frequencies from generation to generation. However, the conflict between the expectation of changing allele frequencies and that of an allelic equilibrium is not real. The equilibrium rule applies to infinitely large populations, but has limitations in smaller populations. Basically, the situation is the same as that regarding Mendelian ratios in small sibships. In Chapter 9 we found that the expectation of a 3:1 or a 1:1 ratio needs modification for small sibships, and that expected deviations from the ideal expectation can be calculated. Similarly, the details of drift are predictable as deviations from equilibrium expected in small populations.

In our discussion of drift, we have made the assumption, among others, of neutral selective value of the various alleles. Drift plays a role even when the selective value of an allele is positive or negative. The interplay of the processes of drift and selection is complex. Their relative strength in changing the genetic composition of a population depends, among other factors, on the population size. Since drift is most effective in small populations, it can overshadow, and even run counter to, the trend which selection alone would favor. Thus, even an allele against which selection would discriminate may become established and fixed by drift as long as it is not so disadvantageous as to lead to the extinction of its carriers, and, conversely, an allele which would be favored by selection may be lost by drift before selection could show its full effect.

Genetic drift, small population size, and isolation are closely interrelated agents of evolution. They may not only be effective in the manner described —that is, acting on individual alleles—but may also be particularly important in the preservation and establishment of special combinations of alleles of different loci. In a large population, two rare alleles A^2 and B^2 will only occasionally happen to form the combination $A^2A^2B^2B^2$. Regardless of the selective value of such a combination, a cross with any one of the prevalent genotypes which is not homozygous for A^2 and B^2 will immediately break up the $A^2A^2B^2B^2$ combination, so that it would not reappear in the next generation. The situation might be different in a small isolate within the population. If chance had given the otherwise rare alleles A^2 and B^2 a relatively large share of the allele frequencies, the danger of loss of the combination $A^2A^2B^2B^2$ would be decreased. The higher allele frequencies of A^2 and B^2 will increase the likelihood of an A^2B^2 gamete from $A^2A^2B^2B^2$ meeting an A^2B^2 gamete produced in the isolate. Drift or selection, or both, may lead to the establishment of the new combination $A^2A^2B^2B^2$ and the disappearance of all other genotypes.

If mankind were, and had always been, a single interbreeding population, then genetic drift with its shifting allelic ratios and potentially complete loss or fixation would have been of minor consequence. In reality, mankind has always consisted of more or less separate isolates, owing to geographical and social barriers. Particularly in prehistoric times, the total number of men was small and was distributed discontinuously over many parts of the globe, and, very frequently, groups were divided into reproductively segregated tribes. Furthermore, fluctuations in the size of these isolates must have been great, as the result of famines, epidemics, and wars. During each such low in population number, the sample of alleles that passed through the narrow "bottleneck" of the few parents which connected an earlier, relatively large, with a later, relatively large, population provided a striking opportunity for a demonstration of the effect of drift and often must have resulted in greatly different allelic ratios before and after the bottleneck generation.

Similarly, migration of a fraction of a population to a new region constituted opportunities for drift. The migrants may, in many genetic respects, have been a random sample of the original group, but if they were few enough in number, this random sample may not have been a representative one. In other words, the allelic ratios found in the migrants may have deviated considerably from those of the original group, and, in any case, these ratios may often have undergone great changes during the early generations when the migrated population remained small.

The Role of Selection and Drift in Specific Cases

In a general fashion, the origin of racial diversity can be explained by the action of the various evolutionary processes which have been outlined:

mutation, recombination, selection, and drift. Added to these, the interbreeding of already diverse populations must have led to new types of gene pools,
for instance, as in the American negro and Australian aborigine (to be discussed below). In most specific instances of racial diversity, it is, at present,
difficult if not impossible to say whether selection or drift has been the sole
or at least major agent, or whether an interplay of the two has been decisive.
What, for instance, is the explanation for the fact that all South American
Indians, and many of the North American Indians, possess only the blood-
group allele I^O? Since the ancestors of the Indians were Asian Mongoloids
who presumably came to the Americas across the Bering Strait, they should
have brought with them the three alleles I^A, I^B, and I^O. It has seemed likely
that the loss of I^A and I^B was due to drift in one of two different ways:
either the probably small number of prehistoric migrants who came to North
America all happened to belong to blood group O; or they and their descendants did carry all three I alleles but ultimately happened to transmit to
a small number of surviving children the I^O allele only. One or the other of
these happenings may indeed constitute the whole explanation of the origin
of the isogeneity for I^O in the Amerindian. But one wonders whether selection
can be disregarded. Since we know that the populations of the earth fail
significantly to cover the whole possible array of allele frequencies for I^A,
I^B, and I^O (Fig. 237, p. 623), that maternal-fetal ABO and Rh incompatibilities have complex selective effects, and that selection finds at least
one more point of attack on the ABO blood groups in their relation to
various diseases, it is an open question whether selection was not important
in making the American Indian $I^O I^O$.

Similarly, one may ask: Are the observed relative differences in ABO
blood-group frequencies of Egyptians and Central Arabs, who otherwise
are racially similar, the result of chance processes that acted during earlier
periods when small, isolated populations were forming the ancestors of the
contemporary larger groups? Or did ill-defined different modes of life favor
selectively different allele frequencies? Conversely, did the observed similarities in ABO blood-group frequencies between the Central Asian Mongoloids
and the Hindus, who are racially so different, come about by chance shifting
of allelic ratios, or did selective forces play a role? Only future discoveries
will permit decisive answers to these questions. In the meantime, one can
point to some important examples of diversity in which chance and others
in which selection seem to have been of main importance.

Probable Examples of Drift.   The Blood and Blackfeet Indians of North
America are exceptional in that they contain, in addition to I^O, the I^A allele,
in frequencies of more than 50 per cent. This is not only higher than in
other North American Indian groups, but also higher than in any other
population. It would seem likely that this is the result of shifting allele
ratios in initially small populations. Perhaps the immigrant Asian ancestors
of these American Indian tribes did bring with them the I^A allele, and drift

brought it to a high frequency. Or, perhaps, even the Bloods and Blackfeet were first all $I^O I^O$ and mutation secondarily led to I^A alleles. Even with a low rate of mutation, a new allele, once originated, may by chance escape extinction and become numerous, particularly in a small population.

Other examples in which it is unlikely that selection was important are the peculiarities in blood-group frequencies of certain Eskimos. The Aleutians and the Eskimos inhabiting the areas from western Alaska to eastern Greenland have allele frequencies of I^A of about 30 per cent and of I^B of about 6 per cent. But small tribes of the Polar Eskimos have only 7 per cent I^A and 1 per cent I^B, and those from Baffin Island and Labrador, while having I^A in high frequency, have almost no I^B. For the MN group, most Eskimos, like most American Indians, have the high frequencies of 78–91 per cent L^M, but again the Eskimos from Baffin Island and Labrador diverge greatly by having only 56 per cent L^M.

A direct demonstration of changes in allele frequencies can be made only by comparisons of successive generations. Glass has studied the blood groups of a very small religious isolate—a community of Dunkers in Pennsylvania. The ancestors of this sect were 27 families who, in the early eighteenth century, came from German Rhineland to North America. At present, their ABO frequencies differ significantly from those typical for Germans in the Rhineland as well as for Americans. Thus, the frequency of group A among the Dunkers is nearly 60 per cent, as contrasted to 40–45 per cent in the related populations; O group is somewhat rarer in Dunkers than in Germans or Americans; and the I^B allele is nearly absent among the Dunkers. It is not known when these changes in allele frequencies occurred—whether they were a result of initial deviations from the general population or whether they occurred during the 200 years in which the Dunkers remained a small isolate. Although there is no difference, at the present time, between the ABO frequencies in three different age groups of Dunkers (representing more or less three generations), there is a significant difference in frequencies of the MN groups. The age group of fifty-six years and older has a L^M frequency of 55 per cent, which is similar to that of West German and American populations. In contrast to this, the middle-age group, from twenty-eight to fifty-five years, contains 68 per cent of L^M alleles. In the youngest group, from one to twenty-seven years, the frequency has risen to 73 per cent. Because of the small numbers of subjects, the differences between adjoining age groups are not statistically significant, but the difference between the oldest and youngest groups is highly significant. It is hard to avoid the conclusion that the shift in allele frequency in the Dunker isolate is the result of drift.

There is also evidence for drift of some clearly unfavorable genes. Porphyria is a metabolic disorder in which excessive amounts of porphyrin, an essential part of the hemoglobin molecule, are secreted in the urine. Affected individuals are liable to develop blisters and abrasions on those parts of the skin which are exposed to light. They can become acutely ill, suffering abdominal pain and other symptoms, particularly after the use of barbiturates and certain other drugs. The condition is caused by a dominant gene. It is rare, though not absent, in most parts of the world, but seems to occur in 1 per cent of the Afrikaner population of South Africa. These people are descendants of Dutch and French settlers who arrived in Africa during the latter part of the seventeenth century.

Why is the allele for porphyria so frequent in the Afrikaners? The answer seems to be that it is due to chance! The present population of about two million Afrikaners is descended from a rather small number of original immigrants who raised large families. Their descendants too had large families, as may be seen by the fact that the affected great-grandfather of an affected proposita left 478 descendants. A careful search of the genealogies of South African porphyrics makes it probable that all of them are descendants of a single Dutch settler who immigrated to Cape Town in 1686. Since the total number of original settlers was small, the one allele for porphyria present in the original carrier corresponded to a rather high allele frequency, which is reflected in its rather high frequency in South Africa at the present time.

Similar chance sampling of genes among the small numbers of original ancestors of specific populations probably accounts for unusual incidences of other abnormal alleles. The high frequency of an albino allele among the San Blas Indians of Panama is one example, and the high frequency of an albino allele in an isolated population of mixed negro-white-American Indian origin is another. The absence, or an unusually low incidence, of alleles for given diseases in some populations may likewise be due to chance phenomena. Böök has noted the near absence of manic-depressive psychosis, but not that of schizophrenia, in a north Swedish isolate, and Eaton and Weil have found the reverse, namely low incidence of schizophrenics but high incidence of manic-depressives, among the Hutterite isolates of North America. These data on psychoses are subject to not only genetic but also cultural interpretations, and the reference to genetic drift at present cannot be more than a suggestion.

The interpretation of striking differences in the incidence of clearly unfavorable traits as the result of drift presupposes genetic determination of the traits. Sometimes it is difficult to establish such genetic bases even if numerous pedigrees show an accumulation of affected individuals in sibships, successive generations, and collateral families. Although such pedigrees suggest genetic determination, the possibility of unknown external causative agents often remains. This may be illustrated by two fatal diseases of the nervous system.

Amyotrophic lateral sclerosis is a disease in which slowly progressive degeneration of nerve cells in the spinal cord and in the brain stem leads to progressive muscular wasting and other degenerative changes. The disease is found in persons of middle age and older. Death occurs, on the average, within three years after the onset of the disease. In most parts of the world amyotrophic lateral sclerosis is very rare, accounting for only one death annually among one hundred thousand people. In contrast to this over-all low frequency is the very high incidence among the Chamorro people of the Marianas

Islands, including Guam. There the incidence of the disease is at least one hundred times higher than in the rest of the world; nearly 10 per cent of all adult deaths are due to it. Among white and negro Americans and Europeans, most cases of the disease are sporadic, but a number of kindreds have been found in which inheritance by means of a dominant, incompletely penetrant gene is strongly indicated. The sporadic cases are probably of heterogeneous nature. Some cases may be from kindreds in which there are other affected members who have not been reported, some may be due to new mutations, some may be caused by genes with unusually low penetrance, and some may be nongenetic in origin. Among the Chamorro people in Guam, most cases are familial. This could be due to the common presence of a responsible gene, but could also be due to a high incidence of some unknown nongenetic condition. If the pattern of recurrence of affected individuals in pedigrees is analyzed, usually it is relatively easy to distinguish between these two possibilities. But the family histories in Guam are not very reliable since there is a tendency not to reveal the existence of affected relatives, the family relationships are often not clear, and the church and civil records were destroyed during World War II. Nevertheless, Kurland is inclined to interpret the evidence as indicative of dominant inheritance with incomplete penetrance. This interpretation is strengthened by the finding that amyotrophic lateral sclerosis is rare among other people than the Chamorros living on Guam, and by the fact that the disease is common not only among the Chamorros in Guam but also among those Chamorros who have settled in California and live like other Californians of their socioeconomic groups. If the genetic interpretation is correct, the population of Guam was probably very small some two and a half centuries ago, and the occurrence of a mutation, or the presence of the mutant gene, in one or a few individuals may have provided the opportunity for drift, which led to a high frequency of the deleterious allele.

A fatal disease of still higher incidence is kuru, which occurs among the Fore natives of New Guinea, and is unknown elsewhere. Kuru is a paralysis due to rapidly progressive malfunction of the cerebellum. Approximately one-half of the affected females and one-tenth of the affected males in many parts of the eastern highlands die within a few months after onset of the disease. Most males become affected as children or adolescents, but affected females fall into two overlapping groups, those with onset during childhood and adolescence and those with late onset of maximum occurrence between the ages of 25 to 35. Various facts indicate that kuru is probably not due to an external agent, and Bennett has proposed a genetic interpretation based on extensive genealogical data. It has been postulated that an abnormal allele Ku is recessive in males and has intermediate expression in heterozygous females: $Ku\ Ku$ males and females are potentially affected, suffering early onset, $Ku\ ku$ females suffer late onset, and both $Ku\ ku$ and $ku\ ku$ males and $ku\ ku$ females remain healthy. It should be emphasized that the lack of evidence for an external cause of kuru is not proof of genetic determination. However, if it should be true that a special genotype is the main cause of the disease, its high frequency in the Fore natives is probably due to genetic drift.

Probable Examples of Selection.   Drift, as an explanation for the origin of racial diversity, accounts primarily for differences determined by single gene substitution. Polygenically determined traits are less easily changed by chance assortment, since random processes are likely to shift some allelic proportions in one direction and others in an opposite direction. Moreover, if the hypothesis is true that many of the characteristics of different races are adaptations to their specific environments, present or past, then selection must have been instrumental in their establishment.

Among the differences between racial groups that depend on single genic loci are some for which selective forces, and not drift, are clearly responsible. The foremost example of these is that of sickle-cell hemoglobin. The allele $Hb_1{}^S$ is nearly absent in most human populations, but occurs in frequencies as high as 10–20 per cent in a broad belt across Central Africa, in Madagascar, and in high or low (but still clearly elevated) frequencies in most North African and southern European countries which surround the Mediterranean. In irregular fashion, hemoglobin S has also been found in certain racial groups in Arabia and India (Fig. 260). The sickle-cell trait is thus a characteristic of many African populations, but its presence in other groups suggests either migrations and separation of subgroups or admixture by interbreeding. It is likely that such processes have served to distribute the $Hb_1{}^S$ allele over wide areas. It is also clear that an additional factor must exist which accounts for important, detailed features of the distribution as well

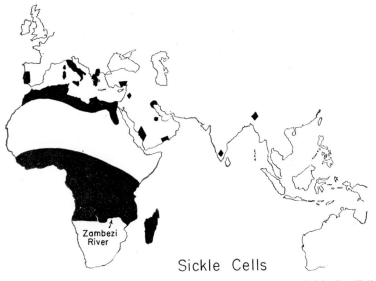

Sickle Cells

FIG. 260. Sickle cells. The distribution of the gene for hemoglobin-S. (Edington and Lehmann, *Man,* **36,** 1956.)

as for the unexpectedly high frequencies of this homozygously lethal, or at least severely deleterious, allele. This additional factor is selection for the $Hb_1^A Hb_1^S$ heterozygote, accomplished, according to Allison's theory, by greater resistance to malaria of the heterozygotes than of normal $Hb^A Hb^A$ homozygotes.

In favor of this theory is the considerable positive correlation between the incidence of malaria and the frequency of the sickle-cell allele in various areas. The correlation breaks down, however, in certain places where African tribes living in malaria-infested regions have only low frequencies of the Hb_1^S allele. Livingstone has analyzed these relations in West Africa. He considers that selection for sickle-cell heterozygotes is a phenomenon which has come relatively recently to mankind in general, and to West Africa in particular. He believes that malaria began to attack man on a large scale only after the invention of agriculture led to the clearing of forests and to the rise in population densities. The clearing of the tropical rain forests, as well as man's refuse and his villages, provided new and abundant breeding places for the malaria-carrying mosquito, and the increasing population density created a favorable situation for the persistence of the parasite. According to this view, in many populations the frequency of the sickle-cell allele is not yet in equilibrium with its selective attributes. Its existence, in minimal numbers, depends on its initial presence in certain tribes, its spread on their migration into new areas, and the "diffusion" of the gene, by miscegenation, into other populations. But the actual frequencies of the gene are not determined by the initial state or the degree of admixture. Rather, they are the result of selective forces which, in a malarian environment and an agricultural mode of life (which favors exposure), lead to high frequencies of Hb_1^S, or which, in a relatively malaria-free environment and a mode of life such as hunting in the forest (which decreases exposure), lead to low frequencies. The Hb_1^S allele may well have originated by mutation, in other populations of the world. Its near absence in them may be no more than a reflection of the fact that most individual mutations never are established but become extinct by random sampling soon after they appear.

Among various other genes for abnormal hemoglobins are the allele Hb_1^C for hemoglobin C and the gene for thalassemia. The occurrence of Hb_1^C is nearly restricted to West Africa, where it overlaps the distribution of Hb_1^S. It may reach a frequency of more than 10 per cent. Homozygous hemoglobin C individuals are affected by an anemia in a much milder way than are sickle-cell homozygotes. Compound heterozygotes for Hb_1^S and Hb_1^C are severely affected, although less so than Hb_1^S homozygotes. There is thus selective pressure against Hb_1^C in $Hb_1^C Hb_1^S$ heterozygotes and in homozygotes. Its high frequency, in spite of this negative selection, requires the existence of compensating positive selection. It has naturally been wondered whether resistance to malaria, in the case of hemoglobin C, also provides the agent for such selection.

The frequency of the gene for thalassemia offers problems similar to those

FIG. 261. The distribution of the gene for thalassemia in Italy. The numbers represent allele frequencies in per cent. (After Bianco, Montalenti, Silvestroni, and Siniscalco, *Ann. Eugen.,* **16,** 1952.)

of the $Hb_1{}^S$ and $Hb_1{}^C$ alleles. Thalassemia occurs primarily in the Mediterranean area, but also in various Asian areas, particularly in Thailand. Careful studies of its distribution in Italy have been made by Silvestroni and his associates. In Figure 261 it is seen that the thalassemia allele is very unequally distributed, having frequencies of less than 1 per cent in Florence and Bologna, and reaching peaks of 3 and 5 per cent in Sicily and Ferrara, respectively. Since the reproductive fitness of the homozygotes is practically zero, the high frequencies of the gene for thalassemia must be maintained by the increased fitness of the heterozygotes. The nature of this increased fitness is not yet clear, but there are again suggestive correlations between the incidence of the allele for abnormal hemoglobin and the presence of malarial environments.

Selective Migration and Stratification.   Genetic diversity of populations can also be brought about by the separation of subgroups within a common gene pool. It has often been asked whether emigrants form a group which is somewhat genetically distinct from the group which stays at home. It is likely that emigrants often have different mental attributes than the sessile group—for instance, a higher initiative—but the genetic basis of such properties is doubtful. Emigrants as a group conceivably may also have different morphological traits, be it a greater physical strength which might favor the overcoming of physical hardships, or a smaller body size which might permit more individuals to occupy a primitive boat.

Some modern anthropometric measurements seem to indicate that there are no differences between Mexican and Chinese immigrants to the United States and the native populations from which they stemmed, although it is clear that the new environment, if effective early in life, can strikingly modify such traits as stature. In other, historical migrations, differences between migrants and nonmigrants may well have existed. The type of selection involved in such migrations has been referred to as "sifting."

Within a population, different socioeconomic layers may to some degree represent different gene pools. If the stratification of such a population becomes relatively fixed, a genetic diversity of subpopulations is thereby originated.

Gene Flow and Gradients in Allele Frequency.   Selection and drift lead to diversity in human populations, but such diversity has a tendency toward equalization. Matings between neighboring, genetically diverse populations result in the introduction of genes from one to the other. Migrations of populations into new territories may lead to contacts, accompanied by gene exchange, between diverse populations formerly separated by great distances. Migrations of groups of people may be likened to the coming together of separate rivers which flow into the same sea. The consequent intermingling of the water molecules from different rivers into a homogeneous body of water may be likened to the interbreeding of initially separate populations.

The formation of new gene pools by interbreeding is often a slow process. Populations are known that have lived side by side for hundreds or even thousands of years and yet have retained genetic diversity. Thus, Sanghvi has shown that different castes in India have strikingly different frequencies for ABO, MN, P, and Rh blood groups as well as for taster ability and color blindness. Conversely, the gypsies of Hungary resemble in their ABO frequencies the Indian immigrants who came to Europe from Asia in the fifteenth century and who have remained different from the population by which they are surrounded. Such retention of diversity depends on cultural factors which prescribe endogamy. Sometimes these factors restrict gene diffusion primarily in one direction: the African Negroes brought to North America experienced an influx of genes from Caucasoids; whereas the latter did not acquire any appreciable admixture of genes from Negroids. Even if a social system does not place legal barriers in the way of gene exchange, personal preferences often lead to positive assortative mating and thus counteract tendencies toward panmixis.

If two genetically diverse populations, I and II, occupy different but adjoining areas, gene exchange should result in gradients of allele frequencies. An allele A^1 which is more common in population I than in II would be expected to be relatively frequent in II near the border of I and II and to decrease in frequency in II farther away from the border. Similarly, if there are migrations of individuals of population I into the territory occupied by II, gradients of the frequency of A^1 among II may reflect the number of migrants who penetrated into specific regions and there mixed with the indigenous population. A famous example is the gradient of frequencies of the I^B allele from Central Asia to western Europe (Fig. 262): from a peak frequency of 25–30 per cent in Central Asia, this allele becomes less and less common closer to western territories. Candela has explained this gradient by assuming it to be

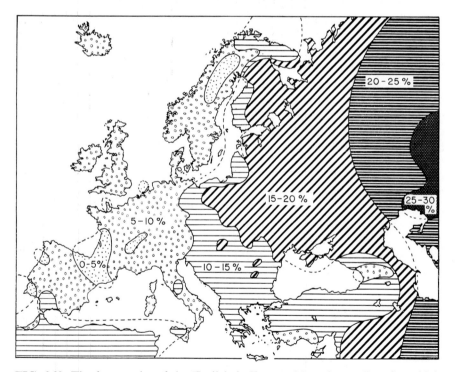

FIG. 262. The frequencies of the I^B allele in Europe. Note the gradient from high frequencies in the east to low frequencies in the west. (After Mourant, 1954; and Manuila, *Am. J. Phys. Anthrop.*, **14**, 1956.)

a consequence of the invasions of the Mongoloids who, from about 500 A.D. to 1500 A.D., pushed westward in numbers which decreased with distance from their region of origin. Miscegenation of the invaders with the native populations, in which the I^B allele is supposed to have been absent, led to "diffusion" of I^B from Central Asia to the west. The gradient of I^B concentration, therefore, is a reflection of the diminished contact between Mongoloids and populations farther west. The external features of the Mongoloids are not found strikingly in the present populations of Europe, since polygenic combinations determining racial characters were broken up in miscegenation. The singly determined blood-group traits, however, still bear witness to the influx of many other eastern alleles. It should be added that there are pockets of increased frequencies of the I^B allele in some of the most western areas of Europe, making it unlikely that all I^B alleles on that continent are derived from those of the eastern invaders. And there remains the slight possibility that a gradient in a blood-group allele may reflect not only gene flow but also unknown selective influences which follow a geographic gradient.

A similar penetration of I^B alleles into a region known to have been free of I^B alleles has been noted in Australia. On most of this continent the aborigines possess only I^O and I^A alleles, but tests of individuals from the northern coastal areas have revealed I^B frequencies of 8–20 per cent (Fig. 263). It seems that the I^B allele was introduced from two separate sources: the Papuans of New Guinea, northeast of Australia, and the Malayans, northwest of Australia. It may be expected that in the course of time a gradient toward the south of decreasing frequency of the I^B allele will be formed.

Birdsell, who has summarized the data on I^B in Australia, has also considered various other traits. One of his many interesting uses of population genetics in the exploration of anthropologic problems concerns the question of the racial origin of the aborigines. It is believed (but not generally so) that these people were derived from three different racial groups which reached

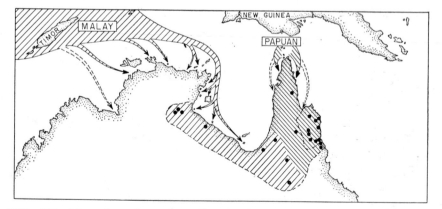

FIG. 263. Map of northern Australia, showing areas of penetration of the I^B allele from adjacent regions. The black dots signify locations of aborigines possessing I^B. (Birdsell.)

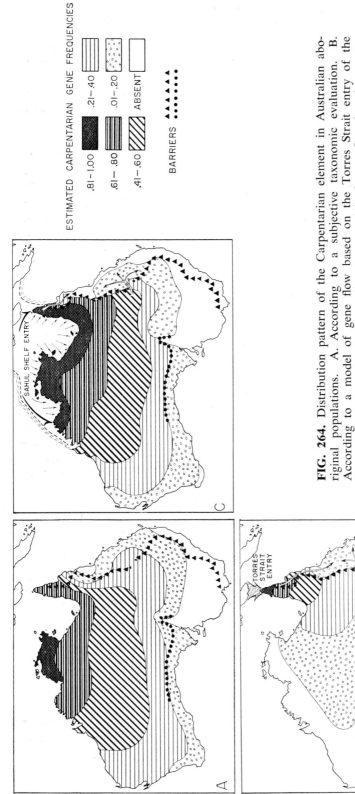

FIG. 264. Distribution pattern of the Carpentarian element in Australian aboriginal populations. A. According to a subjective taxonomic evaluation. B. According to a model of gene flow based on the Torres Strait entry of the Carpentarian element. C. According to a model of gene flow based on entry across the Sahul Shelf. (Birdsell.)

ESTIMATED CARPENTARIAN GENE FREQUENCIES

.81–1.00 .21–.40

.61–.80 .01–.20

.41–.60 ABSENT

BARRIERS

Australia in successive periods: first, Negritos; second, primitive Caucasoids, related to the Ainus of northern Japan; and, third, a group called Carpentarian, which seems closest to some of the aboriginal tribes of India. Birdsell has constructed a map, based on a subjective taxonomic evaluation, which presents estimated Carpentarian gene frequencies. They show a general gradient from north to south with some interesting irregularities (Fig. 264, A). Thus, there is a small region of zero frequency in the northeast, a large zone of very low frequency along most of the eastern shores, and a tongue of zero frequency protruding from the south into the otherwise even southern contour of the lowest frequency belt. These irregularities are correlated with physical or geological barriers. Birdsell has worked out two theoretical models to explain, by means of gene flow, the observed gradients of Carpentarian elements. These models take into account the existence of not only physical and ecological barriers but also cultural barriers to gene flow. Foreign alleles arriving in a given tribe will easily become distributed in it, but endogamic rules and preferences will form relative barriers to penetration into adjacent tribes. Thus "genetic space," defined in relation to the number of tribes between two regions rather than to the geographic distance between them, will determine the speed of gene flow along the gradient.

Any detailed model of gene flow will have to make unproven, and at present unprovable, assumptions concerning the genetic space involved. The consequences of gene flow derived from models must therefore be regarded as highly hypothetical. Nevertheless, models are valuable in clarifying concepts and suggesting interpretations.

Birdsell's first model assumes the entry of the Carpentarian element by way of the Torres Strait. Its detailed elaboration results in an expected gradient of estimated allele frequencies that is very unlike that derived from taxonomic observations (Fig. 264, B). The second model assumes a wide area of entrance, along much of the northern coast of Australia. This model results in an expectation of the gradient distribution which is surprisingly similar to that based on observation (Fig. 264, C). It therefore seems possible that the second model reflects the prehistoric actuality of Carpentarian gene flow into Australia.

Birdsell's models did not involve direct knowledge of allele frequencies. They made use of taxonomic observations which were interpreted in terms of population genetics. The validity of such interpretations has been tested in certain situations where degree of relationship of hybridizing populations could be expressed in terms of both taxonomic similarities and specific allele frequencies. How closely these two methods lead to the same conclusion can be seen for the example of four populations represented by West African Negroes, Caucasoids, and two groups of hybrids between them—a typical American negro group, and the negroes of Charleston, South Carolina. Owing to isolating factors, the last group has experienced less gene flow from the Caucasoids than have most other American negroes. The graphic representa-

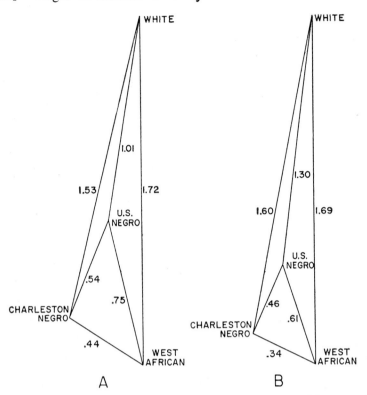

FIG. 265. Diagrammatic representation in terms of "distance" of four populations from one another. A. According to morphological criteria. B. According to indexes computed from allele frequencies for blood groups and hemoglobin types. (After Pollitzer, *Am. J. Anthrop.*, **16**, 1958.)

tions of relationships according to morphological and genetic evaluation of subgroups are very similar (Fig. 265).

The Future

In the attempt to predict the future biological evolution of man, two main facts may serve as guides. The first is biological, the second cultural. Biologically, man became a large species in terms of breeding population. Furthermore, this large species is becoming less and less subdivided into relative isolates of some permanence, but is tending to form increasingly larger interbreeding groups. This by itself should result in a decisive slowdown, if not a cessation, of changes so far as these are caused by genetic drift in its various forms.

Mutation pressure in the future may lead to the further reduction and disappearance of organs or functions which have already ceased to be vital. The loci which are, at present, concerned with the retention of vestigial properties are likely to give rise, by mutation, to new alleles which will result in loss of these properties. These mutant alleles will accumulate in the population, since selection will not act against them.

Interbreeding of different racial groups will lead to the appearance of many hitherto unknown combinations of alleles which, until now, had been kept isolated from one another. While these new variants may possess selective advantages or disadvantages over the already known types, natural selection in the large interbreeding species *Homo sapiens* will have little effect, since good and bad combinations alike will be broken up in each generation.

Changes in the physical environment of man will hardly act as stimulants for evolution. Such changes force other organisms to, so to speak, "explore" their genetic potential for necessary new adaptations. Man's techniques have made him so largely independent of physical environmental influences that he will succeed in stabilizing his surroundings and thus escape the need of adapting himself to new ones. Hence, it appears likely that the normal agents for evolutionary biological change will be greatly reduced in efficacy.

Opposed to this conservatism of biological influences are the revolutionary potentialities of cultural ones. At present, differential reproduction of different genetic groups is a cultural phenomenon which produces changes in the allele frequencies of mankind. The reality of such changes in the over-all genetic composition is beyond doubt, in so far as it concerns the differential reproduction of the major races. On changes in allele frequencies within racial groups, the evidence is less decisive, but it is likely that such alterations are also taking place. As we have seen, there is little reason for being too alarmed about such present phenomena, since only long-continued trends will appreciably change the genetic composition of large populations. Human societies have been so unstable that persistent genetic trends have been virtually impossible.

The endeavors of eugenicists to check undesirable trends and to further desirable ones may be the precursors of human actions which will become evolutionary agents of incalculable influence. Natural selection will be superseded by socially decreed selection.

Man may even learn to cause the appearance of specific mutations in his genes, or to incorporate by chemical means selected genetic materials into his chromosomes. Whether such actions will be directed toward human uniformity or toward variability, and what traits will be set up as desirable ones, will not be decided soon. In the course of time, however, the control by man of his own biological evolution will become imperative, since the power which knowledge of human genetics will gradually place in man's hands cannot but lead to action. Such evolutionary controls will be world-wide in scope, since, by its nature, the evolution of mankind transcends the bounds of unrestricted national sovereignty. It will be a difficult problem to direct the actions of individuals toward a socially desired long-range goal, and to retain at the same time the essential aspects of personal freedom. This, however, is not a new problem. The resolution of the conflict between freedom and organization is a permanent theme in human history.

References

Bennett, J. H., Rhodes, F. A., and Robson, H. N., 1959. A possible genetic basis for Kuru. *Am. J. Human Genet.,* **11:** 169–187.

Birdsell, J. B., 1950. Some implications of the genetical concept of race in terms of spatial analysis. *Cold Spring Harbor Symp. Quant. Biol.,* **15:** 259–314.

Böök, J. A., 1953. A genetic and neuropsychiatric investigation of a North-Swedish population. *Acta Genet. et Stat. Med.,* **4:** 1–100.

Candela, P. B., 1942. The introduction of blood group B into Europe. *Hum. Biol.,* **14:** 413–443.

Dean, G., and Barnes, H. D., 1958. Porphyria. *Brit. Med. J.,* **1:** 298–301.

Dobzhansky, Th., 1951. *Genetics and the Origin of Species.* 3rd ed. 364 pp. Columbia University Press, New York.

————, and Allen, G., 1956. Does natural selection continue to operate in modern mankind? *Am. Anthrop.,* **58:** 591–604.

Eaton, J. W., and Weil, R. J., 1955. *Culture and Mental Disorders.* 254 pp. Free Press, Glencoe.

Fisher, R. A., 1930. *The Genetical Theory of Natural Selection.* 272 pp. Oxford University Press, London (also 1959, 2nd rev. ed. 291 pp. Dover, N. Y.).

Glass, B., 1954. Genetic changes in human populations, especially those due to gene flow and genetic drift. *Adv. Genet.,* **6:** 95–139.

————, 1956. On the evidence of random genetic drift in human populations. *Am. J. Phys. Anthrop.,* n.s. **14:** 541–556.

Haldane, J. B. S., 1932. *The Causes of Evolution.* 235 pp. Harper, New York.

Hulse, F., 1957. Some factors influencing the relative proportions of human racial stocks. *Cold Spring Harbor Symp. Quant. Biol.,* **22:** 33–46.

Kurland, L. T., 1958. Descriptive epidemiology of selected neurologic and myopathic disorders with particular reference to a survey in Rochester, Minnesota. *J. Chronic Dis.,* **8:** 378–418.

Lasker, G. W., 1954. The question of physical selection of Mexican migrants to the U.S.A. *Hum. Biol.* **26:** 52–58.

Livingstone, F. B., 1958. Anthropological implications of sickle cell gene distribution in West Africa. *Am. Anthrop.,* **60:** 533–562.

Mourant, A. E., 1954. *The Distribution of the Human Blood Groups.* 438 pp. C. C. Thomas, Springfield, Ill.

Sanghvi, L. D., and Khanolkar, V. R., 1949. Data relating to seven genetical characters in six endogamous groups in Bombay. *Ann. Eugen.,* **15:** 52–64.

Schwidetzky, Ilse, 1950. *Grundzüge der Völkerbiologie.* 312 pp. Ferdinand Enke, Stuttgart.

Wiener, A. S., 1943. *Blood Groups and Transfusion.* 3rd ed. Chapters 18 and 19, pp. 295–360. C. C. Thomas, Springfield, Ill.

Wright, S., 1932. The roles of mutation, inbreeding, crossbreeding and selection in evolution. *Proc. VIth Intern. Congr. Genetics,* **1:** 356–366.

AUTHOR INDEX

SUBJECT INDEX

Initiate CHD twin study

CHD at operon or regulon level?

Study post-op pt's now
in reproductive age p 523
persistence mutational load — greatly increased
Empiric risk figure for each
defect

Triglyceride + other studies
in childhood for potential coronary
type — ? methane thiol